D1478244

Series Editor: Rhodes W. Fairbridge
Columbia University

Published Volumes

ENVIRONMENTAL GEOMORPHOLOGY AND LANDSCAPE CONSERVATION, VOLUME I: Prior to 1900 / Donald R. Coates
RIVER MORPHOLOGY / Stanley A. Schumm
SPITS AND BARS / Maurice L. Schwartz
TEKTITES / Virgil E. Barnes and Mildred A. Barnes
GEOCHRONOLOGY: Radiometric Dating of Rocks and Minerals / C. T. Harper
SLOPE MORPHOLOGY / Stanley A. Schumm and M. Paul Mosley
MARINE EVAPORITES: Origin, Diagenesis, and Geochemistry / Douglas W. Kirkland and Robert Evans
ENVIRONMENTAL GEOMORPHOLOGY AND LANDSCAPE CONSERVATION, VOLUME III: Non-Urban Regions / Donald R. Coates
BARRIER ISLANDS / Maurice L. Schwartz
GLACIAL ISOSTASY / John T. Andrews
GEOCHEMISTRY OF GERMANIUM / Jon N. Weber
PHILOSOPHY OF GEOHISTORY: 1785–1970 / Claude C. Albritton, Jr.
ENVIRONMENTAL GEOMORPHOLOGY AND LANDSCAPE CONSERVATION, VOLUME II: Urban Areas / Donald R. Coates
GEOCHEMISTRY AND THE ORIGIN OF LIFE / Keith A. Kvenvolden
SEDIMENTARY ROCKS: Concepts and History / Albert V. Carozzi
GEOCHEMISTRY OF WATER / Yasushi Kitano
METAMORPHISM AND PLATE TECTONIC REGIMES / W. G. Ernst
GEOCHEMISTRY OF IRON / Henry Lepp

Additional volumes in preparation

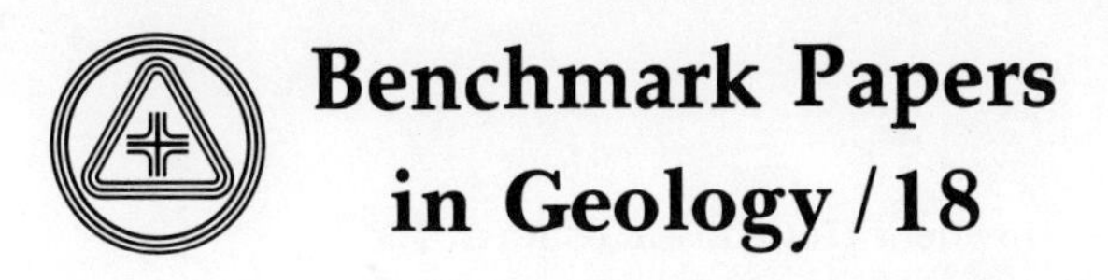

A *BENCHMARK*® Books Series

GEOCHEMISTRY OF IRON

Edited by
HENRY LEPP
Macalester College

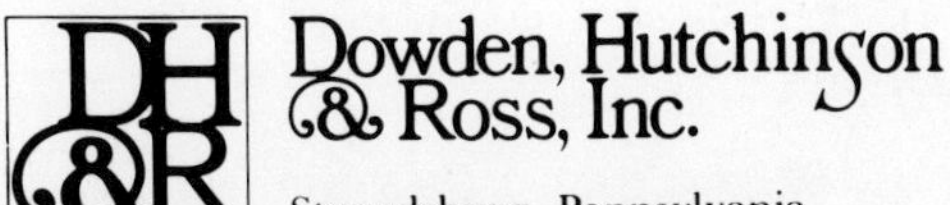

Stroudsburg, Pennsylvania

Distributed by
HALSTED PRESS *A Division of John Wiley & Sons, Inc.*

Benchmark Papers in Geology, Volume 18
Library of Congress Catalog Card Number: 74-23287
ISBN: 0-470-52776-5

77 76 75 1 2 3 4 5
Manufactured in the United States of America.

Library of Congress Cataloging in Publication Data

Lepp, Henry, comp.
Geochemistry of iron.

(Benchmark papers in geology ; v. 18)
1. Iron--Addresses, essays, lectures. I. Title.
QE516.F4L46 553.3 74-23287
ISBN 0-470-52776-5

Exclusive distributor: **Halsted Press**
a division of John Wiley & Sons, Inc.

Acknowledgments and Permissions

ACKNOWLEDGMENTS

DEPARTMENT OF IRON RANGE RESOURCES AND REHABILITATION OF THE STATE OF MINNESOTA AND THE MINNESOTA GEOLOGICAL SURVEY—*The Mineralogy and Geology of the Taconites and Iron Ores of the Mesabi Range, Minnesota*
Hematite–Limonite Deposits

SWEDISH GEOLOGICAL SURVEY—*Sveriges Geologiska Undersöknig*
On the Geochemistry of Swedish Iron Ores and Associated Rocks

U.S. GEOLOGICAL SURVEY
Data of Geochemistry
Chemistry of the Iron-Rich Sedimentary Rocks
Geology and Ore Deposits of the Iron River-Crystal Falls District, Iron County, Michigan

PERMISSIONS

The following papers have been reprinted with the permission of the authors and the copyright holders.

AMERICAN JOURNAL OF SCIENCE (YALE UNIVERSITY)—*American Journal of Science*
Sedimentary Pyrite Formation

ECONOMIC GEOLOGY PUBLISHING COMPANY—*Economic Geology*
Discussions of "Origin of Precambrian Iron Formations"
The Environmental Control of Sedimentary Iron Minerals
Facies Relations in the Gunflint Iron Formation
The Formation of Sedimentary Iron Minerals
Hydrothermal Leaching of Iron Ores of the Lake Superior Type—A Modified Theory
The Iron Ore Deposits of the Pacific Basin
Origin of Precambrian Iron Formations
Sedimentary Facies of Iron-Formation
Supergene Iron Ores of Minas Gerais, Brazil

ELSEVIER PUBLISHING COMPANY–Carbonate Rocks
Carbonate Rocks and Paleoclimatology in the Biochemical History of the Planet

GEOLOGICAL SOCIETY OF AMERICA—*Geological Society of America Bulletin*
Hydrothermal Magnetite
Origin of Banded Iron Formations
Structure, Straitigraphy, and Origin of Iron Formations, Michipicoten Area, Algoma District, Ontario, Canada
Three Great Basins of Precambrian Banded Iron Formation Deposition: A Systematic Comparison

INSTITUTION OF MINING AND METALLURGY, LONDON
Bulletin of the Institution of Mining and Metallurgy
Genesis of Marine Sedimentary Iron Ores
Transactions of the Institution of Mining and Metallurgy
The Lateritic Iron Deposits of Conakry

MACMILLAN JOURNALS LTD.—*Nature*
Depositional Environment of British Liassic Ironstones Considered in the Context of Their Facies Relationships

MICROFORMS INTERNATIONAL MARKETING CORPORATION—*Geochimica et Cosmochimica Acta*
Carbon Isotopic Evidence for the Origin of a Banded Iron-Formation in Western Australia
Role of Clay Minerals in the Transportation of Iron
Separation of Manganese from Iron in Sedimentary Processes

W. W. NORTON & COMPANY, INC.—*Evolution of Sedimentary Rocks*

PLENUM PUBLISHING CORPORATION—*Applied Capillary Microscopy: The Role of Microorganisms in the Formation of Iron-Manganese Deposits*
The Formation of Manganese-Iron Layers in Mud as a Biogenic Process

SPRINGER-VERLAG, BERLIN—*Handbook of Geochemistry*
Abundance in Common Igneous Rock Types
Abundance in Natural Waters

UNESCO—*Proceedings of the Kiev Symposium on Genesis of Precambrian Iron and Manganese Deposits*
Significance of Carbon Isotope Variations in Carbonates from the Biwabik Iron Formation, Minnesota

Series Editor's Preface

The philosophy behind the "Benchmark Papers in Geology" is one of collection, sifting, and rediffusion. Scientific literature today is so vast, so dispersed, and, in the case of old papers, so inaccessible for readers not in the immediate neighborhood of major libraries that much valuable information has been ignored by default. It has become just so difficult, or so time consuming, to search out the key papers in any basic area of research that one can hardly blame a busy man for skimping on some of his "homework."

This series of volumes has been devised, therefore, to make a practical contribution to this critical problem. The geologist, perhaps even more than any other scientist, often suffers from twin difficulties—isolation from central library resources and immensely diffused sources of material. New colleges and industrial libraries simply cannot afford to purchase complete runs of all the world's earth science literature. Specialists simply cannot locate reprints or copies of all their principal reference materials. So it is that we are now making a concerted effort to gather into single volumes the critical material needed to reconstruct the background of any and every major topic of our discipline.

We are interpreting "geology" in its broadest sense: the fundamental science of the planet Earth, its materials, its history, and its dynamics. Because of training and experience in "earthy" materials, we also take in astrogeology, the corresponding aspect of the planetary sciences. Besides the classical core disciplines such as mineralogy, petrology, structure, geomorphology, paleontology, and stratigraphy, we embrace the newer fields of geophysics and geochemistry, applied also to oceanography, geochronology, and paleoecology. We recognize the work of the mining geologists, the petroleum geologists, the hydrologists, the engineering and environmental geologists. Each specialist needs his working library. We are endeavoring to make his task a little easier.

Each volume in the series contains an Introduction prepared by a specialist (the volume editor)—a "state of the art" opening or a summary of the objects and content of the volume. The articles, usually some thirty to fifty reproduced either in their entirety or in significant extracts, are selected in an attempt to cover the field, from the key papers of the last century to fairly recent work. Where the original works are in foreign languages, we have endeavored to locate or commission translations. Geologists, because of their global subject, are often acutely aware of the oneness of our world. The selections cannot, therefore, be restricted to any one country, and whenever possible an attempt is made to scan the world literature.

To each article, or group of kindred articles, some sort of "highlight commentary" is usually supplied by the volume editor. This should serve to bring that article into historical perspective and to emphasize its particular role in the growth of the field. References, or citations, wherever possible, will be reproduced in their entirety—for by this means the observant reader can assess the background material available to that particular author, or, if he wishes, he too can double check the earlier sources.

A "benchmark," in surveyor's terminology, is an established point on the ground, recorded on our maps. It is usually anything that is a vantage point, from a modest hill to a mountain peak. From the historical viewpoint, these benchmarks are the bricks of our scientific edifice.

Rhodes W. Fairbridge

Preface

Iron is an element of special interest to earth scientists; consequently the periodical literature that deals with its geochemistry is voluminous. There are many reasons why so much has been written about iron. It is one of the major elements in the earth's crust, and of these, it alone may be oxidized or reduced in surface environments. Iron is thus an indicator of oxidation potential, and the study of its geochemical cycle is related to that of the evolution of the earth's atmosphere. Furthermore, because iron has long been the foremost industrial metal, its economic deposits, including those formed by weathering, by sedimentation, and by plutonic processes, have been the subject of intensive research for well over a century.

The extensive literature on iron has made the task of selecting papers for this volume a most difficult one. In addition, many of the classic papers are quite long, thus compounding the problem of selecting articles that would provide a measure of breadth, historical perspective, and geographic representation within the limits of a single volume. In preparation for this selection process I sought assistance from a number of researchers in the field, including P. E. Cloud, Jr., S. S. Goldich, A. M. Goodwin, G. A. Gross, H. L. James, R. W. Marsden, G. B. Morey, and A. F. Trendall. I wish to take this opportunity to thank them for their valuable and varied suggestions. I must, however, take the full responsibility for the final selections because each of them would doubtless have assembled a somewhat different grouping of papers.

To assure a breadth of coverage in this volume it was necessary to focus on a particular aspect of the geochemistry of iron. I have chosen to emphasize the surface cycle of iron, because (1) it has produced the greatest known anomalous concentrations of iron in the crust and (2) it appears to have changed with the evolution of the earth's atmosphere. Moreover, as proposed by Landergren in the first paper and to some extent by Park in the last paper, many iron deposits of hydrothermal or magmatic affiliation may in fact be composed of material that was initially concentrated by the surface processes.

The articles herein have been grouped into six topics: (1) Geochemistry and Abundance, (2) Solution, Deposition, and Transport, (3) Weathering and High-Grade Iron Deposits, (4) Iron-rich Sedimentary Rocks, (5) The Surface Cycle of Iron, and (6) Hydrothermal Iron Deposits. To adhere to this subdivision a number of individual articles were split so that excerpts might appear under several subheadings. Initially it was my intention to arrange the contributions within each section historically. It soon became clear that space did not permit the historical approach and many fine contributions made early in this century had to be omitted. Most of the classic early papers on the subject are fortunately reviewed or referred to in articles that are published in this volume.

Henry Lepp

Contents

Contents by Author

Introduction

Iron is the most important metal in the universe. It is considered the most abundant element in the earth as a whole and it ranks fourth in abundance in the crust after oxygen, silicon, and aluminum. It occurs as a major or minor constituent of all mineral classes. Of the major chemical elements in the earth's crust, iron is unusual in that it occurs in several valence states. The fact that it may be oxidized or reduced in natural environments markedly affects its geochemical cycle. Ferric oxide may oxidize organic matter and thus become reduced to the ferrous state. The ferrous solutions thus formed may in turn be reoxidized by atmospheric oxygen. Iron thus acts as a catalyst in the cycle of carbon, and its cycle is also closely bound to that of oxygen.

Iron plays an important role in the biosphere. In animals it acts in transporting oxygen from air or water to the body tissues. In green plants iron is necessary for the formation of chlorophyll. Some bacteria possess an enzyme system that transfers electrons from ferrous iron to O_2, thus freeing them from dependence on organic matter as an energy source.

It is a difficult task to determine the average composition of the earth's crust because of the diversity of materials and because only a small portion of the whole is accessible for sampling. Over the years, however, many thousands of rock analyses have been made and a number of scientists have reported on the average abundances of the chemical elements. Some values for the average iron tenor of the crust are listed in Table 1. They show the crust to contain about 5 percent iron by weight with the small spread indicating the uncertainty.

Table 2 contains reported values for the average iron tenors of various rock types. Although iron is locally markedly enriched in bodies considered to have been formed by either magmatic or hydrothermal processes, by far the most extensive anomalous concentrations are found in the group of sedimentary rocks called iron-formations and ironstones.

Because iron is such an important and ubiquitous element, the literature dealing

Table 1. Estimates of the average iron content of the earth's crust

Source	Fe_2O_3	FeO	Total Fe	Remarks
Clarke, 1924	3.2	3.8	5.2	
Goldschmidt, 1933	3.3	3.5	5.0	
Vinogradov, 1962	2.5	3.7	4.6	
Taylor, 1949			5.6	Continental crust
Poldervaardt, 1955	2.3	5.0	5.5	Continental crust
Poldervaardt, 1955	2.8	5.8	6.5	Entire lithosphere
Pakiser and Robinson, 1967	2.3	5.5	5.9	Continental crust
Ronov and Yaroshevsky, 1969	2.6	3.9	4.9	Continental crust
Ronov and Yaroshevsky, 1969	2.6	4.4	5.2	Entire lithosphere

Table 2. Average iron content of various rocks

Rock Type	Fe_2O_3	FeO	Total Fe	Source
Igneous rocks				
Average	2.9	3.3	4.6	Brotzen (1966)
Granites	1.6	1.8	2.5	Daly (1933)
Granodiorites	1.3	2.6	2.9	Nockolds (1954)
Diorites	2.7	7.0	7.3	Nockolds (1954)
Olivine basalts	3.7	8.1	8.9	Poldervaardt (1955)
Peridotites	2.5	9.9	9.4	Nockolds (1954)
Sedimentary rocks				
Average	3.5	2.6	4.5	Garrels and Mackenzie (Paper 11)
Sandstones	1.7	1.5	2.4	Pettijohn (1963)
Shales	4.2	3.0	5.3	Clarke (1924)
Limestones			0.36	Clarke (1924)
Iron formations			28.0	Lepp and Goldich (Papers 22 and 28)
Metamorphic rocks				
Quartzo-feldspathic gneisses	1.6	2.0	2.7	Poldervaardt (1955)
Mica schists	2.1	4.6	5.0	Poldervaardt (1955)
Precambrian slates	4.1	6.7	8.1	Nanz (1953)
Amphibolites	3.7	8.9	9.5	Lapadu-Hargues (1953)

with various aspects of its geochemistry is voluminous. To achieve some depth in this selection of articles it was necessary to focus on some aspect of iron geochemistry. The focus here is on the anomalous concentrations of iron in the earth's crust and on the processes that have produced these enrichments. Moreover, because the most extensive iron deposits are those formed by the surface processes, this series of articles is devoted chiefly to the exogenic cycle of iron.

The Cycle of Iron

Figure 1 shows the cycle of iron in the lithosphere as modified after Landergren (Paper 1). The various stages of the cycle, such as the ferruginous laterites, bog ores,

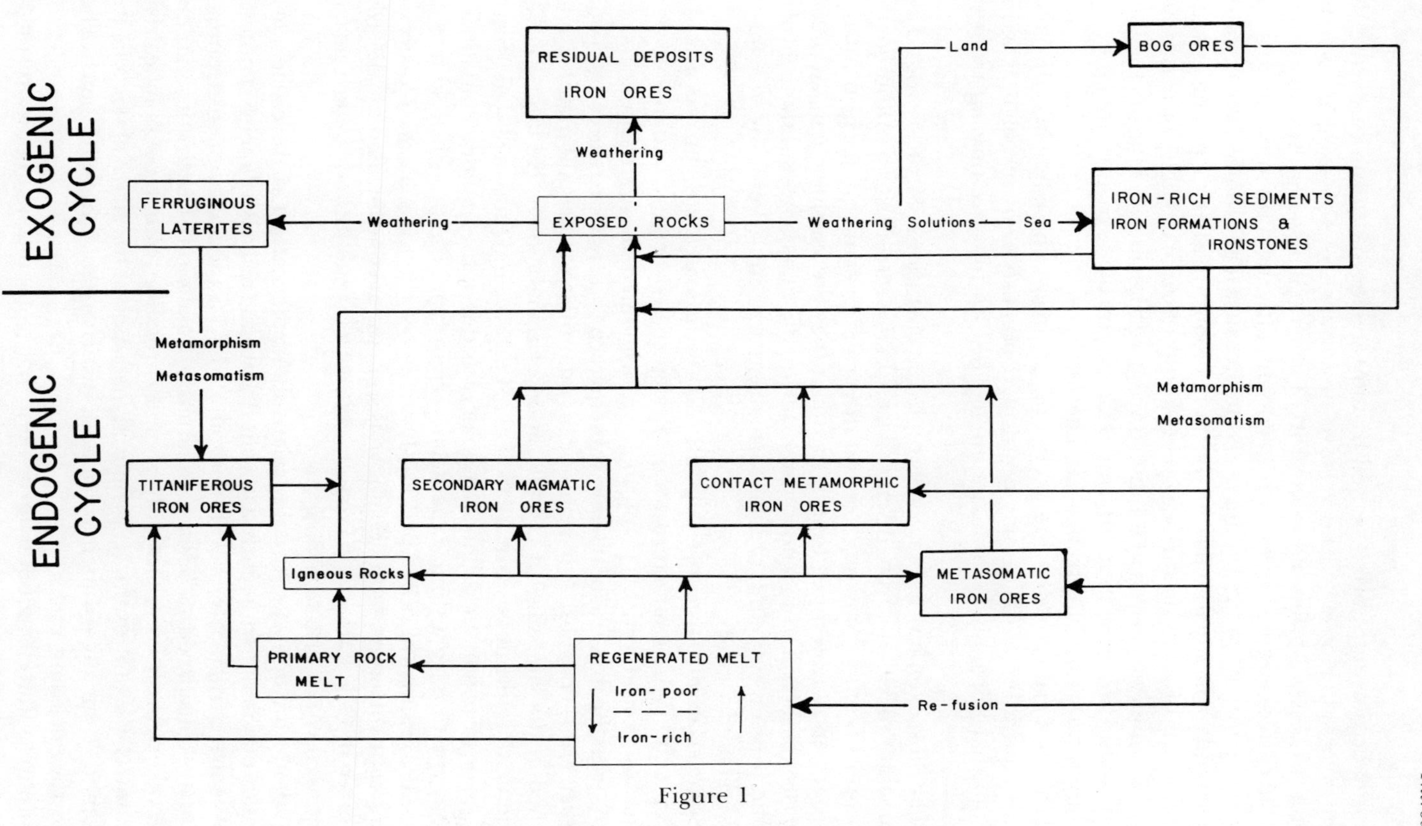
EXOGENIC
CYCLE
ENDOGENIC
CYCLE
RESIDUAL DEPOSITS
IRON ORES
Weathering
Land
BOG ORES
FERRUGINOUS
LATERITES
Weathering
EXPOSED ROCKS
Weathering Solutions
Sea
IRON-RICH SEDIMENTS
IRON FORMATIONS &
IRONSTONES
Metamorphism
Metasomatism
Metamorphism
Metasomatism
TITANIFEROUS
IRON ORES
SECONDARY MAGMATIC
IRON ORES
CONTACT METAMORPHIC
IRON ORES
Igneous Rocks
METASOMATIC
IRON ORES
PRIMARY ROCK
MELT
REGENERATED MELT
Iron-poor
Iron-rich
Re-fusion

Figure 1

metasomatic ores, etc., are accepted by most geologists and in this sense the cycle is uncontroversial. However, the relative importance of the exogenic versus the endogenic processes as prime concentrators of iron remains a highly controversial subject.

When deep-seated rocks with predominantly ferrous minerals are exposed to weathering, iron is oxidized to ferric oxide. Because it is insoluble, the ferric oxide thus formed tends to be separated from the more mobile weathering products, such as Mg^{2+}, Ca^{2+}, Na^{+}, and K^{+}, in the surface cycle. Under tropical to subtropical conditions even silica is sometimes removed in solution during weathering, resulting in the formation of lateritic soils. Large quantities of iron oxide or iron oxide hydrate together with hydrated aluminum oxides are trapped in laterites.

Where lateritic weathering occurs on an iron-rich sediment, concentrations of relatively pure ferric oxide may be formed because elements such as aluminum or titanium that normally accumulate in laterite with iron are missing from the source rock.

The most extensive anomalously high concentrations of iron are found in iron-rich sedimentary rocks, which are discussed later in this introduction. Although there is still not consensus among investigators on the origin of sedimentary iron-formations and ironstones, most now agree that in the main they are marine chemical precipitates of materials weathered from land masses. During the first quarter of this century, the idea that the iron in sedimentary iron-formations was contributed by volcanism was the more accepted view.

Some relatively large iron deposits such as those in the Kiruna district of northern Sweden exhibit the characteristics of a deep-seated origin. The magnetite bodies at Kiruna are considered by many to have originated by segregation in an iron-rich magma with the iron fraction being subsequently injected into the country rocks. A. M. Bateman (1951) proposed that significant quantities of iron and titanium may become enriched in the late stage of crystallization of a mafic melt. He interpreted the large magnetite-ilmenite deposits at Allard Lake, Quebec, and those near Lake Sanford, New York, to be of magmatic origin. Bateman considered the magnetite-apatite ores of the Kiruna type to have a similar magmatic origin from a more silicic source magma. P. Geijer (1931) and others had previously attributed the Kiruna ores to processes related to magmatic differentiation. That iron is sometimes concentrated by differentiation is supported by C. F. Park's (1961) observation of a magnetite body in northern Chile with the characteristics of a lava flow.

Other iron deposits, usually relatively small, consist of cross-cutting irregular bodies of magnetite frequently associated with skarn. Park (Paper 37) noted that such deposits are particularly prevalent around the Pacific basin. Such deposits are most frequently considered to be of contact metasomatic or of hydrothermal origin. The mode of origin, however, is only an interpretation; other possibilities exist. H. G. Backlund (1952), for example, proposed that some of the skarn and leptite iron ores of Sweden were initially sedimentary deposits which were highly modified by rheomorphism of the enclosing rocks.

Whereas there is general agreement that iron-enriched bodies result from both surface and deep-seated processes, there is not consensus on the source of the iron for the deposits. In a way the literature on iron deposits and the iron cycle is like the neptunist–plutonist controversy of the late eighteenth century. If for the purpose of our analogy we interpret "neptunist" as formed by surface processes we have, on the one hand, men like Landergren, who concluded as a result of an extensive chemical investigation of iron ores (Paper 1) that most, if not all, enrichment of iron occurs in the surface cycle and that deposits classed as magmatic or hydrothermal consist of iron initially concentrated by the exogenic processes that has been remobilized in the endogene cycle. This idea of iron being concentrated chiefly in the surface cycle and remobilized at depth receives support from studies of the geochemistry of oxygen. T. F. W. Barth (1948) calculated that the oxygen in the atmosphere would suffice to oxide the iron in only 1.4 percent of the upper crust. The fact that the atmospheric oxygen has not been used up in the oxidation of iron suggests that there must be some process of returning oxygen that has been trapped with iron at the surface back to the atmosphere. Iron may thus act as a respiratory agent in the lithosphere, trapping oxygen near the surface and releasing it in the endogene cycle.

If "plutonist" is taken to mean with magmatic or volcanic affiliation, then those who propose that the sedimentary iron-formations received their iron from volcanic sources may be considered plutonists. According to their interpretation, even the large bodies of iron-rich sediments ultimately depend upon the endogene process of vulcanism. The endogene–exogene controversy extends also to the high-grade oxide ores associated with iron-formations in many parts of the world. J. W. Gruner (1930, Paper 15) proposed that the secondary enrichment of iron in the Lake Superior iron-formations was caused by hydrothermal oxidation and leaching, a position supported by subsequent workers in other parts of the world. Van Hise and Leith (1911), White (1954), James et al. (Paper 17), and others believe that the high-grade ores were concentrated by the surface processes.

An additional problem related to the surface cycle of iron is the chemical difference between some Precambrian and younger sediments. Nanz (1953) demonstrated that Precambrian shales contain less CaO and more Fe, FeO, Al_2O_3 and K_2O than their modern equivalents. Geologists have long known that most Precambrian iron-formations are highly siliceous and impoverished in Al_2O_3, P_2O_3, and TiO_2 relative to their younger counterparts. Not all investigators, however, are convinced that such chemical differences are real. O'Rourke (1961), for example, cites numerous examples of what he considers to be Phanerozoic siliceous banded iron-formations, and others have described Precambrian iron-rich sediments with the characteristics of younger ironstones. Most geologists are now agreed, however, that there are distinct chemical differences between Precambrian and younger iron-rich sediments and that these differences reflect a secular change in the surface cycle of iron.

MacGregor (1927) first proposed that the differences in iron sedimentation with time are related to the evolution of the earth's atmosphere. He postulated that the extensive development of iron-formations in the Precambrian was due to a higher CO_2 and a lower O_2 pressure in the atmosphere of that era, which allowed iron to be mobilized in the ferrous state. Rankama (1955) described the predominance of FeO over Fe_2O_3 in the Precambrian weathering product of a diorite. He suggested that the

Precambrian conglomerate must have formed in an atmosphere devoid of oxygen. Until the 1960s most geologists were reluctant to accept the idea of an oxygen-poor Precambrian atmosphere, and some considered it a violation of uniformitarianism. The idea persisted, however. Tyler and Twenhofel (1952) invoked differences in the earth's atmosphere to account for the restriction of the cherty iron-formations to the Precambrian, as did White (1954), Lepp and Goldich (Papers 22 and 28), Cloud (1965), James et al. (Paper 17), and others. The conclusion that the atmosphere was deficient in oxygen prior to about 1,800 million years ago is now widely accepted partly because scientists such as Miller and Urey (1959), Holland (1962), Berkner and Marshall (1965), and others working on the problem of the origin of life and the origin of the atmosphere came to a similar conclusion on other evidence.

The November 1973 issue of *Economic Geology* is devoted to the Precambrian iron-formations of the world. Although there is not consensus among contributors on the question of how iron-formations were formed, almost all agree that the surface cycle of iron was much different before about 1,900 million years ago than it has been since, and that this difference is directly or indirectly related to unique properties of the Precambrian atmosphere and hydrosphere. Moreover, radioactive dating of iron-formations and associated rocks has shown that the period between 1,800–2,600 million years ago was exceptional from the standpoint of iron sedimentation. The great iron-formations of the Lake Superior region, the Labrador Trough, the Krivoy Rog of the USSR, the Hammersley Range of Australia, and many others formed during this interval.

In the Precambrian the surface cycle of iron was such that iron accumulated with silica in the extensive cherty iron-formations. Large deposits of chert are known in Paleozoic and younger rocks, as are moderately extensive beds of ironstone, but the iron and chert are rarely found together.

Iron-Formations and Ironstones

The iron-rich sediments vary in texture, mineralogy, degree of metamorphism, and chemistry, and they have been variously called jaspillite, taconite, ferruginous quartzite, clay ironstone, etc. Brandt et al. (1972) recently reviewed the problem of nomenclature for these rocks. Most American geologists follow James (Paper 20) and use the term iron-formation for the cherty, frequently banded, iron-rich rocks. Ironstone is used most often for those oolitic and commonly fossiliferous iron sediments of the minette type that are associated with lime or clastics.

Because iron-formations and ironstones are either directly or in weathered form the principal sources of iron for commerce, they have been extensively studied. Much progress has been made in understanding the environments of deposition of these unique sediments, particularly as a result of the work of Castano and Garrels (1950), Krumbein and Garrels (1952), and more directly of James (Paper 20). On the question of origin, however, there still is considerable controversy. The problem of genesis is made difficult by the fact that similar rocks do not appear to be forming today.

Almost half a century ago, Moore and Maynard (1929), in summarizing the problem of the origin of the Lake Superior iron-formations, stated: "That the iron formations are of sedimentary origin is accepted by the great majority of geologists. The main points of difference in the various theories are: the source of the iron and silica, the means by which they were transported and precipitated, and the forms in which they were originally laid down." Although much has been learned since the above was written, these remain the main points of difference in the various present sedimentary models that are proposed to explain the iron-rich sediments.

Early in this century, most geologists were convinced that weathering solutions were inadequate to account for the iron and silica in, for example, the Biwabik iron-formation of Minnesota, which extends for a length of some 130 miles, is about 600 feet thick, and contains an average of 28 percent iron. Consequently, the favored interpretation was that the iron and silica had somehow been derived from contemporaneous volcanism. Gruner (1922) was instrumental in convincing many that weathering was indeed an adequate source when he calculated that the Amazon River moves an amount of iron equal to the total iron in the Biwabik formation in the short time of 176,000 years.

Most proponents of a weathering source for the iron and silica in iron-formations favor weathering of a low-lying land mass under humid tropical to subtropical conditions. This not only provides a possible source for the silica by lateritic weathering, but it also helps, in part, to account for the paucity of clastics in iron-formations. Gruner (1922), Gill (1927), Moore and Maynard (1929), Taylor (1949), Sakamoto (1950), Tyler and Twenhofel (1952), James (Paper 20), Hough (1958), Alexandrov (1955), Lepp and Goldich (Papers 22 and 28), Govett (Paper 33), and others have supported the idea of a weathering source.

Some geologists have looked to the sea as the source of the chemical elements in the iron sediments. This idea is attractive because it overcomes the problem of the near absence of clastics in iron-rich sediments. Until recently, however, it has not met with much favor because present-day seawater contains only minute concentrations of iron and silica. Borchert (Paper 26) suggested that the iron-rich sediments are the result of solution and reprecipitation of iron on the sea floor. Strahkov (1959) proposed that diagenetic enrichment through reactions with seawater was a factor in the buildup of iron-rich sediments. More recently Holland (1973) showed that seawater would have contained an adequate supply of dissolved iron in the Precambrian when the partial pressure of oxygen was much lower than it is now. He proposed that upwelling of the anoxygenic iron-enriched deep-water masses supplied the iron for Precambrian iron-formations.

An oceanic source for the iron ties in with the observation that many Precambrian iron-formations occupy the positions filled by limestones in more recent sedimentary sequences. Dimroth (1973) has described the marked textural and structural similarities between the iron-formations of the Labrador Trough and limestones.

Although a volcanic source for the iron and silica is no longer favored by most geologists, a few still look to volcanic activity as the ultimate contributor of the materials. It appears that volcanic solutions do indeed locally cause some iron enrichment in sediments. Zelenov (1958) showed that iron in solution was contributed to the sea by thermal springs of the Ebeko volcano. Bostrom (1970) demonstrated that iron is slightly enriched in some sediments of the Pacific floor by submarine volcanic activity. However, most ironstones and many iron-formations are not associated with volcanic or igneous rocks, which would seem to rule out a volcanic source. Moreover, Gruner (1922) and, more recently, Holland (1973) showed that the volume of volcanic solutions needed to supply the materials of the larger iron-formations is so large as to require a period of truly unusual volcanic activity. Certainly there should be a record of such intensive activity. In many iron districts, however, there is no evidence for exceptional volcanic activity.

Except for the Devonian iron sediments of the Lahn-Dill region of Germany, most Phanerozoic ironstones fail to show any evidence of volcanic affiliation, and they have been interpreted as sediments that acquired their materials from weathering solutions. The Lahn-Dill ores are thought by many to be related to volcanic activity. Harder (1964) investigated these deposits and concluded that they could not have accumulated directly from volcanic exhalations because other volatile metals that should have accompanied iron are lacking in the ores. He postulates that the iron and silica of the Lahn-Dill iron deposits were most likely contributed by low-temperature carbonate springs.

The early Precambrian iron-formations of the Keewatin type are another matter. Most are small, lens-like bodies, and many are intimately associated with volcanic rocks. For these formations many geologists who otherwise support a nonvolcanic source for the materials of iron-formation still favor a genetic relationship with vulcanism.

Although there is still debate about the source of the chemical elements in iron formation, most geologists now agree that they were transported in solution. The classic early work on the dissolution of iron and silica from various rock types was conducted by Gruner (1922) and by Moore and Maynard (1929). They concluded that the iron was carried as ferric oxide hydrosol stabilized by organic matter. Their proposal for colloidal transport has lost favor in recent years possibly because the concept of chemical facies (Paper 20) requires that iron be in solution at least at the site of deposition.

The above experiments were conducted in air. If it is agreed that the Precambrian atmosphere was deficient in oxygen, there is no problem in explaining the transport of dissolved iron in surface waters. However, this does not account for the situation in the younger ironstones, which clearly formed under an atmosphere similar to the present. In fact, the difficulty in explaining the transport of iron in the more recent ironstones is what makes Borchert's (Paper 26) idea of the solution of iron in anoxygenic portions of the oceans such an attractive explanation. Garrels et al. (1973), in discussing the iron-formation problem, recently noted that: "The diminution in importance of the cherty iron-formations during the later Proterozoic and their virtual absence during Phanerozoic time, may be an expression of the gradual diminution of ferrous iron as a significant means of iron transport in surface waters."

According to H. L. James (Paper 20), each of the various facies (oxide, carbonate, silicate, sulfide) of iron formation and ironstone represent a particular depositional environment. The iron minerals present reflect this environment, with the oxide facies being representative of an oxidizing to neutral environment on the one hand and the sulfide facies representing a strongly reducing environment. Deposition, therefore, is controlled by the chemical parameters of the depositional environment, which suggests that the iron is in the dissolved rather than colloidal state, at least at the time of deposition.

Since James published his classic paper on the sedimentary facies of iron-formations in 1954, geologists have mapped and studied the facies within iron-formations and ironstones in many parts of the world. That varying mineralogies (facies) exist is an established fact. There is, however, still uncertainty in some cases whether the iron minerals now present are primary or whether they are the result of diagenetic or low-grade metamorphic changes.

This problem of the primary versus a secondary replacement origin for the iron minerals is one that has long been debated. Cayeux (1922), for example, proposed for the oolitic ironstones of France that iron silicate (chamosite) formed by replacement of siderite and that goethite and sometimes hematite or magnetite were formed by subsequent oxidation of the ferrous minerals. A. F. Hallimond (1925), on the other hand, believes that the chamosite and siderite in the ironstones of England are primary. La Berge (1964), on the basis of extensive microscope study, concluded that much of the magnetite in the Lake Superior iron formations formed from siderite. Gunderson and Schwartz (1962) argue for a primary origin for the magnetite in the same rocks. Lepp and Goldich (Papers 22 and 28) concluded that the proportions of iron minerals versus gangue can best be explained by assuming an initial precipitate of calcite and siderite. Replacement by silica and diagenetic modifications are thought to have provided the present minerals. Govett (Paper 33) proposed that hematite is the only primary mineral in iron-formations and that the other iron minerals are diagenetic products.

This brief review has covered some of the many suggestions that have been proposed to explain the accumulation of the iron-rich sedimentary rocks. Other unresolved problems include the origin of the banding in iron-formations, the role of organisms in the development of the iron sediments, and the manner in which the chert of iron-formations was precipitated. A puzzling chemical aspect of Precambrian iron-formations is their remarkable uniformity in iron tenor. Those formations that have not been affected by secondary enrichment processes consistently average about 30 percent total iron by weight. Rocks with 10 to 20 percent iron are rare by comparison. Moreover, the tenor of iron appears to be related to the dominant iron mineral in a way that suggests a replacement relationship between the iron minerals.

Although significant progress has been made during the past half century in our knowledge of the iron-rich sediments and in our understanding of the cycle of iron in the lithosphere, there remain many unsolved problems. In fact, most of the current ideas on how the iron-rich sediments were formed can be traced back to the early part of this century. Today's scientists are better equipped with analytical data, fundamental thermodynamic data, and instruments to quantitatively test the various hypotheses. Much testing, however, remains to be done before there is consensus on the details of the iron cycle.

References

Alexandrov, E. A., 1955, Contribution to studies of origin of Precambrian banded iron ores: Econ. Geol., v. 50, p. 459–468.

Backlund, H. G., 1952, Some aspects of ore formation, Precambrian and later: Edinburgh Geol. Soc. Trans., v. 14, pt. 3, p. 302–335.

Barth, T. F. W., 1948, The distribution of oxygen in the lithosphere: Jour. Geol., v. 56, p. 40–49.

Bateman, A. M., 1951, Formation of late magmatic ore deposits: Econ. Geol., v. 46, p. 404–426.

Berkner, L. V., and L. C. Marshall, 1965, On the origin and rise of oxygen concentration in the earth's atmosphere: Jour. Atmospheric Sci., v. 22, p. 225–261.

Bostrom, K., 1970, Submarine volcanism as a source for iron: Earth Planet. Sci. Lett., v. 9, p. 348–354.

Brandt, R. T., et al., 1972, Problems of nomenclature for banded ferruginous cherty sedimentary rocks and their metamorphic equivalents: Econ. Geol., v. 67, p. 682–684.

Brotzen, D., 1966, The average igneous rock and the geochemical balance: Geochim. Cosmochim. Acta, v. 30, p. 863–868.

Castano, J. R., and R. M. Garrels, 1950, Experiments on the deposition of iron with special reference to the Clinton iron ore deposits: Econ. Geol., v. 45, p. 755–770.

Cayeux, L., 1922, Études des gîtes minéraux de la France. Les minerais de fer oolithique de la France, Fasc. II: Minerais de fer secondaire: Paris, Imprimerie Nationale, 1051 p.

Clarke, F. W., 1924, The data of geochemistry: U.S. Geol. Surv. Bull. 770, 841 p.

Cloud, P. E., Jr., 1965, Significance of the Gunflint (Precambrian) flora: Science, v. 148, p. 27–35.

Daly, R. A., 1933, Igneous rocks and the depth of the earth: McGraw-Hill Book Co., New York, 598 p.

Dimroth, E., 1973, Petrography of the Sokoman iron formation in part of the central Labrador trough, Quebec, Canada: Geol. Soc. America Bull., v. 84, p. 111–134.

Garrels, R. M., E. A. Perry, Jr., and F. T. Mackenzie, 1973, Genesis of Precambrian iron-formations and the development of atmospheric oxygen: Econ. Geol., v. 68, p. 1173–1179.

Geijer, P., 1931, Iron ores of the Kiruna type: Sver. Geol. Unders. ser. C, no. 367.

Gill, J. E., 1927, Origin of the Gunflint iron-bearing formation: Econ. Geol., v. 22, p. 687–728.

Goldschmidt, V. M., 1933, Grundlagen der quantitativen Geochemie: Fortschr. Mineral. Krist. Petrogr., v. 17, p. 112–156.

Gruner, J. W., 1922, The origin of sedimentary iron formations: Econ. Geol., v. 17, p. 407–460.

——, 1930, Hydrothermal oxidation and leaching experiments; their bearing on the origin of Lake Superior hematite-limonite ores: Econ. Geol., v. 25, p. 697–719, 837–867.

Gunderson, J. N., and G. M. Schwartz, 1962, The geology of the metamorphosed Biwabik iron formation, eastern Mesabi district, Minnesota: Minnesota Geol. Surv. Bull. 41, 193 p.

Hallimond, A. F., 1925, Iron ores—Bedded ores of England and Wales—Petrography and chemistry: Great Britain Geol. Surv. Mem., Spec. Rept. Min. Res., v. 29, 139 p.

Harder, H., 1964, Können Eisensäuerlinge die Genese der Lahn-Dill-Erze erklären? Beitrage Miner. Petrog., Bd. 9, 379–422.

Holland, H. D., 1962, Model for the evolution of the earth's atmosphere; *in* Petrologic studies: a volume to honor A. F. Buddington, Geol. Soc. America, New York, p. 447–477.

——, 1973, The oceans: A possible source of iron in iron-formations: Econ. Geol., v. 68, p. 1169–1172.

Hough, J. L., 1958, Fresh-water environment of deposition of Precambrian banded iron formations: Jour. Sed. Petrology, v. 28, p. 414–430.

Krumbein, W. C., and R. M. Garrels, 1952, Origin and classification of chemical sediments in terms of pH and oxidation–reduction potentials: Jour. Geol., v. 60, p. 1–33.

La Berge, G. L., 1964, Development of magnetite in iron formations of the Lake Superior region: Econ. Geol., v. 59, p. 1313–1342.

Lapadu-Hargues, P., 1953, Sur la composition chimique moyenne des amphibolites: Soc. Géol. France Bull., 6th ser., v. 3, p. 153–173.

MacGregor, A. M., 1927, The problems of the Precambrian atmosphere: South Africa Jour. Sci., v. 24, p. 155–172.

Miller, S. L., and H. C. Urey, 1959, Organic compound synthesis on the primitive earth: Science, v. 130, p. 245–251.

Moore, E. S., and J. E. Maynard, 1929, Transportation and precipitation of iron and silica: Econ. Geol., v. 24, p. 272–303, 365–402, 506–527.

Nanz, R. H., Jr., 1953, Chemical composition of pre-Cambrian slates with notes on the geochemical evolution of lutites: Jour. Geol., v. 61, p. 51–64.

Nockolds, S. R., 1954, Average chemical composition of some igneous rocks: Geol. Soc. America Bull., v. 65, p. 1007–1032.

O'Rourke, J. E., 1961, Paleozoic banded iron formation: Econ. Geol., v. 56, p. 331–361.

Pakiser, L. C., and R. Robinson, 1967, Composition of the continental crust as estimated from seismic observations: *in* The earth beneath the continents, Am. Geophys. Union Monogr. 10, p. 620–626.

Park, C. F., Jr., 1961, A magnetite "flow" in northern Chile: Econ. Geol., v. 56, p. 431–436.

Pettijohn, F. J., 1963, Chemical composition of sandstones: U.S. Geol. Surv. Prof. Paper 440-S, 119–144.

Poldervaart, A., 1955, Chemistry of the earth's crust: Geol. Soc. America Spec. Paper 62, p. 119–144.

Rankama, K., 1955, Geologic evidence of chemical composition of the Precambrian atmosphere: Geol. Soc. America Spec. Paper 62, p. 651–664.

Ronov, A. B., and A. A. Yaroshevsky, 1969, Earth's crust geochemistry: *in* Encyclopedia of geochemistry and environmental sciences, R. W. Fairbridge, ed., Van Nostrand Reinhold Co., New York, p. 243–254.

Sakamoto, T., 1950, The origin of Pre-Cambrian banded iron ores: Amer. Jour. Sci., v. 248, p. 449–474.

Strakhov, N. M., 1959, Schéma de la diagenèse des dépots marins: Eclogae Geol. Helv., v. 51, p. 761–767.

Taylor, J. H., 1949, Petrology of the Northampton Sand ironstone formation: Great Britain Geol. Surv. Mem., 111 p.

Tyler, S. A., and W. H. Twenhofel, 1952, Sedimentation and stratigraphy of the Huronian of Upper Michigan: Amer. Jour. Sci., v. 250, p. 1–27, 118–151.

Van Hise, C. R., and C. K. Leith, 1911, The geology of the Lake Superior region: U.S. Geol. Surv. Monogr. 52, 641 p.

Vinogradov, A. P., 1962, Average content of chemical elements in main types of igneous rocks of the earth's crust: Geokimiya, No. 7, p. 555–571 (in Russian).

White, D. A., 1954, The stratigraphy and structure of the Mesabi range, Minnesota: Minnesota Geol. Surv. Bull. 38, p. 1–92.

Zelenov, K. K., 1958, On the discharge of iron in solution into the Okhotsk Sea by thermal springs of the Ebeko volcano (Paramushir Island): Akad. Nauk SSSR Doklady, v. 120, p. 1089–1092 (English translation by Consultants Bureau, Inc., New York, 1959, p. 497–500).

I
Geochemistry and Abundance

Editor's Comments on Papers 1 Through 4

The papers in this section were selected primarily to provide data on the distribution of iron in various earth materials. In addition, the section is intended as an introduction to the geochemical behavior of the element. Because the classic papers dealing with the distribution of iron are long, it was necessary to select portions of the original works for reproduction.

The first paper is from an extensive study of the geochemistry of Swedish iron ores by Sture Landergren. Although this work was published in 1948, it remains one of the principal sources of information on the abundances of certain minor elements in various iron ores and related rocks.

Landergren began work on this project in 1937 while he was studying spectrographic research methods in the geochemical laboratory of the late V. M. Goldschmidt at the University of Oslo. In 1940, the Geological Survey of Sweden founded a geochemical laboratory and he continued the work there. An initial report on the geochemistry of the apatite iron ores of the Grängesberg mines was published in 1943.

Landergren reports in the preface that his original intent was to study the distribution of some significant minor constituents in Swedish Precambrian iron ores. As the study progressed, however, it became clear that additional information on the abundance of iron in other ores and rocks was necessary in order to interpret the data for the Precambrian ores. The study was thus expanded to provide sufficient data for an evaluation of the geochemical behavior of iron in the upper lithosphere.

The main body of Landergren's work contains abundance and statistical data on the distribution of the ferrides (Ti, V, Cr, Mn, Fe, Co, Ni) in various iron ores, iron formations, ironstones, and in the important rock types. In addition, the report contains information on the abundances of Li, Mg, Rb, K, Be, B, Mo, W, Ca, Na, and some of the lanthanides in the same crustal units. Numerous ratios, such as the quartz ratio (qv) and the MgO/FeO ratio (mgf) are reported, and since they are not defined in the chapter reproduced herein, they are listed below:

$$\text{quartz ratio (qv)} = \frac{100\ SiO_2}{SiO_2 + CaO + MgO + FeO + MnO}$$

$$\text{degree of oxidation (og)} = \frac{100(0.300 + 0.222p)}{(0.700 + 0.778p)\dfrac{0.3}{0.7}} \qquad p = FeO/Fe_2O_3 \text{ ratio (wt \%)}$$

$$\text{MgO/CaO ratio (mc)} = \frac{100\ MgO}{MgO + CaO}$$

The MgO/FeO (mgf), K_2O/Na_2O (kn), and Mn/Fe (mf) ratios were calculated in the same way that mc was calculated. All are molecular ratios.

The chapter reproduced as Paper 1 contains Landergren's interpretation of the data. He concludes that the primary enrichment of iron even in ores such as those at Kiruna and Grängesberg, which exhibit intrusive characteristics, must have occurred in the exogenic (surface) cycle. Most other geologists, such as Geijer (1931, 1935), conclude that these ores formed by magmatic processes.

Paper 2 in this series is an excerpt from U.S. Geological Survey Professional Paper 440-W, "Chemistry of the Iron-Rich Sedimentary Rocks," by Harold L. James. Other excerpts of this Professional Paper appear as Papers 21 and 32. To my knowledge, the section reproduced is currently the most complete compendium of data on the compositions of iron sediments from various parts of the world. Moreover, it contains excellent descriptions of the mineralogical and textural characteristics of the principal groups and facies of iron sediments and a fine commentary on the chemical properties of the various types of iron-rich sediments.

H. L. James received the Ph.D. from Princeton University and he has spent most of his professional career with the U.S. Geological Survey. From 1965 to 1971 he was Chief Geologist of the U.S.G.S. and he is currently a Research Geologist with that organization. Early in his career he was stationed for nearly a decade in the Iron River district of Michigan, and it was during this period that he published his now classic papers on the sedimentary facies of iron formation (James 1951, Paper 20). His facies concept has since been applied by others to iron-rich sediments throughout the world. James remains active in the field of iron deposits and iron geochemistry. He was one of the principal organizers of a Symposium on Precambrian Iron-Formations of the World held in Duluth in November 1972, and he is coeditor of and a contributor to a volume of *Economic Geology* (Vol. 68, No. 7, 1973) containing papers from the symposium.

Papers 3 and 4 are from the section on iron in the *Handbook of Geochemistry* edited by K. H. Wedepohl. They were selected to provide information on the abundance of iron in igneous rocks, on its behavior in the magmatic cycle, and on the abundance of iron in natural waters.

Paper 3 is by Robert F. Mueller, who is currently a Scientist at NASA's Goddard Space Flight Center. Mueller received his doctorate from the University of Chicago and spent the period from 1959–1962 at Scripps Oceanographic Institute. From 1962 to 1967 he taught at the University of Chicago, leaving there in 1967 for his present post.

Robert A. Berner, the author of Paper 4, also contributed Paper 8. He received his doctorate from Harvard University. After one year at Scripps Institute of Oceanography, he joined the faculty at the University of Chicago, where he taught from 1963 to 1965. Since 1965 he has been on the staff of Yale University.

References

Geijer, P., 1931, The iron ores of the Kiruna type: Sver. Geol. Unders. ser. C, no. 367.

———, 1935, Die nordschwedischen Eisenerze und verwandte Lagerstätten als Beispiele eruptiver Spaltungsprozesse: Geol. Rundschau, v. 26.

James, H. L., 1951, Iron formations and associated rocks in the Iron River district, Michigan: Geol. Soc. America Bull., v. 62, p. 251–266.
Landergren, S., 1943, Geokemiska studier över Grängesbergsfältets järnmalmer: Ingeniorsvetenskapsakademien, Stockholm, Handl. 172.
Wedepohl, K. H., ed., 1970, Handbook of geochemistry: Springer-Verlag, Berlin.

1

Reprinted from *Sveriges Geol. Under.*, Ser. C, **42**(5), 112–124, 129–138 (1948)

On the Geochemistry of Swedish Iron Ores and Associated Rocks

STURE LANDERGREN

Part Two.

Chapter IV. On the Geochemistry of the Ferrides.

Introduction.

Geochemists, geologists, and geophysicists have advanced several hypotheses on the constitution and history of the interior of the Earth. A valuable survey of the 20th century concepts on this matter is given by A. F. Buddington (12).

When dealing with the problems of the distribution of the elements in the Earth's crust, it would naturally be desirous to know as much as possible regarding the relative abundance of elements in the primary stage of evolution, *i.e.* in an undifferentiated matter. The greatest difficulty encountered in our endeavours to obtain numerical values of the relative abundance in this case is that of defining a fair sample. The Earth as a whole may be considered such a sample, but since the main part of the interior is inaccessible, we have got to find other methods to arrive at a reasonable conception of what may be regarded as a primary distribution of elements.

If we desire a distribution principle of elements of sufficient universality, the rule suggested by William D. Harkins is the first to be considered. Harkins pointed out that the elements with even atomic numbers are more abundant than those with odd numbers. Further, he arrived at the conclusion that the even-numbered members are always more abundant than the adjacent odd-numbered elements (56, p. 862).

In a series of important laboratory studies on the relative abundance of the lanthanides in the Earth's crust, V. M. Goldschmidt and L. Thomassen (48) found that Harkins' rule is strictly applicable in this coherent group of elements. Other investigations by Ida Noddack (92), E. Minami (88), Th. G. Sahama and V. Vähätalo (104), and the author (67) (cf also Table 35), have shown that, even in vastly different milieus, no deviations from Harkins' rule have so far been found as regards the relative abundance of the lanthanides.

Thus, the chemical differentiation is too feeble in the lanthanides to permit of any deviation from Harkins' rule, and the reasons are plain enough when considering the atomic structure of the lanthanides. The electrons (neglecting the inner ones) are grouped as follows:

Editor's Note: A row of asterisks indicates that material has been omitted from the original article.

$4s^2 4p^6 4d^{10} 4f^{0-14} 5s^2 5p^6$. The construction of the 4f-group continues while the outer electrons remain constant.

Now, when dealing with the alterations in the distribution of elements under different conditions, it would be more profitable to study alterations in the relative abundance of a coherent group of elements where the chemical differentiation is less feeble than that of the lanthanides, so that alterations in the relative abundance might be put in relation to differences in the milieus investigated.

The ferrides will be such a coherent group. Here the electrons are arranged as follows: $3s^2 3p^6 3d^{2-8}$. Thus, the completion of the 3d-group continues, but in this case the electrons belong to an outer "shell" (the M-shell). The next shell (the N-shell) is the seat of the valency electrons. This arrangement of the electrons finds an expression in a certain coordination of the ferrides in Nature, but the chemical differentiation is strong enough to effect alterations in the relative abundance of the ferride members in different milieus.

When dealing with problems connected with the enrichment of iron, the most abundant member, it is evidently of importance to study the distribution of all ferrides in different milieus. The geochemistry of the ferrides will consequently be closely discussed.

The "even-odd" rule for the distribution of elements, advanced by William D. Harkins (56), holds good also for the relative abundance of isotopes, as shown by F. W. Aston (3) and V. M. Goldschmidt (46). Since the abundance of elements discussed by Goldschmidt in his work quoted above refers to the mass-number (M), the author considers it suitable to choose the same x-axis, *viz.* the mass-numbers 46—62, to illustrate the relative abundance of the ferrides in different milieus. In the calculations are included the two calcium-isotopes $M = 46$ and $M = 48$, and the unimportant nickel isotope $M = 64$ is excluded.

The Abundance of the Ferride Isotopes in different Milieus.

Cosmos. On the basis of the data available on the distribution of elements, V. M. Goldschmidt has calculated the average abundance of elements in Cosmos, supposing that the relative abundance of isotopes for each element is similar to that found in material emanating from the Earth's crust (46), p. 120). The relative abundance of the ferride isotopes has been recalculated from Goldschmidt's tables and is shown in the diagram, fig. 19.

As seen from the diagram the even-odd rule for the abundance of isotopes is very well illustrated.

The abundance in Meteorites. The distribution of the ferrides in meteorites is well known to us thanks to investigations by O. C. Farrington (25), G. P. Merrill (87), G. Hevesy (58), I. and W. Noddack (90), V. M. Goldschmidt (44), and others. To ascertain the average contents of the various elements in mete-

8

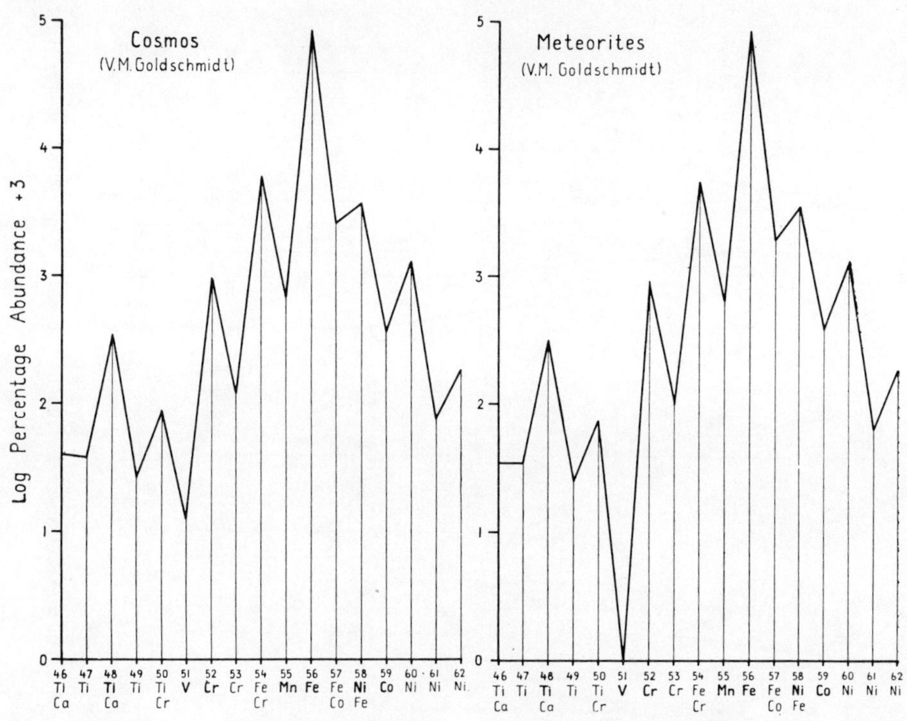

Fig. 19. Diagram of the percentage abundance of the ferride isotopes with mass-numbers 46—62 in Cosmos and Meteorites (mean).

orites V. M. Goldschmidt has made an estimate, assuming that the average composition of the meteorites is as follows: ten parts of stony meteorites, two parts of iron meteorites and one part of troilites. He arrives at the relative abundance — recalculated for the mass-numbers 46—62 — illustrated in fig. 19.

The correctness of Goldschmidt's assumption regarding the proportion of the three meteoritic phases may be discussed, but the estimate of the relative abundance seems to be reasonable. Thus, the similarity between the relative abundance of the ferride isotopes in Cosmos, on the one hand (fig. 19), and in the average of the meteorites, on the other (fig. 19), is obvious. In both cases the even-odd rule is strictly valid.

Now the question may be asked: What is the relative abundance of the ferride isotopes in the three phases (the iron, stone, and sulphide phase, respectively) after the primary endogene differentiation? It is well known that the lithophile tendency of the ferrides increases as the atomic number decreases, *viz.* from 28 Ni to 22 Ti. On the other hand, the chalcophile and siderophile tendency is greatest for the triade Fe-Co-Ni. These elements also show the greatest similarity in their atomic structure. The features mentioned find an expression in their relative abundance in the three meteoritic phases.

On the basis of investigations by Goldschmidt and I. and W. Noddack on

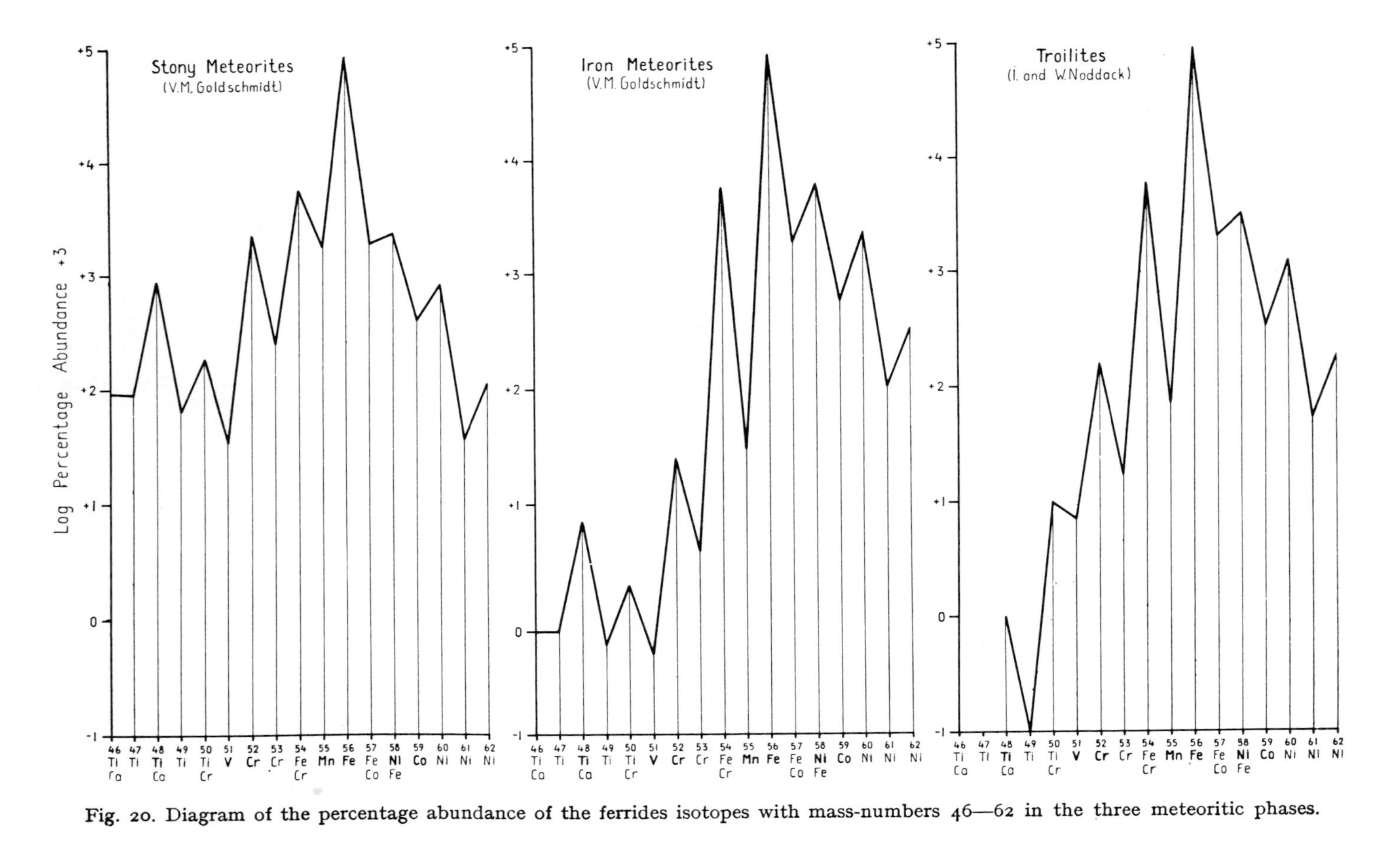

Fig. 20. Diagram of the percentage abundance of the ferrides isotopes with mass-numbers 46—62 in the three meteoritic phases.

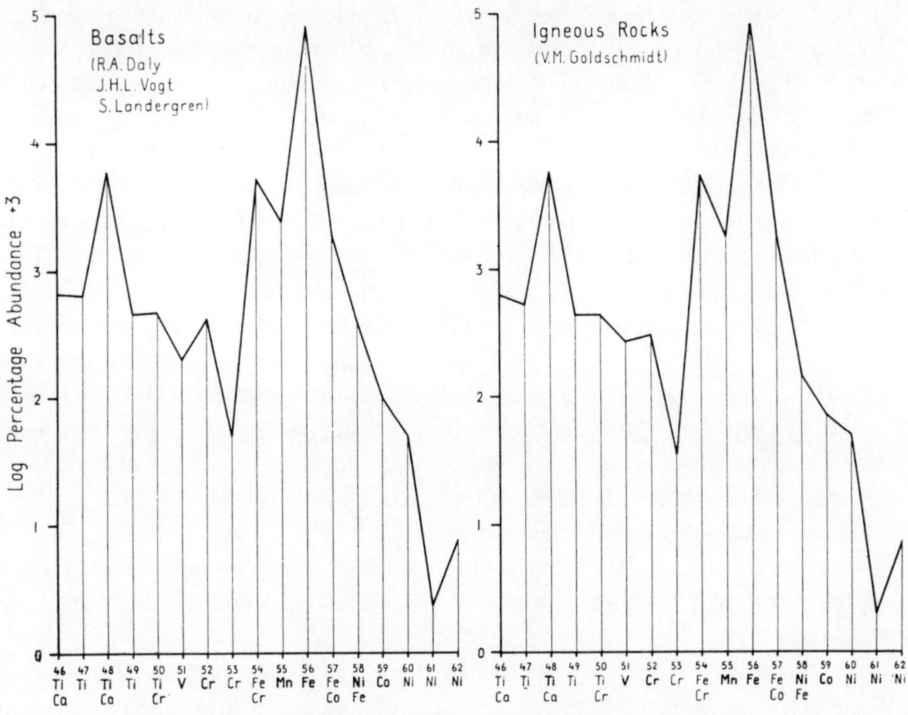

Fig. 21. Diagram of the percentage abundance of the ferride isotopes with mass-numbers 46—62 in basalts and in the igneous rocks (mean).

the distribution of elements in meteorites, the author has calculated the relative abundance of the ferride isotopes in the three meteoritic phases, using Aston's figures for the percentage abundance of isotopes in his work quoted above (3). This is shown in fig. 20.

It is evident that the data available must be regarded as approximations, and their validity as average values may be discussed. However, they show the tendency in the distribution of the ferrides, and the main geochemical features of the various members of the ferrides appear in the diagrams in fig. 20. Thus, the isotopes of the members with a lithophile tendency (M: 46—55) are most abundant in the stony meteorites but decrease considerably in the iron and sulphide meteorites. The proportion between the lithophile isotopes, on the one hand, and those with siderophile and chalcophile tendency (M: 56—62), on the other, varies exactly as might be expected. However, the remarkable constancy in the relative abundance of the latter isotopes should be noted. The author will return to this question later.

Igneous rocks. Fig. 21 above illustrates the average abundance of the ferride isotopes in the basalts and in the igneous rocks of the upper lithosphere. The figures for the igneous rocks are from Goldschmidt's work quoted above. The figures for the basalts are recalculated from the works of R. A. Daly (17),

J. H. L. Vogt (119), H. S. Washington (120), and some complementary analyses by the author on rock samples from the Mineralogical Department of the University of Stockholm. The figures for vanadium, chromium and cobalt cannot be regarded as good mean values, but they give a conception of the distribution tendency.

If we assume that the composition of the stony meteorites approximately corresponds to that of the peridotites of the interior of the Earth beneath the basaltic substratum (cf. Buddington (12), it can be said that the relative abundance of the ferrides from the peridotitic to the basaltic stage of evolution has undergone a remarkable alteration. Thus, titanium has increased considerably, chromium, cobalt and nickel, on the other hand, have decreased to the same extent and manganese has remained practically constant. The alterations mentioned involve, *inter alia*, that the even-odd rule, which is strictly valid for the meteorites (peridotites), is not valid for the basalts, especially with regard to the relative abundance of the isotopes of iron, cobalt and nickel.

If the composition of the igneous rocks estimated by Goldschmidt approximates an average of the Earth's crust, we find that the relative abundance of the ferrides in the igneous rocks shows a striking similarity to that of the basalts.

The geochemical features mentioned must not be overlooked when dealing with problems connected with the origin of the upper lithosphere. Since the average composition of the upper lithosphere is influenced by the composition of the sediments, some data on the relative abundance of the ferrides in some sediments are presented below.

Sediments. The relative abundance of the ferride isotopes in the following sediments will be illustrated: marine bottom sediment from the Tyrrhenian Sea, the Mediterranean, post-glacial clay-gyttja from the Viskan Valley, Sweden, Ordovician alum shale, Sweden, and lateritic iron ore, N. Ireland. The relative abundance is illustrated in the diagrams of fig. 22.

In the Mediterranean sediments we find a relative abundance of ferride isotopes, which — apart from some unimportant details — is fairly similar to that in the igneous rocks (fig. 21). However, there are some trends in the distribution that differ from the trends in the igneous rocks and should be noted. The vanadium isotope ($M = 51$) is more abundant than in the igneous rocks. Thus, the content of V^{51}_{23} is greater than that of the two adjacent odd members, $Ti^{50}_{22} + Cr^{50}_{24}$, on the one hand, and Cr^{52}_{24}, on the other. This is quite contrary to the even-odd rule. Further, $Fe^{57}_{26} > Fe^{58}_{26} + Ni^{58}_{28} > Co^{59}_{27} >$ $> Ni^{60}_{28}$, quite as in the igneous rocks.

The post-glacial clay-gyttja (cf. Landergren (70) p. 4 and fig. 2) shows a relative abundance of ferride isotopes, very similar to that of the sediment discussed above and requires no special comment.

The general trend in the abundance of the ferride isotopes in the Ordovician

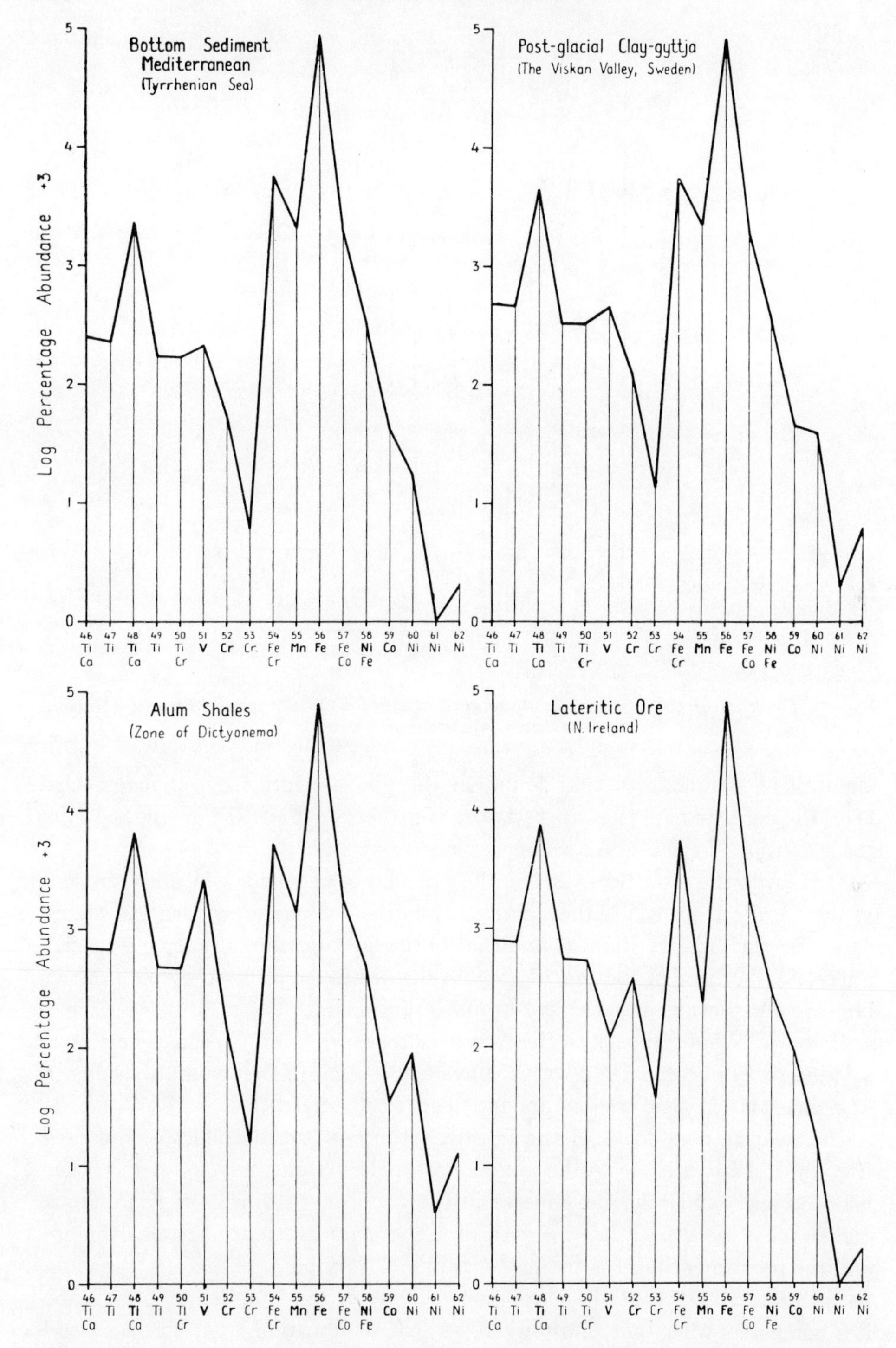

Fig. 22. Diagram of the percentage abundance of the ferride isotopes with mass-numbers 46—62 bottom sediment from the Tyrrhenian Sea (Mediterranean), post-glacial clay-gyttja from the Viskan valley, Sweden, alum shale, Sweden, and lateritic sediment, N. Ireland.

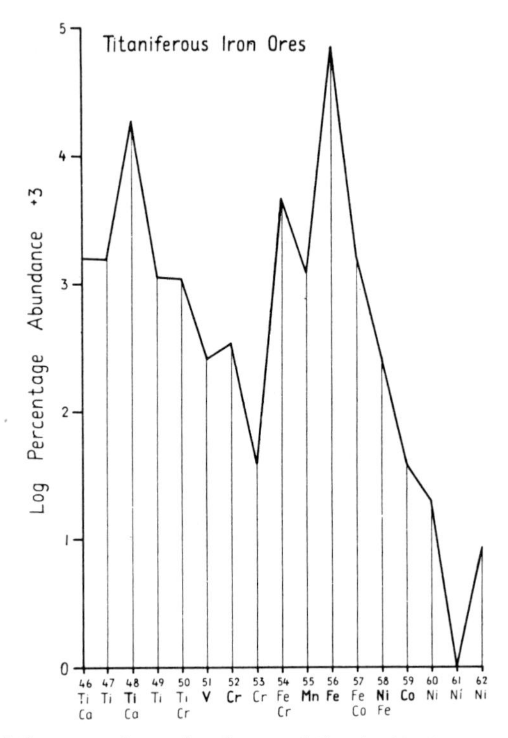

Fig. 23. Diagram of the percentage abundance of the ferride isotopes with mass-numbers 46—62 in titaniferous iron ores.

alum shale is similar to that found in the above-mentioned sediments, but here the content of V^{51}_{23} is appreciable. Further $Co^{59}_{27} < Ni^{60}_{28}$, contrary to the conditions in the other sediments discussed.

As regards the lateritic sediment the abundance of ferrides depends on that in the basalts from which they derive. Thus the similarity between the abundance in the basalts (fig. 21) and that in the laterites shows that no essential alteration in the distribution of the ferrides has taken place on account of the lateritic weathering and the ore-forming processes.

Iron ores. What happens to the ferride isotopes when iron becomes enriched, say, ten times in comparison with the average content of the upper lithosphere? The diagrams in figs. 23—28 are intended to illustrate this.

The relative abundance of the ferride isotopes in the titaniferous iron ores (fig. 23) is fairly similar to the abundance in the basalts, which, on the other hand, is approximately the same as in the gabbros, to which the titaniferous ores in most cases are related genetically. The main difference between the ore and the rocks mentioned is the higher content of titanium in the ore. It should be mentioned, too, that the chromium content of the titaniferous ores is too low compared with that of titanium, so that a deviation from the even-odd rule appears in the relative abundance of the two isotopes $Ti^{49}_{22} > Ti^{50}_{22} + Cr^{50}_{24}$.

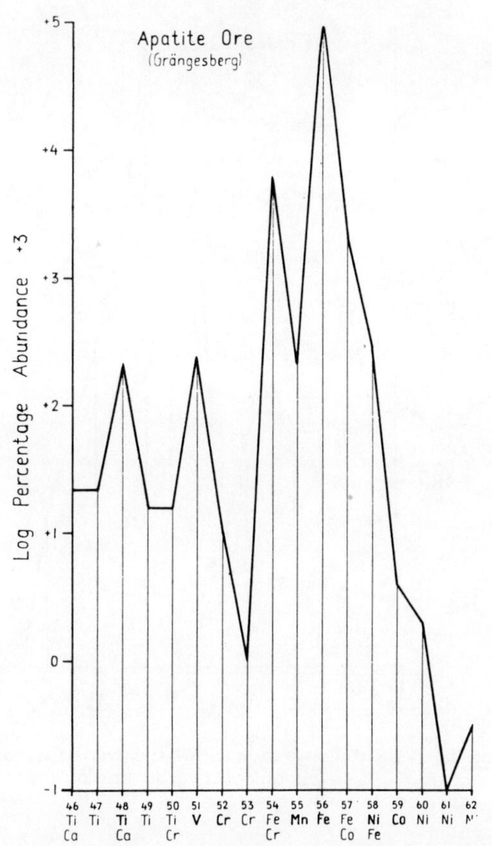

Fig. 24. Diagram of the percentage abundance of the ferride isotopes with mass-numbers 46—62 in apatite iron ores of Grängesberg, Sweden.

The most remarkable feature in the distribution of the ferrides in the apatite ores is the high vanadium content. Thus V^{51}_{23} is much greater than the two adjacent members $Ti^{50}_{22} + Cr^{50}_{24}$ and Cr^{52}_{24}. Further $V^{51}_{23} > Cr^{48}_{20} + Ti^{48}_{22}$ and $V^{51}_{23} > Mn^{55}_{25}$, as seen from fig. 24 above.

Fig. 25 shows the distribution of the ferride isotopes in the oolitic ores. In this ore type we again meet with the characteristic fairly great abundance of the vanadium isotope V^{51}_{23}, which is greater than the abundance of the adjacent members $Ti^{50}_{22} + Cr^{50}_{24}$ and Cr^{52}_{24}, respectively. Further, the isotopes of cobalt and nickel are more abundant than in the apatite ore of Grängesberg (fig. 24).

In the sideritic and the bog ores the abundance of ferride isotopes has decreased considerably as compared with conditions in the oolitic ores, as seen from fig. 26. Thus, the content of vanadium in the sideritic ores is small, so that $Ti^{50}_{22} + Cr^{50}_{24} > V^{51}_{23} > Cr^{52}_{24}$. The abundance of cobalt is approximately the same as in the oolitic ores. In the bog ores the distribution is rather irregular, partly due to the high content of manganese and partly to the low content of

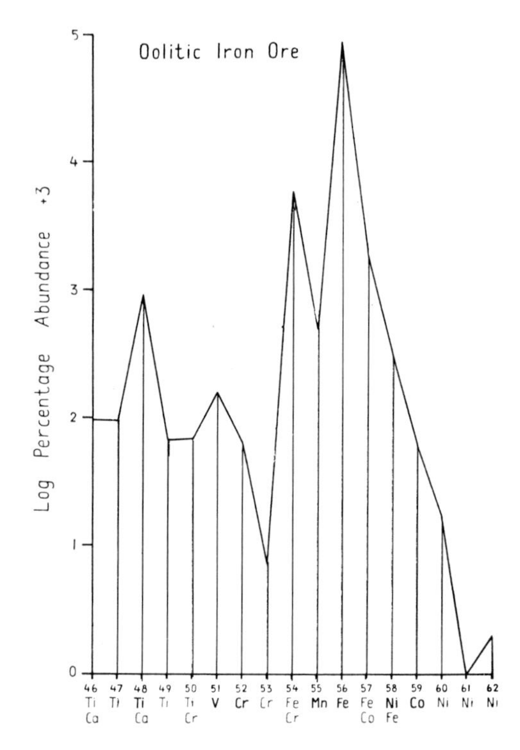

Fig. 25. Diagram of the percentage abundance of the ferride isotopes with mass-numbers 46—62 in oolitic iron ores.

titanium, vanadium and chromium. The distribution of the ferride isotopes in the lateritic ores is illustrated in fig. 22.

Let us turn, finally, to the relative abundance in the pre-Cambrian iron-ore types from central Sweden. The diagrams will be found in figs. 27 and 28. The most characteristic feature that these ores have in common is the great difference in the abundance of iron, on the one hand, and of the other ferrides (in some cases apart from manganese), on the other.

Fig. 27 shows the abundance of ferrides in the skarn and lime-dolomite ores. The diagram of the skarn ores shows a remarkable deficiency in the contents of ferrides, both the lithophile and the chalcophile members. The lime-dolomite ores are characterized by the high content of manganese, and here, again, one can observe that the vanadium isotope is more abundant than the adjacent even-numbered members.

The distribution of the ferride isotopes in the quartz ores is interesting, as seen from the diagrams in fig. 28.

In the banded quartz ores the great abundance of V^{51}_{23} is significant, and $V^{51}_{23} = Ti^{48}_{22} + Ca^{48}_{20}$. Thus, there is a striking similarity in the distribution of the ferrides in the banded quartz ores and in the marine sedimentary oolitic

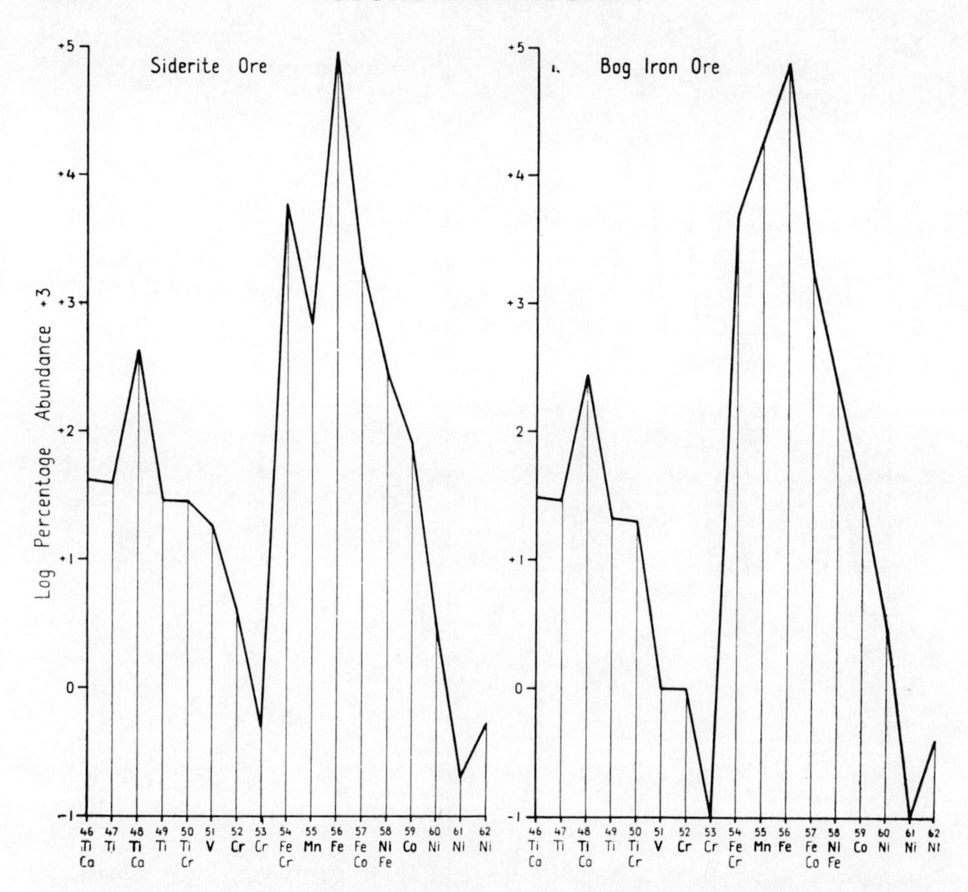

Fig. 26. Diagram of the percentage abundance of the ferride isotopes with mass-numbers 46—62 in siderite ores and in the bog iron ores of Finland.

ore type, but it should be emphasized that the content of ferrides in the oolitic ores is greater than in the banded quartz ores. In the not banded quartz ores the contents of ferrides are low and the diagram shows no feature worth mentioning.

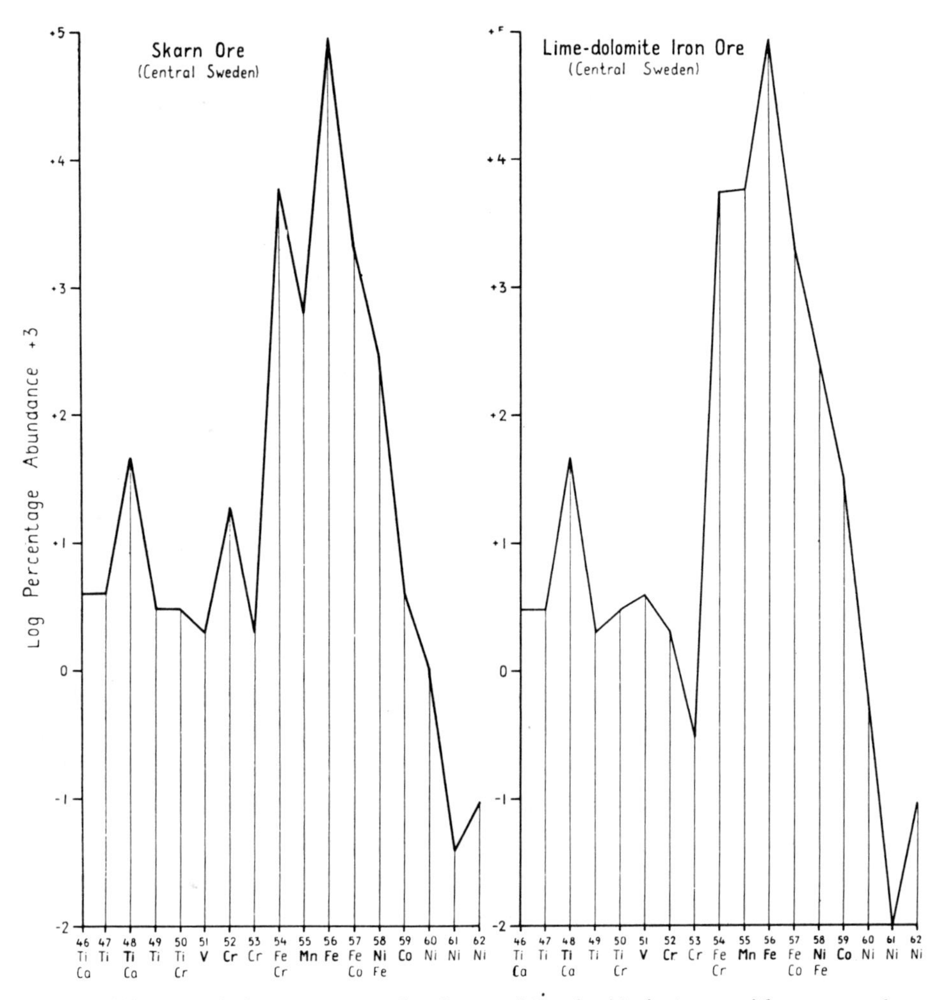

Fig. 27. Diagram of the percentage abundance of the ferride isotopes with mass-numbers 46—62 in skarn and lime-dolomite ores from central Sweden.

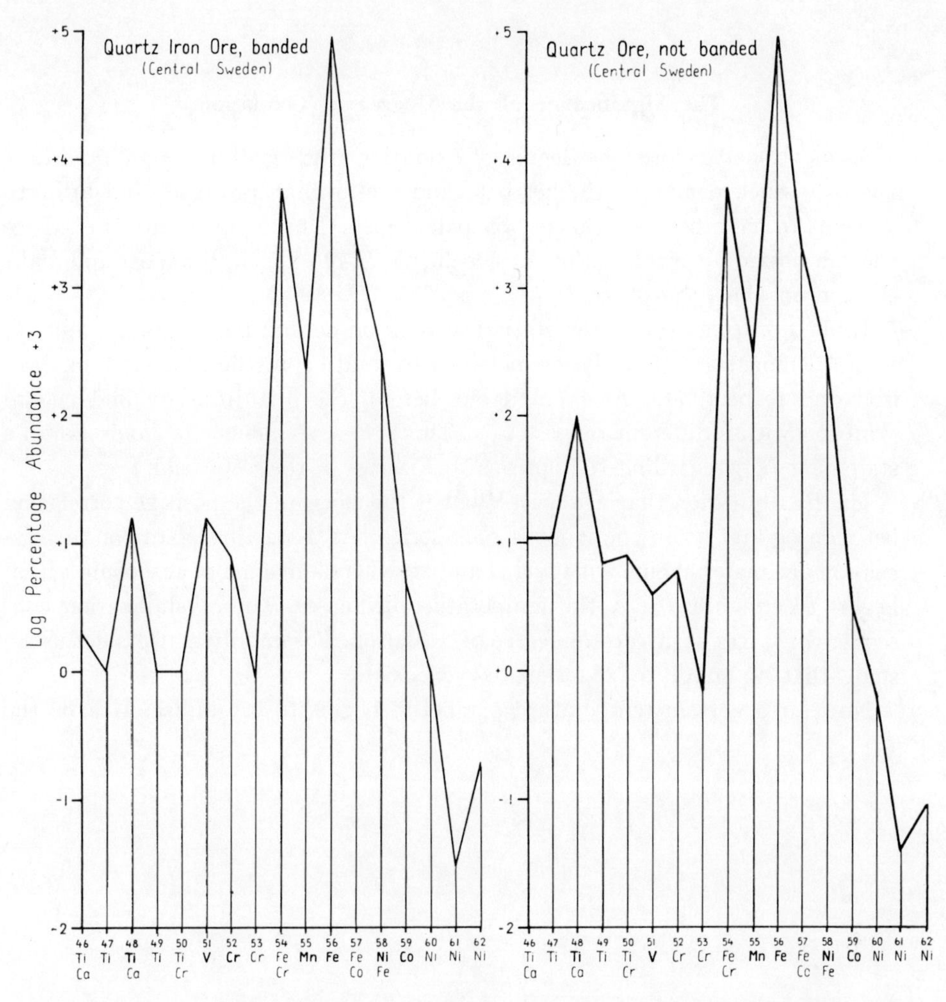

Fig. 28. Diagram of the percentage abundance of the ferride isotopes with mass-numbers 46—62 in banded and not banded quartz iron ores from central Sweden.

* * * * * * *

The Significance of the Degree of Oxidation.

As mentioned before, the degree of oxidation (the og-value) is an important quantity when dealing with the rock- and ore-forming processes and hitherto it seems to have been overlooked by petrologists. Through the ratio Fe^{2+}/Fe^{3+} one can obtain a conception of the geochemistry of oxygen, the most abundant element in the lithosphere.

Table 2 on p. 25 shows the statistical data on og and figs 12, p. 47, and 16, p. 49, demonstrate the relation between qv and og in the igneous rocks and iron ores respectively. As pointed out before, the quantities qv and og are symbatic within different ranges of qv. This is in agreement with Goldschmidt's statement (47) regarding the igneous rock series in the Oslo field.

The first question that arises is: What is the cause of the positive correlation between og and qv in the igneous rock series? As a starting point for the discussion one may imagine a magma chamber, where a magma of any composition begins to crystallize, *i. e.* the temperature decreases. The crystallization consequently starts at a certain degree of oxidation. To simplify matters, let us assume that no supply of external oxygen exists.

Now, at a certain temperature magnetite begins to crystallize. If a be the primary content of Fe^{3+} and b that of Fe^{2+}, where $a < b$, the primary ratio $Fe^{3+}/Fe^{2+} = a/b$. When c molecules of magnetite have crystallized the ratio Fe^{3+}/Fe^{2+} gets the value $\frac{a-c}{b-c} < \frac{a}{b}$, *i. e.* the degree of oxidation decreases in the melt.

According to Wickman in his paper quoted above, it is reasonable to believe that all ions with high charges and coordination numbers between four and six have large E-values when in the most favourable coordination. This is certainly true of trivalent iron and it is therefore probable that $E_{Fe^{3+}} > E_{Fe^{2+}}$. In this connection Wickman may be cited again: "During the course of differentiation one can therefore reckon with a steady production of trivalent iron, which apart from the amount incorporated in the silicate structures forms magnetite, when a sufficient concentration is reached. As a rule the content of divalent iron is sufficiently large to prevent the formation of hematite." (125) p. 385).

Consequently it might be expected that the degree of oxidation would decrease or possibly remain constant during the course of differentiation. An increase in the degree of oxidation under pure endogene conditions is exceedingly unlikely for reasons mentioned.

Nevertheless, the degree of oxidation increases in the igneous rock series, as shown in Table 2 on p. 25. This can be explained in two ways: On the one hand, an oxidation of the crystallizing system may take place due to successive assimilation of external material with a higher degree of oxidation than that of the primary system. On the other hand, a reaction with the volatiles present in the crystallizing system may take place.

However, the latter alternative seems to be the less probable, for reasons which will now be discussed. The two by far most abundant volatiles are H_2O and CO_2. The oxidation of Fe^{2+} to a higher degree of oxidation takes place due to the two reactions:

$$\text{I.} \quad 3\,FeO + H_2O = Fe_3O_4 + H_2$$

$$\text{II.} \quad 3\,FeO + CO_2 = Fe_3O_4 + CO.$$

These two well-known "furnace reactions" have been closely investigated by several authors. The equilibrium constant (K_p) has been calculated at different temperatures by M. Tigerschiöld (115) and is given in Table 60 below.

As seen from the table reactions I and II run in favour of magnetite formation as the temperature decreases. However, the two oxidation processes I and II correspond to the following reduction processes:

$$\text{III.} \quad H_2 + 3\,Fe_2O_3 = 2\,Fe_3O_4 + H_2O \text{ and}$$

$$\text{IV.} \quad CO + 3\,Fe_2O_3 = 2\,Fe_3O_4 + CO_2,$$

the equilibrium constants of which are given in Table 61.

Table 60.

I: $3\ FeO + H_2O = Fe_3O_4 + H_2$

Temperature (Centigrade)	K_p
570	3.85
615	2.27
640	1.75
700	0.97
725	0.78
768	0.54
770	0.53
800	0.41
805	0.40
885	0.22
900	0.20
950	0.14

II: $3\ FeO + CO_2 = Fe_3O_4 + CO$

Temperature (Centigrade)	K_p
627	0.76
662	0.66
720	0.54
863	0.34
963	0.26
1 070	0.19
1 175	0.15

Table 61.

III: $3\ Fe_2O_3 + H_2 = 2\ Fe_3O_4 + H_2O$.

Temperature (Centigrade)	K_p at an og-value of	
	99.7	90.0
527	$3.21 \cdot 10^5$	$6.40 \cdot 10^4$
727	$1.50 \cdot 10^5$	$4.13 \cdot 10^4$
927	$1.01 \cdot 10^5$	$3.43 \cdot 10^4$
1 127	$8.22 \cdot 10^4$	$3.27 \cdot 10^4$

IV: $3\ Fe_2O_3 + CO = 2\ Fe_3O_4 + CO_2$.

Temperature (Centigrade)	K_p at an og-value of	
	99.7	90
527	$1.80 \cdot 10^6$	$3.51 \cdot 10^5$
727	$2.14 \cdot 10^5$	$5.80 \cdot 10^4$
927	$5.83 \cdot 10^4$	$1.97 \cdot 10^4$
1 127	$2.51 \cdot 10^4$	$9.86 \cdot 10^3$

The values of K_p indicate that the reactions in question also run in favour of magnetite formation at any temperature that may reasonably be taken into account. As M. Tigerschiöld has pointed out, reactions III and IV are practically irreversible (115). Thus, we are concerned with redox-systems that have no other influence on the degree of oxidation in the crystallizing system than that discussed before.

Finally, the thermal dissociation of Fe_2O_3 should be mentioned in this connection. The dissociation runs as follows:

$$6\ Fe_2O_3 = 4\ Fe_3O_4 + O_2.$$

The reaction has been investigated by Sosman and Hostetter (10) and the pressure of dissociation of Fe_2O_3 (p) at different temperatures and degrees of oxidation was estimated by M. Tigerschiöld in the paper quoted above. Some of the figures are given below:

Temperature (°C)	p at an og-value of:	
	99.7	90.0
1 027	$4.55 \cdot 10^{-5}$	$6.10 \cdot 10^{-6}$
1 227	$1.81 \cdot 10^{-2}$	$3.17 \cdot 10^{-3}$

Temperature (°C)	p at an og-value of:	
	99.7	90.0
1 327	0.219	$4.29 \cdot 10^{-2}$
1 527	16.03	3.76
1 727	$5.78 \cdot 10^{2}$	$1.65 \cdot 10^{2}$

Thus, heated in air (0.21 atm. of O_2) Fe_2O_3 begins to dissociate a little below 1 325 centigrades to a remarkable extent. At 1 727° C the dissociation has become considerable (of the magnitude 10^2 atm.).

From the figures presented it is evident that mineral facies containing highly oxidized minerals are not stable at the temperatures of a crystallizing magma presumed by R. A. Daly (17) and J. H. L. Vogt (117).

As discussed before, the fractional crystallization of a magma probably takes place at a decreasing degree of oxidation. Since the correlation between qv and og is positive and the degree of oxidation increases as the acidity of rocks increases, it is plausible that the first alternative to explain the increasing degree of oxidation in the igneous rock series, *viz.* the influence of external material in the rock-forming processes, should be taken into account.

Thus, we have to reckon with an endogene-exogene redox system in the lithosphere: Highly oxidized material from the surface of the Earth's crust enters the endogene phase, where a corresponding reduction takes place and oxygen is given off. Consequently, oxygen takes part in the cyclic migration of elements and iron can be looked upon as the "respiratory organ" of the lithosphere.[1]

The arguments of the significance of the degree of oxidation in the igneous rock series can be employed for the iron ores too. The author has chosen the iron-ore types from central Sweden to illustrate that the formation of essential quantities of magnetite and hematite requires a degree of oxidation much higher than that for the igneous rock series, as seen from fig. 16. The upper curve represents the og-values for the iron ores of Central Sweden. There is a strong relationship between qv and og, quite similar to that of the igneous rock series, the lower curve in fig. 16. In fact, the two curves in question run parallel to each other.

If, now, we must reckon with the symbaty between qv and og in the igneous rocks indicating an addition of external material oxidized in the exogene phase in the rock forming-processes as qv increases, it is obvious that this claim should be valid for the formation of iron ores too, especially since their

[1] Quite recently a very interesting paper by Tom. F. W. Barth has become available: The Distribution of Oxygen in the Lithosphere (Journ. of Geology, vol. 56: 1,1948, pp. 40—49). The author has not the opportunity to discuss Barth's paper in this connection. However, as far as the author can see there is full agreement between Barth's and the author's conceptions regarding the geochemistry of oxygen.

og-values in general are higher than those of the igneous rocks with corresponding qv-values.

Thus, for the formation of iron ores it is not only a question of enrichment of iron, it is also a question of enrichment of oxygen necessary for the formation of ore minerals. Generally the oxidation of iron will take place at the surface of the Earth's crust. However, in such cases where we have to reckon with the formation of sideritic sediments, there seems also to be another source of oxygen which may affect the formation of magnetite: the reaction between Fe^{2+} and the volatiles (H_2O, CO_2) at a moderatly increased temperature (contact metamorphism, for example), as discussed before.

It is plausible, too, that the increasing formation of magnetite in a comparatively late stage of the development of titaniferous iron ores, basalts, diabases, etc., often met with, may be due to reaction between divalent iron ions and volatiles.

To sum up: it is quite unreasonable to assume a primary endogene connection between the formation of iron ores and the formation of igneous rocks, if the distribution of oxygen is to be considered. Generally, the oxidation of iron necessary for the formation of the oxide ore minerals takes place at the surface of the Earth's crust. In some cases of formation of magnetite the reaction between divalent iron and volatiles (H_2O, CO_2) at a moderatly increased temperature, should also be taken into account.

Clearly magmatic differentiation of some kind may take place to a limited extent but the processes are regulated not only by the conditions in the primary magma but also by the composition, quantity and degree of oxidation of the material incorporated in the endogene processes. Phenomena of local significance are, of course, not included in this conception.

In the following discussion it will be shown that many features in the distribution of the elements can be explained by this conception. On the other hand, if we assume that the distribution of the elements in the endogene development are solely or even preferably regulated by pure endogene differentiation processes practically undisturbed by external material the distribution of elements will continue to be a mystery.

Comments on the Distribution of the Ferrides in the Exogene Development.

V. M. Goldschmidt has emphasized (40) that the endogene processes lead to homogeneity of matter, exogene, on the other hand, to separation and consequently to enrichment of elements.

Clearly the by far most important separation and enrichment takes place through the activity of water. The solutions and the changes in their physico-chemical conditions are, therefore, the great factor regulating the distribution of elements.

The pioneer investigations of Goldschmidt and his collaborators should be noted also as regards the geochemistry of sediments. Goldschmidt has laid down the principles for the distribution of elements in the sedimentary development. We can share his opinion that the importance of this field of geochemistry may be judged by the fact that a very great percentage of ores and other useful minerals and rocks is associated with sediments. The processes of weathering, transportation and redeposition of matter at the surface of the Earth's crust involve a great number of chemical reactions including all chemical elements (45).

For the processes in the endogene development the crystal-chemical properties — ionic charge and size — and temperature are, as already mentioned, the controlling factors in the distribution of elements. In the processes of sedimentation the deformability and polarisability of ions are also of importance when considering phenomena of ionic adsorption, as shown by W. Noll (93).

For more detailed information in this part of geochemistry the works by Goldschmidt and Noll quoted above may be referred to. A very valuable survey on this subject is also given by K. Kalle (66).

V. M. Goldschmidt's well-known diagram may serve (45) as a basis for the discussion on the distribution of the ferrides in the sedimentary cycle.

The diagram in fig. 29 is divided into three sections. In the upper section are found elements with relatively large ionic size and low charge. They are the elements that occur in true ionic solutions. The middle section of the diagram shows the ions which preferably precipitate through hydrolysis or remain in solutions as sols. The lowest section of the diagram shows the ions with high ionic charge and small ionic radii. They form complex anions containing oxygen and can remain in true ionic solutions. In the diagram the ferrides are represented by filled circles, the other ions by open circles.

As seen from the diagram, the ferrides, on account of their different charges and sizes, behave differently in solutions. Thus, Mn^{2+}, Fe^{2+}, Co^{2+}, and Ni^{2+} can occur in ionic solutions. As hydrolysates occur Ti^{4+}, V^{3+}, Cr^{3+}, Mn^{4+} and Fe^{3+}. Finally V^{5+} and Cr^{6+} can form complex anions. Consequently, the redox-potential in the solutions is essential for the enrichment and separation of the ferrides during the transport from the weathering milieu to the precipitation milieu.

The ratio Mn/Fe (mf) attracts special interest. The formation of sedimentary iron and manganese ore deposits has been the subject of very important laboratory research, especially by F. Behrend (8). The main results of Behrend's investigations into the conditions during weathering, transportation and redeposition of iron and manganese may, therefore, be mentioned.

By the weathering of rocks iron and manganese become dissolved mainly

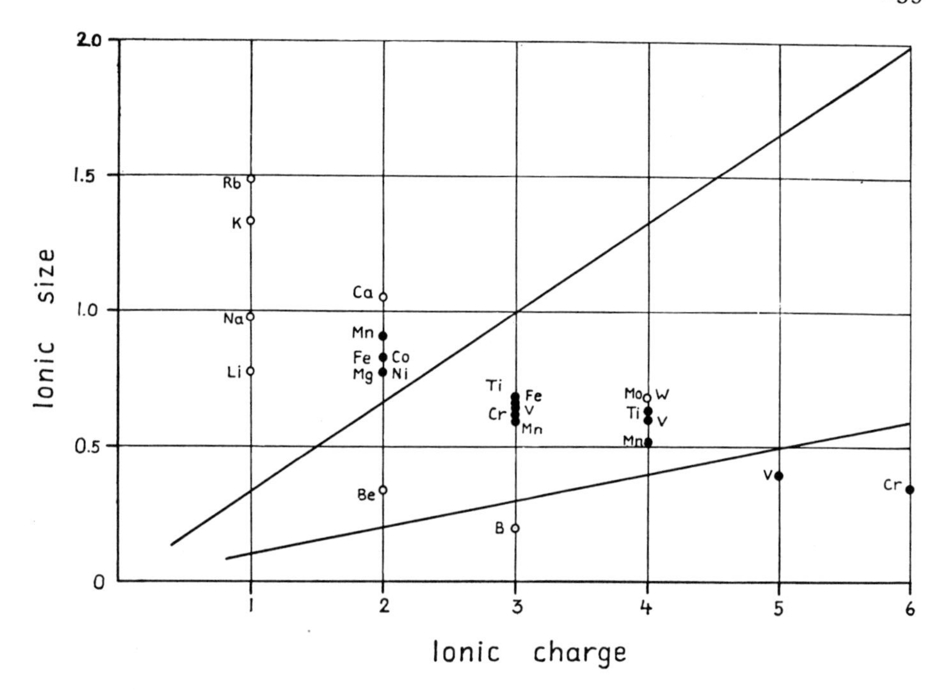

Fig. 29. Diagram of the distribution of elements in solution. (After V. M. Goldschmidt.) Filled circles are ferrides.

as bicarbonates and to some extent also as sulfates. The solubility of manganese is greater than that of iron, and Mn is more stable in solution. When oxidation takes place by the aid of atmospheric oxygen, Fe $(OH)_3$ and Mn $(OH)_4$ are formed under certain conditions and remain in the solution as sols. The former sol has a feebly basic character, the latter a feebly acid one. The former, therefore, has a positive charge, the latter a negative one. Consequently, the two sols in question either flocculate each other or — if there is a great excess of one of them — the less abundant sol becomes recharged. In the presence of other ions in the solution, flocculation can take place and then in the order manganese → iron.

During the lateritic weathering process an oxidation takes place. The uni- and divalent cations (Ca, Mg, Co, Ni, K, and Na) dissolve together with SiO_2. Thus the residue becomes enriched in the hydrolysates, *i. e.* Ti^{4+}, V^{3+}, Cr^{3+}, Mn^{4+}, Fe^{3+}, and Al^{3+}.

The manganese sol preferably adsorbs cations, the iron sol preferably anions. The well-known occurrence of cations such as Li, K, Ba, Co, Ni, Zn, Tl, Pb, and W in manganese deposits indicates that these elements are enriched through the adsorbtion of the manganese sol. This has been shown experimentally by N. G. Chatterji and N. R. Dhar (13). The adsorbtion of anions by iron sols is well-known, too. As and Sb, for example, are often enriched in sedimentary iron deposits (cf Goldschmidt (43). The Långban manganese-iron deposit in Central Sweden may be mentioned as an example of enrichment of a number of elements through adsorbtion (se p. 169).

The concentration of hydrogen ions in the transporting solutions is of great importance for the precipitation of iron and manganese. In the table below are shown some p_H -values for precipitation of some hydroxides.

p_H	ion	milieu	p_H	ion	milieu
10	Mg^{2+}		6	Cu^{2+}	rain water
9			5	Al^{3+}	
8	Mn^{4+}	sea water	4		
7	Fe^{2+}	fresh water	3	Fe^{3+}	

The table shows the great effect of changes in the p_H-conditions on the selective precipitation of elements. Thus, for example, a high oxidation potential leads to the precipitation of $Fe(OH)_3$ even at $p_H = 3$. At a high reduction potential, on the other hand, divalent iron becomes dissolved at $p_H \leq 7$. Further, Mn^{4+} and Fe^{3+} can become separated within the p_H-region 3—8 at a high oxidation potential.

As seen from Table 1 on p. 21, the correlation between qv and mf is positive but rather feeble. In many cases there is practically no correlation at all. It is true that the M-values for mf tend to increasing values as qv increases, but the relation between the two quantities is fairly irregular, as mentioned before and as is seen from fig. 14 on p. 48. Again, it is very unlikely that endogene differentiation processes lead to an increase of mf as qv increases in the rock-forming processes. The irregularity in the relation between qv and mf is more likely due to the influence of exogene processes where several factors regulate the magnitude of the ratio mf.

As regards the iron ores investigated, it has been shown that there exists a negative correlation throughout between qv and mf (see Table 10). However, it should be noted that a decrease of qv in the ores generally means an increasing content of carbonate. Thus there is a tendency towards a positive correlation between mf and the content of carbonate in the ores, showing the great importance of the CO_2-pressure in the transporting solutions, which certainly influences the magnitude of mf. Evidently, there are ores rich in carbonate but relatively poor in manganese, on the one hand, and quartz ores relatively rich in manganese, on the other, but if we bear in mind that the ratio mf is also dependent on the magnitude of mf in the primary source of the iron- and manganese-bearing sediments, these exceptions from the rule can be explained.

It is obvious that there are many factors regulating the sediment-forming processes that must be taken into account. As regards the relative abundance of the important ferride group, one has to reckon with the redox potential, the p_H-value, the pressure of CO_2, and the adsorption phenomena in the colloidal stage. Thus the distribution of the ferrides in the rocks and iron ores investigated is seemingly irregular.

Summary.

In this chapter some features of the geochemistry of the ferrides have been discussed. As regards the relative abundance of the ferride isotopes it has been shown that the even-odd rule for the mass-numbers 46—62 holds good only in the meteoritic-peridotitic stage of development but is not valid for the igneous rocks and iron ores mainly occurring in the upper lithosphere. There is a striking similarity between the relative abundance of the ferrides in the basalts, on the one hand, and the bulk of the igneous rocks, on the other.

The sediments and most iron ores show very characteristic deviations in the relative abundance of the ferrides when compared with the abundance in the meteorites, which probably represent the primary distribution.

The proportion Fe : Co : Ni and the ratio Co/Ni in the rocks and ores investigated have been discussed. A conception has been expressed that the ionic size of Co and Ni seem to have no essential influence on the magnitude of the ratio Co/Ni in the upper lithosphere.

V. M. Goldschmidt's and Frans E. Wickman's suggestions have been used as a basis for the discussion on the significance of the magnitude of the degree of oxidation. The increasing values of og as qv increases have been discussed with reference to the conceptions mentioned.

Finally, the principal factors regulating the distribution of the ferrides in the sediment-forming processes have been mentioned.

With the aid of geochemical premises the following conclusions have been drawn:

The formation of igneous rocks and the iron ores associated with these rocks must be regarded as endogene, and processes of differentiation of some kind must be considered to have played a part and have left their geological impression on the rocks and ores. But these endogene processes worked on a material which essentially depended on the quantity, composition, and degree of oxidation of external material which successively entered in the endogene phase of development during the orogenetic cycles within the upper lithosphere. The "igneous" character of the rocks decreases successively towards the most salic members.

As regards the iron-ore formation the primary enrichment of iron occurred mainly in the exogene phase of the cycles. This can explain the seeming irregularity in the relative abundance of the ferrides in the igneous rocks and iron ores.

References

(3) Aston, F. W.: Mass Spectra and Isotopes. Second Edition. London, 1942.

(8) Behrend, F.: Über die Bildung von Eisen- und Manganerzen durch deren Hydroxydsole auf Verwitterungslagerstädten. Zeitschr. f. prakt. Geol. Bd. 32, pp. 81 and 102, 1924.

(10) Bowen N. L.: The Evolution of the Igneous Rocks. Princeton 1928.

(12) Buddington, A. F.: Some petrological Concepts and the Interior of the Earth. Am. Mineralogist 28:3, 1943.

(13) Chatterji, N. G., Dhar, N. R.: Adsorbtionsstudien I. Ionenadsorbtion durch frischgefälltes und lufttrocknes Mangandioxyd. Kolloid-Zeitschrift 33:1, 1943.

(17) Daly, R. A.: The Igneous Rocks and the Depth of the Earth. New York, 1933.

(25) Farrington, O. C.: Analyses of stony Meteorites. Field Columbian Museum, Geol. Ser. Bd 3:9, 1911.

(40) Goldschmidt, V. M.: Der Stoffwechsel der Erde. Vidensk. selsk. skrift. Mat.-Naturv. Kl. II. Kristiania (Oslo), 1922.

(43) ———, Drei Vorträge über Geochemie. G. F. F. Bd 56:3, 1934.

(44) ———, Grundlagen der Quantitativen Geochemie II. (Seltene Elemente in Meteoriten). Fortschr. d. Min. Krist. u. Petr. Bd. 19, 1935.

(45) ———, The Principles of Distribution of Chemical Elements in Minerals and Rocks. J. Chem. Soc., pp. 655–673. London, 1937:1.

(46) ———, Geochemische Verteilungsgesetze der Elemente IX. Norske Vid. Akad. Mat.-Naturv. Kl. 1 no. 4. Oslo, 1937.

(47) ———, Oksydasjon og reduksjon i geokjemien, G. F. F. Bd 65:1, 84, 1943.

(48) Goldschmidt, V. M., Thomassen, L.: Geochemische Verteilungsgesetze der Elemente III. Röntgenographische Untersuchungen über die Verteilung der Seltenen Erdmetalle in Mineralen. Vid. selsk. skr. Mat.-naturv. kl. 1 no. 5. Kristiania (Oslo), 1924.

(56) Harkins, W. D.: The Evolution of Elements and the Stability of complex Atoms. J. Am. Chem. Soc. 39:1, p. 856, 1917.

(58) Hevesy, G.: Chemical Analyses by X-Rays and its Applications. New York, 1932.

(66) Kalle, K.: Der Stoffhaushalt des Meeres. Probleme der Kosmischen Physik Bd. XXIII Leipzig, 1943.

(67) Landergren, S.: En orienterande undersökning över elementfördelningen i några svenska järnmalmstyper. J. K. A. 12, 1936.

(70) ———, Contribution to the Geochemistry of Boron. II. The Distribution of Boron in some Swedish Sediments, Rocks and Iron Ores. The Boron Cycle in the upper Lithosphere. K. V. A. Ark. f. Kemi, Geol., Min. Bd 19A, no. 26, 1945.

(87) Merrill, G. P.: Report on Researches on the chemical and mineralogical Composition of Meteorites, with especial Reference to their minor Constituents. Mem. National Ac. Sciences, Washington, Bd 14:1, 1916.

(88) Minami, E.: Gehalte an Seltenen Erden in europäischen und japanischen Tonschiefern. Nachr. Ges. d. Wiss. Göttingen, Math.-Phys. Kl. 14, 1935.

(90) Noddack, I., and W.: Die Haufigkeit der chemischen Elemente. Naturw. Bd 18, 1930.

(92) Noddack, I.: Die Häufigkeit der Seltenen Erden in Meteoriten. Z. An. Chemie Bd 225:4, 1935.

(93) Noll, W.: Ueber die geochemische Rolle der Sorbtion. Chemie d. Erde 6, 1931.

(104) Sahama, Th. G., Vähätalo, V.: X-Ray spectrographic Study of the Rare Earths in some Finnish eruptive Rocks and Minerals. Bull. Comm. Géol. Finlande No. 126, 1941 (1939).

(115) Tigerschiöld, M.: Järnets oxider från termodynamisk synpunkt. J. K. A. 78, 1923.

REFERENCES

(117) Vogt, J. H. L.: Über die Schmelzpunkt-Erniedrigung der Silikatschmelzlösungen und über die Kalorischen Konstanten der Silikate Videnskabs-Selsk. Skrifter Mat.-Naturv. Kl. No. 1, Christiania (Oslo), 1904.

(119) ———, Nickel in Igneous Rocks. Ec. geol. 18, pp. 307–353, 1923.

(120) Washington, H. S.: Chemical Analyses of Igneous Rocks. U. S. G. S. Prof. Paper No. 99, 1927.

(125) Wickman, F. E.: Some Aspects of the Geochemistry of Igneous Rocks and of Differentiation by Crystallization. G. F. F. 65:4, 1943.

2

Reprinted from *Data of Geochemistry* (U.S. Geol. Survey Prof. Paper 440–W), Chap. W, 1966
pp. 1–2, 17–27

CHEMISTRY OF THE IRON-RICH SEDIMENTARY ROCKS

By Harold L. James

ABSTRACT

The iron-rich sedimentary rocks, defined as those containing 15 percent or more iron of depositional or diagenetic origin, have a wide range of physical and chemical properties, in part because of gradations into more common sedimentary types and in part because of the wide variety of iron minerals possible. The iron may be in the form of goethite (limonite), hematite, and magnetite; siderite, with a substantial range in amounts of manganese, magnesium, and calcium in solid solution; chamosite, greenalite, and glauconite (which upon slight metamorphism may be converted into thuringite and other chlorites); minnesotaite, and stilpnomelane; and pyrite and marcasite. Many of these minerals may be preceded by metastable species of uncertain status, such as ferric hydroxide and hydrotroilite. Other minerals, of rare occurrence, are lepidocrocite, maghemite, the tetragonal iron sulfide, greigite, smythite, and pyrrhotite.

By custom, the noncherty and generally oolitic iron-rich rocks, most of which are of post-Precambrian age, are referred to as ironstone (including the "minette type"), whereas the chert-banded rocks, most of which are of Precambrian age, are called iron-formation. Both ironstones and iron-formations may be divided into four major facies—oxide, silicate, carbonate, and sulfide—on the basis of the dominant iron mineral. This facies classification has a theoretical base established by the distribution of stability fields of the iron species, expressed most effectively in terms of redox potential (Eh) and pH. Examples of stability-field diagrams show that at given anion concentrations almost any combination of oxides, silicates, carbonates, and sulfides of iron can exist stably at some geologically reasonable value of Eh and pH. The dominant aspect, however, is one of sequential appearance of stable fields for oxide, carbonate, and sulfide with decrease in Eh. In an idealized restricted basin in which iron sediments are being formed, this corresponds to progressive decrease in available oxygen in the bottom environment. The facies, therefore, are a direct reflection of depositional environments.

Chemical analyses of the iron-rich rocks are organized and presented according to facies and in part according to age (Precambrian and post-Precambrian), and the distribution in space and time is summarized in a series of tables. The major differences in bulk compositions are inherent in the classification—as in the ratio of FeO to Fe_2O_3 and the content of CO_2—the silicate facies being significantly higher in Al_2O_3. The SiO_2 content varies chiefly according to the relative amounts of clastic quartz (in ironstone) or chert (in iron-formation).

Data on minor-element content are relatively scarce. The information available shows the amounts to be generally low in comparison with crustal abundance. Differences between facies are slight, except for higher chromium and vanadium in chamositic rocks, and commonly are submerged by local differences related to the geochemical nature of the terrain adjacent to basins of deposition.

The origin of the iron-rich sedimentary rocks remains a matter of speculation, as no modern-day examples exist. A few deposits, exemplified by the ironstone of the Lahn-Dill district of Germany and the Helen iron-formation of the Michipicoten district of Canada, appear to have a genetic relation to volcanic and igneous activity and may be classed as "exhalative-sedimentary." The more typical and more extensive ironstones and iron-formations, however, are entirely lacking in volcanic and igneous associations; for these the iron seemingly must be derived by weathering of exposed land, although the large chemical and physical differences between ironstone and iron-formation imply some significant difference in the nature of the process. It is suggested, by analogy with bog-iron deposition, that for both types the iron is extracted and transported by ground waters of low pH, and that this process was more effective in Cambrian and pre-Cambrian time, possibly because of a significantly higher content of CO_2 in the earth's atmosphere.

INTRODUCTION

Iron, which is estimated to make up about 4.7 percent of the earth's crust, is present in significant amounts in almost all sedimentary rocks. The average sandstone, including graywacke, contains 1.7 percent Fe_2O_3 and 1.5 percent FeO (Pettijohn, 1963, p. 15); the average shale contains 4.2 percent Fe_2O_3 and 2.45 percent FeO, and the average limestone 0.54 percent combined Fe_2O_3 and FeO (Clarke, 1924, p. 25, 564). Each of these rock types, however, ranges in composition into facies in which the iron content is 20 percent or more. The iron-rich sedimentary rocks, here defined as those containing 15 percent or more Fe of primary origin (depositional or diagenetic), in part therefore can be considered a family of end members of the sedimentary series. These rocks commonly are referred to as ironstone or iron-formation.

The iron-rich rocks have a great range of physical and chemical characteristics. In part this is due to gradations from the common sedimentary rocks—sandstone, shale, limestone, chert—with retention of attributes of the parent stem. In larger part, however, the diversity is due to the extraordinary ability of iron to form dif-

Editor's Note: A row of asterisks indicates that material has been omitted from the original article.

ferent minerals in response to different conditions of the bottom and diagenetic environment. Iron may precipitate as ferric oxide or hydrate (hematite, maghemite, goethite, lepidocrocite), as a ferrous-ferric oxide (magnetite), as a ferric-ferrous silicate (glauconite), as a ferrous-ferric silicate (greenalite, chamosite), as a carbonate (siderite), or as a sulfide (pyrite, marcasite, or less stable precursors). Inasmuch as the classification of the iron-rich rocks is based in large part on the mineralogy of the iron, the character, composition, and occurrence of the iron minerals found in sedimentary rocks are reviewed in the following section. The discussion will deal only with those aspects of importance to the problem at hand; more complete data on the optical, structural, and chemical properties of the pure minerals are available in standard texts and references.

* * * * * * *

CHEMISTRY OF IRON-RICH ROCKS, ACCORDING TO GROUPS AND FACIES

Tables 8 to 19 present selected analyses of iron-rich rocks, grouped according to facies and to some extent according to age, and some of the more significant aspects of each group are given in summary fashion below. The separation according to age is to permit isolation of differences between the Precambrian iron-formations and the younger ironstones; these differences are discussed in a later section.

Except where otherwise stated, the analyses are known or believed to be of representative samples of particular rock types—in general of hand specimen size or somewhat larger.

OXIDE FACIES

The oxide facies of the normal iron-rich sedimentary rocks comprises the oolitic limonitic and hematitic ironstones of post-Precambrian age, banded hematitic iron-formation of Precambrian age, and magnetite-rich rocks of both Precambrian and younger age. In the tables these are grouped according to subfacies—for example, limonitic ironstone—and according to age (Precambrian and post-Precambrian).

OOLITIC LIMONITE IRONSTONE

The oolitic limonites are very largely restricted to ironstones of Tertiary and Mesozoic age. An exception is that of the Mayville ore of Ordovician age (table 8, analyses Q–R).

The rocks typically consist of oolitic or pelletal grains of limonite, many with cores of clastic material, in a matrix of chamosite or calcite. Some consist of mixtures of chamosite and limonite ooliths, with the chamosite either partly altered to limonite or containing limonite in alternating layers with chamosite. The rocks are chemically heterogeneous and doubtless are the products of a primary chemical precipitation followed by mechanical transport and sorting of the ooliths. Siderite, present in quantities of as much as 10 percent or more, is of diagenetic origin.

Chemically the rocks are marked by a wide range in composition that is related in considerable part to the rudely inverse relation between quartz and calcite content, and to the amounts of chamosite and of secondary siderite. The P_2O_5 content is generally high, reflecting the presence of pelletal collophane.

HEMATITIC ROCKS OF MESOZOIC AND PALEOZOIC AGE

Most of the hematitic ironstones listed in table 9 are oolitic rocks similar in physical character to the oolitic limonites and with similar associations and origin. As in the limonites, an inverse relation between CaO and SiO_2 reflects the dominance of either clastic quartz or clastic or interstitial calcite. Chemically the chief difference is in the lesser H_2O content, represented mineralogically in the dominance of hematite.

Two analyses, L and M, are of ironstone of the "Lahn-Dill" type, as contrasted to the "minette" type. The Lahn-Dill ironstone is a type example of the so-called exhalative-sedimentary class (Borchert, 1960b, p. 25; Oftedahl, 1958), produced by sedimentary deposition of materials derived from submarine volcanic and fumarolic activity. The Lahn-Dill ironstone, which includes both quartz-rich and calcite-rich varieties, has a distinctly lesser content of P_2O_5, Al_2O_3, and MgO than do ironstones of the normal minette type.

Two analyses, Q and R, are quartz-banded ores of the Dunderland belt of Norway. These rocks, which consist chiefly of interlayered quartz and crystalline iron oxides, are of early Paleozoic age and have been metamorphosed. Physically and mineralogically they are very similar to many of the Precambrian iron-formation rocks.

HEMATITIC IRON-FORMATION OF PRECAMBRIAN AGE

The hematitic variety (or subfacies) of the oxide facies (table 10) is one of the more common types of Precambrian iron-formation, though in some places there is some question as to the primary nature of the hematite. Edwards (1936) and Miles (1941), in discussing the now dominantly hematitic rocks of South and Western Australia, for example, note that much of the hematite is secondary after magnetite; according to Johnson (1962, p. 31), residual magnetite is present

TABLE 8.—*Analyses of oolitic limonite (goethite) ironstone*

	A	B	C	D	E	F	G	H	I	J	K	L	M	N	O	P	Q	R
SiO_2	8.60	17.75	25.03	5.39	8.64	8.44	7.83	10.40	6.55	3.45	10.45	23.85	14.32	3.90	9.25	13.77	6.90	5.12
Al_2O_3	3.72	3.38	4.60	4.32	4.89	5.27	4.62	7.89	6.91	3.56	5.28	7.57	5.20	3.34	4.6	4.77	4.72	3.25
Fe_2O_3	35.82	47.36	41.61	40.45	35.07	36.78	43.14	50.48	62.88	36.40	39.00	39.46	43.22	19.4	24.86	38.71	60.50	72.34
FeO	9.57	7.37	7.46	8.72	12.02	14.27	8.23	.93	.18	.18	.28	8.78	1.31	11.31	10.66	6.56	.604	.44
MnO	.39	.45	.39	.36	.33	.26	.34	.16	.38	.31	.33	.29	.36	1.58	1.4	.167	.20	-------
MgO	2.10	1.72	2.10	1.63	1.95	1.94	2.10	1.47	1.10	.58	.41	1.95	1.03	1.3	1.83	2.92	2.97	.61
CaO	15.90	5.25	4.85	15.13	14.05	11.30	12.75	7.67	6.06	27.08	20.07	4.91	14.66	26.3	21.1	11.18	6.70	5.98
H_2O+ } H_2O-	6.84	8.23	7.68	7.20	7.16	7.78	7.94											
H_2O+								11.64	10.24	6.56	7.59	8.23	7.99	-------	-------	(1)	7.06	4.90
H_2O-								1.66	[2] 1.44	[2] 1.60	[2] 1.72	[2] 1.85	[2] 1.64	-------	-------	-------	.95	.32
TiO_2	-------	-------	-------	.17	-------	-------	-------	.19	-------	-------	-------	-------	-------	-------	-------	-------	-------	-------
P_2O_5	1.67	2.20	1.88	1.67	1.86	2.06	1.95	2.35	1.83	1.05	1.10	.96	1.35	.77	.85	.917	3.33	3.73
CO_2	15.10	6.08	4.67	15.00	13.84	12.04	12.00	2.52	3.33	20.64	15.11	3.26	10.32	-------	-------	[3] 20.13	5.86	3.60
S	.18	.04	.07	.04	.07	.05	.07	-------	.004	.009	.045	.25	.032	.41	.27	.055	.048	-------
Subtotal	99.89	99.83	100.34	[4] 100.18	99.88	100.19	100.97	[5] 99.82	99.46	99.82	99.67	99.51	99.79	-------	-------	99.18	99.84	100.29
Less O for S	.09	.02	.03	.02	.03	.02	.03	-------	-------	-------	.02	.12	.02	-------	-------	.03	.02	-------
Total	99.80	99.81	100.31	[4] 100.16	99.85	100.17	100.94	[5] 99.82	99.46	99.82	99.65	99.39	99.77	-------	-------	99.15	99.82	100.92

[1] Included under CO_2.
[2] Not included in total. Reported as "hydration grad" in original reference.
[3] Includes H_2O.
[4] Total includes 0.08 percent V_2O_5, 0.02 percent As.
[5] Total includes 2.24 percent SO_3, 0.13 percent V_2O_5, 0.01 percent NiO, 0.08 percent C.

A-G. Minette ores of the "Grise," "Noire," and "Verte" horizons of Landres-Amermont basin, Lorraine: A-C from Coche and others, 1954; D-G from Cocke and others, 1955, analyses credited to Ecole de Mines, Nancy. Calculated modes as follows:

	A (Couche Grise)	B (Couche Noire)	C (Couche Verte)	D (Couche Grise)	E (Couche Grise)	F (Couche Grise)	G (Couche Grise)
Goethite	40.9	54.1	47.6	43.76	39.8	37.0	45.4
Siderite	10.3	9.2	5.5	13.17	9.2	10.3	8.7
Ankerite	2.1	-------	1.0	-------	-------	-------	-------
Chamosite	14.9	9.9	19.5	14.22	20.9	29.1	19.4
Calcite	23.2	5.9	4.5	22.71	23.4	17.5	19.1
Quartz	4.0	15.2	17.6	1.45	2.0	.7	2.9
Phosphate	3.7	5.0	4.1	5.67	4.4	4.8	4.3
Other	.9	.6	.5	1.40	.1	.3	1.1

H. Ore from the Lias-γ horizon, north Göttingen, Germany, between Harz and Solling (Harder, 1951, p. 465). H. Harder, analyst. Calculated mode: calcite, 4.9 percent, gypsum 4.8 percent, apatite 5.5 percent, goethite (with minor chamosite and siderite) 84 percent.

I-M. Minette ores of Luxembourg, stratigraphically assigned as follows: I, Rotes Haupt Lager 3; J, Gelbes Neben Lager 2a; K, Gelbes Haupt Lager 2; L, Braunes Lager I; M, Rotes Lager I. Separate values given in original reference for quartz and combined SiO_2. Quartz content of samples as follows: I, 0.05 percent; J, 0.11 percent; K, 6.46 percent; L, 11.46 percent; M, 8.90 percent. From Lucius (1945, table B); analyses by technical laboratory of Konzerns A.R.B.E.D.

N-O. Partial analyses of unweathered "* * * chamosite-siderite mudstone * * * crowded with limonite ooliths"; from Frodingham ironstone, North Lincolnshire, England. N is from "Appleby bore 2"; O is from Yarborough Pit. Analysis of separated limonite ooliths from this bed given in table 1, this report. Hallimond (1925, p. 78); analyses by Frodingham Iron Co., Ltd.

P. Limonite oolite of Jurassic age (Corallian Beds), from East Kent, England (Lamplugh, Wedd, and Pringle, 1920, p. 225). Sample from drill core: analysis credited to E. O. Forster Brown.

Q-R. Mayville ironstone from the Neda Formation of Ordovician age, Mayville, Wisconsin (Hawley and Beavan, 1934, p. 505). Q is composite analysis of run-of-mine ore, made in 1925 by E. J. Wechter and Mayville Iron Co; R. by E. J. Beavan, analyst. Ore chiefly goethite and calcite, with a wide variety of other minerals in minor quantity.

TABLE 9.—*Analyses of hematite-rich sedimentary rocks of Paleozoic and Mesozoic age*

	A	B	C	D	E	F	G	H	I	J	K	L	M	N	O	P	Q	R
SiO_2	11.51	13.36	10.94	4.21	11.98	12.59	9.85	4.66	15.29	8.90	-------	2.59	46.79	13.60	30.82	19.08	34.35	36.32
Al_2O_3	6.85	7.89	3.72	4.38	5.13	5.71	3.23	3.05	9.63	2.79	-------	.75	.25	5.17	10.33	4.45	3.73	4.58
Fe_2O_3	29.90	29.62	42.88	37.72	75.90	75.12	67.79	52.08	44.17	66.55	52.83	52.56	50.80	55.56	43.13	55.48	50.41	43.47
FeO	12.08	2.69	7.67	7.27	(1)	(1)	10.03	21.17	19.38	1.13	-------	.88	.40	.23	.45	.18	1.17	2.35
MnO	.058	.33	.29	.18	.23	.06	-------	.78	.26	1.13	.81	.11	.01	.14	.21	.15	.39	.35
MgO	1.82	.93	5.90	1.68	.21	.42	0.37	1.14	1.45	1.39	5.70	.21	.02	1.49	1.01	2.05	.20	2.66
CaO	16.97	21.90	10.80	22.49	2.71	1.49	2.42	2.88	1.54	9.40	14.61	22.40	.80	10.26	2.16	7.14	3.85	4.25
Na_2O	.019	.014	.05	.01	-------	-------	-------	-------	.46	.15	-------	.05	.05	.07	.07	.07	} 1.1	1.7
K_2O	.30	.50	.02	.00	-------	-------	-------	-------	.08	.43	-------	.03	.04	1.22	2.36	1.05		
H_2O+	4.15	1.85	1.76	1.98	[2] 1.86	[2] 2.17	2.35	1.72	5.80	} 2.12	4.75	{ 1.12	.27	1.88	4.78	1.87	} .50	.64
H_2O-	.30	1.48	.12	.21	-------	.52	.32	.27	.83			.21	.08	.80	2.05	.67		
TiO_2	.39	.45	.14	.12	-------	.27	.40	.28	-------	-------	-------	.1	.05	.22	.34	.20	.23	.32
P_2O_5	1.27	2.35	.71	1.00	2.02	1.63	2.26	2.11	1.07	1.02	.32	.084	.12	1.80	1.34	1.41	.46	.55
CO_2	11.97	14.59	14.98	18.62	-------	-------	1.05	10.78	.43	5.73	18.14	18.50	.06	7.36	.10	6.02	2.9	2.8
S	.10	.32	-------	.00	.03	.00	-------	-------	-------	-------	-------	.31	.028	.03	.02	.03	.04	.19
SO_3	1.90	1.05	.00	.00	-------	-------	-------	-------	-------	1.31	.32	.009	.17	.00	.00	.00	-------	-------
C	.38	.33	-------	-------	-------	-------	-------	-------	-------	[3] .38	[3] 1.30	.08	.09	-------	-------	-------	-------	-------
Subtotal	[4] 100.13	[5] 99.93	[6] 100.03	99.87	100.07	99.98	100.07	100.92	100.39	102.43	98.78	100.12	[8] 100.14	99.83	99.17	99.85	99.33	100.18
Less O	.05	.16	.03	-------	.02	-------	-------	-------	-------	-------	-------	.15	.01	.02	.01	.02	.02	.10
Total	[4] 100.08	[5] 99.77	[6] 100.00	99.87	100.05	99.98	100.07	100.92	100.39	102.43	98.78	[7] 99.97	[8] 100.13	99.81	99.16	99.83	99.31	100.08

[1] All iron reported as Fe_2O_3.
[2] Reported as "loss on igition"; includes CO_2.
[3] "Organic matter".
[4] Total includes 0.116 percent V_2O_5, 0.001 CoO, 0.05 NiO.
[5] Total includes 0.28 percent V_2O_5.
[6] Total includes 0.05 percent F.
[7] Total includes 0.05 percent V_2O_5, 0.08 percent B_2O_3.
[8] Total includes 0.015 percent V_2O_5, 0.1 percent B_2O_3.

A–B. Oolitic hematite in chamosite-siderite matrix, from the Lias (Lower Jurassic) of north Göttingen (Harder, 1951, p. 463–464); analyses by H. Harder. Calculated modes as follows, in percent:

	A	B
Hematite	46	54
Calcite	24.83	32.09
Chamosite	15	4
Siderite	12.52	1.25
Apatite	3.00	5.53
Gypsum	4.09	2.27
Pyrite	.17	.60
Humus	.65	.56

C. Oolitic hematite of Westmoreland bed of the Clinton Group (Silurian), Kirkland, N.Y. Rock is dominantly hematite and calcite. Analysis by Paula M. Buschman, U.S. Geological Survey. Sample F-2640, collected by R. P. Sheldon.

D. Hematitic ironstone, from base of Keefer Sandstone of Clinton Group (Silurian) age. Sample F-2635, collected by R. P. Sheldon from road cut 1 mile south of Allenwood, Pennsylvania; analysis by Paula M. Buschman, U.S. Geological Survey. Sample consists of hematite, calcite, dolomite, minor quartz.

E–F. Dominion bed (Lower Ordovician), Wabana, Newfoundland. Analysis E by Nova Scotia Steel and Iron Co.; analysis F by T. G. McFarlane. Reported as analyses C and D in Hayes (1915, p. 45), from "average" samples of Zone 2. Specific gravity of No. F is 4.10. Average mode for analyses E and F in percent: hematite 65.5 percent; chamosite 23.9 percent; phosphate (shell fragments) 4.4 percent; quartz 6.0 percent (Hayes, 1915, p. 47).

G–H. Ore bed of zone 4, Wabana, Newfoundland. Analysis G of lower part of ore zone 4, specific gravity 4.23; analysis H is of upper part of ore zone 4. A. V. Seaborn, analyst, as reported by Hayes (1915, p. 52–53).

I. Ore bed of zone 4 (lower part), Wabana, Newfoundland. C. O. Hayes (1915, p. 53), analyst. Oolitic hematite and chamosite.

J. Rhubina hematite (Carboniferous), South Wales. Analysis made in laboratories of Geological Survey of Great Britain; quoted by Hallimond (1925, p. 85). Oolitic hematite with abundant shell fragments. As given by Hallimond, analysis is divided into two parts. The first is of the "soluble part," with 10.36 percent reported as insoluble residue; the second is of the ignited insoluble residue. The total for the first (including 10.36 percent insoluble) is 101.72 percent; the total for the second is 11.07 percent.

K. Cheadle hematite (Carboniferous), Froghall, North Staffordshire, England. Massive hematite with calcite and dolomite. Partial analysis made in laboratory of Geological Survey of Great Britain; reported by Hallimond (1925, p. 86). Total includes 0.04 percent insoluble.

L. Hematite-calcite ore (Devonian), Koenigszug mine, Lahn-Dill region, Germany (Harder, 1954, p. 60). H. Harder, analyst. Sample contains about 0.001 percent NiO, and less than 0.0005 percent CoO.

M. Hematite-quartz ore (Devonian), Constanze mine, Lahn-Dill region, Germany (Harder, 1954, p. 61). H. Harder, analyst. Sample contains about 0.005 percent NiO, less than 0.0005 percent CoO.

N. Oolitic hematite with chamosite, calcite, dolomite, and quartz. From the Martin Formation of Devonian age, Gila County, Ariz. (Willden, 1961). Sample F-2726, analysis by Paula M. Buschman, U.S. Geological Survey. Sample represents the upper 6 feet of the bed (see also Willden, 1960, p. B21–B23).

O. As above. Sample G-2892; represents lower foot of the ore bed; may be slightly oxidized.

P. As above. Sample F-2727, representing 6.2 feet of beds.

Q. Quartz-banded hematite ore, Ørtrann mine, Dunderland, Norway (Bugge, 1948, table 1, borehole sample 115/II). Late Cambrian or Early Ordovician age. Rock contains 48.6 percent hematite, 3 percent magnetite. Analysis made in laboratories of Rana Gruber A/S (Company).

R. Quartz-banded hematite ore, same locality, reference, and analyst as for Q, borehole sample 122/III. Rock contains 38.8 percent hematite, 7 percent magnetite.

in some of the dominantly hematitic rocks of the Cauê Itabirite of Brazil.

The hematitic iron-formation consists of thin layers or laminae of hematite alternating with those of recrystallized chert. In the Lake Superior region, at least, the layers pinch and swell to give rise to "wavy bedded" iron-formation. Oolitic textures are typical of such rock (James, 1954) and are preserved even in areas of moderate to strong metamorphism (James and others, 1961, p. 44–45).

Chemically, the rock is remarkable in its simplicity; SiO_2 and Fe_2O_3 generally account for all but a small percentage of the total. In contrast to hematitic and limonitic rocks of younger age, the phosphorus content is very low—rarely as much as 0.1 percent.

MAGNETITE-RICH ROCKS OF MESOZOIC AND PALEOZOIC AGE

Magnetite-bearing facies are not common in rocks of post-Precambrian age, but they have been described as minor rock types in several unmetamorphosed ironstones. The characteristic occurrence of magnetite in ironstones of the minette type (table 11, analyses A to G) is as fine granules or small crystals of diagenetic origin, clustered within limonite or chamosite ooliths. As Taylor (1949, p. 83) states with respect to magnetite in the Northampton sand ironstone (analysis G):

> Clearly it was not formed normally as a result of the alternation between oxidizing and reducing conditions. This is shown by its complete absence between concentric skins of chamosite and limonite in the ooliths.

Magnetite in the chloritic ironstones of early Paleozoic age in Brittany, Normandy, and Wales (represented by analysis H) may be a metamorphic mineral, the by-product of conversion of an original iron-rich chlorite to chlorite of lower iron content (Pulfrey, 1933).

Analyses I and J are from the same district as analyses Q and R (table 9), the Dunderland belt of Norway. As in the hematitic rocks of that area, the

TABLE 10.—*Analyses of hematite-rich rocks of sedimentary origin, Precambrian age*

[All rocks have been moderately metamorphosed]

	A	B	C	D	E[1]	F[1]	G	H	I	J	K
SiO_2	44.80	39.72	46.81	37.54	40.1	28.30	46.94	51.56	56.23	39.3	51.4
Al_2O_3	.37	.45	.49	.80	.8	3.86	.00	Tr	.45	<.5	<.5
Fe_2O_3	53.08	58.58	46.91	50.41	50.1	63.39	51.00	47.48	34.96	60.1	47.8
FeO	.71	1.03	5.03	10.17	1.6	2.57	1.41	.90	5.67	.3	.4
MnO	Tr	.00	Tr	.00	.2	.00	.02	----	.07	----	----
MgO	.07	.07	.36	.19	2.0	.56	.00	.00	1.13	<.1	<.1
CaO	.28	.03	.14	Tr	1.4	.86	Tr	.00	.81	<.1	<.1
Na_2O	} .12	.07	{ .13	} .03			.00	{ ----	.15	----	----
K_2O			.03		----	----		----	.12	----	----
H_2O+	.04	.28	.28	.26	----	.72	.68	----	.49	.3	.1
H_2O-	.03	.02	.04	.02	----	----	----	----	.03	----	----
TiO_2	.07	Tr	Tr	Tr	----	.00	.00	----	.02	----	----
P_2O_5	----	.02	----	.03	.07	.085	.39	----	05	.03	.12
CO_2	----	.40	----	.58	2.6	----	----	----	.06	----	----
S	----	----	----	----	.009	----	----	----	----	----	----
SO_3	----	.03	----	.02	----	----	----	----	----	----	----
Total	99.57	[2] 100.70	[3] 100.22	100.05	98.9	100.34	100.44	99.94	100.24	----	----

[1] Samples dried at 100° C. before analysis.
[2] Given as 100.60 in original reference.
[3] Given as 100.19 in original reference.

A–B. Banded specularite iron-formation, Krivoi Rog Series, Ukraine, U.S.S.R. (Semenenko and others, 1956, p. 95). Analysis A by S. A. Panchenko; analysis B made in laboratories of Ukranian Geologic Administration.

C–D. Hematite-magnetite iron-formation, Krivoi Rog Series, Ukraine, U.S.S.R. (Semenenko and others, 1956, p. 101). Analysis C by P. P. Makhovka; analysis D made in laboratories of Ukranian Geologic Administration.

E. Hematite iron-formation, Menominee district, Michigan. Composition as recast by James (1954, p. 260; error in P_2O_5 content corrected) from commercial analysis. Representative of shipment of 13,417 tons. Sample dried at 100° C. before analysis. Approximately 47 percent hematite, 40 percent quartz, 5 percent dolomite, 5 percent magnetite, 3 percent kaolin and chlorite.

F. Banded ironstone ("calico rock") of the Swaziland System, Umhlatuzi Valley Zululand, South Africa (Wagner, 1928, p. 71). Name of analyst not given.

G. "Hematite quartzite", Camel Hill, Middleback Ranges, Australia (Edwards, 1953, p. 468). Edwards(?), analyst.

H. Banded ironstone of the Hospital Hill Slate Zone, Witswatersrand System. Johannesburg, South Africa (Wagner, 1928, p. 73). Name of analyst not given.

I. Specularite-magnetite iron-formation, Atlantic City district, Wyoming (Bayley, 1963, p. 10). Chip sample taken from about 200 feet of outcrop. Dorothy F. Powers, analyst, U.S. Geological Survey.

J–K. Banded chert-specularite, Cauê Itabirite, Minas Gerais, Brazil. (J. V. N. Dorr II, written communication of December 12, 1963). Samples are composites of 25–75 chip samples; dried at 110° C. before analysis. Selected from 10 analyses, which show SiO_2 range of 36.3 to 51.4 percent (average 44.2), Fe_2O_3 range of 47.8 to 63.6 percent (average 54.9). M. B. J. Fernandes, analyst.

TABLE 11.—*Analyses of magnetite-rich sedimentary rocks of Mesozoic and Paleozoic age*

	A	B	C	D	E	F	G	H	I	J
SiO_2	3.2	3.4	4.8	7.03	8.20	15.63	6.2	[1] 12.90	35.6	35.94
Al_2O_3	2.2	3.2	4.7	7.13	4.77	7.92	5.9	3.66	4.76	4.49
Fe_2O_3	30.3	20.9	44.1	32.56	14.90	16.21	18.2	34.14	32.73	34.46
FeO	38.3	18.8	24.9	25.92	33.69	32.82	34.8	32.90	14.84	14.99
MnO	.19	.31	.21	.22	.32	----	.3	----	.26	.31
MgO	2.1	1.0	1.2	1.82	1.80	.25	2.4	1.00	2.17	3.04
CaO	4.6	28.2	6.4	2.84	12.45	2.62	4.6	5.00	4.84	3.55
Na_2O	} Tr	{ ----	----	----	----	----	----	----	} 1.2	1.6
K_2O		----	----	----	----	----	----	----		
H_2O+	} 3.1	3.1	9.4	{ 4.88	} 5.60	{ 7.82	4.6	} [2] 7.90	.50	.3
H_2O-				6.20		----	1.3			
TiO_2	Tr	----	----	----	----	1.55	----	----	.38	.32
P_2O_5	1.14	1.4	2.1	1.57	1.72	6.33	1.8	2.25	.44	.55
CO_2	13.0	19.2	1.0	9.38	15.80	8.33	19.0	----	1.86	1.12
S	.55	----	----	.02	.42	.17	.10	.25	.08	.23
SO_3	----	----	----	----	----	----	.04	----	----	----
C	1.1	----	----	.56	----	----	----	----	----	----
Subtotal	99.91	99.51	98.81	100.13	99.67	99.65	99.24	100.00	99.66	100.90
Less O	.28	----	----	.01	.21	.09	.05	.13	.04	.12
Total	[3] 99.63	99.5	98.8	100.12	99.46	99.56	99.2	99.87	99.62	100.78

[1] Reported as "clay and silica."
[2] Reported as "Loss on ignition (carbonic acid, organic matter, etc.)."
[3] Total includes 0.05 percent As, 0.05 percent Zn, 0.03 percent V.

A–C. Magnetite oolite in minette ores of Jurassic age of the Lorraine basin, France (Hoehne, 1955). Sample A from Angevillers; samples B and C from Amermont.

D. Magnetite ironstone of Jurassic age (Upper Lias, Dogger Seam), West Rosedale, Cleveland district, England. Quoted by Lamplugh and others (1920, p. 60) as an average of many analyses of the Dogger, or Top, Seam.

E. Magnetite-siderite ironstone, Couche Grise, of Aalenien (Jurassic) age, Lorraine, France. Mode: Quartz <1 percent, siderite 25.1 percent, magnetite 21.6 percent, phosphate 3.8 percent, calcite 14.3 percent (Deudon, 1955, p. 478). Analysis made in mineralogical laboratory, Facultés des Sciences de Toulouse.

F. Calcitic chamosite-magnetite-siderite ironstone of Dogger (Middle Jurassic) age. Analysis by C. Schmidt. Erzegg-Planplatte region, Switzerland (Deverin, 1945, p. 42). Specific gravity 3.24.

G. Siderite-magnetite-chamosite, Northampton sand ironstone, Middle Jurassic age. Easton Neston, England (Taylor, 1949, p. 60). Calculated mode: Sideritic carbonate 48.5 percent, magnetite 26.4 percent, chamosite 18.9 percent, phosphate 4.0 percent (Taylor, 1949, p. 63). Analyst, C. O. Harvey, Geological Survey of Great Britain.

H. Oolitic magnetite ironstone of Cambrian age. Gareg-fawr mine, Carnarvonshire, Wales (Strahan and others, 1920, p. 24): analysis made by "Dr. Price of Newport."

I. Banded magnetite-quartz rock, Late Cambrian or Early Ordovician age, Ørtvann mine, Dunderland, Norway (Bugge, 1948, table 1, borehole sample 131/II). Rock contains 47 percent magnetite, 0.6 percent hematite. Analysis represents 2.5 m of core. Analyst not specified; analysis presumably made in laboratories of Rana Gruber A/S (Company).

J. Banded magnetite-quartz rock, same locality as sample I (Bugge, 1948, table 1, borehole 123). Rock contains 48 percent magnetite, 1.5 percent hematite. Analysis represents 9 m of core. Analyst not specified; analysis presumably made in laboratories of Rana Gruber A/S (Company).

magnetite-rich rocks are interlayered with quartz and are more like Precambrian iron-formation than they are like the normal minette type.

Except for the quartz-banded ores (analyses I and J), the rocks are not different chemically in any significant respect from the hematitic ironstones, other than in ferrous-ferric ratio.

MAGNETITE-RICH IRON-FORMATION OF PRECAMBRIAN AGE

The magnetite-banded rocks, as represented by analyses A, B, D, E, F, G, and L in table 12, are one of the major types of Precambrian iron-formation. They consist of layers alternately quartz-rich and magnetite-rich. Both chemically and mineralogically the magnetite facies is more complex than the hematite facies with which it commonly is associated. The rock generally contains appreciable quantities of siderite and an iron silicate (greenalite, minnesotaite, stilpnomelane, chlorite), reflected chemically in the significant content of CO_2, MgO, and to a lesser degree, Al_2O_3. The rocks are notably lower in Al_2O_3, CaO, and P_2O_5 than magnetite-bearing rocks of younger age (table 11).

Analyses H to K are of South African rocks from stratigraphically widely separated positions in the Precambrian. Of interest and importance is the occurrence of chamositic rocks (particularly analyses J and K), physically and chemically more closely allied to the post-Precambrian magnetite facies than to the more typical cherty rocks of the Precambrian. The age of the Pretoria Series of the Transvaal System, in which chamositic rocks occur, is believed to be about 2,000 million years (Nicolaysen, 1962, p. 580, 582).

SILICATE FACIES

The silicate facies comprises those rocks in which the primary silicates chamosite, greenalite, and glauconite are dominant, plus those in which minnesotaite, iron-rich chlorite, or stilpnomelane—probably metamorphic in origin—are major constituents.

CHAMOSITIC IRONSTONE

The chamositic rocks are one of the most characteristic facies of the post-Precambrian ironstones (table 13). In some districts they grade into or are interbedded with limonite (or hematite) oolite; in others they grade into or are interbedded with sideritic rocks.

The rocks typically are oolitic, but most do not exhibit chemical heterogeneity to the degree shown by

TABLE 12.—*Analyses of magnetite-rich ironstones of Precambrian age*

	A	B	C	D[1]	E[1]	F[1]	G[1]	H	I	J	K	L
SiO_2	34.44	35.86	2.56	51.52	45.66	39.50	22.70	42.10	50.90	19.05	5.84	47.2
Al_2O_3	.85	1.57	6.20	.08	.28	.44	.31	4.65	6.25	6.60	4.40	1.6
Fe_2O_3	30.54	38.56	21.54	35.37	19.16	29.21	22.07	22.15	20.00	41.30	42.03	38.5
FeO	22.06	20.26	26.57	10.24	21.28	18.51	23.20	17.83	14.40	22.70	34.35	10.1
MnO	.21	.16	.04			.12	1.06	3.35	.85	.25	.90	
MgO	2.30	1.74	6.95	.20	2.73	2.00	3.88	2.25	2.00	1.25	.90	1.3
CaO	1.72	.51	1.85	.02	1.04	2.71	4.49	1.00	.85	1.25	1.50	.8
Na_2O	.00	.02	.60									
K_2O	.13		1.10									
H_2O+	.44	.60	5.66	1.48	1.54			.75	1.30	5.50	2.90	
H_2O-	.17	.06	.53	(1)	(1)	(1)	(1)			.65	.28	
TiO_2	.02	.04	.27			.040	.014	.15	.30	.15	.26	
P_2O_5	.07	.14		.060	.085			.05	.05	.20	1.19	[2] .22
CO_2	7.36	.60	3.99	1.06	7.54	6.22	21.18	4.90	1.10	.60	4.75	
S	.01					.129	.005	.10	.15	.25	.08	.007
SO_3	.00	.17										
C	.04			.00	.12	[3] .017	[3] .016					
Subtotal	100.36	100.29	99.86	100.03	99.44	[4] 98.90	98.92	[5] 99.28	[6] 98.15	99.75	99.38	99.7
Less O	.01					.06		.05	.08	.13	.04	
Total	100.35	100.29	99.86	100.03	99.44	98.84	98.92	99.23	98.07	99.62	99.34	99.7

[1] Samples dried at 100° C. before analysis.
[2] Calculated from 0.088 P.
[3] "Organic C."
[4] Given as 99.90 in original reference.
[5] Given as 99.30 in original reference.
[6] Given as 97.85 in original reference.

A. Banded magnetite iron-formation, Ironwood Iron-Formation, Gogebic district, Michigan (Huber, 1959, p. 100); Lucile N. Tarrant, U.S. Geological Survey, analyst. Calculated mode: Magnetite 44.3 percent, quartz 31.3 percent, sideritic carbonate 17.5 percent, minnesotaite 6.0 percent, excess constituents 1.3 percent. Sample represents 11 feet of drill core.

B. Banded magnetite-quartz rock with minor chlorite, siderite, and cummingtonite. Saksagan (Krivoi Rog) Series, Ukraine, U.S.S.R. (Semenenko and others, 1956, p. 105); O. I. Dokhlenko, analyst.

C. Magnetite-stilpnomelane rock, with minor cummingtonite and carbonate, middle suite of Krivoi Rog Series. From northern part of Saksagan band, U.S.S.R. (Aleksandrov and Zmeenkova, 1958, p. 79); A. V. Zmeenkova, analyst.

D–E. Banded magnetite chert from the Lower Cherty division of Biwabik Iron-Formation, Mesabi district, Minnesota (Gruner, 1946, p. 58–59); analyses by Mines Experiment Station, University of Minnesota; W. E. Apuli, chief chemist. Analysis D is one of 5 given by Gruner of magnetite-rich rock cut by drill hole near Aurora; sample represents 30 feet of core. Analysis E is one of 6 given by Gruner for magnetite-rich rock cut by drill hole near Hibbing; sample represents 20 feet of core. Rocks mostly magnetite and quartz, with siderite and iron silicates (greenalite, minnesotaite, stilpnomelane) in lesser amounts.

F–G. Magnetite chert member of Temiscamie Iron-Formation, Lake Albanel district, Quebec, Canada (Quirke, 1961, p. 312; see also Quirke, Goldich, and Krueger, 1960). Each sample represents 58 feet of core from drill hole. Analysis of major elements by Cleveland-Cliffs Iron Co; CO_2 and C by Mines Experiment Station, University of Minnesota.

H. Magnetite-siderite slate, South Africa. From uppermost part of Pongola beds, Swaziland System (Wagner, 1928, p. 69); analyzed in the Government Chemical Laboratory, Johannesburg. Sample is composite of 37 taken across 40-foot bed in southeastern Transvaal. Reported to contain some chamosite. Specific gravity 3.41.

I. Shaly magnetite ironstone, same locality as H but stratigraphically 40 feet higher (Wagner, 1928, p. 69). Analysis is of a composite sample representing a 20-foot thickness. Analyzed in the Government Chemical Laboratory, Johannesburg.

J. Arenaceous oolitic magnetite-chamosite ironstone (Wagner, 1928, p. 85). From "Magnetic Quartzite Iron Horizon," Pretoria Series. Sample from core of hole drilled near Pretoria, S. Africa; H. G. Weall, analyst. Calculated mode (main constituents): quartz 11.2 percent, magnetite 35.2 percent, hematite 17.0 percent, chamosite 28.6 percent, calcite 1.4 percent (Wagner, 1928, p. 86).

K. Oolitic magnetite-chamosite-siderite ironstone (Wagner, 1938, p.92). From "Clayband Horizon," Pretoria Series. Sample from core of hole drilled near Pretoria, S. Africa. Calculated mode (main constituents): magnetite 60.9 percent, chamosite 22.0 percent, siderite 12.5 percent, phosphate 0.6 percent (Wagner, 1928, p. 93). Major elements determined in "laboratory of the Gutehoffnungshutte"; CO_2 and H_2O determined by Government Chemical Laboratory, Johannesburg.

L. Magnetite-quartz rock (Krishnan, 1952, p. 524), average of "large number of samples." From Kanjamalai deposit, Madras State, India.

777-130—65——4

TABLE 13.—*Analyses of chamositic ironstones*
[See also chamositic siderites]

	A	B	C	D	E	F	G	H	I	J	K	L	M
SiO_2	21.78	16.24	49.64	42.76	13.4	13.70	6.60	26.00	26.20	41.80	16.22	15.60	32.04
Al_2O_3	10.67	8.09	8.82	7.82	7.4	9.04	5.27	14.50	15.71	16.18	7.65	6.96	13.24
Fe_2O_3	6.20	5.10	8.71	12.47	8.5	15.15	24.76	2.03	3.70	4.28	2.99	2.24	2.01
FeO	22.70	15.12	16.70	16.29	31.9	36.47	23.34	29.03	28.45	24.28	35.38	18.25	24.32
MnO	.08	.26	.23	.091	--	--	--	--	1.67	1.86	3.12	.56	.13
MgO	3.61	2.41	3.19	.61	2.5	2.26	.97	3.67	1.36	.43	1.84	8.83	2.78
CaO	12.25	24.15	2.10	1.44	6.1	6.48	19.60	7.30	6.50	1.00	4.01	17.64	8.26
Na_2O	.08	.32	--	.12	--	--	.52	--	--	--	--	.01	.05
K_2O	.09	.024	--	.63	--	--		--	--	--	--	.02	.23
H_2O+	8.36	6.00	5.09	7.23	4.9	6.31	4.27	9.68	7.90	8.44	2.61	3.38	5.60
H_2O-	1.01	.51	(1)	5.66	3.6	(1)	(1)	(1)			.78	.14	.37
TiO_2	.53	.75	--	.50	--	.62	.31	.87	.10	.05	.61	.18	.70
P_2O_5	1.62	1.53	.91	.30	2.8	1.75	1.21	1.34	3.93	1.12	4.91	.80	.97
CO_2	8.45	18.04	5.15	3.37	17.4	8.95	13.32	4.85	3.00	.00	16.64	24.99	8.42
S	.22	.59	.72	[2].043	.5	--	--	--	[3]1.39	[3].56	--	--	--
SO_3	1.47	.01	--	--	--	--	--	--	--	--	--	.00	.00
C	.50	.63	--	.98	--	--	--	--	--	--	--	--	--
Subtotal	[4]99.96	[5]99.99	101.36	100.31	99.0	100.73	100.17	99.27	99.91	100.00	96.76	[6]99.96	[7]99.56
Less O	.11	.30	.36	.02	.3	--	--	--	--	--	--	.15	.19
Total	[4]99.85	[5]99.69	101.00	100.29	98.7	100.73	100.17	99.27	99.91	100.00	96.76	99.81	99.37

[1] Samples apparently dried before analysis.
[2] Reported as S_2.
[3] FeS_2.
[4] Total includes 0.23 percent V_2O_5, 0.05 percent B_2O_3, 0.06 percent NiO.
[5] Total includes 0.17 percent V_2O_5, 0.04 percent NiO, 0.004 percent CoO.
[6] Includes 0.36 percent F.
[7] Includes 0.44 percent F.

A. Chamosite ironstone from the Lias (Lower Jurassic) of north Göttingen, Germany (Harder, 1951, p. 460-462). Rock contains about 72 percent chamosite, 16 percent calcite.
B. Calcitic chamosite ironstone, same locality and reference as above. H. Harder, analyst. Rock contains about 53 percent chamosite, 39 percent calcite.
C. Arenaceous chamosite ironstone of the "Couche Noire" of Middle Jurassic (Aalenian) age, Landres-Amermont basin, Lorraine, France (Coche and others, 1954). Analysis by laboratory of Ecole des Mines, Nancy. Rock contains about 38 percent chamosite ("chlorite"), 37 percent clastic quartz, 10 percent siderite, 10 percent limonite.
D. Arenaceous green chamosite oolite of Early Jurassic (Lias) age, Rödingeberg, Sweden (Palmqvist, 1935, p. 69). Sven Palmqvist, analyst. SiO_2 value divided into "sand" 28.79, percent, "SiO_2 (sol.)" 12.38 percent, "SiO_2" 1.59 percent; Al_2O_3 value divided into "Al_2O_3" 6.46 percent, "Al_2O_3 (clay)" 1.36 percent.
E. Chamosite oolite, Northampton sand ironstone, of Middle Jurassic (Inferior Oolite) age, (Taylor, 1949, p. 60). G. A. Sergeant, analyst, Geological Survey of Great Britain. From Lodge Pit, near Irchester, Northamptonshire, England. Rock contains about 36 percent chamosite, 10 percent goethite, remainder mostly sideritic carbonate.
F-H. Chamosite oolite, Chamosentze, Switzerland, of Middle Jurassic (Dogger) age (Déverin, 1945, p. 24). C. Schmidt, analyst. Average mode for 3 analyses includes chamosite 40 percent, magnetite 14 percent, quartz 13 percent, siderite 11 percent, calcite 10 percent.
I. Oolitic ironstone, quarry near Llangoed, Anglesey, Wales (Strahan and others, 1920, p. 14; see also Pulfrey, 1933, for mineralogic descriptions). E. J. Morris and W. E. Williams, analysts. Ordovician.
J. Oolitic ironstone, Bonw, Mynydd-y-Garn, Anglesey, Wales (same analysts as samples F-H; Strahan and others, 1920, p. 15). Ordovician.
K. Oolitic chamosite, Zone 4, Scotia bed, Wabana, Newfoundland (Hayes, 1915, p. 58). A. O. Hayes, analyst. Ordovician. Specific gravity of rock 3.50.
L. Oolitic chamosite, uppermost 6 inches of Westmoreland bed of Clinton Group (Silurian), Westmoreland, New York. Sample F 2639, collected by R. P. Sheldon; analysis by Paula M. Buschman, U.S. Geological Survey. Modal analysis given in Hunter, 1960, p. 104 (see footnote, p. W7) as follows: Hematite and masked chamosite—9.9 percent; chamosite—36.8 percent; calcite, dolomite, siderite—45.9 percent; pyrite—1 percent; quartz—6.0 percent; collophane—0.4 percent.
M. Oolitic chamosite, uppermost 6 inches of Keefer Sandstone of Clinton (Silurian) age, Piato, Allegheny County, Maryland. Sample F 2642, collected by R. P. Sheldon; analysis by Paula M. Buschman, U.S. Geological Survey. Modal analysis given in Hunter, 1960, p. 104 (see footnote, p. W7), as follows: Chamosite—48.4 percent; Calcite, dolomite, siderite—22.8 percent; pyrite—0.2 percent; quartz—11.6 percent; argillaceous matrix—17.0 percent.

the limonitic and hematitic oolitic ironstones. Nevertheless, they have a wide range in mineralogic and chemical makeup, attributable in part to the amount of clastic material—mostly quartz, calcite, or dolomite—and in part to extensive diagenetic modifications such as development of siderite and magnetite. The rocks are dominantly ferrous, but the chamosite ooliths themselves often contain concentric skins of oxidized material that represent interludes of higher Eh of the bottom environment during accumulation. As is to be expected, the Al_2O_3 content is higher than in most other types of ironstone, and to a considerable degree the chamosite can be considered a product of sea-bottom reactions between ferrous iron in solution with detrital clay particles. The replacement of clastic material by chamosite indicates, however, that the process of formation was not simply that of clay diagenesis. In the Northampton sand ironstone the process of iron enrichment of clay to produce chamosite was locally reversed, with the production of kaolinite that partly retains the oolitic form of chamosite (Taylor, 1949, p. 32).

SILICATE IRON-FORMATION OF PRECAMBRIAN AGE

Most of the analyses listed in table 14 are of rocks that have been metamorphosed to some degree. Of the Precambrian rocks, only that from the Roper River (analysis H) can be considered to be essentially in unaltered form; those from the Mesabi district (analyses A-C) are weakly metamorphosed, with the partial conversion of greenalite to minnesotaite and stilpnomelane; that from the Gogebic district (analysis F) is slightly more metamorphosed with complete loss of original greenalite. Grunerite- and garnet-bearing rocks, representing a higher degree of metamorphism, are arbitrarily excluded in the tabulations.

Most of the rocks consist of quartz (recrystallized chert) in layers alternating with silicate-rich layers that generally contain significant amounts of magnetite and siderite. An exception is represented by analyses D and E, in which quartz, chlorite, siderite, and magnetite occur as fine-grained intergrowths in a laminated rock. The rock, though rich in iron, does not resemble normal iron-formation, and the bulk chemistry can be matched by that of some of the younger chamositic ironstones.

Aside from analyses D and E, the Precambrian silicate rocks are strikingly different in chemical composition from the chamositic ironstones of younger age. Most notable is the much higher content of SiO_2 (original chert) and much lower contents of Al_2O_3 and P_2O_5.

Also included in the tabulation is the analysis of an unusual greenalite-chert rock of Ordovician age (analysis L).

GLAUCONITIC ROCKS

Glauconite, (see table 15) though of widespread occurrence as a minor constituent of ironstones, rarely forms discrete deposits with ironstone associations. An exception is the Seend ironstone of England, represented by analysis I. Most of the larger glauconite deposits (greensands), such as those of New Jersey, have been studied as sources of potash rather than iron. Nevertheless, in the ironstone districts, glauconite as a disseminated mineral bears definite facies relation to other iron minerals. The oolitic hematite-chamosite ironstones of the Clinton Group, for example, are shown by Hunter (See footnote p. W7) to grade to the east into semicontinental hematitic sandstone and to the west into glauconite-bearing marine strata.

The compositions of the glauconitic rocks (table 15) have a wide range, in considerable part due to the variable proportions of clastic material, interstitial calcite, and secondary siderite. Though glauconite, like chamosite, probably in large part originates by reactions between solids and sea water, the actual accumulation into deposits is accomplished by transport and deposition of granules and pellets, along with more usual clastic components. The typical glauconite is dominantly ferric and—depending upon its "maturity"—with a substantial content of K_2O (see table 5). The compositions of the Gulf Coast greensands (analyses E-H, table 15) are therefore unusual, in that the rocks are more ferrous than normal glauconitic rocks and have a very low content of K_2O. In part the ferrous aspect is due to secondary siderite, but this can account only partially for the relatively low ferric-ferrous ratio. The rocks are also high in Al_2O_3. Evidently the pelletal material making up these greensands is far removed from the ordered mica structure of ideal glauconite; quite possibly it includes some chamosite. The association glauconite-chamosite is not particularly common, but it has been described. Chillingar (1956) reviews several occurrences of glauconite and chamosite in the U.S.S.R. Of interest is the extremely low content of K_2O (0.14 percent) of a chamosite-bearing glauconite of Mesozoic age (Chillingar, 1956, p. 495).

CARBONATE FACIES

Aside from the "blackband" and "clayband" siderites, which are discussed later, the rocks included in the carbonate facies are divided into those of Precambrian and post-Precambrian age. These groups are strikingly different in chemical composition and physical character, but they bear entirely comparable facies

TABLE 14.—*Analyses of silicate iron-formation, mostly Precambrian*

	A	B	C	D	E	F	G	H	I	J	K	L
SiO_2	50.96	42.48	65.42	51.18	48.11	29.35	38.51	30.26	52.18	38.85	45.10	71.08
Al_2O_3	1.09	.53	.08	11.95	3.27	.70	2.70	2.26	3.08	2.23	2.16	.55
Fe_2O_3	5.01	5.63	4.19	8.09	13.62	4.41	13.57	16.47	18.30	13.20	17.41	.78
FeO	30.37	33.76	23.63	12.15	16.69	39.51	21.47	37.00	16.68	26.58	20.83	18.53
MnO	.00	----	----	2.71	3.27	1.02	1.81	.78	----	.57	.47	.00
MgO	5.26	4.29	2.45	2.42	2.91	3.81	3.53	2.09	4.36	2.02	1.81	.18
CaO	.04	----	----	1.12	.80	2.10	3.55	Tr	2.90	2.09	2.66	Tr
Na_2O	.00	----	----	2.12	.24	.00	.01	.16	} .58	.11	} .12	----
K_2O	.00	----	----	1.86	2.32	.00	.09	.14		.11		----
H_2O+	6.41	4.80	4.16	1.19	1.74	2.79	----	8.73	} [1].94	.59	.67	} 6.40
H_2O-	.75	(2)	(2)	.07	.44	.06	----	2.15		----	----	
TiO_2	----	----	----	.51	.52	.01	.144	.03	----	.15	.10	.13
P_2O_5	.00	----	----	.54	.44	.14	----	.01	.28	.23	.18	----
CO_2	.00	7.44	Tr	3.70	5.62	16.37	12.70	Tr	(1)	13.52	8.52	.44
S	Tr	----	----	----	----	.06	.005	----	[3].32	.37	.59	----
C	.21	----	----	----	----	.08	.027	----	----	----	----	----
Subtotal	100.10	98.93	99.93	99.61	99.99	100.41	98.12	100.08	99.62	[4]100.87	[5]100.85	98.09
Less O	----	----	----	----	----	.03	----	----	----	.19	.28	----
Total	100.10	98.93	99.93	99.61	99.99	100.38	98.12	100.08	99.62	100.68	100.57	98.09

[1] Loss on ignition, presumably includes CO_2.
[2] Samples dried at 100° C. before analysis.
[3] SO_3.
[4] Includes 0.25 percent SO_3. Total given as 100.69 in origina reference—apparently corrected O for S.
[5] Includes 0.23 percent SO_3. Total given as 100.56 in original reference—apparently corrected O for S.

A. Greenalite rock, Biwabik Iron-Formation, Mesabi district, Minnesota (Leith, 1903, p. 108). Analysis by George Steiger, U.S. Geological Survey.
B. "Taconite consisting of about 8.5 percent quartz, 19 percent carbonate, and 71 percent minnesotaite and greenalite" (Gruner, 1946, pp. 56–57). From "Lower Slaty division," Biwabik Iron-Formation, Mesabi district, Minnesota. Analysis by Mines Experiment Station, University of Minnesota; W. E. Apuli, chief chemist.
C. "Taconite consisting of about 28 percent quartz and 72 percent minnesotaite" (Gruner, 1956, pp. 56–57). From "Lower Cherty division," Biwabik Iron-Formation, Mesabi district, Minnesota. Analysis by Mines Experiment Station, University of Minnesota, W. E. Apuli, chief chemist.
D–E. Laminated chlorite-siderite-magnetite-quartz rock, Stambaugh Formation, Iron River district, Michigan (James, 1954, p. 271). Analyses by Leonard Shapiro and W. W. Brannock, U.S. Geological Survey.
F. Sideritic silicate iron-formation, Gogebic district, Michigan (Huber, 1959,.p 91). Calculated mode: minnesotaite 46.3 percent sideritic carbonate 40.8 percent, magnetite 6.4 percent, quartz 5.8 percent, excess constituents 1.0 percent. Represents 14 feet of drill core. Lucile N. Tarrant, analyst, U.S. Geological Survey.
G. "Upper argillite" member, Temiscamie Iron-Formation, Lake Albanel range, Quebec (Quirke, 1961, p. 306; also Quirke, Goldich, and Krueger, 1960). Main elements determined in laboratories of Cleveland-Cliffs Iron Co., Owen Hassett, chief chemist; C and CO_2 by Mines Experiment Station, University of Minnesota.
H. Magnetite-bearing oolitic greenalite rock, Roper River, Northern Territory, Australia (Cochrane and Edwards, 1960, p. 17; also Edwards, 1958). F. J. J. Sinnott, analyst.
I. Stilpnomelane-actinolite-magnetite-quartz rock, Krivoi Rog Series (Semenenko and others, 1956, p. 374). Verkhtsevskovo region, U.S.S.R. Analyzed in laboratories of Ukrainian Geologic Administration.
J–K. Thuringite-magnetite-siderite-quartz rocks, Krivoi Rog Series (Semenenko and others, 1956, p. 387). Verkhtsevskovo region, U.S.S.R. Analyzed in laboratories of Ukrainian Geologic Administration.
L. Black cherty rock with granules of greenalite, Ordovician in age (Kennedy, 1936, p. 435). From near Glenluce, Wigtownshire, Scotland. W. J. Skilling, analyst.

TABLE 15.—*Analyses of glauconitic rocks (greensand)*

[Values in parentheses reported separately; not included in total]

	A	B	C	D	E	F	G	H	I
SiO_2	68.90	50.74	51.83	50.32	29.40	32.10	28.67	27.21	21.61
Al_2O_3	3.52	1.93	6.23	7.53	7.46	15.54	16.80	18.87	5.82
Fe_2O_3	8.91	17.36	17.15	18.38	5.60	12.71	8.41	9.32	17.48
FeO	1.52	3.34	2.93	3.02	14.54	20.39	20.74	18.55	25.69
MnO							.11	.12	.52
MgO	1.90	3.76	3.66	3.82	2.88	5.20	1.55	1.49	.59
CaO	2.10	2.86	.52	.65	20.00	1.98	.45	.38	2.88
Na_2O	.82	1.53	.76	.22	Tr	2.37	.03	.11	.14
K_2O	3.56	6.68	6.60	7.88	3.41	3.62	.70	.43	.83
H_2O+	7.68 (H₂O+ and H₂O−)	9.08	9.98	8.58	[1] 2.20	[1] 5.20	11.76	13.12	3.05
H_2O-									2.59
TiO_2							.30	.42	.25
P_2O_5	1.05	1.79	.31	.34	Tr	Tr	.25	.31	.96
CO_2	1.00	.88	.36	.15	14.80		10.03	9.85	16.68
FeS_2									.50
Organic C	(.21)	(.10)	(.24)	(.07)			[2]	[2]	.79
Total	100.96	99.95	[3] 100.33	100.89	100.29	[4] 100.09	99.80	100.18	100.38

[1] Includes organic matter.
[2] Reported as "present."
[3] Given as 100.42 in original reference.
[4] Total included 0.98 percent SO_3.

A–D. Greensand from Eocene Manasquan Formation (A) and Paleocene Hornerstown Sand, New Jersey (Mansfield, 1922, p. 124). R. K. Bailey, analyst; organic matter by E. T. Erickson (reported separately on p. 130).
E. Greensand, Texas (Schock, 1918, p. 170). Eocene. Analyst's name not given.
F. Greensand marl of Eocene age, Texas (Schock, 1918, p. 170; see also Baker, 1935) L. E. Magnenat, analyst.
G–H. Greensand, Weches Greensand Member of Mount Selman Formation, Texas; of Eocene age (Eckel, E. B., 1938, p. 25). J. J. Fahey, analyst.
I. Glauconite-limonite oolite from Seend ironstone, Wiltshire, England (Hallimond, 1925, p. 89). Lower Cretaceous. Analyzed in laboratories of Geological Survey of Great Britain.

relations to silicate and oxide rocks in their respective associations.

SIDERITIC ROCKS OF POST-PRECAMBRIAN AGE

The range of physical and chemical characters of sideritic ironstone is exceptionally well displayed in the Northampton Sand ironstone, as described by Taylor (1949, especially pp. 23–29, 33–35) and represented in part by analyses B–G, table 16. In the more common varieties of the Northampton Sand, the siderite may form a groundmass for chamosite or limonite oolite, typically with considerable diagenetic replacement of the ooliths; it may occur in fine-grained sideritic mudstone with sandy and argillaceous material; it may occur in limestone as matrix and partial replacements of shell fragments and calcite ooliths, or replacements of matrix calcite; or it may occur as "sphaerosiderite"—rounded masses and nodules in chamositic or kaolinitic ironstone. Of these several varieties, probably only sideritic mudstone represents a primary sediment. This rock generally is fine grained and massive. In the other varieties the bulk of the siderite is diagenetic, as shown by textural relations to other rock components; it is commonly more coarsely grained; and it has greater range in relative molecular proportions of FeO, MgO, and CaO.

As with other ironstone types, the sideritic rocks have a considerable spread in chemical composition—only in part reflected by the selected analyses in table 16—as a result of gradations into chamositic and limonitic facies and into normal mudstone, sandstone, limestone, and dolomite. Granules of collophane and phosphatized organic debris occur in the varieties containing ooliths of chamosite or limonite; the content of P_2O_5 ranges from low (<0.2 percent) to high (>2 percent), approximately in direct relation to the oolitic component.

SIDERITIC IRON-FORMATION OF PRECAMBRIAN AGE

The typical sideritic iron-formation (see table 17) is a thinly bedded or laminated rock made up almost wholly of alternating layers of dominantly chert and dominantly iron-rich carbonate, in roughly equal proportions by volume. It may grade into or be interbedded with pyritic facies, on the one hand, as in the Iron River district of Michigan (James, 1951) and the Michipicoten area of Ontario (Goodwin, 1962), and into silicate or silicate-magnetite facies, on the other, as in the Mesabi district (Gruner, 1946; White, 1954), the Gogebic district of Wisconsin and Michigan (Huber, 1959), the Gunflint district of Ontario (Goodwin, 1956), and the Labrador trough (Harrison, 1953; Gastil and Knowles, 1960). The transitions into silicate or silicate-magnetite are well illustrated by analyses D to G in table 17 and analysis F in table 14, and accompanying modes of rock from the Gogebic district, in which the silicate is minnesotaite.

Chemically, the greatest range is in the SiO_2:($FeO+CO_2$) relation, reflecting the variable proportions of chert and siderite. As in most Precambrian iron-formation, the alkali content is very low or actually zero. In rocks containing carbonaceous material or associated with pyritic facies the carbonate is notably higher in Mn content (analyses A–C, M–N) and the P_2O_5 content is distinctly higher than in rocks with silicate association. Sideritic iron-formation from the Cuyuna district, Minnesota, contains as much as 12.9 percent MnO (Schmidt, 1963, p. 21).

TABLE 16.—*Analyses of siderite rocks of post-Precambrian age*

	A	B	C	D	E	F	G	H	I	J	K	L [1]	M [1]	N	O	P	Q	R
SiO_2	7.56	9.20	8.03	4.42	4.88	12.73	2.3	8.51	13.5	32.71	7.75	12.70	18.60	9.09	8.20	7.36	13.5	18.63
Al_2O_3	4.10	8.95	8.86	5.40	3.38	9.10	1.3	6.12	10.2	5.54	8.35	4.65	5.31	7.11	5.84	3.77	.7	5.90
Fe_2O_3	1.83	2.64	23.76	1.20	1.20	7.12	1.4	1.77	3.0	2.58	1.71	16.83	21.47	7.34	3.25	4.57	1.8	1.22
FeO	43.86	39.53	27.58	45.14	49.32	32.62	23.4	36.91	32.5	25.17	35.61	27.93	23.06	44.90	42.72	43.23	43.8	42.10
MnO	.13	.05	.17	.18	.37	.16		.42	.7	.46	.37	.76	.76	.20	.36	.84	1.5	.61
MgO	3.92	2.06	3.13	3.69	1.51	4.37	2.4	3.75	3.5	2.30	4.03	4.34	3.26	.53	.84	.33	1.7	1.58
CaO	2.90	6.73	4.65	6.03	3.46	8.70	28.7	5.54	5.0	3.27	10.53	5.98	4.47	2.37	3.94	4.97	3.1	.99
Na_2O	.11							.05			.18			.01	.05	.12		
K_2O	1.13							.03						.34	.51	.70		
H_2O+	.81	4.32	3.95	.14	2.33	.44	.9	4.05	2.90	.72	4.15	4.73	5.77	3.73	1.78	2.11	.9	.58
H_2O-	.28						.2	10.00	8.00	1.27	(2)	(1)	(1)	.80	1.43	.77		
TiO_2	.18							.36	.3		.18			2.44	.39	.24	.03	.28
P_2O_5	.11	2.70	1.84	.108	.618	2.18	.3	1.30	1.0	1.80	1.28	1.53	.60	.81	.21	.39	2.45	.33
CO_2	32.84	23.01	17.35	33.06	32.70	21.78	38.8	20.70	19.0	20.80	25.25	20.80	16.30	19.78	29.41	29.91	29.6	[3] 24.31
S		.036	.014	.111	.119	.216	.4	.05	.2		.102	.11	.21	[4] .013	[4] .19	[4] .16		.44
FeS_2										1.62								
C								.27	.2	[5] 1.33	[6] .36			.28	.62	.61		
Subtotal	[7] 99.82	99.23	99.33	99.48	99.89	99.42	100.1	[8] 99.96	100.0	99.57	99.85	[9] 100.36	[10] 99.81	99.74	99.74	100.08	[11] 99.08	96.97
Less O	.03	.02	.01	.06	.06	.11	.2	.03	.1		.05	.06	.11		.10	.08		.22
Total	[7] 99.79	99.21	99.32	99.42	99.83	99.31	99.9	[8] 99.93	99.9	99.57	99.80	[9] 100.30	[10] 99.70	99.74	99.64	100.00	[11] 99.1	96.75

[1] Sample dried before analysis. Moisture content ("hydratationgrad") of L reported as 2.49 percent; that of M as 2.38 percent.
[2] Sample dried at 212°F before analysis. Moisture loss reported as 6.48 percent.
[3] Reported as loss on ignition in analysis of acid-soluble fraction.
[4] Reported as S_2.
[5] "Coaly matter."
[6] "Carbonaceous matter."
[7] Contains 0.06 percent F.
[8] Total includes 0.03 percent Cr_2O_3, 0.08 "V. oxide," 0.02 As.
[9] Total does not include 0.60 reported as insoluble.
[10] Total does not include 0.80 reported as insoluble.
[11] Contains 0.0005 percent V_2O_5.

A. Siderite bed in upper 6 feet of Brassfield Dolomite of Silurian age. Rose Run pits, Owingsville, Bath County, Ky. Analysis F2641 by Paula M. Buschman, U.S. Geol. Survey, of sample collected by R. P. Sheldon. Subtotal contains 0.06 percent F. Analysis also shows zero SO_3.

B–G. Sideritic rocks from the Northampton Sand ironstone, Middle Jurassic age (Taylor, 1949, pp. 60–61). B, described as "ooliths of chamosite in siderite matrix"; C, "Ooliths of limonite and subordinate chamosite in siderite matrix"; D, "fine-grained siderite mudstone"; E, "fine-grained siderite mudstone [with] scattered chamosite ooliths"; F, "siderite mudstone with chamositic cement and local calcareous debris;" G, "siderite granules scattered through calcite groundmass" (Taylor, 1949, p. 58). Calculated mineral compositions given in original reference. Analyses B–F by Stewarts and Lloyds, Ltd.; Analysis G by G. A. Sergeant, Geological Survey of Great Britain.

H. Cleveland ironstone (Middle Jurassic), Eston, England (Hallimond, 1925, p. 51). Main seam. Rock contains about equal amounts of siderite and chamosite (34 percent each). J. E. Stead, analyst.

I. Cleveland ironstone (Middle Jurassic), Cleveland, England (Hallimond, 1925, p. 51). Main seam. Rock contains approximately equal amounts of siderite and chamosite (about 30 percent each). J. E. Stead, analyst.

J. Cleveland ironstone, "Pecten Seam" (Whitehead and others, 1952, p. 61; analysis quoted from older report). From Glaisdale Mine, Yorkshire, England.

K. Cleveland ironstone, "Two-foot Seam" (Whitehead and others, 1952, pp. 59–60). Analysis by J. and H. S. Pattison, Newcastle upon Tyne.

L. Minette ore from Luxemburg, Jurassic (Aalenian) in age. From upper part of "Grunes" horizon, Lager IV (Lucius, table B). Quartz content reported separately as 1.14 percent, included in total SiO_2. Analysis by laboratory of Konzern, A.R.B.E.D.

M. Minette ore from Luxemburg, Jurassic (Aalenian) in age. From near base of "Schwarzes" horizon, Lager III (Lucius, table B). Quartz content reported separately as 9.48 percent, included in total SiO_2. Analysis by laboratory of Konzern, A.R.B.E.D.

N. Ilmenite-bearing gray oolite, chamositic, from Kurremolla, southern Sweden (Palmqvist, 1935, p. 53). Jurassic (Lias) age. Analysis by Sven Palmqvist. SiO_2 is total of values for "sand" 3.10 percent, "SiO_2 (sol.)" 5.70 percent, "SiO_2" 0.29 percent. Al_2O_3 is total of values for "Al_2O_3" 6.86 percent, and "Al_2O_3 (clay)" 0.25 percent.

O. Greenish-gray, dense siderite rock, locality as for N (Palmqvist, 1935, p. 58). Analysis by Sven Palmqvist. SiO_2 is total of values for "sand" 1.41 percent, SiO_2 (sol.) 1.71 percent, and SiO_2 5.08 percent. Al_2O_3 is total of values of "Al_2O_3" 1.49 percent, and "Al_2O_3 (clay)" 4.35 percent.

P. Light-gray, dense siderite rock, locality as for N (Palmqvist, 1935, p. 89.) Analysis by Sven Palmqvist. SiO_2 is total of values for "sand" 0.15 percent, "SiO_2 (sol.)" 3.03 percent, and "SiO_2" 4.18 percent. Al_2O_3 is total of values for "Al_2O_3" 0.25 percent, and "Al_2O_3 (clay)" 3.52 percent.

Q. Siderite rock ("Weisseisenerzen"), Auerback, Germany (Harder, 1955, p. 516); Analysis by H. Harder. Cretaceous. Contains 0.0005 percent V_2O_5.

R. Siderite rock from western Bashkiria, U.S.S.R., of Devonian age (Florensky, V. P., and Balshina, B. V., 1948, p. 690; sample 702/4). Analyst, B. V. Balshina. Associated with chamositic ironstone. Analysis is total of two parts, acid-soluble, and acid-insoluble (26.36 percent), given in original reference. All TiO_2, Al_2O_3, and Fe_2O_3 is in "acid-insoluble" fraction, as is all but 0.39 percent of the SiO_2. Calculated mode as follows (ibid., p. 691): detrital material 26.36 percent, siderite 67.27 percent, calcite 0.43 percent, magnesite 2.19 percent, pyrite 0.82 percent, apatite 0.78 percent, other 2.58 percent.

SULFIDE FACIES

Although sulfide, principally pyrite, is a constituent of many or most iron-rich sedimentary rocks, rarely does it assume major proportions. As a facies, the sulfide rocks (see table 16) are distinctly subordinate to those of the oxide, carbonate, and silicate, and the defining mineral is almost wholly of diagenetic origin. With a few exceptions, such as the previously noted thin pyritic beds of the Cleveland district of England and at Wabana, Newfoundland, the heavily pyritic rocks are black shales or their equivalents, with a large content of organic matter or carbon. The absence of direct precipitates, the scarcity of rocks of this facies, and the typical association with organic shales are all to some degree reflections of the extraordinarily slow rate at which sulfate in natural solutions is reduced, even in the thermodynamically stable realms of sulfide, except when catalyzed by biochemical agents. Viewed differently, it may also be said that the presence of organic matter, which permits the development of anaerobic sulfate-reducing bacteria, commonly is necessary to create the requisite low Eh for sulfide formation in sedimentary environments.

In table 18 are tabulated chemical analyses of a variety of sulfide-rich sedimentary rocks. The only complete analysis available (analysis A) is of a 50-foot bed of graphitic pyritic slate, the Wauseca Pyritic Member of the Dunn Creek Slate, which underlies the sideritic Riverton Iron-Formation in the Iron River district of Michigan (James; 1951, 1958). The pyrite occurs mostly in separated grains of about 3 microns diameter, and most show crystal outlines. The content of pyrite is nearly constant over a known strike length of about 20 miles. The fine-grained matrix is black with scattered fine flakes of mica and particles of quartz. Similar concentrations of pyrite in slate are known elsewhere, most notably at Mount Isa, Australia (Love and Zimmerman, 1961), and other localities in Australia (Skinner, 1958; Baker, 1960); lesser but still significant concentrations occur in units such as the

TABLE 17.—*Analyses of sideritic iron-formation, Precambrian*

	A	B	C	D	E	F	G	H
SiO_2	24.25	18.11	22.97	39.26	40.09	32.87	30.62	26.97
Al_2O_3	1.71	.18	1.08	2.88	2.23	2.46	.41	1.30
Fe_2O_3	.71	.34	3.59	.63	9.96	4.78	.46	2.31
FeO	35.22	40.68	33.17	24.94	25.84	30.84	34.50	39.77
MnO	2.11	2.56	6.77	1.23	1.25	1.33	.93	.29
MgO	3.16	3.59	2.02	4.62	2.79	3.58	4.41	1.99
CaO	1.78	1.31	1.48	4.62	.50	.62	1.45	.66
Na_2O	.04	.06	.06	.00	.03	.00	.00	.09 (Na_2O + K_2O)
K_2O	.20	.04	.10	.00	.40	.00	.00	
H_2O+	.00	.05	.00	1.23	1.80	1.69	.02	.51
H_2O-	.21	.09	.17	.11	.56	.28	.03	.10
TiO_2	.00	Tr	.10	.07	.23	.27	.02	--
P_2O_5	.91	.47	.62	.11	.13	.09	.10	.03
CO_2	27.60	30.52	26.50	20.46	14.38	20.94	27.03	26.20
S	--	.06	--	.04	.01	.09	.07	--
FeS	--	--	--	--	--	--	--	--
C	1.96	1.41	2.02	.07	.05	.45	.06	--
Subtotal	99.86	99.47	100.65	100.27	[5] 100.26	100.29	100.11	100.22
Less O	--	.03	--	.02	.01	.05	.04	--
Total	99.86	99.44	100.65	100.25	[5] 100.25	100.24	100.07	100.22

	I	J	K	L	M	N	O	P
SiO_2	46.46	45.4	48.10	27.43	30.15	13.91	38.58	58.22
Al_2O_3	.24	1.8	.47	.23	.40	3.63	3.27	.48
Fe_2O_3	.64	8.4	6.79	1.64	5.27	3.28	4.90	2.40
FeO	26.28	21.1	22.36	30.28	31.34	28.62	28.07	20.90
MnO	.21	1.7	--	.77	[1] 2.53	1.73	.04	.01
MgO	3.10	1.9	2.91	5.04	4.77	5.73	.47	.44
CaO	1.87	1.1	.74	6.64	1.25	4.34	1.79	1.33
Na_2O	--	.05	--	--	--	.94	.39	.27
K_2O	--	.07	--	--	--	.45	.12	.04
H_2O+	1.15	.50 (H_2O+ and H_2O-)	1.80	--	.36	1.30	.81	.50
H_2O-	.07		([2])	--	([2])	.10	1.76	2.26
TiO_2	Tr	.03	--	--	.02	.09	.03	.02
P_2O_5	.13	.41	.087	--	.665	.23	--	--
CO_2	19.96	16.7	15.32	28.03	24.65	27.06	19.02	13.00
S	[3] .11	--	--	--	--	--	--	--
FeS	--	--	--	--	--	[4] 8.43	--	--
C	--	--	.40	.016	--	--	--	--
Subtotal	100.22	99.16	98.98	100.08	101.40	99.84	99.25	99.87
Less O	--	--	--	--	--	--	--	--
Total	100.22	99.2	98.98	100.08	101.40	99.84	99.25	99.87

[1] Reported as Mn_2O_3.
[2] Sample dried at 100° C. before analysis.
[3] Given as FeS_2.
[4] Reported as 5.08 percent Fe, 3.35 percent S, with text notation that sulfide is mainly pyrrhotite (8.31 percent) with minor pyrite (0.12 percent).
[5] Total contains 0.01 percent V_2O_3.

A. Banded chert-carbonate rock, Riverton Iron-Formation, Iron River district, Michigan (James, 1951, p. 257); analyst, Leonard Shapiro, U.S. Geol. Survey. Sample represents 3 feet of drill core.

B–C. Carbonate-rich layers in Riverton Iron-Formation, Iron River district, Michigan, (James, 1951, p. 257). Analysis B by Leonard Shapiro; analysis C by Charlotte Warshaw, U.S. Geol. Survey.

D–G. Banded chert-carbonate from the Ironwood Iron-Formation, Gogebic district, Wisconsin-Michigan (Huber, 1959, p. 91). Analyses D and G, by Lucile N. Tarrant, analyses E and F by Lucille M. Kehl, U.S. Geol. Survey. Analyses D, E, F, and G represent, respectively, 17, 12, 14, and 12 feet of drill core. Calculated modes in percent, as follows:

	D	E	F	G
Sideritic carbonate	49.6	35.9	52.4	67.2
Quartz	31.8	34.7	29.5	29.7
Minnesotaite	14.5	10.2	6.5	1.7
Magnetite	.9	14.4	6.9	.7
Excess constituents	3.4	5.0	5.0	.7

H. Carbonate iron-formation, Negaunee Iron-Formation, Marquette district, Michigan (Van Hise and Bayley, 1897, p. 337). Analyses given separately for acid-soluble and acid-insoluble fractions. George Steiger, analyst.

I. Carbonate iron-formation, Gunflint Iron-Formation. From north side Gunflint Lake, Gunflint district, Ontario (Irving and Van Hise, 1892, p. 192; see also Goodwin, 1956). T. M. Chatard, analyst.

J. Chert-siderite rock, Welch mine, Florence County, Wis. Sample 150004, collected by C. E. Dutton; analysis by P. L. D. Elmore, S. D. Botts, M. D. Mack, U.S. Geol. Survey, using "rapid analysis" methods described in U.S. Geol. Survey Bull. 1036–C.

K. Siderite-rich bed in "Lower Slaty division", Biwabik Iron-Formation, Mesabi district near Hibbing, Minn. (Gruner, 1946, p. 59). Sample represents 15 feet of drill core. Analysis by Mines Experiment Station, University of Minnesota; W. E. Apuli, Chief Chemist.

L. Upper sideritic chert member, Temiscamie Iron-Formation, Lake Albanel range, Quebec (Quirke, 1961, p. 308). Sample represents 10 feet of drill core. Major elements determined in laboratory of Cleveland-Cliffs Iron Co.; organic C and CO_2 by Mines Experiment Station, Univ. of Minnesota.

M. Siliceous iron carbonate rock from the Kennedy mine, Cuyuna district, Minnesota (Harder and Johnston, 1918, p. 120–121). Analyst: J. H. McCarthy, Mines Experiment Station, University of Minnesota.

N. Lowermost member of iron-formation at Helen mine, Michipicoten district, Ontario (Collins, Quirke, and Thomson, 1926, p. 69; see also Goodwin, 1962).

O. Quartz-siderite rock, Krivoi Rog Series, Ukraine, U.S.S.R. (Semenenko and others, 1956, p. 147); S. A. Panchenko, analyst.

P. Quartz-rich siderite iron-formation, Krivoi Rog Series, Ukraine, U.S.S.R. (Semenenko and others, 1956, p. 149); analyses by laboratories of Ukraine Geologic Administration.

Chattanooga Shale of the United States (about 11 percent, according to Bates and Strahl, 1957), the Upper Cambrian "alum shale" of Sweden (about 12 percent in the *Peltura* zone, written communication from V. E. McKelvey), and the Kupferschiefer of Germany and its equivalent, the Marl Slate of England. The pyritic deposit of Meggen, Germany, is thought by some to be of sedimentary origin (Lindgren, 1933, p. 269), and by others to be epigenetic; Ehrenberg, Pilger, and Schroder (1954) conclude that it formed as a result of submarine exudation of magmatically derived fluids—that is, it is of "exhalative-sedimentary" origin. In several of these units—notably the Mount Isa rock and the Kupferschiefer—the pyrite is accompanied by a variety of other sulfides.

Analyses G to H, table 18 are of a Precambrian pyritic slate in Minnesota that has been metamorphosed to yield some pyrrhotite—a hydrothermal origin for the sulfides, as proposed by Thiel (1924), seems very unlikely. Analysis F represents a thick unit of pyritic rock—as much as 120 feet thick, with associated pyrrhotite, siderite, magnetite, and quartz—of the Michipicoten district of Ontario; according to Goodwin (1962) the rock is the product of sedimentation of materials derived from submarine hot spring and fumarolic activity—that is, it is of the "exhalative-sedimentary" type. A similar origin is suggested for pyrrhotite-pyrite bodies at Samreid Lake, Ontario (Friedman, 1959).

The occurrence of sulfide as diagenetic replacements in limestone is well known, particularly because of the spectacular preservation of fossils converted entirely to pyrite. In a few places the pyritic replacements assume major proportions as rock constituents; analyzed samples of a 4-foot bed in the Greenhorn Limestone of the Black Hills, for example, contain as much as 25.2 percent pyrite (Rubey, 1930, p. 8).

BLACKBAND AND CLAYBAND SIDERITE

The so-called blackband and clayband (or clay-ironstone) siderites (table 19) occur in clays and shales as thin layers rarely more than a foot or so thick, or as disconnected lenses and nodules. They consist of fine-grained siderite for the most part, with variable amounts of clastic material—sand and clay—and organic matter. Spherulitic structure is common.

TABLE 18.—*Analyses of sulfide-rich rocks*

[Values given in percent]

Sample A. Complete analysis

SiO_2	36.67	Na_2O	0.26	FeS_2	38.70
Al_2O_3	6.90	K_2O	1.81	SO_3	2.60
Fe_2O_3		H_2O+	1.25	C	[1] 7.60
FeO	2.35	H_2O-	.55		
MnO	.002	TiO_2	.39	Total	100.21
MgO	.65	P_2O_5	.20		
CaO	.13	V_2O_5	.15		

Samples B–H. Partial analyses

	B	C	D	E	F	G	H
SiO_2	9.91		13.20		4.69	42.11	36.57
Al_2O_3					.56	8.72	5.28
Fe	35.18	29.00	28.60	31.10	42.1	18.88	27.84
Mn					1.0	.75	.16
MgO					1.90	.20	1.69
CaO	.54		2.80		3.87	.19	1.70
P_2O_5	.35		.52				
P						.063	.119
S	34.46	25.00	24.58	25.70	32.6	14.8	15.6
SO_3							
CuO		.015					
PbO		.140					
Ni, Co		.11					
H_2O							
Loss on ignition						16.24	10.96

[1] Includes organic matter.

A. Pyritic graphitic slate, Iron River district, Michigan. Precambrian (James, 1951). Charlotte M. Warshaw, analyst.
B. Oolitic pyrite, Wabana, Newfoundland (Hayes, 1915, p. 49). Ordovician. A. V. Seaborn, analyst.
C. "Sulphur band" of Cleveland ironstone, Cleveland district, England (Hallimond, 1925, p. 54). Middle Jurassic. J. E. Stead, analyst.
D–E. "Sulphur band" of Cleveland ironstone (Lamplugh, Wedd, and Pringle, 1920, p. 53). Analysis D by A. A. Street, analysis E by Ridsdale and Co., Middlesbrough.
F. Pyritic member of Precambrian iron-formation of Michipicoten district, Goodreau A deposit, Ontario (Goodwin, 1962, p. 577). J. H. Dann, analyst.
G–H. Sulfide-bearing graphitic slate (Precambrian), Aitkin County, Minn. (Pennington and Davis, 1953, p. 9, 14). Sulfides are pyrite, pryrrhotite, and marcasite. Sample G represents 66 feet of drill core; sample H represents 70 feet. Analyses by Lerch Bros., Crosby, Minn.

The typical occurrence is in rocks associated with coal beds, notably those of Carboniferous or Permian age. They are abundant in the Appalachian coal field (see, for example, Stout, 1944; Singewald, 1911), and they are reported to occur at 75 horizons in the lower coal measures of Wales (Tyler, 1950, p. 518). In the U.S.S.R., in the foreland of the Urals in the general vicinity of Perm, siderite forms irregular and lenticular beds as much as several meters thick over a region of thousands of square miles (Belousov, 1933; Miropolskaya, 1949).

The rocks tend to be higher in FeO relative to MnO, CaO, and MgO than the marine siderite facies. The $FeCO_3$ content of the carbonate commonly is 90 percent or more. The calculated molecular composition of siderite from the coal measures of the Lvov basin of the U.S.S.R., for example, in molecular percent is 95.07 percent $FeCO_3$, 2.15 percent $MnCO_3$, and 2.77 percent $CaCO_3$ (Vartanova, Artemenko, and Galkina, 1950, p. 302). The blackband ores are significantly higher in C or organic content than those of the clayband variety and commonly contain several percent marcasite.

Much of the blackband and clayband siderite is of diagenetic origin, but some of the more continuous layers may represent primary sediments, deposited in brackish waters or marine swamps in the presence of abundant vegetal matter.

TABLE 19.—*Analyses of blackband and clay-ironstone siderite*

	A	B	C	D	E	F	G	H	I	J
SiO_2	5.10	6.46	13.50	10.04	12.86	6.83	13.35	0.48	8.67	10.72
Al_2O_3	2.35	2.64	6.13	5.57	6.16	2.85	5.79	.37	4.47	4.45
Fe_2O_3	.00	6.85	1.30	1.49	.39	.43	.41	1.18	.42	1.11
FeO	50.92	42.08	39.87	37.99	43.81	51.45	41.03	41.37	43.11	38.08
MnO	.58	2.32	1.38	1.51	.98	.54	.55	.89	2.07	1.06
MgO	.30	1.76	2.77	3.37	1.15	.42	3.36	4.00	2.09	3.75
CaO	.70	3.87	2.12	4.59	1.67	2.13	3.00	4.53	5.15	5.19
Na_2O										.12
K_2O			.18	.55	.42	.16	.86			.19
H_2O+	2.70 (H₂O+ and H₂O−)	Tr	1.21	1.47	1.32	.54	1.36	4.10 (H₂O+ and H₂O−)	[1] .25	1.10
H_2O-		.15	.59	.74	.54	.19	.57		[2] .12	.77
TiO_2		.21						.02		.22
P_2O_5	.33	.65	.69	.80	.83	.23	.70	1.87	1.176	1.83
CO_2	31.80	32.70	28.47	29.92	28.22	33.31	28.49	31.34	32.74	30.20
S	.18								.178	
SO_3		.20	Tr	Tr	Tr			.30		.02
FeS_2		.11	.05	.06	.30	.02		1.28		.42
C	5.00		[3] .83	[3] 1.42	[3] .88	[3] .67	[3] .07	[3] 8.25		[4] 1.04
Subtotal	99.96	100.00	99.09	99.52	99.53	99.77	99.54	[5] 100.00	100.44	100.27
Less O	.09								.09	
Total	99.87	100.00	99.09	99.52	99.53	99.77	99.54	100.00	100.35	100.27

[1] "Water and organic matter."
[2] "Moisture."
[3] "Organic matter."
[4] Total of carbon, organic 0.92 percent, and hydrogen, organic 0.12 percent.
[5] Total includes 0.02 "arsenic acid."

A. Siderite ironstone ("blackband"), Prestwick Mine, Natal, South Africa (Wagner, 1928, p. 127–128). R. R. Walton, analyst. Associated with coal beds of Karoo System (Carboniferous to Triassic). Calculated mode: quartz 2.33 percent, "clay substance" 7.82 percent, siderite 83.24 percent, calcite 0.48 percent, apatite 0.76 percent, pyrite 0.34 percent, carbon 5.00 percent. Some of "clay substance" is chamosite.
B. "Clay ironstone," Ashburnham, Sussex, England (Lamplugh, *in* Lamplugh, Wedd, and Pringle, 1920, p. 227). Bed in Wadhurst Clay (Cretaceous). Analysis by R.R. Tatlock and Thomson, Glasgow.
C. "Clayband ironstone," Pargate, Yorkshire (Gibson, *in* Strahan and others (1920). Bed of siderite nodules in Coal Measures (Carboniferous). Analysis reported here is total of acid-soluble and ignited acid-insoluble residue. All SiO_2 is in insoluble portion. Analyst not known.
D. Siderite ironstone, Brown Rake, Butterley, Derbyshire, England (Gibson, *in* Strahan and others, 1920, p. 52). Bed in Coal Measures (Carboniferous). Analysis reported here is total of acid-soluble and ignited acid-insoluble residue. Analyst not known.
E. Brooch ironstone, Corngreaves, Staffordshire, England (Gibson, *in* Strahan and others, 1920, p. 62). Thin layer in Coal Measures (Carboniferous). Analysis reported here is total of acid-soluble and ignited acid-insoluble residue. Analyst not known.
F. Sideritic ironstone ("Crawstone"), Madeley Wood, Shropshire, England (Dewey, *in* Strahan and others, 1920, p. 93). Irregular masses in fine-grained sandstone of Coal Measures (Carboniferous). Specific gravity 3.68. Analysis reported here is total of acid-soluble and acid-insoluble residue. Analyst not known.
G. Clay ironstone, Rosser Vein Mine, Dowlais, South Wales (Strahan, *in* Strahan and others, 1920, p. 114). Bed in Coal Measures (Carboniferous). Analyst not known.
H. Blackband ironstone, Dundonald Colliery, Fifeshire, Scotland (MacGregor, Lee, and Wison, 1920, p. 142). Analysis by Lochgelly Iron and Coal Co. Layer 4–6 inches thick above coal bed of early Carboniferous age.
I. Blackband ore, Holmes County, Ohio (Stout, 1944, pp. 168–169). Nodular siderite in Pennsylvanian strata. Analysis by Ohio Geological Survey.
J. Blackband ore, Tuscarawas County, Ohio (Stout, 1944, p. 172). Nodular siderite above Lower Kittanning coal (Pennsylvanian). D. Schaaf, analyst.

Editor's Note: References for this article may be found at the end of Paper 32.

3

Reprinted from *Handbook of Geochemistry,* K. H. Wedepohl, ed., Springer-Verlag, Berlin, 1970, pp. 26-E-1–26-E-6

26-E. Abundance in Common Igneous Rock Types

R. F. MUELLER

The iron content of those igneous rocks and minerals which have come down to us unaltered from the magmatic stage should reflect at least approximately the physico-chemical environment prevailing at the time. In particular the quantities $Mg^{2+}/(Mg^{2+}+Fe^{2+})$ and Fe^{2+}/Fe^{3+} should furnish a record of the fugacity of oxygen. It has been found that a variety of plutonic rocks, including both the calc-alkali batholiths and the differentiated gabbroic complexes, show a decrease in the fraction $Mg^{2+}/(Mg^{2+}+Fe^{2+})$ along the differentiation sequence leading from basaltic magma to granite. This trend is particularly well shown by the minerals of the southern California batholith (nos. 17 to 21, Table 12-E-1) in the sequence ranging from troctolite to granite. It is also shown by the sequence of average calc-alkali rocks of Table 12-E-2 of that chapter. Among the gabbros, the best known example is that of the Skaergaard complex of East Greenland (WAGER and DEER, 1939).

In the case of the calc-alkali sequence, this change in mineral composition corresponds to an absolute decrease in the rock of $MgO+FeO$ with an accompanying increase in SiO_2 and Na_2O+K_2O. But in the gabbroic complexes, a different trend, toward strong iron enrichment, is apparent. This may be seen in Table 12-E-1 if the three members of the Bushveld border facies (nos. 27, 28, and 29) are compared. It is equally well shown by the rocks of the Skaergaard and Stillwater as well as numerous other complexes of this kind.

The two contrasting trends of differentiation are illustrated graphically in Fig. 26-E-1.

It is interesting to compare the iron-titanium oxides of the igneous rocks with the silicates from these rocks and with similar oxides formed under a metamorphic environment. We then see (Table 26-E-1) the same tendency for $Mg^{2+}/(Mg^{2+}+Fe^{2+})$ to decrease during differentiation as in the silicates. We also see that the oxides from igneous rocks accept relatively more magnesium than their metamorphic counterparts, even when the latter are formed in a Mg-rich environment.

The variation in Fe^{2+}/Fe^{3+} is not nearly as systematic among igneous rocks as that of $Mg^{2+}/(Mg^{2+}+Fe^{2+})$. One reason for this appears to be the sensitivity of the former ratio to the influence of other elements such as aluminum and sodium. However if Table 12-E-2 is examined, it will be seen that there is a marked decrease in this ratio in volcanic calc-alkali sequence (basalt to rhyolite) and that it is considerably lower than in the corresponding plutonic member of the sequence (gabbro to granite). Quite generally also, the determination of Fe_2O_3 presents chemical analytical problems[1] so that many published values for this oxide are suspect. This is especially true for such minerals as olivine which appear to have little crystal chemical accommodation for primary Fe^{3+}. Indeed those cases in which a particular effort has been made in the analysis, very low values of Fe_2O_3 are usually obtained. This is illustrated here for a very iron-rich olivine (no. 23, Table 12-E-1).

[1] Fe_2O_3 determinations are inferior to FeO determinations where Fe_2O_3 is a minor constituent as it is in many minerals and rocks.

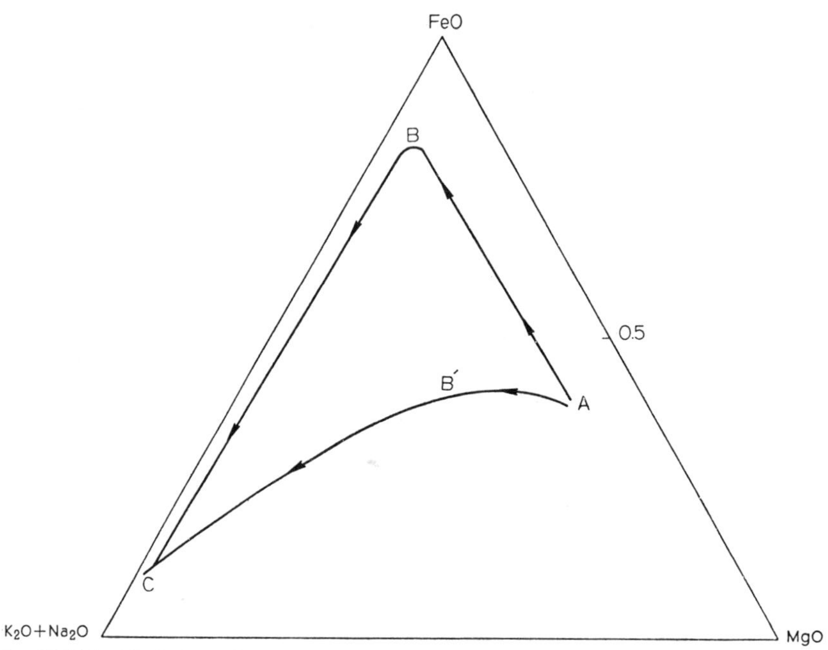

Fig. 26-E-1. Variation diagram, in weight per cent, of the oxides of two contrasting differentiation trends. Curve ABC represents the skaergaard gabbroic complex (WAGER and DEER, 1939) while curve AB′C represents the calc-alkali complexes such as the Southern California batholith

Table 26-E-1. *Compositions and atomic fractions of co-existing titatano-magnetites and ilmenites of successive differentiates from the Skaergaard Complex, East Greenland.* (Data from VINCENT and PHILLIPS, 1954)

Rock type	Mineral	MgO	FeO	Fe_2O_3	$\frac{Mg^{2+}}{Mg^{2+}+Fe^{2+}}$
Hypersthene olivine gabbro	magnetite	1.98	43.07	32.27	0.076
	ilmenite	3.27	39.64	4.25	0.128
Middle gabbro	magnetite	1.19	35.68	42.95	0.055
	ilmenite	2.27	40.39	6.26	0.091
Hortonolite ferrogabbro	magnetite	1.21	41.69	31.26	0.049
	ilmenite	1.48	42.72	2.58	0.059
Ferrohortonolite gabbro	magnetite	0.77	35.69	45.86	0.037
	ilmenite	0.62	43.30	3.92	0.024
Fayalite ferrogabbro	magnetite	0.06	37.01	39.58	0.003
	ilmenite	0.46	42.18	4.19	0.023

In the case of iron determinations by electron microprobe methods, the quantity of Fe_2O_3 present must of course be inferred by other methods. This is illustrated in the case of the minerals from the Stillwater complex (Table 12-E-1, no. 31). Such correction of total iron for Fe_2O_3 assumes great importance in the calculation of D values for mineral pairs which differ greatly in Fe_2O_3 content.

In volcanic rocks which have been subject to strong oxidation, the Fe_2O_3 contents of certain minerals such as hornblende or biotite may be so high that they exhibit peculiar optical properties. These "oxyhornblendes" and "oxybiotites" are usually unstable in that they most frequently represent altered phenocrysts which were originally formed under more reducing conditions at depth. It has been shown (LARSEN, IRVING, GONYER and LARSEN, 1936) that the increase in Fe^{3+}/Fe^{2+} is in these cases due to a loss of hydrogen from the hydrous minerals.

As in cases from meteorites and metamorphic rocks, the compositions of igneous minerals can be understood only in terms of certain reactions of thermodynamic significance. Thus for basic and ultrabasic rocks, one of the most significant reactions is the following:

$$\underset{\text{pyroxene}}{2MgSiO_3} + \underset{\text{magnetite}}{2/3\ Fe_3O_4} \rightleftarrows \underset{\text{forsterite}}{Mg_2SiO_4} + \underset{\text{fayalite}}{Fe_2SiO_4} + \underset{\text{fluid}}{1/3\ O_2} \qquad \text{(E-1)}$$

This reaction, which relates the compositions of the co-existing olivines and pyroxenes to the oxygen fugacity, is applicable to both subliquidus and subsolidus conditions whenever olivine, pyroxene and magnetite are present. It may also be seen that (E-1) is analogous to reaction (C-1) for meteorites except that olivine here appears on the reduced side. It may be shown (MUELLER, 1965) from an equation of equilibrium analogous to (C-3) that in this case also $Mg^{2+}/(Mg^{2+}+Fe^{2+})$ increases with increasing P_{O_2}; this is also in agreement with the experimental data of MUAN and OSBORN (1956) and of SPEIDEL and NAFZIGER (1968) (Fig. 26-E-2).

When the rocks are silica-saturated, as is frequently the case among the calc-alkali differentiates (Table 12-E-1), the following reaction may be appropriate:

$$\underset{\text{quartz}}{SiO_2} + \underset{\text{ferrite}}{1/3\ Fe_3O_4} \rightleftarrows \underset{\text{pyroxene}}{FeSiO_3} + \underset{\text{fluid}}{1/6\ O_2}. \qquad \text{(E-2)}$$

If we apply thermochemical data to this reaction, it may again be shown that as in the case of (E-1), $Mg^{2+}/(Mg^{2+}+Fe^{2+})$ increases with increasing P_{O_2}. If this is true, it is inescapable that we must interpret the observed variation of $Mg^{2+}/(Mg^{2+}+Fe^{2+})$ in the minerals of the calc-alkali series as a reduction of P_{O_2} in the sequence troctolite to granite. Similarly, considerable reduction of P_{O_2} must have occurred during differentiation of the gabbroic complexes which show iron enrichment.

The behavior of iron and magnesium in magmatic differentiation may best be understood if reference is made to the experimental work on the systems MgO—FeO—SiO_2 (BOWEN and SCHAIRER, 1935) and MgO—FeO—Fe_2O_3—SiO_2 (MUAN and OSBORN, 1956). Taken together these systems may be designated as the system MgO—Fe—SiO_2—O_2 and which is applicable to both meteorites and terrestrial rocks. In particular the system MgO—FeO—SiO_2 rather closely approximates the major silicate components of the stony meteorites, and since the experiments of BOWEN and SCHAIRER were conducted in such a way that the silicates were in equilibrium with iron crucibles, the oxygen fugacities should also approximate the meteoritic environment. However, it must be kept in mind that other constituents such as the feldspars in stony meteorites lower the liquidus temperatures.

The system MgO—FeO—Fe_2O_3—SiO_2 as studied by MUAN and OSBORN applies to a region of somewhat higher oxygen fugacities than the system of BOWEN and SCHAIRER and involves (Fe, Mg) Fe_2O_4 (magnetite) as a prominent phase. Accordingly its phase relations are particularly significant in the interpretation of terrestrial

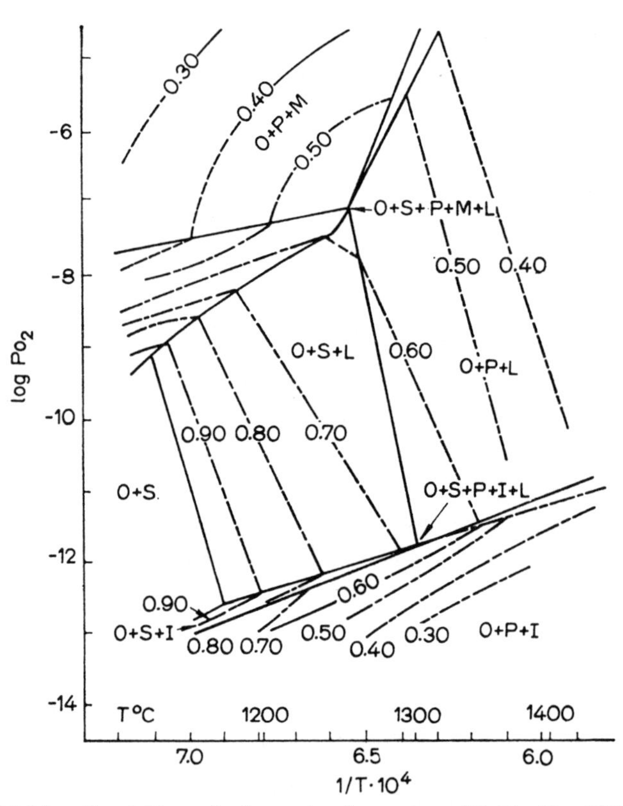

Fig. 26-E-2. Fields of stability of phases in the system $MgO—Fe—SiO_2—O_2$ at one atmosphere total pressure as experimentally determined (SPEIDEL and NAFZIGER, 1968). Phase boundaries are shown as solid lines while the dashed lines show the mole fraction $Fe^{2+}/(Mg + Fe^{2+})$ of the olivine. The symbols are defined as follows: *O* olivine, *P* pyroxene, *M* magnetite, *S* silica, *I* metallic iron, *L* liquid

rocks such as the gabbroic complexes. Fortunately, however, the major trends in igneous equilibrium and fractional crystallization for both meteorites and terrestrial rocks are exhibited by the system $MgO—FeO—SiO_2$ as shown in Fig. 26-E-3. One of the most important characteristics of this system is the great enrichment of FeO in the liquid relative to the crystalline precipitates with which it is in equilibrium. The corresponding effect in the differentiation of a basaltic magma may be seen in Table 12-E-1 if the composition of the quenched border facies rock of the Still-water complex is compared with the composition of minerals in one of the first differentiates, the basal harzburgite. In this case $Mg/(Mg + Fe^{2+})$ of the border facies, which presumably represents the liquid, is only 0.580, while the crystals which precipitated from this liquid all show values of $Mg/(Mg + Fe^{2+})$ greater than 0.86. An important consequence of this iron enrichment in the liquid is that the upward transport of basaltic magma should bring about a continual enrichment of the crust in FeO relative to MgO.

Experimental data for a range of liquidus and subsolidus temperatures in the general system $MgO—Fe—SiO_2—O_2$ were recently presented by SPEIDEL and NAFZIGER (1968) (Fig. 26-E-2). Certain features of this diagram are quite interesting.

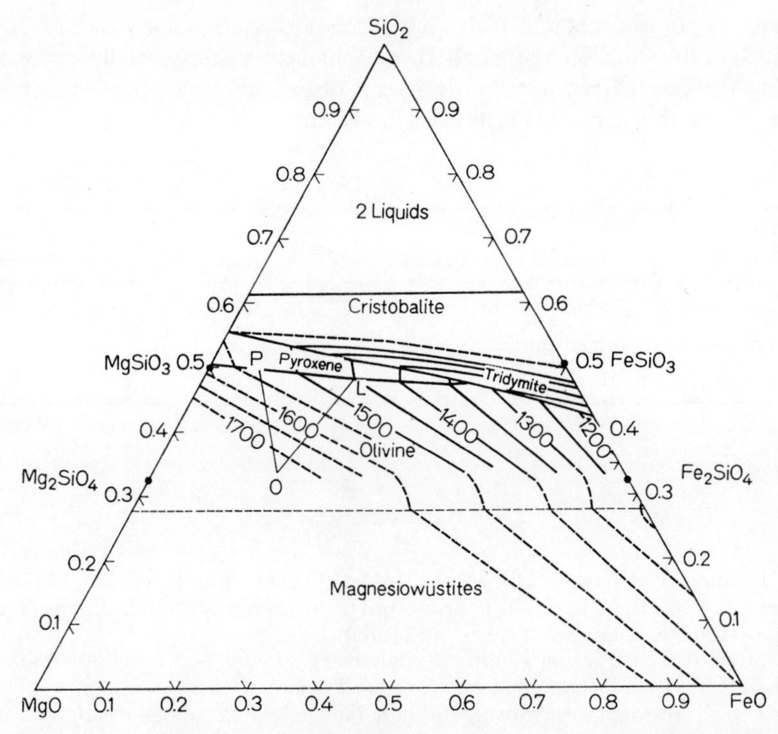

Fig. 26-E-3. Molar plot (MUELLER, 1964) of liquidus relations in the system MgO—FeO—SiO_2 as determined by BOWEN and SCHAIRER (1935). The isotherms are labeled in degrees centigrade. The three phase triangle shows the compositions of co-existing olivine (*O*), pyroxene (*P*) and liquid (*L*) phases at 1,450° C

One of these is the separation, by a field of olivine + silica, of the fields which contain olivine + pyroxene + metal and olivine + pyroxene + magnetite. The last two fields of course correspond to the metallic meteorites and terrestrial rocks respectively. Another interesting feature of the diagram is the considerably greater separation of the lines of equal mineral composition in the field of magnetite compared to the separation in the metallic iron field. This observation accords well with the theoretical predictions from reactions (C-1), (C-2) and (E-1) as formulated in equations of the types (C-3) and (C-4). These equations predict not only the direction of variation of $Mg/(Mg + Fe^{2+})$ in the silicates with temperature and oxygen fugacity but also the relative sensitivities of these variations as revealed by the lines of equal mineral composition.

Although by far the greatest amount of iron in igneous rocks occurs as FeO and Fe_2O_3, a few rocks contain metallic iron. The best known examples are of course the basalts such as those at Disco Island, Greenland (VAASJOKI, 1964) and Buehl near Kassel (Germany), but metallic iron has also been reported from granites and traychtes (PALACHE, BERMAN and FRONDEL, 1944) and from the Muskox gabbroic differentiate (CHAMBERLAIN, MCLEOD, TRAILL and LANCHANCE, 1965). However, in the latter occurrence it has apparently been secondarily derived by reduction of magnetite. As in the case of metamorphic rocks, iron sulfides are minor but almost omnipresent constituents and their abundances are of the same order as in metamorphics (Table 26-E-2). Although these abundances are generally expressed as FeS_2 in chemical analyses, they consist in part of FeS and a variety of more complex species involving such elements as Cu, Ni, Co, etc.

Table 26-E-2. *Iron sulfide content of igneous rocks.* (Data taken from GUPPY and SABINE, 1956)

Rock type	wt.-% FeS_2	No. of Specimens
Basalts, gabbros and diabases	0.25	13
Andesites, diorites and trachyandesite	0.10	4
Granites and granodiorites	0.09	7

References

Bowen, N. L., and J. F. Schairer: The system $MgO–FeO–SiO_2$. Am. J. Sci. **229,** 151–217 (1935).

Chamberlain, J. A., C. R. McLeod, R. J. Traill, and G. R. Lachance: Native metals in the Muskox intrusion. Can. J. Earth Sci. **2,** 188–215 (1965).

Guppy, E. M., and P. A. Sabine: Chemical analyses of igneous rocks, metamorphic rocks and minerals 1931–1934. Mem. Geol. Surv. Great Britain (1956).

Larsen, E. S., Jr., J. Irving, E. A. Gonyer, and E. S. Larsen 3rd: Petrologic results of a study of the minerals from the Tertiary volcanic rocks of the San Juan Region, Colorado. Am. Mineral. **21,** 679–701 (1936).

Muan, A., and E. F. Osborn: Phase equilibria at liquidus temperatures in the system $MgO–FeO–Fe_2O_3–SiO_2$. J. Am. Ceram. Soc. **39,** 121–140 (1956).

Mueller, R. E.: System $Fe–MgO/SiO_2–O_2$ with applications to terrestrial rocks and meteorites. Geochim. Cosmochim. Acta **29,** 967–976 (1965).

Palache, C., H. Berman, and C. Frondel: The system of mineralogy of J. D. Dana and E. S. Dana, vol. 2. New York: John Wiley & Sons, 1944.

Speidel, D. H., and R. H. Nafziger: $P–T–f_{O_2}$ relations in the system $FeO–MgO–SiO_2$ Am.J. Sci. **266,** 361–379 (1968).

Vaasjoki, O.: On basalt rocks with native iron in Disco, West Greenland. Bull. Comm. Geol. Finlande **37,** 85–97 (1964).

Vincent, E. A., and R. Phillips: Iron-titanium oxide minerals in layered gabbros of the Skaergaard intrusion, East Greenland. Geochim. Cosmochim. Acta **6,** 1–26 (1954).

Wager, L. R., and W. A. Deer: Geological investigations in East Greenland, Part III. The petrology of the Skaergaard intrusion, Kangerdlugssuaq, East Greenland, Medd. Groenland **105, 4,** 1–335 (1939).

4

Reprinted from *Handbook of Geochemistry*, K. H. Wedepohl, ed., Springer-Verlag, Berlin, 1970.
pp. 26-I-1–26-I-2

26-I. Abundance in Natural Waters

R. A. BERNER

I. Surface Waters

Most waters at the surface of the earth contain dissolved oxygen. As a result, iron is highly insoluble (see Subsection 26-H-II). Values reported in the literature for iron dissolved in aerated waters, such as sea water, are much higher than the value expected for equilibrium with $Fe(OH)_3$. Thus, natural surface waters appear to be highly supersaturated with respect to ferric hydroxide and hematite. This is shown in Table 26-I-1. The supersaturation, however, is an artifact because the reported "dissolved monomeric" iron is actually the total iron that passes through a filter of a given pore size. In studies conducted within the past 20 years, the pore size used has generally been 0.5 μ (Millipore filters). Iron greater than this size is designated as suspended and less than 0.5 μ (5,000 Å) as dissolved. The size of monomeric dissolved iron species such as $Fe^{3+}_{aq.}$ or $Fe(OH)^{+}_{2\,aq.}$ is on the order of a few angstroms. Therefore, the iron which is less than 5,000 Å can be mostly colloidal and incorrectly reported as monomeric dissolved iron. Proof of this is provided by studies where the concentration of total iron was found to fall off drastically when filters of a pore size less than 0.5 μ or an ultracentrifuge was used (LENGWEILER *et al.*, 1961). Thus, most of the iron reported as simple monomeric species is actually present in a polymeric or colloidal state and the values cited are only maximum values for dissolved iron.

Table 26-I-1. *Concentration of iron in sea water and in river water. Calculated values are for $Fe(OH)_3$ saturation at $pH = 7$ (river water) and $pH = 8$ (sea water) from Fig. 26-H-3*

	Measured Fe ppm	Calculated Fe ppm
Sea water		
(LEWIS and GOLDBERG, 1954)	3.4×10^{-3}	3×10^{-6}
(SPENCER and BREWER, 1969)	2.5×10^{-4}	3×10^{-6}
River water		
(LIVINGSTONE, 1963)	6.7×10^{-1}	3×10^{-5}

In some waters unusually rich in organic matter such as swamps, the formation of chelates with dissolved organic species may enable dissolved iron to be present at appreciable concentrations in the presence of oxygen. For example, the existence of ferrous-tannic acid complexes which are resistant to air oxidation have been reported by HEM (1960) and studied experimentally.

Because of the problem cited above, the values for truly dissolved iron in natural aerobic waters are unknown. "Suspended iron" (>0.5 μ) in natural waters is highly variable and related to nearby sources of sediment (eg. see LEWIS and GOLDBERG, 1954, and SPENCER and BREWER, 1969, for sea water). No meaningful average value can be given.

II. Subsurface Waters

Waters that are not in contact with the atmosphere may lose their dissolved oxygen by reaction with ferrous compounds or by bacterial activity. Thus, many subsurface waters, such as ground waters and marine sediment pore waters, are anaerobic. Under anaerobic conditions the most abundant form of dissolved iron is $Fe^{2+}_{aq.}$ which can be present at reasonably high concentrations in equilibrium with iron compounds (see Figs. 26-H-1 to 26-H-4).

Dissolved iron contents in non-thermal ground waters on the continents range in concentration from <0.01 ppm to about 500 ppm (WHITE *et al.*, 1963). Values greater than 100 ppm are for acid mine waters which often have a pH less than 2 and thus can dissolve considerable ferric as well as ferrous iron. Other more typical ground waters of higher pH (>4) have iron concentrations ranging from <0.01 ppm to 10 ppm (WHITE *et al.*, 1963). No consistent correlation between dissolved iron and rock type is apparent from the data of WHITE *et al.*

The concentration of iron in the pore waters of marine sediments is not well known. BROOKS *et al.* (1968) recently have reported data for sediments of the southern California borderland which show a large range in Eh. Iron concentrations in the interstitial waters fall between 0.001 and 0.07 ppm. Since a 0.5 μ filter was used, these values must be considered maxima for truly dissolved iron.

References

Brooks, R. R., B. J. Presley, and I. R. Kaplan: Trace elements in the interstitial waters of marine sediments. Geochim. Cosmochim. Acta **32,** 397 (1968).

Lengweiler, H., W. Buser, and W. Feitknecht: Die Ermittlung der Löslichkeit von Eisen (III)-hydroxiden mit ^{59}Fe II. Der Zustand kleinster Mengen Eisen (III)-hydroxid in wässeriger Lösung. Helv. Chim. Acta **44,** 805 (1961).

Lewis, G. J., and E. D. Goldberg: Iron in marine waters. J. Marine Res. **13,** 183 (1954).

Livingstone, D. A.: Chemical composition of rivers and lakes. U. S. Geol. Surv. Profess. Papers **440-G** (1963).

Spencer, D. W., and P. G. Brewer: The distribution of copper, zinc, and nickel in sea water of the Gulf of Maine and the Sargasso Sea. Geochim. Cosmochim. Acta **33,** 325 (1969).

White, D. E., John D. Hem, and G. A. Waring: Chemical composition of subsurface waters. U.S. Geol. Surv. Profess. Papers **440-F** (1963).

II
Solution, Deposition, and Transport

Editor's Comments on Papers 5, 6, and 7

5 **Huber:** *The Environmental Control of Sedimentary Iron Minerals*

6 **Krauskopf:** Excerpt from *Separation of Manganese from Iron in Sedimentary Processes*

7 **Curtis and Spears:** *The Formation of Sedimentary Iron Minerals: Part I*

The pioneer experimental work on the solution and deposition of iron by Gruner (1922) and Moore and Maynard (1929) was designed to research the problem of the source of the iron in iron-formations. At the time that their work was conducted it was well known that iron is only a very minor constituent of most natural waters, and it thus appeared that the surface processes were incapable of delivering sufficient iron to form deposits comparable to those in the Lake Superior iron-formations. In experiments that ran for months and even years, both found that carbonated waters, particularly peat solutions, were effective in dissolving iron from various rocks and minerals. They concluded that the iron and the silica of iron-formations was carried by rivers rich in organic matter as protected colloids. As to the deposition of iron, Gruner (1922, p. 455) suggested that: "The precipitation of silica, iron and part of the organic colloids was caused chiefly by algae and bacteria, which used the organic matter for their life processes and the inorganic silica or iron for the building of their cells or sheaths." Moore and Maynard (1929), who similarly believed that the iron and silica were transported in the colloidal state, placed greater emphasis on inorganic precipitation. They proposed that: "The iron would be dissolved and carried as a ferric oxide hydrosol and the silica as colloidal silica, the two being stabilized by organic matter which kept them from mutually precipitating one another until thrown down by the electrolytes of the sea."

By the 1950s it became increasingly accepted that iron-formations are true chemical precipitates. The recognition (Paper 20) that iron may be present in these formations as oxide, carbonate, silicate, or sulfide indicated that dissolved iron must have been available at the depositional sites and that each iron mineral must represent a depositional environment with unique chemical parameters. The problem, therefore, no longer was how the iron was transported, but rather what chemical conditions were necessary to precipitate the individual iron minerals. As long as these conditions were maintained over extended periods at the site of deposition, large deposits of iron could build up from very dilute solutions.

One of the first attempts to delineate the chemical conditions necessary for the formation of an iron sediment (in this case, the Clinton ironstone) is the work by Castano and Garrels (1950). Many subsequent investigations were influenced by this paper and by the more comprehensive report on the origin and classification of chemical sediments in terms of pH and oxidation–reduction potentials by W. C. Krumbein and R. M. Garrels (1952). These authors built upon the work of M. J. N. Pourbaix (1949), who was a pioneer in applying thermodynamics to the chemistry of dilute aqueous solutions.

J. D. Hem and coworkers investigated the solubility of iron in natural waters both experimentally and by calculating activities of dissolved iron for various anionic concentrations from thermochemical data (Hem, 1960a, 1960b; Hem and Cropper, 1959). They published a series of important articles on the solubility of iron and on the stability of the various iron minerals as a number of U.S. Geological Survey Water-Supply Papers.

Paper 5 is by N. King Huber, who began his geologic career investigating iron geochemistry under the guidance of Robert M. Garrels, one of the pioneers in exploring the importance of pH and oxidation potentials in geologic environments at surface temperatures. The principles developed in the present paper were applied in a companion paper to the Ironwood iron-formation of Michigan (Huber, 1959). After joining the U.S. Geological Survey, Huber worked on the granitic rocks of the Sierra Nevada batholith, and he is currently (1973) engaged in making mineral resource studies of the Sierra Nevada. It is interesting to note that in this paper Huber does not consider the Precambrian atmosphere to have been different from the present atmosphere. He thus reflects the position of most geologists during the 1950s, a position that changed drastically during the following decade.

Iron and manganese are chemically similar elements and they are usually closely associated in igneous rocks. Some iron-formations contain Mn/Fe ratios that are the same as those of igneous rocks (Lepp, 1963). There are, however, sedimentary deposits of nearly iron-free manganese minerals and Paper 6 is an excerpt from a paper by Konrad B. Krauskopf designed to explain the conditions necessary for this geochemical separation of these similar elements. K. B. Krauskopf is a professor of geochemistry at Stanford University. He is a most distinguished geochemist, having published extensively on problems involving the application of chemical principles to the interpretation of geologic phenomena. He is the author of a college textbook on geochemistry (Krauskopf, 1967) and of several other books.

Paper 7 is by two British geologists. Only the first half of the paper is reproduced here; the second half, involving the application of the mineral stability diagrams to the Carboniferous and Jurassic iron ores of Britain, appears as Paper 24. Both Charles D. Curtis and David A. Spears are associated with the University of Sheffield in England. Curtis has spent some time at the Denver Research Center of the Marathon Oil Company. He writes that the geochemistry of iron is still his principal interest. D. A. Spears is Lecturer in geology at the University of Sheffield, where he received his Ph.D. in 1963. His doctoral dissertation is on the "Geochemistry of the Mansfield Marine Band," and his interest continues to be the mineralogy and geochemistry of fine-grained sediments.

References

Castano, J. R., and R. M. Garrels, 1950, Experiments on the deposition of iron with special reference to the Clinton iron ore deposits: Econ. Geol., v. 45, p. 755–770.

Gruner, J. W., 1922, The origin of sedimentary iron formations: Econ. Geol., v. 17, p. 407–460.

Hem, J. D., 1960a, Restraints on dissolved ferrous iron imposed by bicarbonate, redox potential, and pH: U.S. Geol. Surv. Water-Supply Paper 1459-B, p. 33–55.

———, 1960b, Some chemical relationships among sulfur species and dissolved ferrous iron: U.S. Geol. Surv. Water-Supply Paper 1459-C, p. 57–73.

———, and W. H. Cropper, 1959, Survey of ferrous-ferric chemical equilibria and redox potentials: U.S. Geol. Surv. Water-Supply Paper 1459-A, p. 1–31.

Huber, N. K., 1959, Some aspects of the origin of the Ironwood iron formation of Michigan and Wisconsin: Econ. Geol., v. 54, p. 82–118.

Krauskopf, K. B., 1967, Introduction to geochemistry: McGraw-Hill Book Co., New York, 721 p.

Krumbein, W. C., and R. M. Garrels, 1952, Origin and classification of chemical sediments in terms of pH and oxidation–reduction potentials: Jour. Geol., v. 60, p. 1–33.

Lepp, H., 1963, The relation of iron and manganese in sedimentary iron formations: Econ. Geol., v. 58, p. 515–526.

Moore, E. S., and J. E. Maynard, 1929, Transportation and precipitation of iron and silica: Econ. Geol., v. 24, p. 272–303, 365–402, 506–527.

Pourbaix, M. J. N., 1949, Thermodynamics of dilute aqueous solutions: Edward Arnold and Co., London, 136 p.

5

Reprinted from *Econ. Geol.*, **53**(2), 124–140(1958)

The Environmental Control of Sedimentary Iron Minerals

N. KING HUBER

ABSTRACT

An Eh-pH stability diagram is developed for hematite, magnetite, siderite, pyrite, and iron sulfide that indicates the relative position of their stability fields in a normal sea water system. With the exception of the magnetite-siderite relationship, Eh is much more critical than pH. In general terms, hematite is stable under oxidizing conditions, siderite and magnetite under intermediate to moderately reducing conditions, pyrite under moderate to strongly reducing conditions, and iron sulfide under still stronger reducing conditions. Because of numerous variables involved the relative positions of the stability fields are stressed rather than their limits on the Eh and pH scales. The inclusion of a magnetite field suggests that magnetite should be much more important as a primary or diagenetic mineral in sedimentary rocks than has been commonly recognized. This is in accord with numerous recent suggestions to that effect. The importance of thermodynamic equilibrium is stressed and it is suggested that differences in rates of formation of the various minerals and the persistence of some metastable phases are among the commonest causes of lack of equilibrium.

INTRODUCTION

Equilibrium relationships between various minerals can be treated by the methods of thermodynamics if certain simplifying assumptions are made. The depositional environment of minerals precipitated from natural waters under earth-surface conditions can be considered one of essentially constant temperature and pressure. In many such natural systems the chemical reactions involved may be controlled almost entirely by the hydrogen-ion concentration (pH) and the oxidation potential (Eh) of the environment. By considering the pH and Eh relationships of a postulated environment, the various mineral associations can be predicted and their fields of thermodynamic stability plotted on an Eh-pH diagram comparable to a temperature-pressure diagram.

Suggestions as to the chemical conditions necessary for the formation of various sedimentary iron minerals have been made by Castaño and Garrels (4), and Krumbein and Garrels (17) have presented an Eh-pH stability diagram for hematite, siderite, and pyrite in a normal sea water system. Further theoretical considerations and some experimental verifications were given by Huber and Garrels (15). These studies were based on data for compounds that approximate the compositions of hematite (actually $Fe(OH)_3$ was used), siderite, and pyrite (actually FeS was used). Magnetite was not considered, nor, except briefly by Castaño and Garrels, were the iron silicates.

Recently, the writer's attention has been called to the work of Pourbaix (22) who has calculated Eh-pH stability fields for hematite, magnetite, and elemental iron in a study of the "corrosion domains" of iron. In a recent continuation of this work Deltombe and Pourbaix (7) presented a diagram indicating the Eh-pH relationships between hematite, magnetite, siderite, and elemental iron. The methods used by Pourbaix and his co-workers are based upon potential equations derived from free energy data allowing application to nearly all mineral species for which free energy data are available. Utilizing the methods of Pourbaix, the present study expands the previous work and presents an Eh-pH stability diagram for hematite, magnetite, siderite, pyrite, and iron sulfide (FeS).

Acknowledgments.—This paper covers some of the theoretical aspects of a larger study of iron-formation sedimentation that is part of a regional study of the Lake Superior iron ranges being made by the U. S. Geological Survey in cooperation with the Geological Survey Division of the Michigan Department of Conservation. Additional assistance for the work described in this paper was provided by the S. F. Emmons Memorial Fellowship, which the writer held while at Northwestern University during the academic year 1953–54. H. L. James of the U. S. Geological Survey, A. L. Howland of Northwestern University, and R. M. Garrels of Harvard University made many valuable suggestions during the development of the study.

DETERMINATION OF MINERAL EQUILIBRIUM RELATIONS

Magnetite-Hematite Equilibrium.—The boundary between the magnetite and hematite stability fields is established by determination of Eh and pH values at which magnetite and hematite can coexist in thermodynamic equilibrium at 25° C.

The relation between magnetite and hematite in an aqueous system can be written as

$$3Fe_2O_3 + 2H^+ + 2e^- = 2Fe_3O_4 + H_2O;$$

or

$$3Fe_2O_3 - 2Fe_3O_4 - H_2O + 2H^+ + 2e^- = 0 \tag{1}$$

with all symbols collected on the same side of the equation and where e^- represents an electron. If this is considered a reaction of the type

$$aA + bB + cH_2O + mH^+ + ne^- = 0 \tag{2}$$

(22, p. 9) then the standard potential for the reaction is given by

$$E° = \frac{a\Delta F_A° + b\Delta F_B° + c\Delta F°_{H_2O} + m\Delta F°_{H^+}}{23{,}060n} \tag{3}$$

(22, p. 9) where $\Delta F_X°$ is the standard free energy ("standard chemical potential" of Pourbaix) for each of the components in the reaction.

The potential, Eh (E of Pourbaix), for such a reaction is given by

$$Eh = E° + \frac{RT}{n\mathfrak{F}} \ln Q. \tag{4}$$

In the above equation E° is the standard potential for the reaction; R, the gas constant, equals 8.314 joules/degree; $\mathfrak{F}$, the Faraday, equals 96,496 coulombs; T is the absolute temperature; and $Q = (a_A)^a(a_B)^b(a_{H_2O})^c(a_{H^+})^m$ or the product of the activities (a_X, expressed in moles/liter) of the various components raised to the power of their coefficients. After substituting the proper constants at 25° C, changing to logarithms of base ten, and replacing $-\log a_{H^+}$ with pH, the equation becomes

$$Eh = E^\circ - \frac{0.0591m}{n} pH + \frac{0.0591}{n} [a \log a_A + b \log a_B] \quad (5)$$

the activity of H_2O being taken as one.

Values for the standard free energies of various components used in the calculation of the stability fields are listed in Table 1.

For the magnetite-hematite relationship given in equation (1), a value for E° may be obtained from equation (3) by proper substitution of standard free energies from Table 1. For this system, then, equation (5) becomes

$$Eh = 0.221 - 0.0591 \, pH \quad (6)$$

the activity of all solids being taken as unity. Equation (6) represents the locus of points lying on the hematite-magnetite boundary (i.e., hematite and magnetite coexisting in thermodynamic equilibrium at 25° C). If a series of pH values is assumed, corresponding Eh values can be calculated and the hematite magnetite boundary plotted on an Eh-pH diagram.

TABLE 1
STANDARD FREE ENERGY AT 25° C (CALORIES PER MOLE)

H^+ aq.	0	$FeCO_3$	−161,060
H_2O	− 56,690	FeS	− 23,320
Fe^{++} aq.	− 20,300	FeS_2	− 39,840
		$S^=$ aq.	+ 22,100
Fe_2O_3	−177,100	$CO_3^=$ aq.	−126,220
Fe_3O_4	−242,400	$SO_4^=$ aq.	−177,340

Values from Latimer (18).

Carbonate Equilibria.—The activity product constant for siderite is given by Latimer (18, p. 222) as

$$a_{Fe^{++}} a_{CO_3^=} = 10^{-10.68}. \quad (7)$$

It is apparent from the above relation that the solubility of siderite (and thermodynamic stability) is dependent upon the activity of carbonate ions in the aqueous system under consideration. The activity of carbonate ions in sea water is dependent upon the pH of the system through the carbon dioxide equilibria

$$CO_2 + H_2O \rightleftharpoons H_2CO_3 \rightleftharpoons HCO_3^- + H^+ \rightleftharpoons CO_3^= + 2H^+. \quad (8)$$

It is also dependent to a lesser degree upon the salinity and chlorinity of the system. Sverdrup, Johnson, and Fleming (29, p. 195–202) present a detailed discussion of the distribution of the CO_2 components in sea water with methods for calculating the concentrations of the various components. The carbonate ion concentrations used in this study for the determination of siderite stability are taken from data supplied by Sverdrup et al. Garrels and Dreyer (11) also discuss the relations between concentrations, activities, and equilibrium constants for the carbon dioxide system in regard to the determination of carbonate ion activity in sea water.

Magnetite-Siderite Equilibrium.—The relation between magnetite, siderite, and carbonate ion activity can be written as

$$Fe_3O_4 - 3FeCO_3 - 4H_2O + 3CO_3^{=} + 8H^+ + 2e^- = 0, \quad (9)$$

where the equilibrium potential for the reaction is

$$Eh = 1.93 - 0.236\,pH + 0.0887 \log a_{CO_3^-} \quad (10)$$

as calculated by the methods of Pourbaix. By substitution in equation (10) of the activity of carbonate ions at various pH values, a series of Eh values can be calculated for magnetite-siderite equilibrium and the boundary between the respective fields can be defined.

Hematite-Siderite Equilibrium.—The equilibrium relations between hematite and siderite can be written as

$$Fe_2O_3 - 2FeCO_3 - 3H_2O + 2CO_3^{=} + 6H^+ + 2e^- = 0 \quad (11)$$

$$Eh = 1.36 - 0.177pH + 0.0591 \log a_{CO_3^-}. \quad (12)$$

As noted in the previous section, at any assumed pH, the carbonate ion activity is fixed and the equilibrium Eh can be calculated from equation (12). A series of such calculations will serve to define the boundary between the hematite and siderite stability fields.

Sulfide Equilibria.—The total sulfur content of normal sea water is approximately $10^{-1.5}$ moles/liter (29, p. 173) and can be considered to be distributed among $S^{=}$, HS^-, H_2S, and $SO_4^{=}$, according to the dissociation constants of H_2S and H_2SO_4. Other sulfur species are negligible for the purposes of this study. The activity of the sulfide ion must also be in equilibrium with the sulfate ion activity through the equations

$$SO_4^{=} - S^{=} - 4H_2O + 8H^+ + 8e^- = 0, \quad (13)$$

$$Eh = 0.148 - 0.0591pH + 0.0074 \log \frac{a_{SO_4^-}}{a_{S^-}}. \quad (14)$$

With these relations the sulfide ion concentration can be calculated for any assumed Eh and pH values.

Magnetite-Pyrite Equilibrium.—The equilibrium relationship between magnetite and pyrite is given by

$$3FeS_2 + 4H_2O - Fe_3O_4 - 6S^{=} - 8H^+ + 4e^- = 0, \quad (15)$$

$$Eh = -2.56 + 0.118pH - 0.0887 \log a_{S^-}. \quad (16)$$

However, because $a_{S^=}$ is fixed for any given Eh and pH conditions, a pair of subsidiary equations are necessary for making the equilibrium calculations:

$$Fe_3O_4 - 3Fe^{++} - 4H_2O + 8H^+ + 2e^- = 0 \quad (17)$$

$$Eh = 0.98 - 0.236pH - 0.0887 \log a_{Fe^{++}} \quad (18)$$

and

$$FeS_2 - Fe^{++} - 2S^= + 2e^- = 0 \quad (19)$$

$$Eh = -1.38 - 0.0296 \log a_{Fe^{++}} - 0.0591 \log a_{S^=}. \quad (20)$$

At any assumed Eh and pH, $a_{S^=}$ is fixed and $a_{Fe^{++}}$ in equilibrium with pyrite can be determined from equation 20. Similarly, $a_{Fe^{++}}$ in equilibrium with magnetite can be determined through equation (18). The magnetite-pyrite equilibrium boundary is then defined by a series of Eh-pH points at which $a_{Fe^{++}}$ is equal for the two relations.

Magnetite-Iron Sulfide Equilibrium.—As previously noted, $a_{S^=}$ is fixed at any given Eh and pH. Thus at any assumed Eh and pH values $a_{Fe^{++}}$ in equilibrium with FeS can be calculated through the use of the activity product constant for FeS (18, p. 222);

$$a_{Fe^{++}}a_{S^=} = 10^{-18.4}. \quad (21)$$

Using equation (21) and equation (18) the magnetite-iron sulfide equilibrium boundary can be determined by exactly the same method used to determine the magnetite-pyrite boundary.

Hematite-Pyrite Equilibrium.—The equilibrium relationship between hematite and $a_{Fe^{++}}$ is given by

$$Fe_2O_3 - 2Fe^{++} - 3H_2O + 6H^+ + 2e^- = 0 \quad (22)$$

$$Eh = 0.727 - 0.177pH - 0.0591 \log a_{Fe^{++}}. \quad (23)$$

The hematite-pyrite equilibrium boundary can be determined through the use of equations (23) and (20) according to the procedure described in the section on magnetite-pyrite equilibrium.

Hematite-Iron Sulfide Equilibrium.—The hematite-iron sulfide equilibrium boundary can be determined through the use of equations (23) and (21) according to the procedure described in the section on magnetite-iron sulfide equilibrium.

Pyrite-Iron Sulfide Equilibrium.—The equilibrium relationship between pyrite and iron sulfide can be written as

$$FeS_2 - FeS - S^= + 2e^- = 0 \quad (24)$$

$$Eh = -0.84 - 0.0296 \log a_{S^=}. \quad (25)$$

If an Eh value is assumed, $a_{S^=}$ in equilibrium with FeS and FeS_2 at that Eh can be determined. As $a_{S^=}$ is fixed for any given Eh and pH, it only remains to find a pH value that will satisfy the above conditions. This can be accomplished through the use of the relations given in the section on sulfide equilibria. Such a series of calculations will serve to define the pyrite-iron sulfide equilibrium boundary.

Siderite-Pyrite Equilibrium.—At any given Eh and pH values a_{S^-} is fixed and $a_{Fe^{++}}$ in equilibrium with pyrite and a_{S^-} can be calculated with equation (20). At any given pH value $CO_3^=$ is also fixed and $a_{Fe^{++}}$ in equilibrium with $CO_3^=$ and siderite can be calculated through the use of the activity product constant for siderite, equation (7). A series of Eh-pH points at which $a_{Fe^{++}}$ is equal for both relations will serve to define the siderite-pyrite equilibrium boundary.

Siderite-Iron Sulfide Equilibrium.—The siderite-iron sulfide equilibrium boundary can be calculated through the use of the activity product constants for siderite (equation (7)) and for iron sulfide (equation (21)). The method requires calculating a_{S^-} and $a_{CO_3^-}$ for a series of assumed Eh and pH values and the subsequent determination of $a_{Fe^{++}}$ values which will satisfy both relations simultaneously.

IRON MINERAL STABILITY DIAGRAM

The methods for calculating boundaries between stability fields for the various mineral pairs under consideration have been discussed in the preceding sections. Such a series of boundaries are shown in Figure 1 for a normal sea water system. To avoid crowding, the hematite-iron sulfide, magnetite-iron sulfide, and siderite-iron sulfide boundaries have been omitted. These boundaries, which would lie approximately 0.03 to 0.05 Eh unit below the respective hematite-pyrite, magnetite-pyrite, and siderite-pyrite boundaries, represent metastable equilibrium in view of the position of the pyrite-iron sulfide boundary and will not affect the final stability diagram.

Upon elimination of the mutually exclusive segments of the boundaries in Figure 1, a diagram showing the Eh-pH stability fields for hematite, magnetite, siderite, pyrite, and iron sulfide is obtained (Fig. 2).

An environmental position within one of the stability fields indicates that that mineral would tend to form in preference to the other minerals on the diagram, assuming of course, that the concentration of iron was sufficient. A position on any of the field boundaries would indicate that the adjacent minerals were in equilibrium with each other and could exist together. At the intersection of any three field boundaries, the three adjacent minerals would be in equilibrium with each other. Because of probable lack of complete thermodynamic equilibrium in most natural environments, it is likely that a zone of apparent stability of adjacent minerals would exist rather than a single boundary line along which they could occur together.

Pyrrhotite and other forms of iron sulfide approaching the composition FeS can form at low temperatures (1, p. 212; 26, p. 1329) and their presence in unmetamorphosed sedimentary rocks has long been reported in the literature (6, p. 234; 14, p. 117; 23, p. 750; 24, p. 6; 27). However, because of the compositional variability of pyrrhotite and the numerous uncertainties regarding the mineralogical form of these other iron sulfides the FeS stability field on the diagram has not been assigned a mineral name.

The mineral smythite (Fe_3S_4) was recently described (9) but as yet details regarding its properties and occurrence have not been published. On the basis of its composition, however, its stability field would be expected to lie between that of FeS and pyrite.[2]

Thermodynamic data for iron silicates such as minnesotaite, chamosite, glauconite, greenalite, and others common to many iron-rich sediments, are

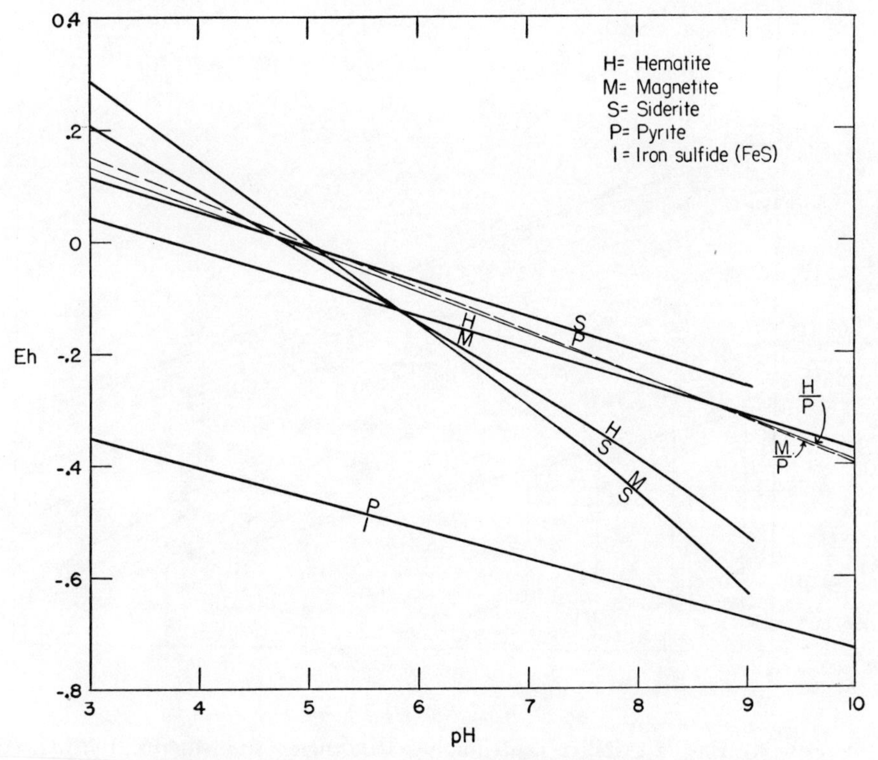

FIG. 1. Boundaries between Eh-pH stability fields for mineral pairs.

not available for use in plotting their stability fields. As ferrous iron generally predominates over ferric iron in these minerals, their stability fields would be expected to lie adjacent to or overlapping the present siderite and magnetite fields. This relationship is indicated by the intimate association of these silicate minerals with magnetite and siderite in many iron-formations.

[2] Since this manuscript was completed, smythite has been described in detail and the low temperature origin of both smythite and pyrrhotite in sedimentary rocks has been discussed (Erd, R. C., Evans, H. T., and Richter, D. H., 1957, Smythite, a new iron sulfide, and associated pyrrhotite from Indiana: Am. Mineralogist, v. 42, p. 309–333).

It is possible that maghemite (γ-Fe_2O_3) plays a role in the sedimentary iron mineral system although its presence as a primary or diagenetic mineral in sedimentary iron formations is uncertain. According to Mason (20, p. 116), maghemite can be formed either by the oxidation of magnetite or by the dehydration of leipdocrocite (γ-FeO·OH). He further notes that maghemite is metastable with respect to hematite and readily inverts to hematite under suitable temperature and pressure conditions.

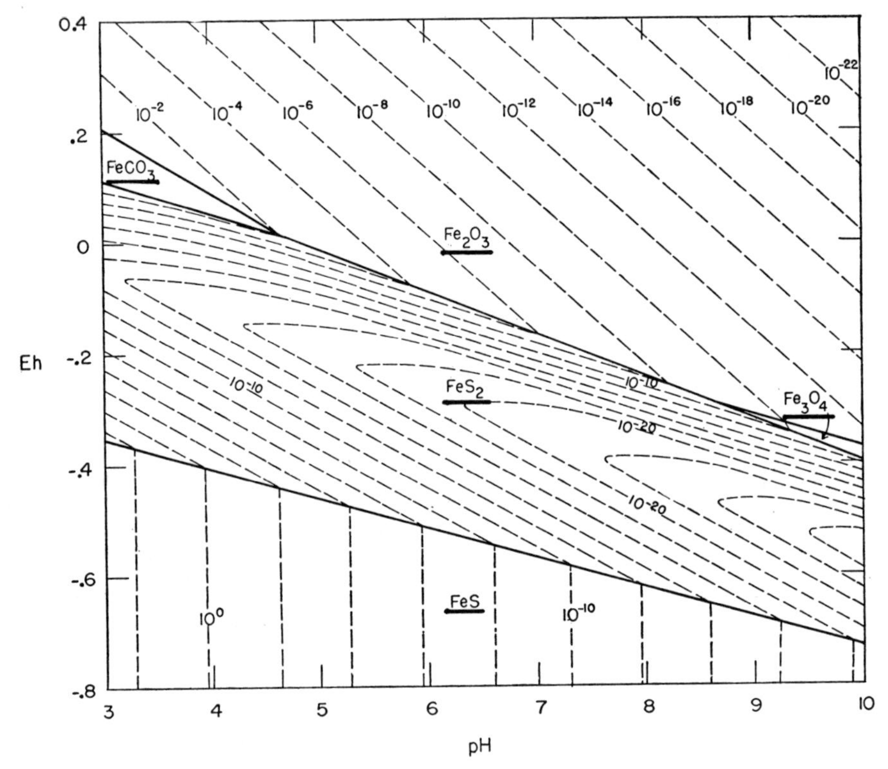

FIG. 2. Eh-pH stability fields for hematite, magnetite, siderite, pyrite, and iron sulfide (FeS) in normal sea water system. Contours indicate $a_{Fe^{++}}$ in equilibrium with the solid phases.

EFFECTS OF ADDITIONAL VARIABLES ON STABILITY FIELDS

Partial Pressure of CO_2.—The pH of most natural waters is chiefly determined by the concentration of carbonic acid and to a much lesser degree boric acid, as these are the only weak acids present in sufficient quantity to affect the hydrogen ion equilibria. Under anaerobic conditions the pH is also affected by H_2S. Figure 3, after Rubey (25, p. 1127) illustrates the relation between pH and the partial pressure of CO_2. The carbonate-ion concentration depends upon the dissociation of carbonic acid through the equilibria given in equation (8). Once the hydrogen ion concentration has been established by the value of the CO_2 partial pressure, the carbonate-ion concentration follows directly. Thus a change in the partial pressure of CO_2 from that normally in equilibrium with the present atmosphere will shift the position of a natural environment in the Eh-pH diagram but will not appreciably change the shape or position of any of the mineral stability fields.

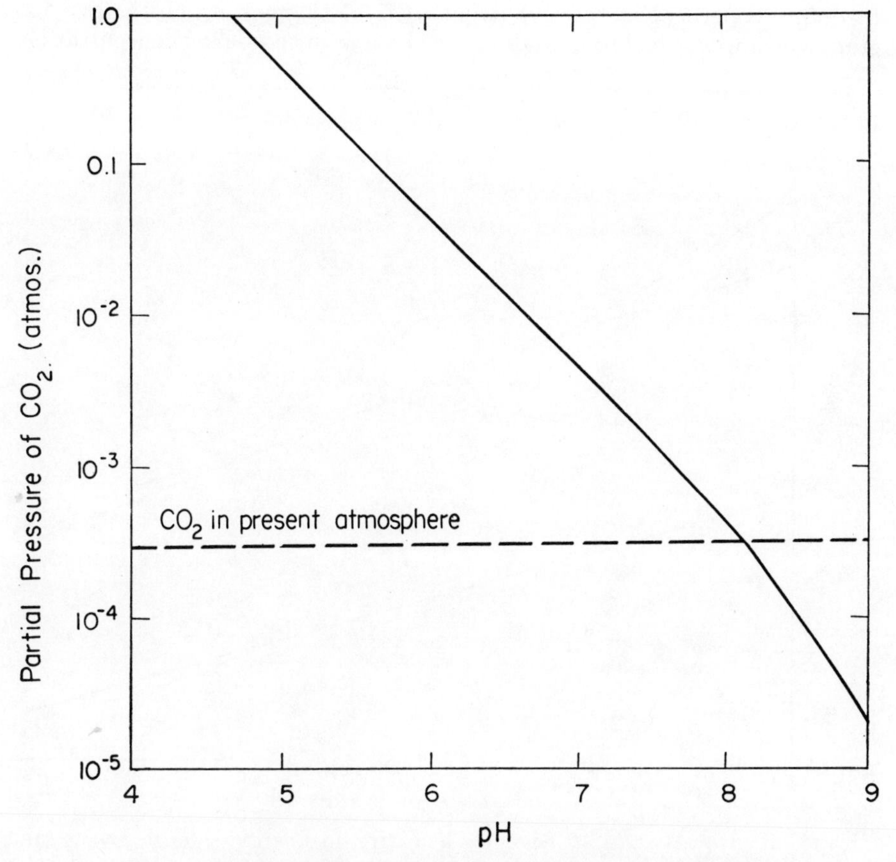

FIG. 3. Variation in pH of sea water as a function of partial pressure of CO_2 (after Rubey, 1951).

Several workers (cf. 19; 30) have suggested that the partial pressure of carbon dioxide in the atmosphere during the Precambrian was very much greater than that at the present time. On the other hand, Rubey (25) in his study of sea water-atmosphere relations concludes that radical changes in the atmosphere have not occurred during recorded geologic time, and James (16) in a discussion of the problem arrives at the same conclusion. The writer favors the latter view, but in either case, because of the direct relationship between pH and carbonate-ion concentration the environmental considerations of this study will apply equally well to Precambrian as to more recent iron-rich sediments.

Sulfide Ion Concentration.—At any given Eh and pH the sulfide ion activity is fixed by the dissociation constants of H_2S and H_2SO_4 and by the potential equation (14) given in the section on sulfide equilibria, once a value for total sulfur in solution has been determined or assumed. Because changes in total sulfur content will produce changes in sulfide ion concentration, it is perhaps instructive to consider the changes in the stability diagram which would be brought about by changes in sulfide ion concentration.

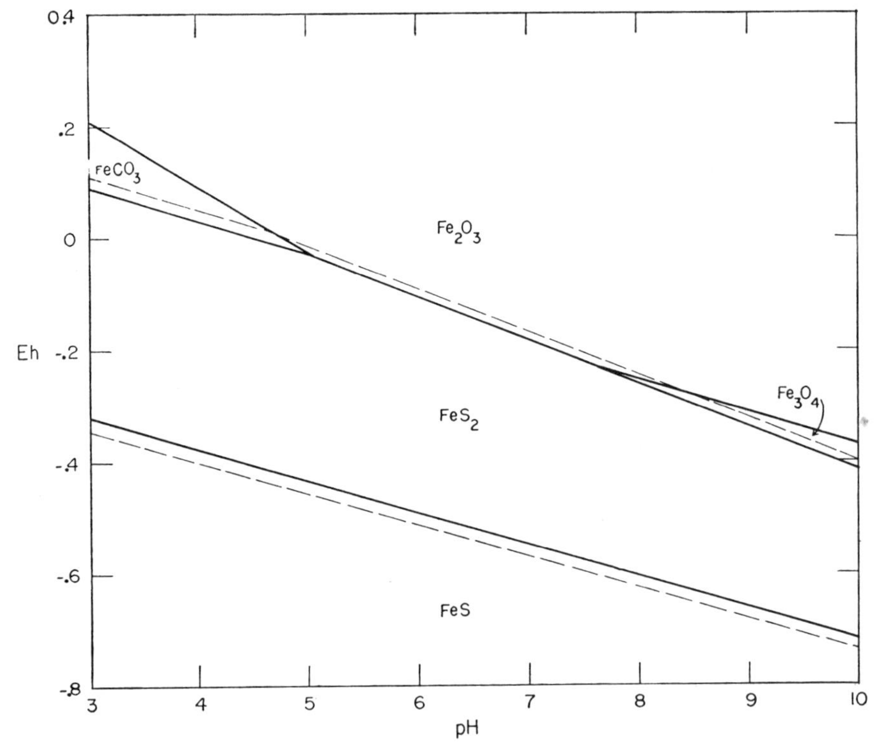

FIG. 4. Eh-pH stability fields for hematite, magnetite, siderite, pyrite, and iron sulfide (FeS) with carbonate equilibria as in normal sea water and total sulfur one-tenth that of normal sea water. Dashed lines for total sulfur as in normal sea water.

Figure 4 illustrates the change in the stability diagram which would be brought about by decreasing sulfide ion concentration to one-tenth that calculated for normal sea water. Figure 5 illustrates the change in the diagram brought about by further reducing the sulfide ion concentration to that encountered in average river or lake water. This is based upon the assumption of 17.7 ppm $SO_4^{=}$ and salinity of 146 ppm for average river and lake water (5) or approximately $10^{-2.2}$ times the concentration calculated for normal sea water.

Figures 4 and 5 show that the siderite-pyrite, hematite-pyrite, and magnetite-pyrite boundaries will be depressed to lower Eh values with decrease in sulfide ion concentration. The dashed lines in the diagram indicate the positions of the boundaries for normal sea water conditions and provide a measure of the amount of changc. The lowering of the aforementioned boundaries produces a concomitant increase in the sizes of the siderite and magnetite fields. Increase in sulfide concentration above that in normal

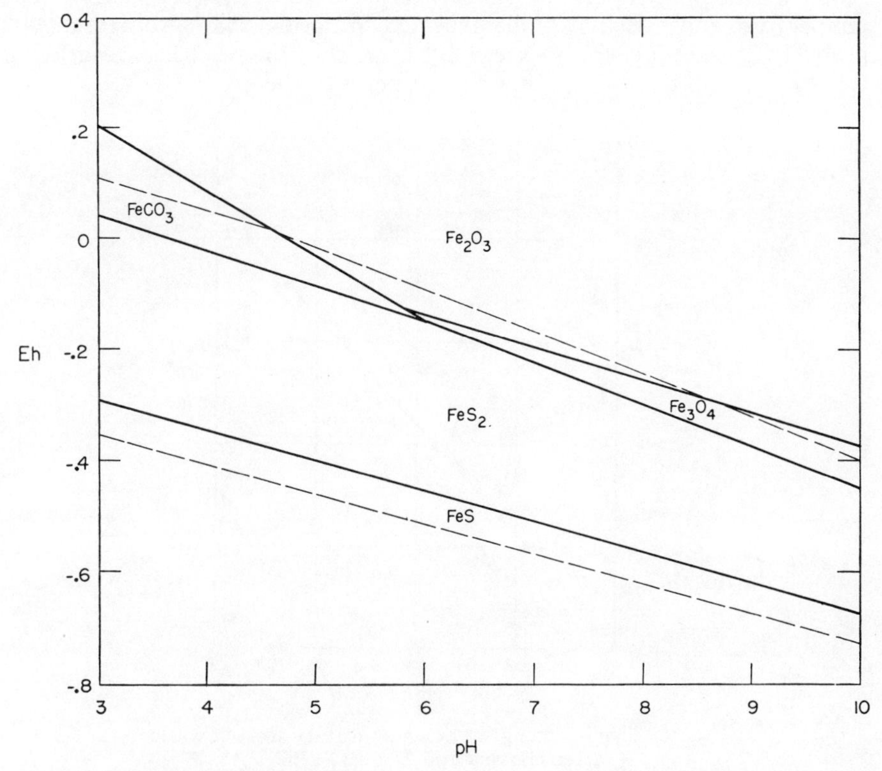

FIG. 5. Eh-pH stability fields for hematite, magnetite, siderite, pyrite, and iron sulfide (FeS) with carbonate equilibria as in normal sea water and total sulfur as in average river and lake water. Dashed lines for total sulfur as in normal sea water.

sea water would produce changes in the opposite direction but of the same magnitude.

Pressure.—The effect of pressure on the various equilibrium constants and relations used to calculate the stability field boundaries is in general not known. For a shallow depositional basin in which only moderate pressure increases will occur, the effect on hematite, magnetite, and pyrite is probably unimportant. The effect of pressure on siderite solubility is greater than that for the other minerals because of the carbon dioxide relations. Garrels and Dreyer (11, p. 340) note a very small increase in the solubility of calcite within the pressure range to be expected in a moderately shallow basin and the effect of pressure on siderite solubility is probably similar.

Temperature.—The solubility of CO_2 in sea water as well as the dissociation constants of carbonic acid are affected by changes in temperature. However, the net effect of these changes is slight and only causes a pH drop of approximately 0.01 pH unit for a rise of 1° C over the intermediate pH range and in the temperature range from 0° C to 25° C (13, p. 54). The temperature range that is to be expected in normal marine environments probably does not generally exceed 10° C, so that the resulting variation of 0.1 pH unit can be neglected for the purposes of this paper.

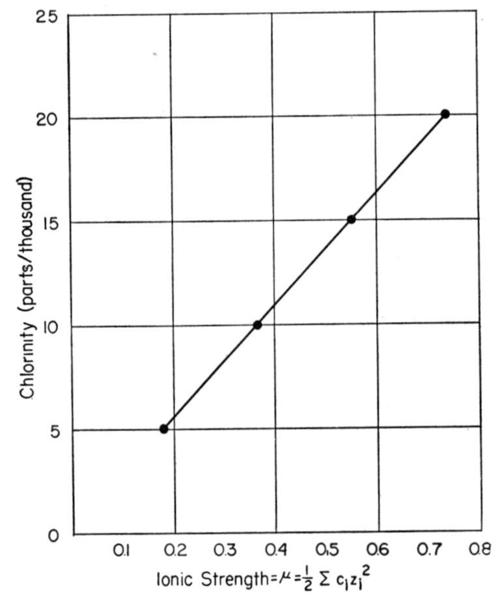

FIG. 6. Ionic strength versus chlorinity for sea water (after Garrels and Dreyer, 1952).

Temperature, as well as pressure, will cause changes in the $\Delta F°$ values of Table 1 used in the calculations. Within the temperature and pressure ranges under consideration these changes will be small.

Salinity.—The activity coefficient relates the activity of a given ion to its stoichiometric concentration through the formula

$$a_i = \gamma_i C_i,$$

where a_i is the activity of the ion, γ_i is the activity coefficient, and C_i is the stoichiometric concentration. The value of γ_i is chiefly dependent upon the valence of the ion and the ionic strength of the aqueous solution. The ionic strength is in turn dependent upon the salinity (or chlorinity) of the sea water system. Figure 6 illustrates the relation between chlorinity and ionic strength and Figure 7 shows the relation between the activity coefficient of the carbonate ion and the ionic strength of the system. As activity coefficients were used only in the calculations that involve the carbonate and the sulfide ions, only those boundaries concerned with these ions will be affected by changes in ionic strength.

Changes in activity coefficients over the probable salinity range will be small. As salinity increases over that of normal sea water, the activity coefficients change very little, having reached nearly constant values under conditions of normal salinity (Fig. 7). As salinity decreases below that of normal sea water, the activity coefficients increase very slowly down to the

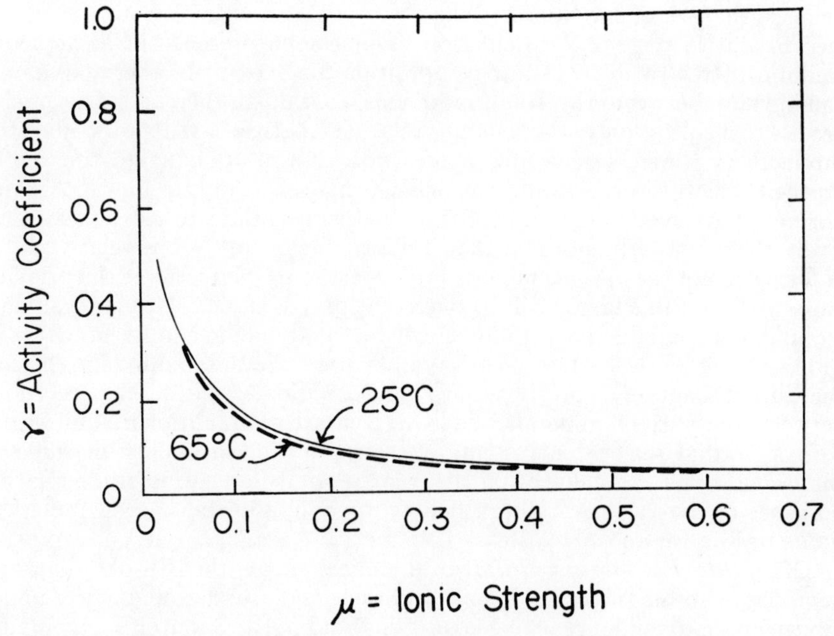

FIG. 7. Activity coefficient of the carbonate ion as a function of ionic strength (after Garrels and Dreyer, 1952). μ = approximately 0.7 for normal sea water.

range of very low ionic strengths. Thus, in any system that has an appreciable quantity of dissolved salts, the activity coefficients are relatively constant and the positions of the various mineral stability fields will not be changed by small variations in the salinity.

APPLICATION OF THE IRON MINERAL STABILITY DIAGRAM

Limitations of the Diagram.—Before considering the application of the Eh-pH diagram to environmental relationships it seems appropriate to review some of the assumptions used in the development of the diagram and to point out some of its limitations.

Some of the free energy values used in the calculations must be considered as only approximate. This is especially true for Fe_2O_3, Fe_3O_4, and FeS, for each of which several $\Delta F°$ values may be found in the recent literature. Any change in the free energy values used in the calculations will cause the field boundaries to shift, but remain parallel, thus causing an increase or decrease in the size of the various fields and a modification of the field intersections. The use of a smaller free energy for magnetite, for example, will shift the magnetite-hematite boundary toward higher Eh values, which would extend the magnetite stability field into part of that now occupied by hematite.

Another factor that might alter the size of the siderite stability field would be the probability of forming solid solution series with Mn, Mg, and Ca. The presence of these ions in the system would probably slightly increase the size of the siderite field.

The entire system of calculation assumes the presence of an aqueous medium of relatively constant composition and complete thermodynamic equilibrium between the solids and ions contained therein. Thermodynamics considers only the energy relations between reactants and the products of the reactions and makes no attempt to indicate the stages through which the reactants may have to pass or the rate at which equilibrium is attained. It is not possible with these data to assess quantitatively the effect of kinetics on the equilibrium systems. The relative rates of formation of the various minerals will exert some control over the primary deposition and this factor will be overcome only if sufficient time (and ionic mobility) is available for attainment of thermodynamic equilibrium.

Assuming that the free energy values used are approximately correct, the Eh-pH diagram as presented in Figure 2 indicates the stability relations between the various minerals under a given set of conditions: equilibrium with a normal sea water system. Because of the variability of some of these conditions, the value of the diagram lies in its indication of the relative positions of the various stability fields rather than in their exact numerical limits on the Eh and pH scales.

Magnetite Equilibrium Field.—As indicated by the Eh-pH diagram, hematite is stable under oxidizing conditions, siderite and magnetite under intermediate to mildly reducing conditions, and pyrite and iron sulfide under moderate to strongly reducing conditions. Magnetite, although stable under approximately the same Eh conditions as siderite, will form in preference to siderite under alkaline pH conditions.

The inclusion of a magnetite field in the iron-mineral stability diagram is in accord with numerous recent suggestions that magnetite is probably much more important as a primary or diagenetic mineral in sedimentary rocks than has generally been assumed.

Brown (3) discusses several occurrences of low-temperature magnetite and possible chemical reactions involved, and concludes that magnetite can be formed by "natural supergene or superficial low-temperature processes." James (16) reviews additional occurrences and the general problem of magnetite as a primary mineral in sedimentary iron-formations and reaches the same conclusion. White (32) in an examination of the mineralogy of the

Biwabik iron-formation of the Mesabi range concludes that much of the magnetite in that formation is of primary or diagenetic origin.

Most of the evidence upon which Brown, James, White, and others have reached their conclusions in regard to low-temperature magnetite has been based upon mineral associations and petrographic features in the rocks as observed in the field and under the microscope. The Eh-pH iron-mineral stability diagram supplements the field evidence by indicating within approximate limits the Eh-pH conditions under which magnetite can exist in a chemical sedimentary environment and its stability relationships relative to other important sedimentary iron minerals.

It has been demonstrated in the laboratory that magnetite can be precipitated from aqueous systems at low temperature and pressure. If alkali is added to a solution containing equivalent amounts of ferrous and ferric salts, a precipitate is obtained that is brownish-black, magnetic, and has an X-ray diffraction pattern identical with that for magnetite from other sources (31, p. 88; 28, p. 818). Hydrous Fe_3O_4 rather than hydrous Fe_2O_3 can be obtained by oxidation of ferrous hydroxide in an alkaline medium provided the rate of supply of oxygen is slow (31, p. 88); however, with a large supply of oxygen (high Eh) the rate of oxidation to ferric oxide is so high that little or no Fe_3O_4 is formed.

Causes and Effects of Lack of Equilibrium.—The failure of a chemical system to maintain equilibrium may permit a thermodynamically unstable mineral to form in preference to a stable one, with resultant anomalous mineral associations.

If magnetite were to be excluded from the Eh-pH mineral stability diagram, the hematite field would be extended into much of what is now the magnetite field. Thus if magnetite were to be retarded from forming because of differences in the relative rates of formation of magnetite and hematite, hematite might first precipitate as a thermodynamically unstable phase under conditions where magnetite is the stable phase. Presumably, as the system approached equilibrium, magnetite would form at the expense of hematite. Lack of complete equilibrium might allow considerable hematite to remain although it would be thermodynamically unstable. This would permit the original precipitation of hematite under conditions of magnetite equilibrium and would also expand greatly the apparent range of conditions under which hematite and magnetite might occur together.

Lack of equilibrium may also result from the failure of a system to respond to environmental changes. If, for example, hematite should form under conditions of hematite stability, and the environmental conditions then be changed to those appropriate for the formation of magnetite, magnetite should tend to completely replace the hematite. The failure of this reaction to proceed to completion because of insufficient time or restriction of ionic mobility would result in lack of equilibrium and the formation of a mixture of hematite and magnetite rather than magnetite alone.

The sulfide-sulfate relationship provides an example in which a biologic catalyst may play an important part in the kinetics of the system. As noted by Pettijohn (21, p. 458) and by Galliher (10) the source of sulfide for the formation of pyrite is twofold; bacterial reduction of sulfates in sea water, and of less importance, sulfur derived by bacterial action on sulfur tied up in previously existing organic compounds. The presence of bacteria for the reduction of sulfate is necessitated by the apparent inability of a natural inorganic system to reduce sulfate to sulfide at ordinary temperatures (2; 12; 33; 8). Therefore, in the absence of sulfide of organic origin or of sulfate-reducing bacteria, iron sulfide (or pyrite) may fail to form even though it is thermodynamically stable and the Eh is low enough to permit reduction of available sulfate. This would produce a metastable extension of the siderite and magnetite fields to lower Eh values.

Seemingly anomalous mineral associations may be produced as a result of extremely local environments, such as in a zone of low Eh surrounding a fragment of organic material in an otherwise oxidizing environment. Under such conditions pyrite might be formed locally in a sediment in which hematite is the stable mineral elsewhere.

In spite of the difficulties involved in its application, the Eh-pH iron-mineral diagram does indicate equilibrium relationships under the specified conditions—relationships that are relatively insensitive to minor changes in these conditions. In addition to predicting the mineral associations to be expected under equilibrium conditions it will to some extent indicate the degree of lack of equilibrium in natural mineral occurrences.

U. S. Geological Survey,
Menlo Park, Calif.,
July 8, 1957

REFERENCES

1. Allen, E. T., Crenshaw, J. L., Johnson, J., and Larsen, E. S., 1912, The mineral sulphides of iron: Am. Jour. Sci., 4th ser., v. 33, p. 169–236.
2. Bastin, Edson S., 1926, The problem of the natural reduction of sulfates: Am. Assoc. Petroleum Geologists Bull., v. 10, p. 1270–1299.
3. Brown, J. S., 1943, Supergene magnetite: Econ. Geol., v. 38, p. 137–148.
4. Castaño, John R., and Garrels Robert M., 1950, Experiments on the deposition of iron with special reference to the Clinton iron ore deposits: Econ. Geol., v. 45, p. 755–770.
5. Conway, E. J., 1942, Mean geochemical data in relation to oceanic evolution: Royal Irish Acad. Proc., v. 48, sect. B, no. 8, p. 119–159.
6. Correns, Carl W., 1949, Einführung in die mineralogie: Springer-Verlag Ohg., Berlin, 414 p.
7. Deltombe, E., and Pourbaix, M., 1954, Comportment électrochimique du fer en solution carbonique: Centre Belge d'etude de la corrosion, Rapport technique No. 8.
8. Emery, K. O., and Rittenberg, S. C., 1952, Early diagenesis of California basin sediments in relation to origin of oil: Am. Assoc. Petroleum Geologists Bull., v. 36, p. 735–806.
9. Erd, R. C., and Evans, H. T., Jr., 1956, The compound Fe_3S_4 (smythite) found in nature: Jour. Am. Chem. Soc., v. 78, p. 2017.
10. Galliher, E. W., 1933, The sulfur cycle in sediments: Jour. Sedimentary Petrology, v. 3, p. 51–63.
11. Garrels, R. M., and Dreyer, R. M., 1952, Mechanism of limestone replacement at low temperatures and pressures: Geol. Soc. America Bull., v. 63, p. 325–379.
12. Ginter, R. L., 1930, Causative agents of sulfate reduction in oil-well waters: Am. Assoc. Petroleum Geologists Bull., v. 14, p. 139–152.
13. Harvey, H. W., 1945, Recent advances in the chemistry and biology of sea water: Cambridge Univ. Press, 164 p.
14. Hatch, F. H., Rastall, R. H., and Black, Maurice, 1938, The petrology of the sedimentary rocks: 3rd. Ed., revised, 383 p., Thomas Murby and Co., London.
15. Huber, N. K., and Garrels, R. M., 1953, Relation of pH and oxidation potential to sedimentary iron mineral formation: Econ. Geol., v. 48, p. 337–357.
16. James, H. L., 1954, Sedimentary facies of iron-formation: Econ. Geol., v. 49, p. 235–293.

17. Krumbein, W. C., and Garrels, R. M., 1952, Origin and classification of chemical sediments in terms of pH and oxidation-reduction potentials: Jour. Geology, v. 60, p. 1–33.
18. Latimer, W. M., 1952, The oxidation states of the elements and their potentials in aqueous solutions: Prentice-Hall, Inc., New York, 2d ed., 392 p.
19. MacGregor, A. M., 1927, The problem of the Precambrian atmosphere: South African Jour. Sci., v. 24, p. 155–172.
20. Mason, Brian, 1943, Mineralogical aspects of the system FeO-Fe_2O_3-MnO-Mn_2O_3: Geol. fören. Stockholm Förh., band 65, häfte 2, p. 97–180.
21. Pettijohn, F. J., 1949, Sedimentary rocks: Harper and Bros., New York, 526 p.
22. Pourbaix, M. J. N., 1949, Thermodynamics of dilute aqueous solutions: Edward Arnold and Co., London, 136 p.
23. Rankama, Kalervo, and Sahama, T. G., 1950, Geochemistry: University of Chicago Press, 912 p.
24. Rubey, W. W., 1930, Lithologic studies of fine-grained upper Cretaceous sedimentary rocks of the Black Hills region: U. S. Geol. Survey Prof. Paper 165-A, p. 1–54.
25. ——, 1951, Geologic history of sea water: Geol. Soc. America Bull., v. 62, p. 1111–1147.
26. Sidgwick, N. V., 1950, The chemical elements and their compounds: v. 2, p. 855–1703, Oxford University Press.
27. Smyth, C. H., Jr., 1911, A new locality of pyrrhotite crystals and their pseudomorphs: Am. Jour. Sci., 4 Ser., v. 32, p. 156–160.
28. Spiroff, Kiril, 1938, Magnetite crystals from meteoric solutions: Econ. Geol., v. 33, p. 818–828.
29. Sverdrup, H. U., Johnson, M. W., and Fleming, R. H., 1942, The oceans; their physics, chemistry, and general biology: Prentice-Hall, Inc., New York, 1087 p.
30. Tyler, S. A., and Twenhofel, W. H., 1952, Sedimentation and stratigraphy of the Huronian of Upper Michigan: Am. Jour. Sci., v. 250, p. 1–27 and 118–151.
31. Weiser, H. B., 1953, Inorganic colloid chemistry, Vol. II: John Wiley and Sons, New York.
32. White, D. A., 1954, The stratigraphy and structure of the Mesabi Range, Minnesota: Minnesota Geol. Survey Bull. 38, 92 p.
33. ZoBell, C. E., and Rittenberg, S. C., 1948, Sulfate-reducing bacteria in marine sediments: Jour. Marine Research, v. 7, p. 602–617.

6

Reprinted from *Geochim. Cosmochim. Acta,* **12,** 61–68 (1957) with the permission of Microforms International Marketing Corporation as exclusive copyright licensee for Pergamon Press journal back files.

Separation of manganese from iron in sedimentary processes

KONRAD B. KRAUSKOPF
Stanford University, California

(*Received* 8 *June* 1956)

Abstract—Thermochemical data on compounds of manganese and iron are in general agreement with reported mineral associations, provided that the more complex mineral compounds, for which data do not exist, be assumed to have somewhat larger stability fields than their nearest simple chemical equivalents. The data show that the iron compounds to be expected in nature are uniformly less soluble than the corresponding manganese compounds, and that ferrous ion is more easily oxidized than manganous ion under any naturally occurring pH-*Eh* conditions. Thus, inorganic processes should always lead to precipitation of iron before manganese from a solution containing both metals, unless the Mn/Fe ratio is very high.

The oxidation of manganous and ferrous ions by atmospheric oxygen takes place by slow reactions which can be utilized as an energy source by bacteria. Selective oxidation and precipitation by different species of bacteria can lead to partial separation of the metals, but this is probably not a major factor in the formation of large, nearly pure deposits of manganese or iron compounds.

Selective dissolution of the metals from igneous rocks, a mechanism of separation often postulated in the literature, was tested by treating basaltic andesite with a number of solvents at temperatures ranging from 25 to 300°C. The ratios of Mn to Fe in the resulting solutions were all approximately the same as in the original rock, showing that this assumed process of separation is ineffective.

Isolation of manganese in solution can be accomplished by precipitating the iron first. This is most effectively done by adding alkali gradually to a solution containing both metals, keeping the solution in contact with atmospheric oxygen. The reaction can be demonstrated in the laboratory under conditions similar to those in nature by letting dilute acid percolate through crushed lava and then through limestone: iron dissolved from the lava is precipitated in the limestone, and the solution is left with a high Mn/Fe ratio. This suggests a possible explanation for the origin of many manganese deposits, especially those associated with lavas and tuffs, but it requires that iron oxide in amounts many times that of the manganese be deposited in the rocks through which the solutions have passed.

THE close chemical similarity between manganese and iron is reflected geologically in their common association in rocks of all kinds. The association is especially marked in igneous rocks, where the ratio Mn/Fe seldom strays outside the limits 1/100 and 1/10, except in rare pegmatites. Sedimentary processes, where oxidation plays a larger role, lead to more effective separation of the two elements. The chemistry of iron and manganese during sedimentation is relatively simple and in its broad outlines is well understood, but the precise mechanism by which the two metals become separated remains mysterious. It is easy to see how manganese in solution may be deposited as carbonate or silicate where the environment is reducing, or as one of the several oxide minerals if oxygen is present, but why iron is not always deposited at the same time is much less clear. This is the essential puzzle in the geochemistry of manganese.

An explanation for the deposition of nearly iron-free manganese minerals can obviously be sought in two directions: either the original solution may have contained no iron, or some precipitation process may remove manganese alone from a solution containing both metals. The stumbling-block in precipitation processes has always been that iron should be more readily deposited than manganese; its carbonate, sulphide, silicate, and hydroxide are all less soluble than the corresponding manganese compounds, and it reacts with oxygen more readily, so that a solution containing both metals should give precipitates of both, either in the same deposit or in close proximity. This difficulty has led most geological writers to

Editor's Note: A row of asterisks indicates that material has been omitted from the original article.

assume solutions containing only manganese, generally derived from volcanic rocks, because manganese deposits are commonly found with such rocks and because springs in volcanic areas have been observed to deposit manganese compounds. This assumption is hardly an explanation, however; it does no more than push the essential process of separation underground, where direct observation is no longer possible.

Such questions about the origin of manganese deposits have been the subject of a voluminous literature. The essential chemistry and the chief problems were outlined in a paper by Vogt (1906) half a century ago; since that time much descriptive information has accumulated and the possible roles of bacteria and colloids in manganese deposition have been explored, but the separation of manganese from iron is still a troublesome question. The object of the present paper is less to solve the problem than to dress it up in modern language and to summarize pertinent work of the past fifty years. A possible hypothesis will be suggested, but its application to field occurrences must remain speculative pending the collection of more data.

The author is indebted to his colleagues, George A. Thompson and Charles F. Park, for critical reading of the manuscript.

Eh-pH Relations

It is common knowledge that neutral and acid solutions can hold large concentrations of Fe^{++} and Mn^{++};* that in alkaline solution these ions can be precipitated as hydroxides, carbonates, silicates, or sulphides, depending on what anions are present; that the divalent ions can be oxidized by moderately powerful oxidizing agents; that the oxidation by atmospheric oxygen is slow; that the oxidation is more complete in alkaline solution than in acid, and at any given acidity more complete for iron than for manganese; and that the products of oxidation are very insoluble oxides and hydroxides which can be represented by such formulas as Fe_3O_4, $Fe(OH)_3$, Fe_2O_3, Mn_3O_4, $Mn(OH)_3$, Mn_2O_3, and MnO_2.

These facts (except the slowness of the oxidation reactions) may be conveniently and quantitatively summarized by means of diagrams showing stability fields of possible compounds at different values of *Eh* and pH. Such diagrams have been extensively used by Garrels and his co-workers (Garrels, 1953; Huber and Garrels, 1953), and Garrels' description of the method of constructing the diagrams makes a detailed explanation unnecessary here (see Appendix). For each metal, two diagrams are given, one showing stability fields for anhydrous oxides and the other showing fields for hydroxides; on each diagram stability fields for the simple sulphides, carbonates, and silicates are also indicated. Each line on a diagram is a boundary between the fields for a relatively more oxidized compound above and a more reduced compound below, the two compounds being named at

* Perhaps it should be pointed out that this statement is merely a generalization of the common assertion in geological literature that "manganese may be transported as the bicarbonate, sulphate, or chloride." To say that manganese (or iron) is present *as* such-and-such a compound puts the emphasis in the wrong place. It is immaterial what particular anions a solution contains—whether chloride, sulphate, bicarbonate, or rarer ones like nitrate, phosphate, or bromide—so long as none of the anions form insoluble compounds with the metal. The essential point is that the ions Fe^{++} and Mn^{++} are not precipitated by any of the anions commonly met with in natural solutions as long as the solution is not alkaline.

the ends of the lines. For example, from Fig, 1, at a pH of 7 and an *Eh* of 0·7 V, MnO_2 is the stable manganese oxide; at a pH of 9 and an *Eh* of 0·3 V, Mn_2O_3 is more stable.

Stabilities of the carbonates, sulphides, and silicates are of course dependent on assumed concentrations of the corresponding anions. Lines on the diagrams are

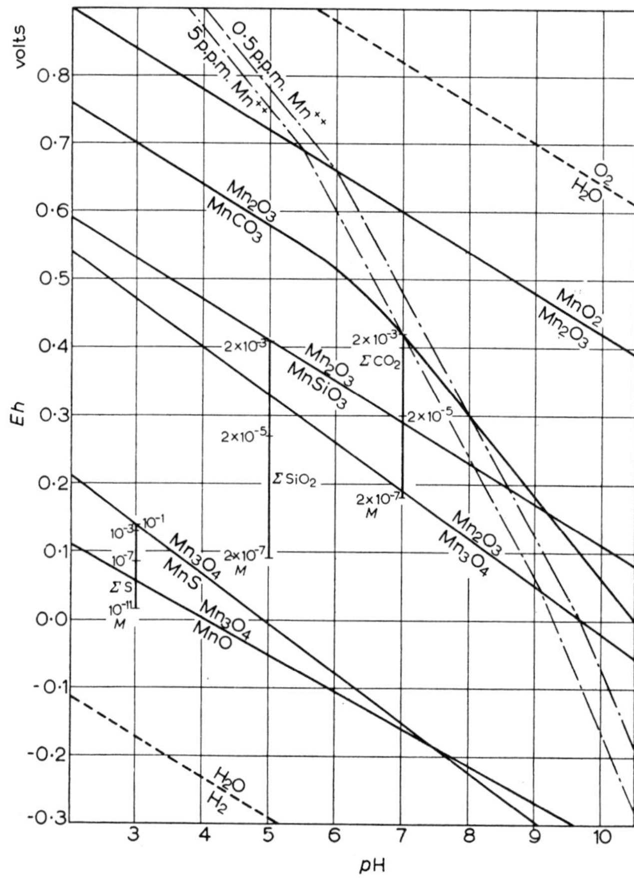

Fig. 1. *Eh*-pH diagram for anhydrous manganese compounds. Solid lines are boundaries of stability fields; each line separates the field of an oxidized form (above) from that of a reduced form (below). Cross-bars on vertical lines show positions of field boundaries at lower concentrations of carbonate, sulphide, and silica. Dashed lines are limits of possible redox potentials in water solution. Dash-dot lines are "isoconcentration" lines, drawn through points where the concentration of Mn^{++} in equilibrium with the oxides is 5 p.p.m. and 0·5 p.p.m. respectively.

drawn for (a) total carbonate $= CO_2 + HCO_3^- + CO_3^{--} = 0{\cdot}002$ M (equilibrium with atmospheric CO_2 at pH 8), (b) total sulphur $= H_2S + HS^- + S^{--} + SO_4^{--} = 0{\cdot}1$ M, and (c) total silica = chiefly $H_4SiO_4 = 0{\cdot}002$ M (amount soluble at 25°). Amounts by which these lines would be shifted by a decrease in concentration are indicated by the vertical lines with crossbars. For example, at pH 5·0 and *Eh* 0·5 V, $MnCO_3$ is the stable Mn compound if total dissolved carbonate is 0·0002 M, but Mn_2O_3 is stable if carbonate is much less than this. Note that the stability of the sulphides is surprisingly little affected by changes in total dissolved sulphur unless the total is less than about 10^{-5} M. At a point like pH 7, *Eh* 0·0, below the lines for $MnCO_3$, $MnSiO_3$, and Mn_3O_4, the compound or compounds formed would depend on what anions are present: $MnCO_3$ if carbonate is in excess of silica, $MnSiO_3$ if silica is in excess, and Mn_3O_4 if both carbonate and silica are minor.

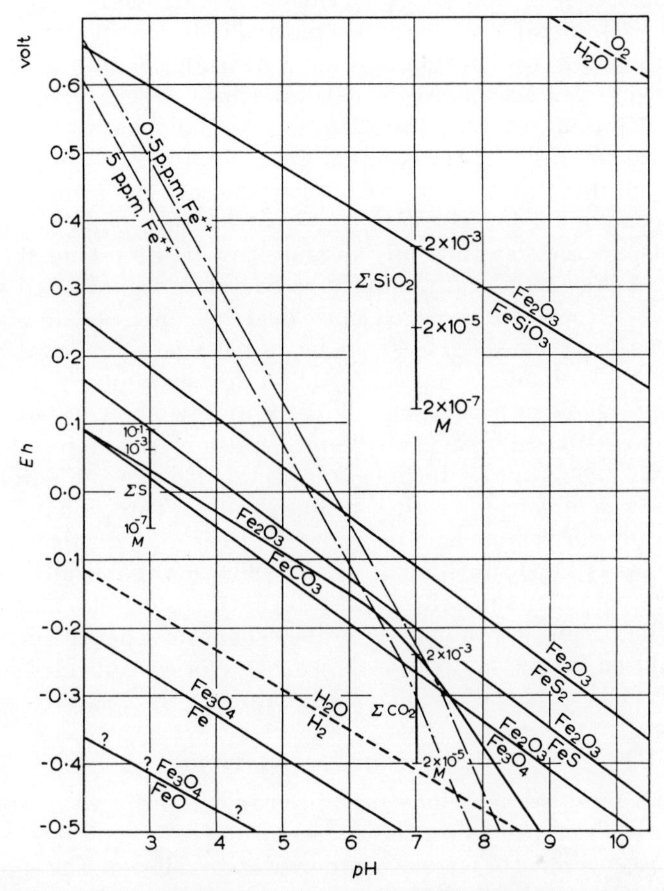

Fig. 2. *Eh*-pH diagram for anhydrous iron compounds. Symbols same as in Fig. 1. Question marks along Fe_3O_4-FeO boundary indicate that under these conditions FeO is unstable with respect to Fe and Fe_3O_4.

Also on the diagrams are shown (dashed lines) the theoretical limits of pH and Eh for natural aqueous solutions imposed by the oxidation of H_2O to O_2 and the reduction of H_2O to H_2. No oxidizing or reducing agent outside these limits can exist in contact with water, because the water would thereby be decomposed.

Theoretically, the equilibrium *Eh* of a solution in contact with atmospheric oxygen should be given by the upper dashed line. The "effective" *Eh*, however, appears to be somewhat less, because one of the steps in oxidation reactions involving O_2 is very slow. Measured *Eh* values in aerated water, both fresh and marine, cluster in the range 0·35–0·45 V for near-neutral solutions, instead of the theoretical 0·75–0·85 V (COOPER, 1937; ZOBELL, 1946; GARRELS, 1953; HUBER and GARRELS, 1953). Probably, as COOPER suggests, the effective *Eh* for slow geologic processes is somewhere between these ranges, but assigning a specific value for a given reaction is not feasible.

The diagrams become more useful if maximum concentrations of Mn^{++} are shown as well as the solid phases with which the Mn^{++} is in equilibrium. Two "iso-concentration lines" are shown on each diagram, one for 5 p.p.m. and one for 0·5 p.p.m. of each metal ion. These are plotted only for the oxides or hydroxides, in other words on the assumption that concentrations of sulphide, carbonate, and silicate are negligible. Manganese in natural solutions seldom has a concentration greater than 5 p.p.m., so that the diagrams actually have their major geologic interest only to the right of the 5 p.p.m. line.

The question inevitably arises with regard to such diagrams: How closely do the artificial compounds for which data are plotted correspond to natural minerals? In other words, are the diagrams only abstractions, of interest chiefly to a theoretical chemist, or can they be usefully applied to the more complicated substances and environments with which a geologist must deal? There is no simple answer, but a few predictions from the diagrams can be tested against natural occurrences, as explained below. It should be emphasized first, however, just how far the diagrams are from actual geologic situations. Figs. 3 and 4, showing stability fields for hydroxides, should be fairly accurate representations of precipitates from laboratory solutions. Figs. 1 and 2 include compounds closer to mineral formulas, but for several the resemblance is rather strained: MnO_2 can perhaps stand for pyrolusite, but hardly for psilomelane or wad; Mn_2O_3 is a poor substitute for braunite or manganite, as is Fe_2O_3 for limonite and $FeSiO_3$ for chamosite. The simple fact that the more complex substances exist in nature suggests that they are more stable than the artificial compounds on the diagrams, hence that their fields of stability would be larger than those shown. One other difficulty in applying this kind of diagram is that the stability fields are strictly accurate only at 25° and 1-atm pressure.

MINERAL ASSOCIATIONS

Despite the serious limitations just discussed, the diagrams show qualitative agreement with observations on the occurrence of manganese and iron minerals. The greater susceptibility of ferrous compounds to oxidation, the effect of increasing pH in making oxidation of both metals more complete, the fact that MnO is stable in natural environments while FeO is not, are all shown clearly by the diagrams. The iron diagram (Fig. 2) shows that any combination of the minerals hematite (or limonite), siderite, pyrite, magnetite, and iron silicate (e.g. chamosite) should be capable of stable coexistance at certain conditions of pH, *Eh*, and anion concentrations, or that any one should be capable of changing to another if conditions are altered. The manganese diagram, on the other hand, suggests that some mineral combinations should be impossible as *primary* associations: pyrolusite can form with no other mineral than braunite or manganite (if these have stability fields like that of Mn_2O_3); braunite and manganite should be able to coexist with hausmannite, rhodochrosite, or rhodonite (or some other manganese silicate), but not with alabandite or manganosite; alabandite and manganosite should not form at all except locally where solutions contain abnormal concentrations of Mn^{++}, and should be accompanied by no primary oxide mineral except possibly hausmannite. A survey of the literature shows that these predictions are generally fulfilled, except that the relations of pyrolusite are uncertain because it is so commonly of secondary origin. (Two articles with especially complete descriptions of manganese mineral associations are THIEL (1924) and LEE (1955).) If psilomelane is considered as a

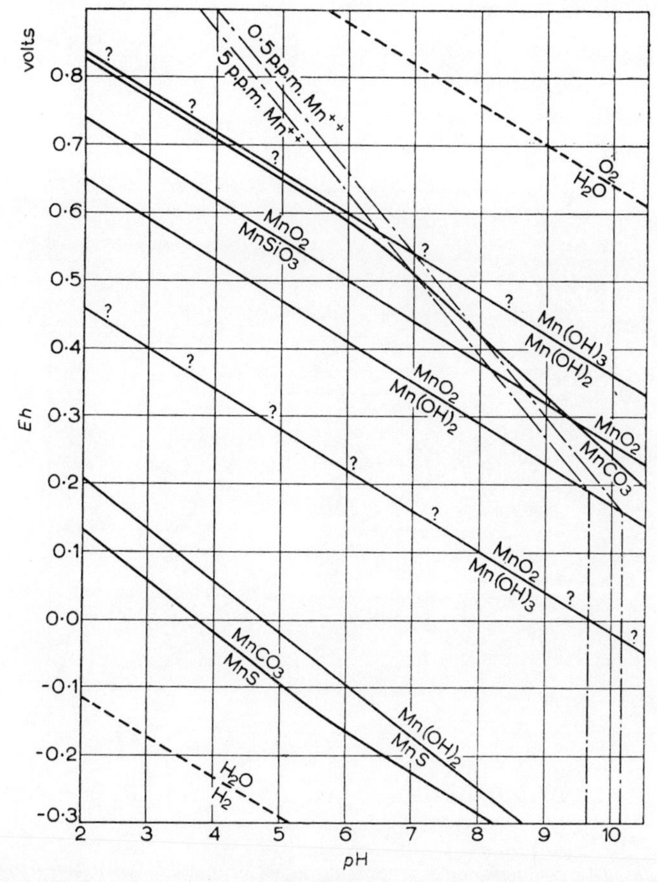

Fig. 3. *Eh*-pH diagram for manganese hydroxides. Symbols same as in Fig. 1. Question marks along stability boundaries for $Mn(OH)_3$ indicate that under these conditions $Mn(OH)_3$ is metastable.

variety of MnO_2, it appears to constitute an exception to the predictions in that the forbidden association psilomelane-hausmannite is well established, although not common; the best-documented example is that described by MISER (1922) at Batesville, Arkansas, where intimate mixtures of the two appear to be unquestionably primary. The anomaly is explainable by assuming that the relatively complicated structure of psilomelane is more stable in mildly oxidizing environments than is pyrolusite, so that its stability field extends well below that of plain MnO_2 and grazes the field of Mn_3O_4.

If the diagrams for manganese and iron are superimposed, the broad Fe_2O_3 field overlaps all the manganese fields down to hausmannite. In other words, where iron and manganese occur together, hematite or limonite should be stable in the presence of any of the manganese oxides except manganosite (and even with this one if the concentration of sulphur is low). The field of pyrite partly overlaps the field of hausmannite, but is far below those of Mn_2O_3 and MnO_2. This does not support PARK's (1942) statement that pyrolusite and pyrite apparently formed

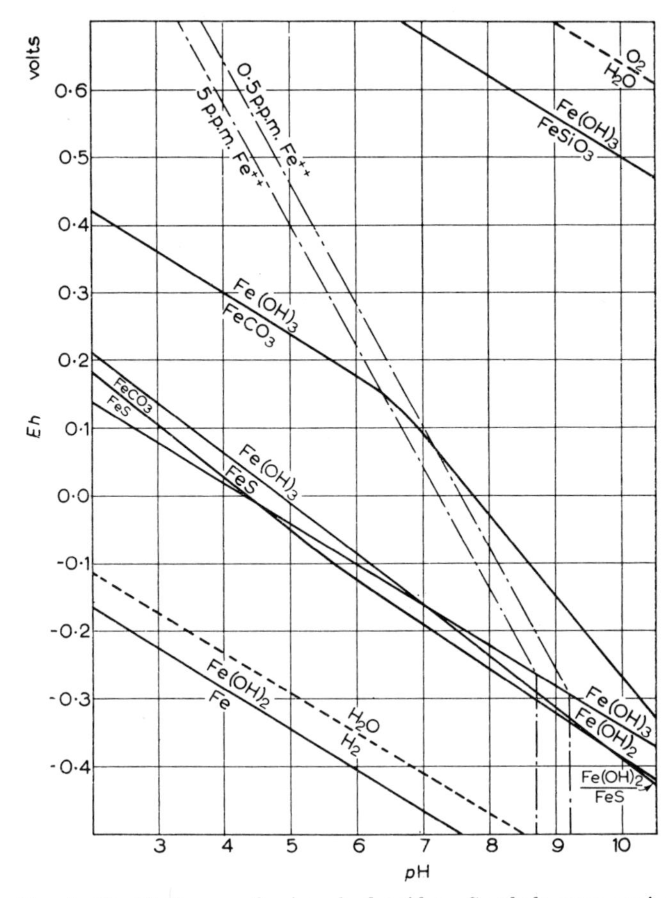

Fig. 4. *Eh*-pH diagram for iron hydroxides. Symbols same as in Fig. 1.

under the same conditions in a Cuban deposit; perhaps the discrepancy means that the stability fields for one or both minerals are broader at temperatures somewhat above 25°.

One other deduction from the diagrams can be checked with the known distribution of iron and manganese minerals. On Fig. 1 the iso-concentration line for 5 p.p.m. Mn^{++} crosses the pH range for normal sea-water at an *Eh* of about 0·2 V, and the line for 5 p.p.b. (or 0·005 p.p.m.) would cross at about 0·4 V. A concentration of 5 p.p.b. is only barely within the normal range for sea-water; THOMPSON and WILSON (1935) give for the normal range 0·7–10 p.p.b. Mn, and HARVEY (1949) suggests that the greater part of this is in filtrable particles rather than true solution. Hence, manganese cannot precipitate as an oxide in the sea except where conditions are strongly oxidizing; ZOBELL (1946) gives −0·5 to 0·35 V as the usual range of *Eh* in marine sediments, and only in the extreme upper part of this range can manganese oxide form (except, of course, locally where manganese may be introduced in exceptionally large concentrations). Even the silicate and carbonate can precipitate from normal sea-water only where the concentrations of the anions or of Mn^{++} are abnormally high, and the precipitation of MnS is completely impossible. Fig. 2, on the other hand, shows the line for 5 p.p.m. Fe^{++} crossing the pH range of sea-water at an *Eh* of about −0·6 V, well below any *Eh* recorded or to be expected in the most reducing of marine environments. Hence, any of the possible iron compounds should be stable in contact with sea-water, Fe_2O_3 wherever conditions are at least mildly oxidizing, and the other compounds where conditions are reducing. In agreement with these predictions, the only manganese compound reported from present-day marine sediments is the dioxide, and this only from oxidizing environments, whereas iron is well known in the form of ferric oxide, pyrite, and glauconite, and less certainly as magnetite and siderite also.

Thus, Figs. 1 and 2, with reasonable modifications for compounds regarding which data are lacking, can be shown to fit most of the observed facts of occurrence and association of manganese and iron minerals. On the other hand, boundaries of the stability fields are so uncertain because of complex mineral compositions and possible temperature effects that the diagrams cannot be regarded as suitable for quantitative predictions.

It should be emphasized again that there is nothing original here in the diagrams or their interpretation. KRUMBEIN and GARRELS (1952) have published an iron diagram including Fe_2O_3, $FeCO_3$, and FeS, and this diagram has been discussed and used by several authors, notably HUBER and GARRELS (1953) and JAMES (1954). The demonstration that magnetite has a field of stability at ordinary temperatures is due to DELTOMBE and POURBAIX (1954) and to HUBER (1956). Manganese diagrams have been published by CHARLOT (1949), BLUMER (1950), and MOUSSARD, BRENET, JOLAS, POURBAIX, and VAN MUYLDER (1954). The diagrams in these papers differ from the ones presented here in that they show the particular compounds that would exist at equilibrium under specific conditions of *Eh*, pH, and concentrations of various anions. The intention here, in Figs. 1–4, is to present the relationships in more general fashion, outlining only the maximum extent of the stability fields under natural conditions and showing alternative precipitates that may form in response to various anion concentrations.

* * * * * * *

References

Blumer M. (1950) Die Existenzgrenzen anorganischer Ionen bei der Bildung von Sedimentgesteinen. Geochemische Untersuchungen IV. *Helv. Chim. Acta* **33,** 1568–81.

Charlot G. (1949) *Théorie et méthode nouvelles d'analyse qualitative* (3rd edition) Paris.

Cooper L. H. N. (1937) Oxidation-reduction potential in sea water. *J. Mar. Biol. Ass.* N.S. **22,** 167–76.

Deltombe E. and Pourbaix M. (1954) Comportement électrochimique du fer en solution carbonique. *Rapport Technique. No.* **8,** p. 5. Centre Belge d'Étude de la Corrosion.

References

Garrels R. M. (1953) Mineral species as functions of pH and oxidation-reduction potentials. *Geochim. et Cosmochim. Acta* **5,** 153–168.

Harvey H. W. (1949) On manganese in sea and fresh water. *J. Mar. Biol. Ass. U.K.* **28,** 155–164.

Huber N. K. and Garrels R. M. (1953) Relation of pH and oxidation potential to sedimentary iron mineral formation. *Econ. Geol.* **48,** 447–457

Huber N. K. (1956) Environmental control of sedimentary iron minerals and its relation to the origin of the Ironwood iron-formation. Ph.D. dissertation, Northwestern University.

James H. L. (1954) Sedimentary facies of iron formation. *Econ. Geol.* **49,** 235–293.

Krumbein W. C. and Garrels R. M. (1952) Origin and classification of chemical sediments in terms of pH and oxidation-reduction potentials. *J. Geol.* **60,** 1–33.

Lee D. E. (1955) Mineralogy of some Japanese manganese ores. *Stanford Univ. Publ., Geol. Sciences* **5,** 1–64.

Miser H. D. (1922) Manganese ore in the Batesville district, Arkansas. *U.S. Geol. Surv. Bull.* **734,** 273.

Moussard A. M., Brenet J., Jolas F., Pourbaix M., Van Muylder J. (1954) Comportement electrochimique du manganèse. *Centre Belge d'Étude de la Corrosion. Rapport Technique No.* 18, p. 7.

Park C. F., Jr. (1942) Manganese deposits of Cubs. *U.S. Geol. Surv. Bull.* **935–B,** 75–97.

Thiel G. A. (1924) The manganese minerals: their identification and paragenesis. *Econ. Geol.* **19,** 107–145.

Thompson T. G. and Wilson T. L. (1935) The occurrence and determination of manganese in sea water. *J. Amer. Chem. Soc.* **57,** 233.

Vogt J. H. L. (1906) Über Manganwiesenerz. *Z. prakt. Geol.* **14,** 217–233.

ZoBell, C. E. (1946) Redox potential of marine sediments. *Amer. Assoc. Petrol. Geol. Bull.,* **30,** 477–513.

7

Reprinted from *Econ. Geol.*, **63**(3), 257–262 (1968)

The Formation of Sedimentary Iron Minerals

C. D. Curtis and D. A. Spears

Abstract

Part I of the paper represents an attempt to combine laboratory and field data (recent sedimentary environment) to produce mineral stability diagrams for use in palaeoenvironmental investigations. This exercise suggests that two distinct situations may be recognized: that of the depositional water and that of the interstitial (sediment) water. In the former only ferric compounds can be truly stable. Ferrous compounds (pyrite, pyrrhotite, magnetite, siderite and chamosite) are stable beneath the sediment/water interface. Anion activity (HS^- and HCO_3^-) appears to be the most important chemical control upon the nature and extent of development of these compounds.

Part II of the paper demonstrates that these essentially theoretical findings are not at variance with petrographic observations made by many workers. Both Carboniferous and Jurassic ores are discussed in some detail.

Part I. Evidence from Thermochemical Considerations and from Present-day Environments

C. D. Curtis

Two valuable techniques for investigating ancient sedimentary environments are comparison with present-day situations and interpretation of equilibrium mineral assemblages with the aid of laboratory attained thermochemical information. The two approaches, however, have not been generally combined. Analyses of the aqueous phase of sedimentary systems indicate that, as well as pH and Eh variation, dissolved iron, carbonate sulfur and silica species exhibit wide concentration ranges. In the past it has been usual for geochemists to represent equilibrium relationships between various iron minerals and dissolved species as two dimensional plots with Eh and pH as variables. Garrels and Christ (1965, p. 239) state, however, that "There is a tendency, for example, to represent relations amongst iron carbonates, oxides and sulfides without regard to the values of ΣS and ΣCO_2 used for calculation. Such disregard is sufficient to invalidate the use of the diagram."

Berner (1964) demonstrated the importance of sulfide activity variation in a combined laboratory/field study of pyrite formation. The present paper represents an attempt to extend these ideas towards a more general appraisal of environmental control upon iron mineral genesis.

Calculations

The mineral equilibria diagrams presented below were constructed according to the procedures developed in Garrels and Christ (1965) and from Free Energy data listed therein. Many of the equations are taken directly from that work, others differ only in that the ionic species considered are chosen to be those that are most abundant in the particular aqueous environments under discussion. Space permits only brief mention of the limitations of the thermochemical approach. Reference to the original text is recommended for a complete discussion. All relationships represent equilibria between pure compounds at 25° C and one atmosphere total pressure. The equations necessary for diagram development are:

1. H_2/HtO_2 — $2H_2O = 2H_2 + O_2$
   lower limit ($PH_2 = 1$): $Eh = 0 - 0.05\ pH$
   upper limit ($PO_2 = 1$): $Eh = 1.23 - 0.059\ pH$
2. Fe_3O_4/Fe_2O_3 — $2Fe_3O_{4c} + H_2O_l = 3Fe_2O_{3c} + 2H_{aq}^+ + 2e$
   $Eh = 0.221 - 0.059\ pH$
3. $FeCO_3/Fe_2O_3$ — $2FeCO_{3c} + 3H_2O_l = Fe_2O_{3c} + 2HCO_{3aq}^- + 4H_{aq}^+ + 2e$
   $Eh = 0.747 - 0.118pH + 0.059 \times \log (HCO_3^-)$
4. $FeCO_3/Fe_3O_4$ — $3FeCO_{3c} + 4H_2O_l = Fe_3O_{4c} + 3HCO_{3aq}^- + 5H_{aq}^+ + 2e$
   $Eh = 1.010 - 0.148\ pH + 0.0885 \times \log (HCO_3^-)$
5. FeS/FeS_2 — $FeS_c + HS_{aq}^- = FeS_{2c} + H_{aq}^+ + 2e$
   $Eh = -0.340 - 0.0295\ pH - 0.0295 \times \log (HS^-)$
6. $FeS/FeCO_3$ — $FeS_c + HCO_{3aq}^- = FeCO_{3c} + HS_{aq}^-$
   $\log (HS^-) = \log (HCO_3^-) - 4.08$

7. FeS/Fe_3O_4
$$3FeS_c + 4H_2O_l = Fe_3O_{4c} + 3HS^- + 5H_{aq}^+ + 2e$$
$$Eh = 1.374 + 0.0885 \log (HS^-) - 0.148\ pH$$

8. $FeS_2/FeCO_3$
$$FeCO_{3c} + 2HS_{aq}^- = FeS_{2c} + HCO_{3aq}^- + H_{aq}^+ + 2e$$
$$Eh = -0.462 - 0.0295\ pH + 0.0295 \times \log (HCO_3^-) - 0.059 \log (HS^-)$$

9. $FeS_2/FeCO_3$
$$FeS_{2c} + 8H_2O_l + HCO_{3aq}^- = FeCO_{3c} + 2SO_{4aq}^{2-} + 17H_{aq}^+ + 4e$$
$$Eh = 0.356 - 0.0716\ pH + 0.00842 \times \log (SO_4^{2-}) - 0.00421 \log (HCO_3^-)$$

10. FeS_2/Fe_3O_4
$$Fe_3O_{4c} + 6HS_{aq}^- + 2H_{aq}^+ = 3FeS_{2c} + 4H_2O_l + 4e$$
$$Eh = -1.199 + 0.0295\ pH - 0.0885 \times \log (HS^-)$$

11. FeS_2/Fe_3O_4
$$3FeS_{2c} + 28H_2O_l = Fe_3O_{4c} + 6SO_{4aq}^{2-} + 56H_{aq}^+ + 44e$$
$$Eh = 0.384 - 0.0751\ pH + 0.00805 \times \log (SO_4^{2-})$$

12. FeS_2/Fe_2O_3
$$Fe_2O_{3c} + 4HS_{aq}^- + 2H_{aq}^+ = 2FeS_{2c} + 3H_2O_l + 2e$$
$$Eh = -1.670 + 0.059\ pH - 0.118 \times \log (HS^-)$$

13. FeS_2/Fe_2O_3
$$2FeS_{2c} + 19H_2O_l = Fe_2O_{3c} + 4SO_{4aq}^{2-} + 38H_{aq}^+ + 30e$$
$$Eh = 0.380 - 0.075\ pH + 0.0079 \times \log (SO_4^{2-})$$

14. HS^-/SO_4^{2-}
$$HS_{aq}^- + 4H_2O_l = SO_{4aq}^{2-} + 9H_{aq}^+ + 8e$$
$$Eh = 0.252 - 0.066\ pH$$

15. Fe^{2+}/Fe_2O_3
$$2Fe_{aq}^{2+} + 3H_2O_l = Fe_2O_{3c} + 6H_{aq}^+ + 2e$$
$$Eh = 0.728 - 0.059 \log (Fe^{2+}) - 0.177\ pH$$

16. Fe^{2+}/Fe_3O_4
$$3Fe_{aq}^{2+} + 4H_2O_l = Fe_3O_{4c} + 8H_{aq}^+ + 2e$$
$$Eh = 0.980 - 0.0885 \log (Fe^{2+}) - 0.236\ pH$$

17. Fe^{2+}/FeS
$$FeS_c + H_{aq}^+ = Fe_{aq}^{2+} + HS_{aq}^-$$
$$\log (Fe^{2+}) = -4.4 - pH - \times \log (HS^-)$$

18. Fe^{2+}/FeS_2
$$2HS_{aq}^- + Fe_{aq}^{2+} = FeS_{2c} + 2H_{aq}^+ + 2e$$
$$Eh = -0.470 - 0.059\ pH - 0.059 \times \log (HS^-) - 0.0295 \log (Fe^{2+})$$

19. Fe^{2+}/FeS_2
$$FeS_{2c} + 8H_2O_l = 2SO_{4aq}^{2-} + Fe_{aq}^{2+} + 16H_{aq}^+ + 14e$$
$$Eh = 0.354 - 0.067\ pH + 0.0084 \log \times (SO_4^{2-}) + 0.0042 \log (Fe^{2+})$$

20. $Fe^{2+}/FeCO_3$
$$FeCO_{3c} + H_{aq}^+ = Fe_{aq}^{2+} + HCO_{3aq}^-$$
$$\log (Fe^{2+}) + \log (HCO_3^-) = -0.330 - pH$$

Natural Environments

Five variables define the chemical system described by the equations listed above: Eh, pH, activity dissolved HS^-, activity dissolved HCO_3^- and activity dissolved Fe^{2+}. Other dissolved species make but small contributions (Garrels and Christ, 1965, p. 196). The variation of each of these parameters in depositional environments is discussed below in order to define the range limits for realistic stability diagrams.

Baas Becking et al. (1957) measured the Eh and pH of 98 estuarine water and 357 estuarine mud samples from a number of localities. The water Eh ranged between +0.150 and +0.500 volts, 83 percent of values being restricted between +0.250 and +0.400 volts. The pH values of the same samples showed small variation, 92 percent lying between 7.5 and 9.0. Bearing in mind the experimental error contribution to the above variation (distributions are normal), marine and estuarine depositional waters can be reasonably characterized by pH 8.0 (or slightly higher) and Eh + 0.250 to +0.500 volts (certainly positive).

In the mud samples of the same investigation, Eh variation proved to be great, some 42 percent of all values being negative. Variation in pH was small, again with normal distribution (85% of all values between 6.5 and 8.5 with a mean between 7.0 and 7.5).

Manheim (1961) made careful in situ pH and Eh measurements in brackish waters and sediments of the Baltic Sea. Values of pH very close to 7.0 were found in pore waters of near-surface sediments and also in immediately overlying anoxic waters. Sediment Eh values were all negative, ranging down to −0.172 volts.

Berner (1963) quotes a large number of Eh values recorded in sediments from tidal flats, brackish bogs and deep-water slope sediments off the Gulf of California. All are negative, the majority being within the range −0.200 to −0.250 volts.

These results indicate that the pH of natural sedimentary environments varies little. Values from depositional waters are somewhat higher (approximately 8) than those from sediment pore waters (approximately 7).

The euxinic marine environment has not so far been considered. Manheim's (1961) insitu water Eh determinations showed a range from positive to −0.155 volts. Very recent data from the Black Sea, due to Skopintsev et al (1966), show the Eh of that highly anoxic water mass to range from −0.110 volts in the upper layers down to a minimum of −0.172 volts in the deeps.

Total Eh variation in the depositional waters of the present day is, therefore, considerable. Highly positive values characterize marine waters with efficient circulation whereas the figure of −0.172 volts must be regarded as being close to the minimum value attainable in stagnant waters. Much lower values are commonly reached in sediment pore waters.

Berner (1963) studied sulfide activity variation in sediments directly by means of a silver/silver sulfide electrode. A range of three or four orders of magnitude was observed. Comparable variation is observed in anoxic water masses.

Carbonate activity variation in natural waters and sediment pore waters is not, in the author's knowledge, particularly well documented. High values are to be anticipated within diagenetic environments where there is bacterial activity. Well circulated freshwaters, on the other hand, can be very poor in carbonates.

Garrels and Christ (18) suggested that if the activity of a dissolved species in equilibrium with a given solid is less than approximately 10^{-6}, the solid will behave as an immobile constituent in its environment. This criterion of solid stability is used in the following diagrams for the depositional water environment. Within the pore-waters of fine-grained sediments, however, cationic activities are maintained at much higher levels than in depositional waters. Some assessment of this stabilizing influence is gained by adopting a solid stability criterion of $a_{Fe_{aq}^{2+}} < 10^{-3}$ for iron minerals in diagenetic environments with severely restricted water circulation.

The above survey, which is based mainly upon data taken from European and North American literature, strongly suggests that the aqueous environments of deposition and diagenesis contrast sharply. Strakhov (1953) reviewed the findings of numerous Soviet field investigations concerning recent sedimentary environments and made just this point his primary conclusion. An attempt to take account of this finding is made, therefore, in the construction of stability field diagrams.

Of the five variables considered in the thermochemical calculations, pH seems to be least important. Diagrams are therefore presented with fixed pH; 7.0 representing the diagenetic environment, 8.0 representing the environment of depositional waters. The remaining variables are considered more fully.

Stability Diagrams

It is unfortunate that thermochemical data for naturally occurring iron silicates are still not available. Garrels and Christ (1965) concluded that these compounds probably occupy much the same stability fields as does magnetite when the system is saturated with amorphous silica. It is certainly difficult to envisage purely ferrous compounds such as chamosite being stable at higher redox potentials than those tolerated by the mixed ferrous-ferric oxide.

Figure 1 demonstrates mineral stability fields as a function of Eh and HS^- or SO_4^{2-} activity at pH 8.0. The fixed carbonate activity is that in equilibrium

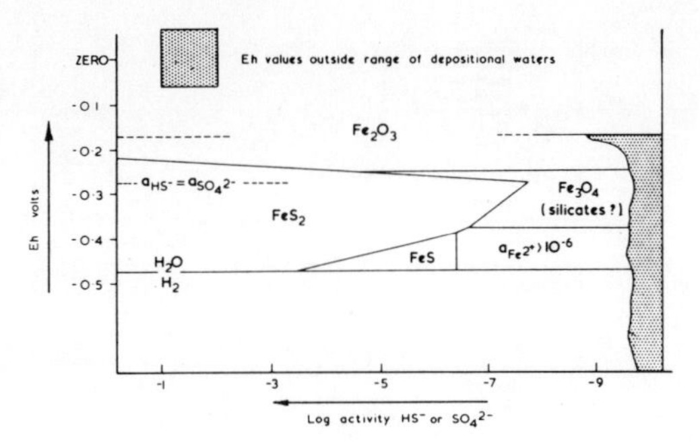

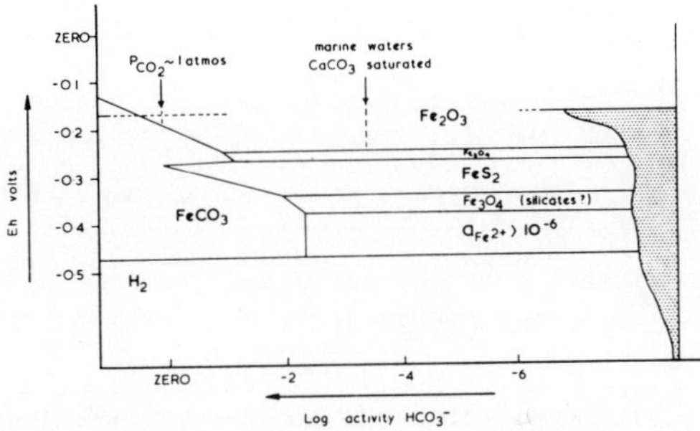

FIG. 1. (Upper) Mineral stability fields as a function of Eh and activity HS^- (conditions comparable with marine depositional waters: pH 8, $a_{HCO_3^-} = 10^{-3.5}$, solid stability at $a_{Fe}2+ < 10^{-6}$).

FIG. 2. (Lower) Mineral stability fields as a function of Eh and activity HCO_3^- (marine depositional waters with trace sulfide present: pH 8, $a_{HS^-} = 10^{-7}$, solid stability at $a_{Fe}2+ < 10^{-6}$).

with calcite at the Ca^{2+} activity of normal marine waters. This diagram spans chemical variation within depositional waters. Ferric compounds are clearly the only stable solid species in normal marine waters even at Eh values down to the lowest recorded in present day anoxic basins.

Figure 2 shows the effects of carbonate activity variation under conditions similar to those stipulated for Figure 1. Plainly, siderite is unlikely to be stable in any depositional water body. The pyrite field is included to show that small sulfide activities stabilize pyrite over a considerable range of Eh and carbonate activity.

In Figure 3, an attempt is made to account for the consequences of bacterial disturbance of SO_4^{2-}/HS^- equilibrium. The diagram and reasoning are but slight adaptations of those used by Berner (1964) who discussed this topic at some length. The net result is that pyrite is stabilized relative to other compounds at higher than true equilibrium Eh values. Direct precipitation of or (more likely) partial transformation of suspended ferric compounds to pyrite could occur, therefore within the depositional water

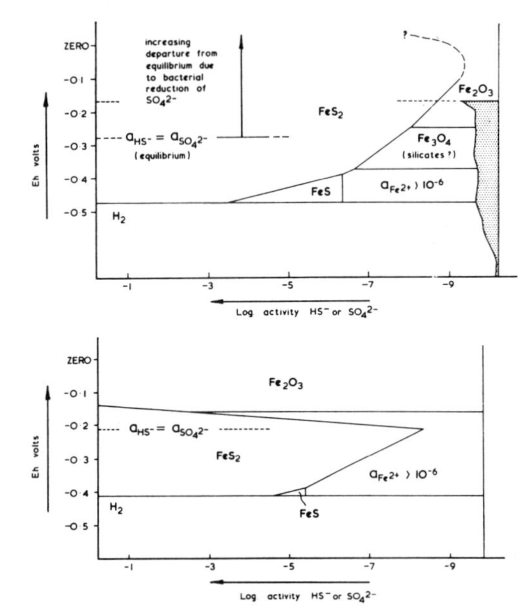

FIG. 3. (Upper) Mineral stability fields as a function of Eh and activity HS^- with SO_4^{2-}/HS^- equilibrium disturbed in favor of HS^- (anoxic marine depositional waters: pH 8, $a_{HCO_3^-} = 10^{-3.5}$, solid stability at $a_{Fe^{2+}} < 10^{-6}$).

FIG. 4. (Lower) Mineral stability fields as a function of Eh and activity HS^- (conditions thought to be more representative of uppermost sediment pore waters: pH 7, $a_{HCO_3^-} = 10^{-2.5}$, solid stability at $a_{Fe^{2+}} < 10^{-6}$).

masses of highly anoxic environments. Such waters are commonly more acidic than normal marine waters (Manheim, 1961). This would cause diminution of pyrrhotite and magnetite fields but would hardly affect that of pyrite.

Figure 4 is a modification of Figure 1 to pH 7, considered to be more typical of interstitial sediment water. Within this environment, Eh values range down (commonly) to −0.25 or −0.30 volts. Even lower values might be encountered in environments supporting hydrogen bacteria. Pyrite is immediately seen to occupy a very wide stability field, even at very low sulfide activities. Pyrrhotite is theoretically stable but requires extremely low Eh values and a narrow sulfide activity range.

Figure 5 shows that siderite, magnetite and ferrous silicates can be stable in the presence of maintained ferrous ion activities, such as might be anticipated in sediment pore waters. Severely restricted water circulation is encountered near to the sediment/water interface in fine-grained argillaceous sediments but only at greater depth in coarser material. Within the zone of intense bacterial activity (especially in organic-rich sediments) any sulfide generation would inevitably stabilize pyrite relative to all other possible diagenetic minerals. In the absence of sulfate reducing bacteria or in abiotic environments, siderite, magnetite, or ferrous silicates would be stable depending upon carbonate activity and the presence or absence of amorphous silicates.

Figure 6 further illustrates the relative effectiveness of anionic components by reducing carbonate activity below that of calcite saturation. Magnetite or silicates will only form when the sulfide activity of the diagenetic environment is vanishingly small and the carbonate activity quite low. This diagram also illustrates the maximum stability field of pyrrhotite. It must be concluded that the very low Eh values and narrow sulfide activity range required to stabilize this mineral will not commonly be encountered in the natural environment.

The specific requirements for siderite formation are indicated by Figure 7. Interaction of moderate sulfide with carbonate variation demonstrates that the most likely environment for siderite growth is one of low Eh (−0.25 to −0.35 volts), zero sulfide activity and severely restricted water circulation.

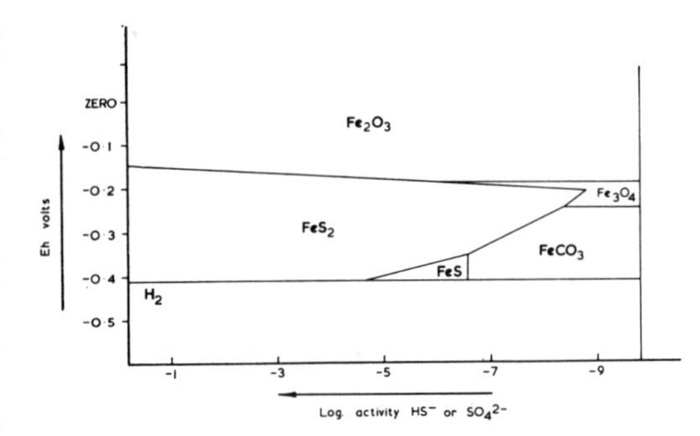

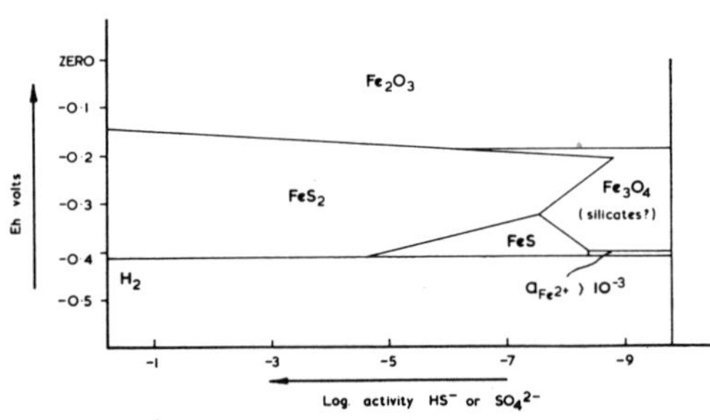

FIG. 5. (Upper) Mineral stability fields as a function of Eh and activity HS^- (conditions thought to be similar to those in sediments with restricted pore-water circulation: pH 7, $a_{HCO_3^-} = 10^{-2.5}$, solid stability at $a_{Fe^{2+}} < 10^{-3}$).

FIG. 6. (Lower) Mineral stability fields as a function of Eh and activity HS^- (conditions of low carbonate activity: pH 7, $a_{HCO_3^-} = 10^{-4.4}$, solid stability at $a_{Fe^{2+}} < 10^{-3}$).

Conclusions

Information gained from stability field diagrams used in conjunction with available data from present-day depositional environments may be summarized as follows:

(a) Hematite and other ferric compounds are the only iron minerals that can exist in true equilibrium with depositional waters.

(b) Pyrite is a metastable phase in anoxic water masses in which sulfide activities are maintained at non-equilibrium levels by bacteria.

(c) With the exception of pyrite as in (b) above, ferrous minerals (pyrite, pyrrhotite, magnetite, siderite, chamosite etc.) can only attain equilibrium with sediment pore waters. They are only stable, therefore within sediment masses.

(d) Pyrite is stable relative to all other possible phases even in the presence of low sulfide activities.

(e) The optimum chemical environment for siderite appears to be one with zero sulfide activity, low Eh (−0.25 to −0.35 volts) and severely restricted circulation.

(f) The environmental requirements for ferrous silicate stability are those for siderite modified by low carbonate activity and saturation with some active silica form.

(g) The fact that a different solid stability criterion (i.e., $Fe^{2+}aq$ maintained at high levels) has to be adopted to demonstrate siderite, magnetite, and silicate stability fields implies that these compounds will be relatively mobile in real systems.

These conclusions stem from thermochemical data for pure compounds. They are not seriously affected, however, by boundary errors of Eh ± 0.05 volts, sulfide activity ± one order of magnitude and carbonate activity ± half an order. These errors are likely to encompass free energy uncertainties or changes due to minor lattice substitutions. The exact meaning of the solid stability boundaries with respect to $Fe^{2+}aq$ is obscure. Conclusion (g) above is the optimum interpretation and is merely qualitative.

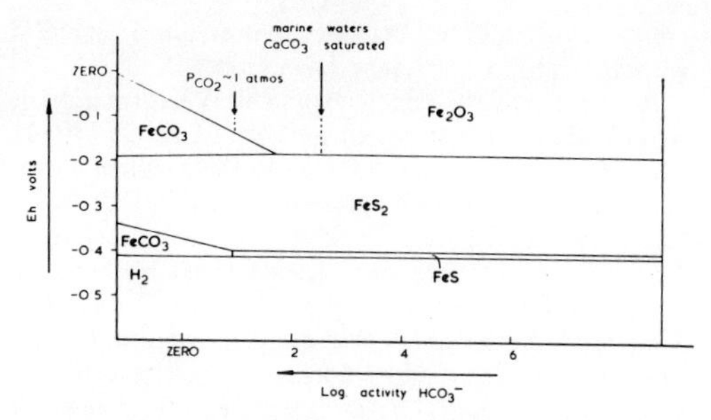

FIG. 7. Mineral stability fields as a function of Eh and activity HCO_3^- (conditions within sediments with restricted pore-water circulation and with sulfate reducing bacteria present: pH 7, $a_{HS^-} = 10^{-5}$, solid stability at $a_{Fe^{2+}} < 10^{-3}$).

Discussion

Stability diagrams describe equilibria between pure solids and dissolved species. Interpretation in terms of reaction mechanisms demands that all other compounds will transform to the stable compound at defined sets of environmental parameters. No account can be taken, for example, of the fact that pyrite generally forms via an intermediate iron monosulfide phase in the natural environment. The end (equilibrium) situation is represented.

Berner (1963), however, showed that in the specific case mentioned above, iron monosulfide was actively transforming to pyrite in natural environments where measurements of Eh, pH, and sulfide activity suggested that pyrite was the stable phase. Data for other transformations are lacking. It is, therefore, necessary to assume that transformations towards equilibrium are not kinetically prohibited: reactions in the natural environment will be towards the situations presented in the stability diagrams. This assumption enables the following deductions to be made:

(a) Only ferric compounds (mostly likely hydrated ferric oxides) can precipitate from normal depositional waters. The exception to this may be precipitation of metastable pyrite from anoxic waters with finite dissolved sulfide activity.

(b) Ferrous compounds (other than pyrite) can only form at Eh values realized within sediment pore waters. Their most likely mechanism of formation involves transformation of precipitate ferric compounds.

(c) Diagenetic environments characterized by slow detrital addition, abundant organic matter and readily available sulfate maintain high sulfide activities. Therein, all iron compounds will tend to transform to pyrite.

(d) Where, for any reason, sulfide activity in the diagenetic environment is very low, abiotic reaction between organic matter and precipitate ferric compounds would be likely to create conditions favorable for siderite formation (i.e., high $Fe^{2+}aq$ and carbonate activity):

$$4Fe(OH)_3 + 3C_{org.} \rightarrow 3CO_2 + 6H_2O + 4Fe^{2+} - 4e.$$

In an earlier paper (Curtis, 1967), it was implied that bacterial involvement in the above hypothetical reaction was a very likely mechanism in siderite formation. In the marine environment (SO_4^{2-} rich), however, it is difficult to envisage the simultaneous presence of sulfate, organic matter, and bacteria without significant sulfide formation.

An alternative mechanism of siderite formation is suggested by the work of Castano and Garrels (1950) who demonstrated that Fe^{2+}aq solutions, when introduced to a calcite/water system, cause calcite to go into solution, whereas ferric hydroxides precipitate. The equilibrium state was characterized by high Eh and negligible iron in solution. Calcite and ferric compounds thus stably coexist under conditions typical of the environment of normal depositional waters and of the sediment/water interface. In diagenetic environments, however, the unstable situation would prevail: ferrous iron together with calcite at maintained negative Eh values. The obvious possibility of siderite replacing calcite is not at variance with simple free energy calculations.

(e) The specific environmental requirements for chamosite (or other similar ferrous compounds) formation have been outlined above. Simultaneous precipitation of silica, alumina, and ferric oxides from depositional waters is not unlikely. Reduction of the iron in the diagenetic environment followed by dehydration (promoted by sediment compaction) would favor transformation to chamosite. Such a mechanism is entirely plausible but certainly cannot be substantiated by factual evidence.

(f) As previously mentioned, comparatively high ferrous ion activities must be maintained to stabilize siderite and ferrous silicates under typical diagenetic conditions (compare Figs. 4 and 5). Dissolution and redistribution of these compounds are likely processes during compaction of the sediments.

Editor's Note: References for this article may be found at the end of Paper 24.

Editor's Comments on Papers 8, 9, and 10

Papers 8 through 10 continue exploration of the subject of the solution and deposition of iron. At first glance they may appear unrelated, because the first considers the formation of sedimentary pyrite, the second the role of clay minerals in the transportation of iron, and the third the role of microorganisms in the formation of iron-rich layers in muds. There is, however, a common thread in that all are concerned with the importance of bacteria and organic matter in the formation of sedimentary iron minerals.

The idea that bacteria may play a significant role in the deposition of iron is not new and there is much early literature on their role in the formation of the bog-iron ores of Sweden. Harder and Chamberlin (1915) suggested that bacteria may have caused the precipitation of the iron oxide in the itabirite of the Minas Gerais region of Brazil. Subsequently Harder (1919) reported on a series of experiments which demonstrated the ability of some bacteria to precipitate iron under certain conditions. He divided the iron-depositing bacteria into the following three main groups: (1) those that require ferrous bicarbonate for their life processes, precipitating ferric hydroxide; (2) those that do not require ferrous bicarbonate but can cause the deposition of ferric hydroxide from either organic or inorganic iron salts; and (3) those that attack organic iron salts using the organic radicle as food and precipitating ferric hydroxide. Moore and Maynard (1929) repeated a number of Harder's experiments with similar results.

Gruner (1922) believed that bacteria were important in the precipitation of iron. He published photomicrographs of rod-like structures in the chert of the Biwabik iron-formation which were identified as bacilli. Gruner noted that similar structures had been reported from oolites of the Minette ores of France.

A number of more recent studies have focused on the role of microbes in the cycle of iron. L. G. M. Baas-Becking et al. (1960) reported on the Eh and pH limits within which microbial oxidation of iron has been observed in nature. Baas-Becking was a most distinguished Dutch microbiologist who went to work in the Australian C.S.I.R.O. laboratories at Canberra and experimentally observed bacterial production of several "high-temperature" iron minerals. H. L. Ehrlich (1972) recently summarized the role of microbes in the oxidation and reduction of iron. He states that microbes cause iron oxidation or reduction either by enzyme catalysis or indirectly by forming metabolic end products, which in turn promote oxidation or reduction.

Pyrite is often an abundant constituent of black shales. One of the classic examples of such a rock is the slate underlying the Riverton iron-formation in the Iron River district of Michigan. This 50-foot unit described by James in Paper 2 contains a uniform 38 percent FeS_2 over a strike length of some 20 miles. Similar pyritic slates have been explored as possible sources of sulfur in other parts of the Great Lakes region. They are common in the shield areas of the world.

Paper 8 is an excerpt of a paper by Robert A. Berner of Yale University on sedimentary pyrite formation. Although Berner uses the recent sediments of the Connecticut coastal plain to demonstrate the conditions necessary for the formation of sedimentary pyrite, his conclusions apply equally well to the ancient enriched pyritic slates. In the excerpt Berner uses the symbol *P*, which is defined in a nonreproduced part of the paper as:

$$P = \frac{\%\text{Fe (pyrite)}}{\%\text{Fe (pyrite)} + \%\text{Fe (HCl-soluble)}}$$

We noted in the introduction that there is compelling evidence for the conclusion that the atmosphere during the early and middle Precambrian contained little or no free oxygen. Under such conditions the transport of iron in solution presents no problem. However, the Paleozoic and younger ironstones must have formed under oxidizing conditions similar to the present, which puts great restrictions on the solubility of iron in waters that are in contact with the air. Paper 9 suggests one way in which significant quantities of iron could be moved to a marine basin even in such an oxidizing atmosphere.

The article is an excerpt of a paper by the late Dorothy Carroll. Carroll was educated at the University of Western Australia and at the University of London. After several research and teaching engagements at institutions of higher learning, she spent most of her career with the U.S. Geological Survey. In addition to numerous publications in geological journals she authored the book *Rock Weathering,* published in 1970 by the Plenum Publishing Company, New York, as one of their Monographs in Geosciences series.

In a 1965 work titled *Applied Capillary Microscopy,* published in the United States by Consultants Bureau, New York, a group of Russian scientists describe some ingenious methods of studying bacterial reduction and oxidation of iron. Paper 10 is one of the several papers in the volume.

References

Baas-Becking, L. G. M., I. R. Kaplan, and D. Moore, 1960, Limits of the natural environment in terms of pH and oxidation–reduction potentials: Jour. Geol., v. 68, p. 243–284.

Ehrlich, H. L., 1972, Iron, oxidation and reduction-microbial; *in* Encyclopedia of geochemistry and environmental sciences, R. W. Fairbridge, ed., Van Nostrand Reinhold Co., New York, p. 610–612.

Gruner, J. W., 1922, The origin of sedimentary iron formations: Econ. Geol., v. 17, p. 407–460.

Harder, E. C., 1919, Iron-depositing bacteria and their geologic relations: U.S. Geol. Surv. Prof. Paper 113, 89 p.

———, and R. T. Chamberlin, 1915, The geology of central Minas Gerais, Brazil: Jour. Geol., v. 23, p. 341–378, 385–424.

Moore, E. S., and J. E. Maynard, 1929, Transportation and precipitation of iron and silica: Econ. Geol., v. 24, p. 272–303, 365–402, 506–527.

8

Reprinted from *Amer. Jour. Sci.*, **268**, 1, 13–23 (1970)

SEDIMENTARY PYRITE FORMATION

ROBERT A. BERNER

Department of Geology and Geophysics, Yale University,
New Haven, Connecticut 06520

ABSTRACT. Experimental study indicates that pyrite can be synthesized at neutral pH in concentrated sulfide solution and in natural sediments by the reaction of precipitated FeS with elemental sulfur at 65°C. Similar reaction at sedimentary temperatures is probable but should require several years for completion. Synthetic pyrite formed by this reaction is framboidal.

The major steps in the process of sedimentary pyrite formation are: bacterial sulfate reduction, reaction of H_2S with iron minerals to form iron monosulfides, and the reaction of iron monosulfides with elemental sulfur to form pyrite. Accordingly the important factors limiting pyrite formation in marine sediments are: the availability of organic matter that can be metabolized by sulfate-reducing bacteria, the diffusion of sulfate into sediments, the total concentration and reactivity of iron minerals, and the production of elemental sulfur.

In sediments from the coastal region of central Connecticut, the main factor limiting pyrite formation is the availability of metabolizable organic matter. Reactive iron and dissolved sulfate are present to excess, and essentially all FeS is transformed by elemental sulfur to pyrite. These sediments are probably typical of many terrigenous marine sediments overlain by aerobic waters. In lower iron sediments, especially carbonates, the principal limiting factor is more likely to be the concentration of reactive iron. In most sediments total iron content and diffusion of sulfate are not limiting.

* * * * * * *

FACTORS LIMITING PYRITE FORMATION IN MARINE SEDIMENTS

Organic matter.—As pointed out in the introduction, the principal source of sulfide for pyrite formation in marine sediments is sulfate dissolved in sea water. To bring about reduction of sulfate to sulfide organic matter is required as an energy source for bacteria. (Non-bacterial reduction does not occur.) Without metabolizable organic matter there is no sulfate reduction and no pyrite formation. Thus, available organic matter, defined as that which can be metabolized by sulfate reducing bacteria, is a primary factor limiting the amount of pyrite that can be formed in a sediment. A crude measure of available organic matter is the concentration of organic carbon. Organic carbon is a reasonably accurate measure of total organic matter in sediments (Emery, 1960). Of course all organic matter is not available for sulfate reduction, but it can be assumed, as a first approximation, that a constant ratio of metabolizable to total organic matter exists at the time of deposition. This would be the case if organic remains of essentially the same biochemical com-

Editor's Note: A row of asterisks indicates that material has been omitted from the original article.

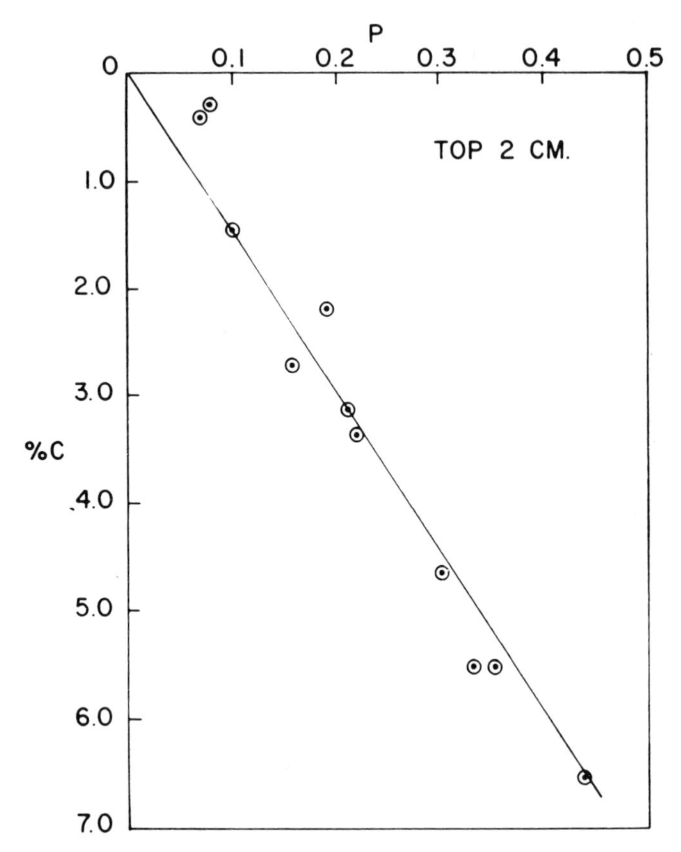

Fig. 6. Plot of P, the degree of pyritization, versus percent organic carbon for the top 2 cm of some Connecticut coastal sediments.

position serve as sources of organic matter for all the sediments of a given area.

Besides acting as a capacity factor in controlling how much pyrite may theoretically form, organic matter may also act as an intensity factor limiting the actual amount formed. It has been suggested by the writer (Berner, 1964c) that the rate of sulfate reduction in sediments is a direct function of the concentration of available organic matter. If this is true, sediments high in available organic matter should also be high in dissolved sulfide. This is because a high reduction rate enables the attainment and maintenance of high H_2S concentrations in the presence of continuous loss of H_2S by diffusion out of the sediment. Because different detrital iron compounds exhibit widely differing reactivities toward H_2S, it would be expected that at higher H_2S concentrations a greater proportion of total iron in a sediment would react with H_2S to form pyrite. If so, then the degree of pyritization of iron should be related directly to the concentration of available organic matter, if organic matter is a limiting factor.

In the Connecticut coastal sediments originally deposited organic carbon, as a measure of available organic matter, appears to be a limiting

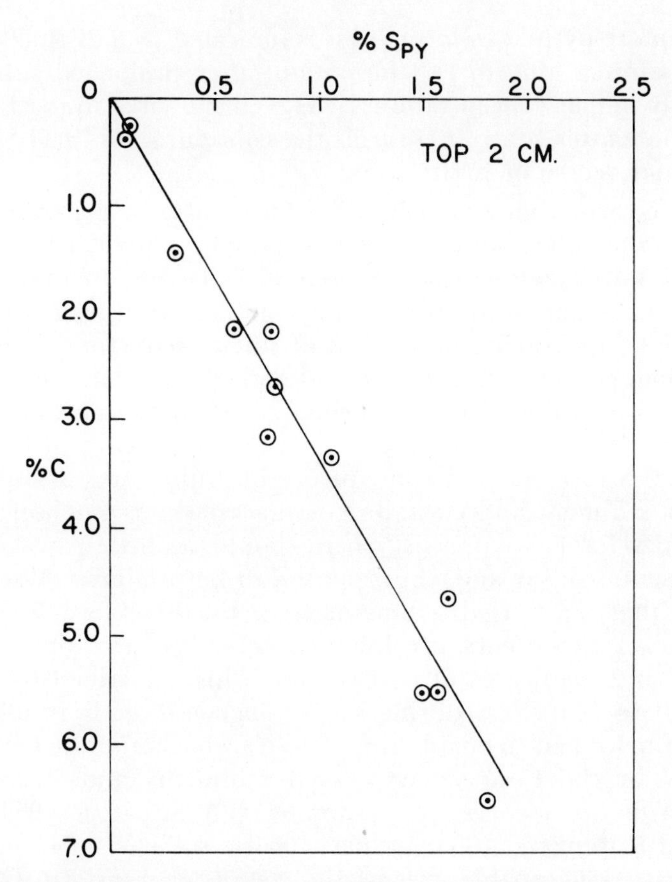

Fig. 7. Plot of percent pyrite sulfur ($S_{py.}$) versus percent organic carbon for the top 2 cm of some Connecticut coastal sediments.

factor. In the topmost portion of the sediments (upper 2 cm) where organic carbon concentrations are as near as possible to those at the time of deposition, there is a good linear correlation between the degree of pyritization, P, and the concentration of organic carbon. This is shown in figure 6. The amount of pyrite formed in the top 2 cm is also a linear function of organic carbon as shown in figure 7. Both regression lines extrapolate to zero at zero percent carbon as would be expected if organic carbon were limiting.

Below 2 cm some additional pyrite is formed (see figs. 2-5). Accompanying this is a loss of FeS and of organic carbon. The decrease in FeS is presumably due to transformation to pyrite, and the loss of organic carbon is due to metabolism by sulfate reducing and other bacteria. After a depth of about 10 cm is reached, the degree of pyritization essentially levels off (fig. 5) indicating cessation of further pyrite formation. The reason for this levelling off is that no more iron is able to react at the concentration of H_2S in the sediment to form pyrite. Additional iron, soluble in HCl, is available for further possible pyrite formation as shown by the relatively low maximum values of P. At higher H_2S concentration more pyrite can form. This is indicated by a distinct darkening of several samples, due to FeS formation, after prolonged subjection to considerably higher concentrations of H_2S in the laboratory. Thus, available organic matter, since it controls the concentration of H_2S, also controls the final degree of pyritization.

Organic carbon may be a limiting factor also in the transformation of FeS to pyrite. The transformation, as pointed out earlier, involves the addition of sulfur, rather than the removal of iron. In some situations the excess elemental sulfur needed for complete transformation may be lacking due to an insufficient amount of sulfate reduction resulting from a low original concentration of available organic matter. In other words, sufficient H_2S is initially formed to convert rapidly a small proportion of very reactive detrital iron to FeS, but not enough is present to transform further all FeS to FeS_2. As a consequence of "sulfur starvation" FeS may persist in a sediment and crystallize as mackinawite, pyrrhotite, or greigite. In order for FeS to persist, there should be little excess H_2S from which elemental sulfur and, thus, pyrite can be produced. Volkov (1961) has shown that old buried sediments from the Black Sea, in which appreciable black FeS occurs, are low in total sulfur and very low in dissolved H_2S and the degree of pyritization. This is ascribed by Volkov to limited sulfate reduction during early diagenesis with insufficient elemental sulfur formed to enable complete transformation of FeS to pyrite. Apparently in the Connecticut coastal sediments and in most other marine pyrite occurrences (for example, van Straaten, 1954; Kaplan, Emery, and Rittenberg, 1963; Berner, 1964b), there is sufficient available organic matter to enable essentially complete transformation. Black FeS is not found at depth.

Iron.—For a given fixed concentration of H_2S the amount of pyrite that forms in a sediment should be directly controlled by the concentration and reactivity of detrital iron compounds. The higher the iron content and the greater its reactivity, the higher should be the resulting concentration of pyrite. If abundant available organic matter is present so that the H_2S concentration is maintained at a very high value for a long time, the total amount of pyrite may be limited by the total quantity of iron. In such a case the value of P should approach, or even exceed one. This situation, however, is almost never achieved as evidenced by the very common occurrence in ancient pyritic sediments of metastable, HCl-soluble iron minerals (for example, Strakhov, 1958; Berner, 1964d; Curtis, 1967).

In the Connecticut coastal sediments total iron is not a limiting factor in pyrite formation. If it were, all reactive iron would be used up to form pyrite. However, relatively low values of P (<0.5) shown in table 3 indicate incomplete pyritization of HCl-soluble iron. Further proof of incomplete pyritization is shown by a blackening of sediment samples in the laboratory when exposed to saturated H_2S solution for a few days. Figure 8 shows no clear-cut correlation between pyrite sulfur

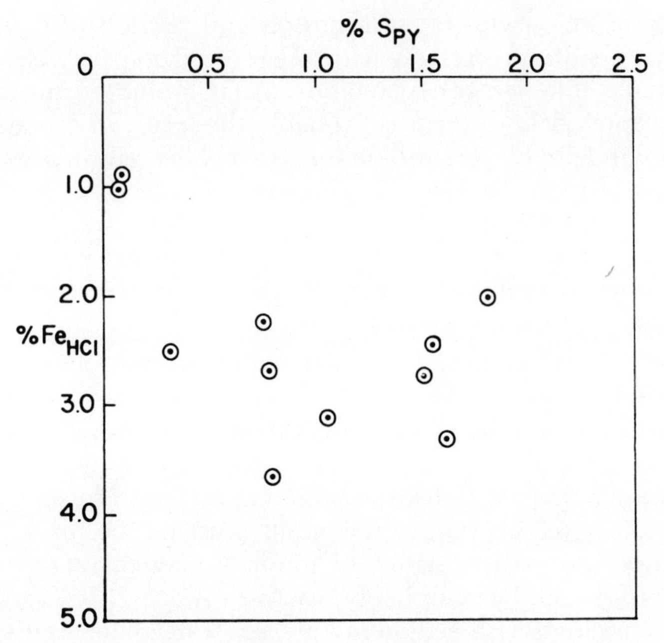

Fig. 8. Plot of percent pyrite sulfur ($S_{py.}$) versus percent HCl-soluble iron (Fe_{HCl}) for the top 2 cm of some Connecticut coastal sediments.

and HCl-soluble iron for the topmost sediment from different locations. This also indicates that iron is not a limiting factor.

Although no apparent correlation between pyrite sulfur and HCl-soluble iron exists when comparing sediments from different locations, there does appear to be some correlation within a single core for samples taken below depths of about 10 cm. This is shown by a rough parallelism of the curves for pyrite sulfur and HCl-soluble iron in figures 3 and 4 and the approximate constancy of P with depth. If P is constant, then:

$$\frac{Fe_p}{Fe_p + Fe_{HCl}} = k \tag{13}$$

and:

$$Fe_p = \left(\frac{-k}{k-1}\right) Fe_{HCl} \tag{14}$$

$$S_p = 1.15\left(\frac{-k}{k-1}\right) Fe_{HCl} \tag{15}$$

where:

$$k = \text{constant}$$
$$Fe_p = \text{pyrite iron}$$
$$Fe_{HCl} = \text{HCl-soluble iron}$$
$$S_p = \text{pyrite sulfur}$$

Curve parallelism and equation (15) are not brought about by a direct relation between pyrite formation and reactive iron. Instead they more probably result from a secondary correlation resulting from the primary correlations of Fe_{HCl} with organic carbon and pyrite sulfur with organic carbon. Pyrite sulfur correlates with organic carbon because carbon is a limiting factor. The weaker correlation of HCl-soluble iron with organic carbon at depths below 10 cm is probably the result of the association of higher iron and higher organic matter with finer grain sizes. Finer particles consist of more HCl-soluble chlorite and adsorbed iron oxides and tend to settle out along with light suspended organic detritus. The covariation of both pyrite sulfur and HCl-soluble iron with organic carbon is, thus, due to a variable sand plus silt content in the sediments. This is supported by grain size determinations.

Although the Connecticut coastal sediments may be typical of iron-rich terrigenous muds (Love, 1967), they are not representative of iron-poor sediments, especially carbonates. The iron content of pure carbonate sediments is low because of a lack of detrital iron minerals. As a result, carbonate muds may be rich in organic matter and H_2S but very low in pyrite. Certainly in this case iron content must be the principal limiting factor in pyrite formation. Much of the iron may emanate from organic iron compounds and be completely reactive toward H_2S. A good example of pyrite-poor, high H_2S sediments are the carbonate muds of Florida Bay.

Probably in most sediments pyrite formation takes place in the presence of overlying partly aerobic water. An outstanding exception is the Black Sea where waters below about 150 m depth are anaerobic and contain dissolved H_2S (Skopintsev, 1961). In this situation it is possible that pyrite formation may take place at, or even above, the sediment-water interface. If most pyrite is formed at the sediment-water interface, the amount formed should be controlled by the amount of detrital iron that can react at the H_2S concentration of the overlying water (Ostroumov, Volkov, and Fomina, 1961). The H_2S concentration is a property of the water mass and not related to local organic carbon concentrations in the sediments. In this situation iron, and not organic carbon, should be the limiting factor. However, additional sulfate reduction occurs within the sediments (Shishkina, 1959), which suggests additional pyrite formation within the sediments. Therefore, reactive iron may be a primary limit on pyrite formation in euxinic environments such as the Black Sea, but metabolizable organic carbon should exert an additional influence.

Sulfate.—If pyritic sulfur emanates mainly from dissolved sulfate, the amount of pyrite formed may be limited by the diffusion of sulfate into a sediment from the overlying water. The importance of diffusion in building up high concentrations of pyrite has already been pointed out in the introduction. A situation might exist where an iron and organic-rich sediment is deposited so rapidly that diffusion of sulfate cannot keep pace with reduction. As a result dissolved sulfate will disappear rapidly at shallow depths and not be replenished from above. The limiting amount of sulfate would then be simply that contained within pore waters buried with the sediment at the time of deposition. For typical marine sediment this would be equivalent to 0.3 percent pyrite sulfur by dry weight.

Diffusion of sulfate is not a limiting factor in the Connecticut coastal sediments. This is shown by the presence of appreciable concentrations of dissolved sulfate in sediment pore waters at and below depths where active pyrite formation occurs and by the presence of pyrite sulfur in concentrations far exceeding 0.3 percent. The Connecticut sediments are probably typical of most marine sediments.[2] In the Gulf of California (Berner, 1964b) and the Santa Barbara Basin off southern California (Kaplan, Emery, and Rittenberg, 1963) concentrations of dissolved sulfate in sediments at depths many tens of centimeters below the depth where pyritization is essentially complete are at least half that in the overlying water. Reduction and removal of all interstitial sulfate at shallow depths, which is necessary for sulfate diffusion to become limiting, does not occur. Also, the concentration of pyrite sulfur generally far exceeds 0.3 percent.

Elemental sulfur.—The transformation of FeS to FeS_2 is an oxidation, and if no active oxidizing agent is present in a sediment, even though there may be a high concentration of H_2S, no pyrite can form. In the present study it is suggested that the only oxidizing agent capable of bringing about this transformation is elemental sulfur. If true, elemental sulfur may be a limiting factor in pyrite formation.

In most sediments elemental sulfur is not limiting since, as pointed out earlier, incomplete transformation of FeS to pyrite is a relatively rare phenomenon. This is especially true of sediments overlain by aerobic waters, such as those from the Connecticut coast, where elemental sulfur readily forms as a result of the oxidation of H_2S and FeS by dissolved oxygen. The oxygen is mixed into the anaerobic sediment by the burrowing activity of benthonic organisms, by current and wave stirring, and by diffusion. The oxidation process can be inorganic but is more commonly mediated by microorganisms such as the Thiobacilli (Thimann, 1963) which not only produce elemental sulfur but also oxidize elemental sulfur to sulfate ion. Oxidation to sulfate explains why elemental sulfur does not normally accumulate in sediments (note low concentrations in table 3).

In sediments overlain by anaerobic waters (that is, euxinic basins) the origin of elemental sulfur is more problematical. It is generally assumed that bacteria that produce elemental sulfur are aerobic, photosynthetic, or use dissolved nitrate as an energy source (ZoBell, 1946; Thimann, 1963). In a sulfidic sediment or a deep sulfidic water there is no oxygen or light, and nitrate is either absent or present in very low concentrations; yet complete transformation of FeS to FeS_2 in sediments of euxinic basins is common as shown by the Black Sea (Ostroumov,

[2] From unpublished studies, the writer has found that in some unusually organic-rich sediments, especially those affected by human pollution, all dissolved sulfate may be removed at shallow depths. However, these sediments are atypical of pyritic sediments in general.

1953; Volkov, 1961). If pyrite formation is dependent upon elemental sulfur, the elemental sulfur must either be added by deposition from above or it must form by some unknown anaerobic process.

The most plausible origin for "detrital" sulfur is formation in the water column at the shallow depth where H_2S-containing deep water contacts oxygenated surface water. In the Black Sea this elemental sulfur is distributed by surface currents and subsequently falls to the bottom (Ostroumov, Volkov, and Fomina, 1961). Volkov (1961) states that elemental sulfur is also formed directly by bacteria in the sediments of the Black Sea. However, microbiological studies of the Black Sea have so far failed to demonstrate conclusively anaerobic sulfur formation at depth (H. Jannasch, personal commun.).

Formation of elemental sulfur anaerobically by a strictly inorganic process is possible; however, the suggested mechanism of Feely and Kulp (1957), whereby elemental sulfur is formed by the reaction of H_2S with dissolved sulfate ion, is unlikely. The non-reactivity of sulfate toward inorganic reducing agents even stronger than H_2S is a well known phenomenon. The writer has never seen any evidence for the Feely and Kulp reaction in experiments at low or elevated temperature whenever air was scrupulously excluded from solutions. Also, Voge (1939) has demonstrated non-reactivity between H_2S and SO_4^{--} through the use of radioactive sulfur. The possible biological or inorganic formation of elemental sulfur by anaerobic processes requires further proof and much additional study. Only then can the role of elemental sulfur as a possible factor controlling pyrite formation be better evaluated.

RATE OF PYRITE FORMATION

The rate of pyrite formation, regardless of mechanism, can be estimated from data available for the Connecticut coastal sediments. Rates of deposition in this general area based on rates of coastal subsidence and sedimentation on tidal marshes (Bloom, 1967) average about 0.1 cm per year. For one of the specific areas studied by the writer some additional depositional rate data exists. The sediments from Joshua Cove (H-1, H-2, H-3) consist of about 2 to 3 cm of mud lying atop the surface of a dead marsh. The mud has been deposited since the opening of the main tidal creek to Long Island Sound during the late 1950's (A. Bloom, personal commun.). Before this the marsh had been artificially closed to the sea, and as a result the grass had died. Thus, the total time of deposition of the mud is about 10 years. Since the mud contains 1.5 to 1.8 percent pyrite sulfur (table 3), the minimum rate of pyrite formation is approximately 0.2 percent S per year. This is a minimum rate because formation may occur over an interval less than 2 cm sampled. There is little FeS in the mud, and degree of pyritization is comparatively high. Thus, pyrite formation may be complete. The rate of formation is undoubtedly higher than in many other areas because of the very high concentration of organic carbon which, due to rapid reduction of sulfate to H_2S, helps to accelerate the overall pyrite forming process. However, it does give an idea of how fast pyrite can form in a sediment under optimum conditions. The rate is of the same order of magnitude as that expected for the reaction of FeS with elemental sulfur at neutral pH and sedimentary temperatures. This is based on room temperature experiments and reasonable extrapolations of rate data obtained at 65°C.

CONCLUSIONS

According to the above discussion and results and the results of other studies, the process of sedimentary pyrite formation in marine sediments proceeds as follows:

1. Organic matter derived from dead marine organisms and iron contained within or adsorbed upon fine grained detrital minerals is deposited in relatively quiet water where the light particles may settle out.

2. Upon removal of dissolved oxygen from associated waters by aerobic metabolism of the organic matter, anaerobic bacterial sulfate reduction occurs within sediments and more rarely in waters overlying the sediments. As a result of sulfate reduction, H_2S is formed.

3. Dissolved H_2S reacts immediately with the most reactive forms of iron present to form black non-crystalline FeS. If H_2S formation ceases at this point and no extra elemental sulfur is added to the sediment, no further reactions, other than the crystallization of FeS to various iron monosulfides, occur. The result is greigite, mackinawite, or pyrrhotite and little or no pyrite (or marcasite).

4. If continued sulfate reduction takes place, the H_2S concentration in the sediment increases which brings about the conversion of additional detrital iron to FeS. The amount of FeS (and ultimately pyrite) that can form is limited by the rate of production and concentration of H_2S and/or by the amount and reactivity of detrital iron.

5. Simultaneously with step 4 the concentration of sulfate in the sediment pore water falls and additional sulfate is made available for reduction by diffusion down the concentration gradient from the overlying water. Likewise, the produced H_2S builds up in the pore water and begins to diffuse out of the sediment. The concentration of available (metabolizable) organic matter controls the rate of sulfate reduction and, consequently, the concentration of H_2S that can be maintained in the presence of loss by diffusion.

6. Some of the H_2S is oxidized, either inorganically or by sulfur oxidizing bacteria, to elemental sulfur. Under aerobic bottom conditions considerable elemental sulfur is formed by the reaction of FeS and H_2S with dissolved oxygen which is stirred into the sediment from the overlying water by burrowing organisms or by storm waves and currents. Part of the elemental sulfur is subsequently oxidized by bacteria to dissolved sulfate.

7. The remaining elemental sulfur slowly reacts with FeS in the sediment to form pyrite which crystallizes as minute framboidal micro-

spheres. The time for complete transformation of FeS to FeS_2, in the presence of abundant H_2S and elemental sulfur, is on the order of several years.

ACKNOWLEDGMENTS

This research was supported by NSF Grant GA-1441 and American Chemical Society PRF Grant 1937-A2. Chemical analyses were performed by Mrs. C. Thomlinson. The writer thanks Dr. F. T. Manheim of the Woods Hole Oceanographic Institution and U. S. Geological Survey for helpful discussion and critical review of the manuscript. Dr. H. Jannasch also of the Woods Hole Oceanographic Institution is thanked for his helpful discussion of bacterial sulfide oxidation.

References

Allen, E. T. and Crenshaw, J. L., 1914, Effect of temperature and acidity in the formation of marcasite and wurtzite: Am. Jour. Sci., 4th ser., v. 38, p. 71-392.

Allen, E. T., Crenshaw, J. L., Johnston, J., and Larsen, E. S., 1912, Mineral sulphides of iron: Am. Jour. Sci., 4th ser., v. 33, p. 169-236.

Baas-Becking, L. G. M., Kaplan, J. R., and Moore, D., 1960, Limits of the natural environment in terms of pH and oxidation reduction potentials: Jour. Geology, v. 68, p. 243-284.

Berner, R. A., 1964a, Iron sulfides formed from aqueous solution at low temperatures and atmospheric pressure: Jour. Geology, v. 72, p. 293-306.

——— 1964b, Distribution and diagenesis of sulfur in some sediments from the Gulf of California: Marine Geology, v. 1, p. 117-140.

——— 1964c, An idealized model of dissolved sulfate distribution in recent sediments: Geochim. et Cosmochim. Acta, v. 28, p. 1497-1503.

——— 1964d, Stability fields of iron minerals in anaerobic marine sediments: Jour. Geology, v. 72, p. 826-834.

——— 1967a, Diagenesis of iron sulfide in recent marine sediments, *in* Lauff, George, Estuaries: Am. Assoc. Adv. Sci. Pub. 83, p. 268-272.

——— 1967b, Thermodynamic stability of sedimentary iron sulfides: Am. Jour. Sci., v. 265, p. 773-785.

——— 1969, The synthesis of framboidal pyrite: Econ. Geology, v. 64, p. 383-384.

Bloom, A. L., 1967, Coastal geomorphology of Connecticut: Office Naval Research Contract Nonr-401(45) Final Rept. Task No. NR 388-065, 72 p.

Curtis, C. D., 1967, Diagenetic iron minerals in some British Carboniferous sediments: Geochim. et Cosmochim. Acta, v. 31, p. 2109-2124.

Emery, K. O., 1960, The sea off southern California: New York, John Wiley and Sons, 366 p.

Feely, H. W., and Kulp, J. L., 1957, Origin of Gulf Coast saltdome sulfur deposits: Am. Assoc. Petroleum Geologists Bull., v. 41, p. 1802-1853.

Feld, W., 1911, Über die Bildung von Eisenbisulfid (FeS_2) in Lösungen und die Entstehung der natürlichen Pyritlager: Zeitschr. für angew. Chemie, v. 24, p. 97-103.

Garrels, R. M., and Christ, C. L., 1965, Solutions, minerals, and equilibria: New York, Harper and Row, 450 p.

Gluskoter, H. J., 1965, Electronic low temperature ashing of bituminous coal: Fuel, v. 44, p. 285-291.

Jedwab, Jacques, 1967, Mineralization engreigite de debris vegetaux d'une vase recente (Grote Geul): Soc. belge géologie Bull., v. 76, p. 1-19.

Kaplan, I. R., Emery, K. O. and Rittenberg, S. C., 1963, The distribution and isotopic abundance of sulphur in recent marine sediments off southern California: Geochim. et Cosmochim. Acta, v. 27, p. 297-332.

Love, L. G., 1957, Micro-organisms and the presence of syngenetic pyrite: Geol. Soc. London Quart. Jour., v. 113, p. 429-440.

——— 1967, Early diagenetic iron sulphide in recent sediments of the Wash, England: Sedimentology, v. 9, p. 327-352.

Nriagu, J. O., 1968, Sulfur metabolism and sedimentary environment; Lake Mendota, Wisconsin: Limnology and Oceanography, v. 13, p. 430-439.

Ostroumov, E. A., 1953, Different forms of combined sulfur in the sediments of the Black Sea: Akad. Nauk SSSR, Inst. Okeanologii Trudy, v. 7, p. 70-90.

Ostroumov, E. A., Volkov, I. I., and Fomina, L. C., 1961, Distribution pattern of sulfur compounds in the bottom sediments of the Black Sea: Akad. Nauk SSSR, Inst. Okeanologii Trudy, v. 7, p. 93-129.

Polushkina, A. P., and Sidorenko, G. A., 1963, Melnikovite as a mineral species: Zapiski Vses. Mineralog. Obshch., v. 92, p. 547-554.

Rickard, D. T., 1969, The chemistry of iron sulphide formation at low temperatures: Stockholm Contr. Geology, v. 20, p. 67-95.

Sandell, E. B., 1959, Colorimetric determination of traces of metals: New York, Intersci. Publishers, 1032 p.

Shishkina, O. V., 1959, The sulfates in the mud waters of the Black Sea: Akad. Nauk SSSR, Inst. Okeanologii Trudy, v. 33, p. 178-193.

Skinner, B. J., Erd, R. C. and Grimaldi, E. S., 1964, Greigite, the thio-spinel or iron; a new mineral: Am. Mineralogist, v. 49, p. 543–555.

Skopintsev, B. A., 1961, Recent work on the hydrochemistry of the Black Sea: Okeanologiya, v. 1, p. 243-250.

Strakhov, N. M., 1958, The forms of iron in Black Sea sediments: Akad. Nauk SSSR Doklady, v. 118, p. 803-806.

Thimann, K. V., 1963, The life of bacteria: New York, The Macmillan Co., 775 p.

Van Straaten, L. M. J. V., 1954, Composition and structure of recent sediments of the Netherlands: Leidse Geol. Mededel., v. 19, p. 1-110.

Voge, H. H., 1939, Exchange reactions with radiosulfur: Am. Chem. Soc. Jour., v. 61, p. 1032-1035.

Volkov, I. I., 1961, Iron sulfides, their interdependence and transformation in the Black Sea bottom sediments: Akad. Nauk SSSR, Inst. Okeanologii Trudy, v. 50, p. 68-92.

ZoBell, C. E., 1946, Marine microbiology: Waltham, Mass., Chronica Botanica Co.

9

Role of clay minerals in the transportation of iron*

DOROTHY CARROLL
U.S. Geological Survey, Washington 25, D.C.

(*Received* 3 *July* 1957)

Abstract—The clay minerals have iron associated with them in several ways: (1) as an essential constituent, (2) as a minor constituent within the crystal lattice where it is in isomorphous substitution and (3) as iron oxide on the surface of the mineral platelets. Nontronite, "hydromica," some chlorites, vermiculite, glauconite and chamosite contain iron as an essential constituent. Kaolinite and halloysite have no site within the lattice for iron, but in certain environments iron oxide (goethite or hematite) is intimately associated as a coating on the micelles. Analyses of clay minerals show that the content of Fe_2O_3 varies: 29 per cent (nontronite), 7·3 per cent (griffithite), 4·5 per cent ("hydromica"), 5·5 per cent (chlorite), 4 per cent (vermiculite) and 18 per cent (glauconite). The FeO content is: 40 per cent (chamosite), 7·8 per cent (griffithite), 1–2 per cent ("hydromica"), 3 per cent (glauconite) and 2 per cent (chlorite).

The iron associated with the clay minerals remains stable in the environment in which the minerals occur, but if either pH or Eh or both are changed the iron may be affected. Change of environment will cause: (1) removal of iron by reduction of Fe^{3+} to Fe^{2+}; (2) ion-exchange reactions; (3) instability of the crystal lattice.

Experiments using bacterial activity to produce reducing conditions with kaolinite and halloysite coated with iron oxides and with nontronite in which ferric iron is in the octahedral position within the lattice showed that ferric oxide is removed at Eh +0·215 in fresh water and at Eh +0·098 in sea water. Hematite, goethite, and indefinite iron oxides were removed at different rates. Red ferric oxides were changed to black indefinite noncrystalline ferrous sulphide at Eh −0·020 but reverted to ferric oxide under oxidizing conditions. Nontronite turned bright green under reducing conditions and some of the ferrous iron remained within the lattice on a return to oxidizing conditions. Bacterial activity seems to be necessary for maintaining reducing conditions in the environments studied.

* * * * * * *

* Publication authorized by the Director, U.S. Geological Survey.

Editor's Note: A row of asterisks indicates that material has been omitted from the original article.

Discussion

Effect of marine environment on iron oxides associated with clay minerals

The kinds of clay minerals transported to a marine environment will depend, as GRIM (1951, p. 229) has pointed out, on those present in the area. Iron oxides, if present as films on the clay mineral micelles, will be carried along with the clay minerals, and if conditions of pH and Eh do not change the iron oxides will be incorporated in the resulting sediments. The experiments described here indicate the course of events that may take place after deposition in a marine environment. Several possibilities are to be considered:

Iron oxide films are not removed from clay particle surfaces. Red, brown or yellow sediments indicate the presence of ferric oxides, hematite, goethite or indefinite iron oxides which are stable in sea-water with Eh +0·1 to 0·3 (KRUMBEIN and GARRELS, 1952, p. 3) at the bottom; that is, oxidizing. It should be noted that although both Eh and pH measure the solubility of ferric oxide, there is a very narrow range in pH for normal sea-water, so that the relationship to pH is not nearly so important as that to Eh. Sea-water alone will not dissociate ferric oxides from clay minerals, as the Eh is similar to that for many soils in which iron oxide films and coatings are formed. Some loss of weight in the minerals may occur (Table 10). Exchangeable ions are important in all clay minerals except kaolinite and halloysite, in which the total exchange capacity is practically unchanged from its original quantity, although the exchangeable cations may be present in different proportions.

Iron oxide films are removed from clay particle surfaces. The stability field for the existence of solid ferric oxide and ferrous oxide is governed by the oxidation–reduction potential present according to the equation (CASTANO and GARRELS, 1950, p. 757):

$$\mathrm{Eh} = +0{\cdot}06 \log \frac{a\mathrm{Fe}^{3+}}{a\mathrm{Fe}^{3+}}$$

Lowering Eh (conditions become more anaerobic) will increase Fe^{2+} at the expense of Fe^{3+} and at the same time decrease the pH (STARKEY and HALVORSON, 1927, p. 382). Conversely, raising the Eh (conditions become more aerobic) will increase the amount of Fe^{3+} at the expense of Fe^{2+}. Ferrous ions will be in solution, probably in equilibrium with $Fe(OH)_2$ at low Eh values, but if the Eh is raised, Fe^{2+} changes to $Fe_2(OH)_3$, which will precipitate if the amount exceeds the solubility in sea-water. COOPER (1938, Table VI) has summarized the activities of Fe^{3+} and Fe^{2+} in equilibrium with sea-water containing solid ferric hydroxide.

The fluctuation between oxidizing and reducing ions will determine the quantities of Fe^{3+} and Fe^{2+} present. There are two important environments: the interface between the sea-water and the ocean floor; and the sediments below the ocean floor. These have been illustrated by KRUMBEIN and GARRELS (1952, p. 20) and HUBER and GARRELS (1953). Several environments may now be examined:

Marine environments and their influence on iron oxides associated with clay minerals

Unrestricted marine environment with little or no bacterial activity. The sea-floor interface in an unrestricted sea subject to circulation of water will have pH and Eh similar to that of ordinary sea-water; e.g. pH 7–8, Eh +0·1–0·3 V. Under these conditions iron oxide films will be stable on the clay particles and no removal will take place. The resulting sediments will be similar in colour to those being transported by the rivers to the area. Some adjustment of crystal lattices may take place with time. Exchangeable cations will be readjusted to those of the marine environment. It is supposed that in this environment the addition of organic matter is at a minimum and that bacterial activity is not marked.

Shallow marine environment with little or no bacterial activity. In such an environment bacterial activity will reduce the Eh, but the pH remains approximately the same as in normal sea-water. This is an environment similar to that of the experiment with sea-water and Bahama Bank bacteria. As the Eh is lowered, ferric iron becomes unstable and is removed with consequent bleaching of the clay particles. Below the interface, bacterial activity may increase but will depend on the availability of organic matter for growth of the bacteria. This environment could well occur on wide shallow estuaries with little movement of water; it is aerobic in that some circulation of water occurs.

Restricted shallow water, marine environment with bacterial activity. The abundance of organic matter and bacteria results in strongly reducing conditions, as in stagnant water inside offshore bars. The experiment with inoculant from Martha's Vineyard was designed to examine this type of environment. The Eh is sufficiently low for reduction of ferric oxide to ferrous oxide, which is unstable and will change to Fe_3O, but in addition the presence of sulphides causes deposition of uncrystallized $FeS \cdot nH_2O$, and if sufficient time elapses pyrite and possibly marcasite develop. EDWARDS and BAKER (1951) have observed that pyrite forms in marine muds that have an alkaline or neutral reaction. Ferric oxide in clay mineral lattices is changed to ferrous. A feature of this type of deposit is that the iron is not removed but remains in its new form associated with the clay minerals except for a small quantity that has crystallized as pyrite. At the interface where the Eh is higher, oxidation occurs and the black clay changes to brown. If the whole surface is exposed, oxidation similarly takes place and goethite and hematite, probably with indefinite iron oxides, result. Such situations have been described for Wadden Sea in Holland, and similar conditions are found in many near-shore areas.

The results of the fresh-water experiment indicate that at the interface of the floor of a fresh-water lake containing clay-bearing sediments, ferric iron can be reduced to ferrous iron if bacterial activity takes place. It should be noted, however, that pH is a limiting factor for bacterial growth. The iron removed from the surfaces of the clay particles is in the ferrous form and later forms a ferrous organic salt. The organic salt may be one method of transporting iron in solution.

The chamosite environment. One of the difficulties of explaining the large quantities of chamosite that occur in such formations as the Northampton sand ironstone has been the lack of sufficient iron solution in sea water. TAYLOR (1949, p. 80) has discussed the various theories of transportation of iron into the basin in which the Northampton sand ironstone was formed. The association of chamosite with siderite indicates a definite environment limited by a pH of 7·0 to 8·0 and Eh of +0·05 to −0·10 V, but probably mainly below the zero Eh line (organic matter fence) as shown by KRUMBEIN and GARRELS (1952, Fig. 8, p. 26). In this field chamosite and siderite coexist; the presence of a small quantity of pyrite indicates the lower part of this field. HALLIMOND (1925, p. 98) regards chamosite as a result of the interaction of clay and ferrous iron. The clay derived from the weathering and erosion of land surface can carry with it sufficient iron to provide the iron in the chamosite which has subsequently developed in a shallow marine environment. For example, the kaolinite (fraction $<2\ \mu$) used in the experiments described in this paper has 15 per cent free iron oxide attached to the outside of the particles. This is equal to 336 lb ferric oxide in 13 ft^3 (1 ton) or in 52 ft^3 of soil, assuming that the soil contains 25 per cent clay. In the experiment with bacteria in sea-water ferric iron was changed to ferrous at +0·055, which is just on the lower edge of the stability field for hematite. Further evidence is provided by the ironstone mineralogy. The presence of both siderite and pyrite indicates that probably the condition under which the change from ferric to ferrous took place was more nearly like that of black mud with much bacterial activity to keep the Eh low. Experiments with fresh water and with a black sulphide inoculant show that in minerals such as nontronite the ferric iron will change to ferrous iron in conditions with a higher Eh in the presence of organic acids. Kaolinite present in the ironstones may be evidence that this mineral acted as a carrier of iron and that it is residual; further evidence is the fact that the chamosite is the kaolinitic type (BRINDLEY, 1951, p. 520), the structure being a disordered one such as is very often found in soil clays. Further information given by YOUELL (1955) indicates that there is a range in the disorder of the chamosite lattice. Another piece of evidence suggested by TAYLOR (1949, p. 80) is that the climate of the land surrounding the depositional basin was warm and humid with abundant vegetation. Such a climate at the present time would have deep reddish-brown to red kaolinitic or halloysitic soils with abundant ferric oxide films on the clay particles and would be similar to those described by FRIPIAT and GASTUCHE (1952) or by MOHR and VAN BAREN (1954).

The glauconite environment. Hendricks and Ross (1941) have reviewed the literature on glauconite formation. Glauconite has formed from muds—its immediate parent material—that are associated with decaying organic matter and pyrite or marcasite, or both. This observed association brings glauconite into the same stability field as chamosite, but rather lower than the position shown by KRUMBEIN and GARRELS (1952, Fig. 3, p. 26) because of the very common association with pyrite. The pH will be between 7·0 and 8·0 and the Eh near −0·20 V. The constancy of the magnesium content in glauconites from many localities is an important indicator of uniformity of environment (sea-water). It was noted in an earlier section of this paper that soaking of montmorillonite in sea water causes a rearrangement of the proportions of the exchangeable cations as reported by KELLEY and LIEBIG (1934). HENDRICKS and ROSS (1941) reported a similar increase in magnesium in a montmorillonite that had developed from volcanic ash in a marine environment. It is suspected that for hydrous mica a similar rearrangement may also take place.

The shallow-water marine environment with restricted circulation and abundant organic matter for bacterial activity, similar to that described in the experiment, could very well be the natural habitat for glauconite formation. The clay minerals entering such an environment from land masses in temperate climates would be hydrous mica and degraded chloritic and vermiculitic minerals rather than kaolinite or halloysite. The Wadden Sea clays, for example, consist of 80 per cent or more of hydrous mica (FAVEJEE, 1951, p. 140). Both ferric and ferrous iron are present in the octahedral layer of glauconite. Experiments with nontronite have shown that under reducing conditions part of the ferric iron will change to the ferrous state. In nontronite allowed to remain only a short time in reducing conditions, most of the ferrous iron reverts back to the ferric state when the mineral is placed in oxidizing conditions, but less reversion may occur if the reducing conditions continue for long periods of time, i.e. the clay mineral lattice may become stable in its environment. The weathering product of both chamosite (TAYLOR, 1949, p. 53) and glauconite (COLE, 1941, p. 242) is a ferric oxide which has been referred to as limonite, but the change to limonite is a very slow one. This suggests that beds of chamosite and of glauconite have been under reducing conditions for very long periods of time; during that time reducing conditions must have been maintained by bacterial action because sea-water is oxidizing, and mineralogical changes would take place. The non-removal of iron from these environments is probably due to several factors, among which are: reducing conditions maintain the iron in a ferrous condition which is nevertheless still closely associated with the clay mineral to which it was originally attached, either as a film of ferric oxide or as a part of the mineral lattice as in nontronite; slow sedimentation of new material would not change conditions from reducing to oxidizing; low solubility of ferrous and ferric hydroxide in sea-water would prevent removal of iron from its site of deposition. The total quantity of iron in true solution in sea-water after equilibrium has been obtained is not more than 4×10^{-7} mg Fe/m^3 at pH 8·0 (COOPER, 1938, p. 306). Ferrous hydroxide is soluble to $10^{-2 \cdot 7}$ moles/l. at the same pH.

In many publications the importance of iron-reducing or sulphate-reducing bacteria has been discussed, and it is true that such bacteria do have important effects on the precipitation of ferric hydroxide or of iron sulphides. However, the effect of both aerobic and anaerobic bacteria of many kinds is to produce reducing conditions in the cultures, and presumably also in the natural environments in which they grow (HEWITT, 1950, p. 98 *et seq.*). The reduction (lowering of Eh) is caused by the metabolism of the bacteria, which requires the oxidation of the nutrient material available to produce energy for growth. Each type of bacterium will have optimum pH conditions for growth. The range of Eh produced by the activities of aerobic bacteria is about +0·4 to −0·2 V; that for the anaerobic bacteria is about +0·5 to −0·4 V (HEWITT, 1950, p. 117). The nutrient material in cultures or in natural environments causes variations in the Eh conditions. HEWITT

(1950, p. 120) discusses the effect of glucose, which is often used in bacterial cultures and has a reducing effect that alone would be sufficient to reduce Fe^{3+} to Fe^{2+} without any bacterial activity; it therefore should not be used in experiments with ferric iron without due recognition of its reducing capacity.

Experiments in the bacterial reduction of iron should be interpreted with caution; the reduction is a side-effect of the growth of the bacteria and not a consequence of any particular species of bacteria.

THEIL (1927) noted that bacteria, through their metabolic processes, can also affect clay minerals by causing solubility of alumina and silica. He found that five times as much alumina was removed by solutions in which bacteria were actively growing as by sterile solutions. In the experiments described here, alumina was removed from nontronite in a similar manner.

CONCLUSIONS

The association of iron with clay minerals is an important means whereby iron is transported by rivers to a site of deposition either in freshwater lakes or in marine environments. The free iron oxide films on minerals such as kaolinite and halloysite account for the addition of considerable quantities of ferric oxide to a sedimentary basin, and the iron content of clay minerals in which iron has a position in the lattice also contributes. The free iron oxide films can be removed by lowering the redox potential through the metabolic processes of bacterial growth in culture media supplied with nutrients. In natural environments the nutrients are supplied by organic matter growing and decaying *in situ* or transported into the sedimentation area.

Reducing conditions influence ferric iron in the lattice of nontronite, changing it partly to the ferrous form; on return to oxidizing conditions the ferrous iron changes back to the ferric state though the reversion may not be complete. Reduction and oxidation may be an important means of clay mineral change in such minerals as montmorillonite and hydrous micas. Sea-water causes a change in the proportion of exchangeable cations in montmorillonite and may well do so in other clay minerals.

Iron oxide films on clay particles as well as iron within the lattices form the source of much of the iron deposited as amorphous ferrous sulphide in restricted marine environments in which black muds develop. Black ferrous oxide may accompany the amorphous ferrous sulphide; the black material remains attached to the clay mineral particles and reverts to ferric oxide if the Eh is raised. This was observed in the laboratory but also occurs in natural situations if black muds of this type are exposed to the air.

Bacterial activity seems to be necessary to maintain reducing environments such as those in which chamosite and glauconite are believed to form; also in this category are the iron sulphides that occur as thin layers in shales like the Kupferschiefer, as suggested by EDWARDS (1956, p. 106).

The experiments described here suggest a number of points that should be investigated. Among these are: changes in the proportion of exchangeable cations in various clay minerals soaked in sea-water; solubility of clay minerals in sea-water with varying redox potentials; influence of structure on stability in sea-water; removal of silica and alumina from clay minerals soaked in sea-water for varying periods of time; effects of any of these treatments on the structure of the clay mineral lattices.

Acknowledgement—Members of the sedimentary petrology laboratory of the U.S. Geological Survey helped with various aspects of the experiments described here: J. C. HATHAWAY made X-ray and electron micrographic examinations of the clay minerals and supplied the black muck from Martha's Vineyard; H. C. STARKEY made pH and Eh readings while the author was away for a few days; G. W. CHLOE prepared the clay samples and assisted with the ion-exchange determinations; P. D. BLACKMON advised concerning the use of calcareous mud from the Great Bahama Bank as a source of bacteria. The sea-water used was collected by P. E. CLOUD, Jr., for use in these and other experiments.

References

Brindley G. W. (1951) The crystal structure of some chamosite minerals. *Miner. Mag.* **29,** 57–70.

Castano J. R. and Garrels R. M. (1950) Experiments on the deposition of iron with special reference to the Clinton iron ore deposits. *Econ. Geol.* **45,** 755–770.

Cole W. F. (1941) X-ray analysis (by the powder method) and microscopic examination of the products of weathering of the Gingin upper greensand. *J. Roy. Soc. W. Aust.* **27,** 229–307.

Cooper L. H. N. (1937–38) Some conditions governing the solubility of iron. *Proc. Roy. Soc.* B, **24,** 299–307.

Edwards A. B. (1956) The present state of knowledge and theories of ore genesis. *Proc. Aust. Inst. Min Engrs.* **177,** 69–116.

Edwards A. B. and Baker G. (1951) Some occurrences of supergene iron sulphides in relation to their environments of deposition. *J. Sediment Petrol.* **21,** 34–46.

Favejee J. C. L. (1951) The origin of the "Wadden" mud: *Meded. LandbHoogesch., Wageningen* **51,** 5, 113–141.

Fripiat J. J. and Gastuche M. C. (1952) Etude physico-chimique des surfaces des argiles. Les combinaisons de la kaolinite avec les oxydes der fer trivalent (Series scientifique no. 54) p. 60. INEAC.

Grim, R. E. (1951) The depositional environment of red and green shales. *J. Sediment. Petrol.* **21,** 226–232.

Grim R. E. and Rowland R. A. (1942) Differential thermal analysis of clay minerals and other hydrous materials. *Amer. Min.* **27,** 746–761.

Hallimond A. F. (1925) Iron ores: Bedded ores of England and Wales: Petrography and Chemistry. *Spec. Report on Mineral Resources Great Britain Mem. Geol. Surv. U. K.,* **29,** 139.

Hendricks S. B. and Ross C. S. (1941) Chemical composition and genesis of glauconite and celadonite. *Amer. Min.* **26,** 683–708.

Hewitt L. F. (1950) *Oxidation-reduction potentials in bacteriology and biochemistry,* (6th Ed) p. 215. E. & S. Livingstone, Edinburgh.

Huber N. K. and Garrels R. M. (1953) Relation of pH and oxidation potential to sedimentary iron mineral formation. *Econ. Geol.* **48,** 337–357.

Kelley W. P. and Liebig G. F. (1934) Base exchange in relation to composition of clay with special reference to effect of sea-water. *Bull. Amer. Ass. Petrol. Geol.* **18,** 358–367.

Krumbein W. C. and Garrels R. M. (1952) Origin and classification of chemical sediments in terms of pH and oxidation-reduction potentials. *J. Geol.* **60,** 1–33.

Mohr E. C. J. and van Baren F. A. (1954) *Tropical Soils,* p. 498. Interscience, New York.

Starkey R. L. and Halvorson H. O. (1927) Studies on the transformations of iron in nature—II: Concerning the importance of micro-organisms in the solution and precipitation of iron. *Soil Sci.* **24,** 381–401.

Taylor J. H. (1949) Petrology of the Northampton sand ironstone formation. *Mem. Geol. Surv. U.K.*

Theil G. A. (1927) The enrichment of bauxite deposits through the activity of micro-organisms. *Econ. Geol.* **22,** 480–493.

Youell R. F. (1955) Mineralogy and crystal structure of chamosite. *Nature, Lond.* **176,** 560–561.

10

Reprinted from *Applied Capillary Microscopy: The Role of Microorganisms in the Formation of Iron–Manganese Deposits,* B. V. Perfil'Ev et al., eds., Consultants Bureau, New York, 1965, pp. 88–105

THE FORMATION OF MANGANESE-IRON LAYERS IN MUD AS A BIOGENIC PROCESS

D. R. Gabe, É. P. Troshanov, and É. É. Sherman

In geological literature the formation of iron-manganese deposits in waters is usually regarded as a purely physicochemical phenomenon. According to the prevalent view in geology, iron and manganese dissolved in feeder waters entering lakes or seas with higher pH are oxidized and precipitated in the form of hydroxide deposits (Pustovalov [1940]; Kazakov, Sokolova, Vainshtein [1957]; Listova [1961]; etc.). Only an indirect role in this process is attributed to the microflora. For instance, as Krotov [1950, 1951] reports, in the "bloom" period the planktonic algae use up the carbon dioxide, thus increasing the pH of the water and causing the precipitation of the Mn and Fe dissolved in it. According to Strakhov [1954, 1956, 1957a, 1957b], these two elements are carried mainly in the oxidized form, as a suspension, into the water by feeder waters. They are deposited on the bottom (stage of sedimentogenesis) and enter a reduced milieu created by the vital activity of an abundant and diverse microflora. In these conditions the oxidized forms of manganese and iron are reduced. Though recognizing the role of bacteria in diagenetic transformations, Strakhov [1947, 1956, 1957a, 1957b] treated the deposition of Mn and Fe oxides as a purely physicochemical process: "In the mud solution all these almost insoluble compounds are in the state of saturated solutions, from which authigenic diagenetic minerals are formed by purely chemical means. Direct biological extraction of substances from solution, a process which plays such an important role in the precipitation of many components from the water mass, does not occur at all in the formation of minerals in the deposit (in diagenesis)" (Strakhov [1957b], p.161). In other words, biocatalysts in the form of specific microorganisms are not required for the precipitation of manganese and iron from a mud solution saturated with them, since at the high oxidation potential characteristic of the upper layer of bottom deposits the lower oxide forms of Mn and Fe are precipitated from solution by autoxidation, i.e., spontaneous oxidation at normal temperature, without the participation of extraneous energy.

As Perfil'ev [1932, 1952] showed, the diagenesis of bottom deposits with the redistribution and concentration of manganese and iron oxides in the form of visually distinct layers can be reproduced in laboratory conditions. Thoroughly mixed mud installed even in a small glass vessel, such as a tea glass, becomes distinctly stratified after some time. This new structure is the secondary diagenetic microzonal profile, which is characterized by a pronounced vertical differentiation of the redox potential (Eh) in a thin (4-5 cm) layer of mud.

The top layer (8-12 mm) is distinguished by a high Eh (500-800 mV), while the underlying layer of mud is characterized by pronounced reducing conditions: The dissolved oxygen content usually drops to zero (Rabinovich, Gal'perina, Sapotnitskii [1964]; Rabinovich and Sherman [1964]) and the Eh becomes negative or close to zero (Gabe and Rabinovich [1964]). The situation is fundamentally similar to that directly observed in the mud of some lakes with iron-manganese deposits (Semenovich [1958]; Sokolova [1962] – for Punnus-Yarvi; Kuznetsov [1938] – for Gabozero). As Strakhov [1956, 1957b] indicates, a pronounced difference in the oxidation-reduction properties of the water and the bottom is characteristic of all bodies of water.

An investigation of the new manganese-iron microbe Metallogenium personatum (first discovered by Perfil'ev [1937, 1952] and fully described by Perfil'ev and Gabe [1961, 1964]) in the secondary microzonal profile is of particular importance for a conclusive answer to the question of the role of microbes in ore formation.

Formation of Manganese–Iron Layers in Mud as a Biogenic Process

The structure of this microbe, its developmental cycle, the chemical composition of its deposits, and the physicochemical conditions of its habitat have been discussed in other papers in this collection – those of Perfil'ev and Gabe, Shapiro, and Gabe and Rabinovich. Here we will discuss only one question: Is the concentration of manganese and iron in mud actually due to the vital activity of Metallogenium and similar microbes, or should the process be regarded as abiogenic?

We must point out that it is not always possible, even when Metallogenium is abundant, to distinguish a layer enriched with deposits of this microbe in the oxidizing mud horizon, which also contains manganese oxides formed by autoxidation. If Metallogenium is gradually displaced during the formation of the mud, then the bulk of the manganese deposited by it in the course of several years will be scattered throughout the oxidized horizon and it will be impossible to separate the product of biogenic oxidation from the product of autoxidation.

In certain conditions, however, the Metallogenium microzone is fairly distinctly demarcated above and, particularly, below. In this case stratification of the mud develops in the following way. Soon after the thoroughly pale brown mud has been put into the glass, the upper 3- to 5-mm thick layer becomes darker owing to the precipitation of manganese oxides from the solution. No Metallogenium or similar manganese-oxidizing microbes are found in this layer. Hence, in this case the deposition of manganese must be regarded as an abiogenic process: Owing to the penetration of oxygen into the mud the Eh of the top layer is greatly increased and the manganese in the oxidizing horizon is precipitated from the mud solution and imparts a darker hue to the mud. After 2-3 months a blackish-brown or almost black layer begins to form at the lower boundary of the oxidizing horizon. This layer may descend a little by accretion on the underside and can be found at a depth of 8-10 mm from the mud surface. At first the layer is very thin and discontinuous, but its separate parts gradually merge into one another and the layer becomes thicker and darker, sometimes black, frequently with a metallic sheen. A microscopic examination of this horizon in peloscopes invariably reveals the development of an abundant enrichment culture of Metallogenium, usually in the trichospherical stage (Perfil'ev and Gabe [1961]). In the course of 2-3 years the black layer formed by Metallogenium can attain a thickness of 3-4 mm. It also becomes much more compact than the rest of the mud owing to cementation by the deposits of the microbe. The reducing horizon of the mud during the formation of the profile becomes appreciably lighter in color, since the manganese contained in it enriches the mud in the microzone of development of Metallogenium. This is illustrated by the diagram in Fig. 1.

If Metallogenium develops as described above, then it becomes possible not only to detect the redistribution of manganese in the mud profile between the reducing and oxidizing horizons, but also to distinguish in the oxidizing horizon the upper part of the microzone, paler and loose, containing mainly the autoxidation

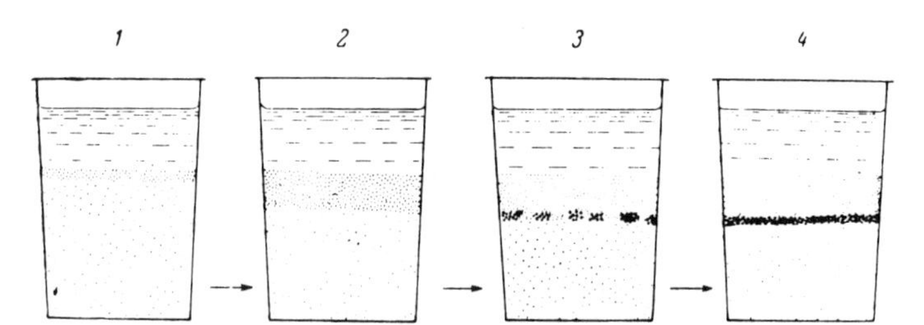

Fig. 1. Diagram of formation of Metallogenium microzone in the development of the secondary microzonal profile. 1) Start of formation of oxidation microzone due to autoxidation; 2) increase in thickness of oxidizing horizon due to penetration of atmospheric oxygen into mud; 3) start of formation of Metallogenium microzone in lower part of oxidizing horizon; 4) formation of continuous manganese-iron layer as a result of oxidizing activity of Metallogenium.

product, and the underlying compact black layer formed mainly by Metallogenium deposits.

Redistribution of Mn and Fe in the Process of Diagenesis in the Secondary Profile of Ore-Bearing Mud

Mud samples taken with a drag from the ore field in Lake Ukshezero and freed from concretions by sieving were put into vessels (tea glasses). Sixteen glasses (5118-5133) altogether were set up. In all the glasses the mud profile developed in the way described above.

To determine the manganese and iron content of three horizons of the diagenetic mud profile [the upper brown oxidized layer (OH), the blackish-brown Metallogenium microzone (MM), and the pale brown reducing horizon (RH)] we selected at first five vessels with distinct stratification (5119, 5121, 5129, 5131, 5133). Later, after 8 months, we tested another three vessels with mud of similar composition (5126, 5127, 5128).

We took a core sample from each glass by the following method. The water was carefully drawn out of the glass with a pipet. A thin-walled stainless-steel tube (wall thickness 0.2 mm) with an internal diameter of 18 mm was pushed vertically into the mud. If the top end of the tube after immersion in the mud was tightly sealed with the palm, then a mud core remained inside the tube when the latter was withdrawn from the glass. If the tube was then held at an angle over a white glass plate and the top end opened a little, the core slid out of it and lay on the surface of the glass with its stratification undisturbed. The Metallogenium microzone was then carefully removed from the core with a knife, the top layer was separated, and part of the lower region of the core was cut off. The three samples (from the top layer of the oxidizing horizon, from the Metallogenium microzone, and from the reducing horizon) were put into three bottles and were subsequently used for the chemical analyses. At the same time we withdrew slit peloscopes with Metallogenium microaccretions from the glasses. The strips were examined under microscope, dried to constant weight, and in the coating formed by this microorganism we determined the content of manganese (di-, tri-, and tetravalent, separately) and iron (see below, Table 4).

Each of the mud samples, dried to constant weight, was separated into four parts. The first two parts were used for repeated separate determinations of manganese of different valence. From the other two parts of the sample we made repeated determinations of the total manganese and total iron.

For the separate determination of manganese of different valence we used the method proposed by Lavrukhina [1949], which is as follows: A 25-100 mg portion of the mud sample dried to constant weight at 105° C was put into an Erlenmeyer flask, to which 20 ml of 6 N ammonium sulfate solution was added. The mixture was mixed for 20-25 min on a boiling water bath. The solution was then filtered through a Gooch No. 4 filter, and the deposit on the filter was washed several times with distilled water. The Mn^{+2} content of the filtrate was determined by the persulfate method. For this purpose the filtrate was transferred to a 150-ml conical flask, to which 10 ml of nitric acid (1:5), 10 ml of 0.5% $AgNO_3$, and 10 ml of 20% $(NH_4)_2S_2O_8$ were added. The solution was boiled on a water bath for not less than 1 min and was then cooled under a stream of water. When the sample contained divalent manganese (which is oxidized by ammonium persulfate to the heptavalent form) the solution became colored after heating. The colored solution was transferred to a measuring flask, diluted to the mark with water containing no reductants and the concentration of divalent manganese ions introduced with the sample was determined on a colorimeter. For this purpose we used a FEK-M photoelectric colorimeter, usually with a 20-mm cuvette (occasionally 30-mm and 50-mm cuvettes) and a green filter.

To extract Mn^2O^3 from the sample we treated the deposit on the filter for 1 h at 70-75° in a thermostat with a solution containing 15 g of metaphosphoric acid in 100 ml of concentrated H^2SO^4. The deposit was then washed several times with small batches of a 25% solution of H^2SO^4. The Mn_{3+} content in the filtrate was determined by the persulfate method, as described above for divalent manganese.

From the deposit left on the filter after this we extracted Mn_{4+} by treatment with a mixture of 0.1 N $Na_2C_2O_4$ solution (10 ml) and a 25% H_2SO_4 solution (10 ml). Solution was effected at 70° C in a thermostat for 1-1.5 h. In the solution filtered through a Gooch No. 4 filter and washed with several batches of hot distilled water we determined the Mn^{4+} content, also by the persulfate method, on the photoelectric colorimeter.

Formation of Manganese–Iron Layers in Mud as a Biogenic Process

In a separate dry weighed batch of the same sample we determined the total manganese and iron content. For this purpose we first prepared a hydrochloric acid extract of the batch. Since Cl^- ions prevent the use of the persulfate method, we had to replace the hydrochloric acid in the extract by nitric acid to determine the total manganese. To avoid the laborious and inconvenient operation of evaporation we subsequently obtained the extract by using the same solvent which we used to extract tetravalent manganese, i.e., we treated the batch with a mixture of 0.1 N $Na_2C_2O_4$ solution and 25% H_2SO_4 solution or with a mixture of concentrated H_2SO_4 and H_3PO_4 (Ponomarev [1955]). The greater part of the solution was used for the determination of the concentration of total manganese by the persulfate method. In 1-3 ml of this solution we determined the content of iron in trivalent form by means of sulfosalicylic acid. For this purpose we put the solution for the Fe determination into a 50-ml measuring flask, added 5 ml of sulfosalicylic acid (10 g of acid and 18-20 g of urotropin were dissolved in water and brought to 100 ml). To the colored solution we added acetate buffer, pH = 5.2 (100 ml of 6 N HCl solution and 380 ml of 50% CH_3COONa solution) with a slight excess after change of color, topped the solution up to the mark with distilled water and after 10 min we measured it with a colorimeter in conjunction with a blue filter (Babko and Pilipenko [1951]; Shidlovskaya-Ovchinnikova [1955]).

The results of chemical determinations of the manganese and iron content in the three horizons of the mud profile are given in Table 1.

For greater clarity the figures indicating the distribution of Mn and Fe in the horizons of the mud profile are presented in the form of a graph (Fig. 2). The manganese content, determined as a percentage of the dry weight of the mud from the analysis for total Mn, is represented by the blank columns; the three thin black columns inside the latter represent the percentage content of the three forms (di-, tri-, and tetravalent) found by separate determination by Lavrukhina's method [1949].

TABLE 1. Mn and Fe Content (as % of Dry Weight) of Different Horizons of Mud Profile With a Metallogenium Microzone

No. of vessel	Time of development of microzonal profile	Horizon of mud profile	Thickness of layer (mm)	No. of sample	From separate determinations				Total Mn	Total Fe
					Mn^{2+}	Mn^{3+}	Mn^{4+}	Total		
5121	3 yr	OH	7	26	0.32	1.87	0.52	2.71	2.60	5.38
		MM	4	27	0.61	4.57	0.63	5.81	6.85	5.76
		RH	35	28	0.49	1.01	0.64	2.15	2.21	6.56
5119	3 yr	OH	9	29	0.31	1.79	0.44	2.54	2.75	3.50
		MM	3	30	0.61	3.98	1.79	6.38	6.38	5.45
		RH	32	31	0.33	1.05	0.48	1.86	2.19	6.39
5133	3 yr	OH	9	32	0.33	1.31	0.49	2.13	1.97	6.10
		MM	3	33	0.61	4.29	1.30	6.00	5.78	6.77
		RH	40	34	0.60	0.38	0.19	1.17	1.10	6.39
5131	3 yr	OH	10	42	0.24	1.36	0.19	1.80	1.74	5.65
		MM	2.7	43	0.52	4.95	0.37	5.84	5.98	5.51
		RH	34	44	0.74	0.44	0.13	1.31	1.40	6.09
5129	3 yr	OH	8.5	45	0.25	1.21	0.31	1.77	1.83	2.50
		MM	3	46	0.42	5.43	0.59	6.44	6.21	2.20
		RH	39	47	0.46	0.38	0.20	1.04	1.26	4.70
5127	3 yr 8 mo	OH	10	69	0.42	2.56	0.11	3.09	3.91	8.71
		MM	3	70	0.08	9.01	0.83	9.92	9.97	10.21
		RH	32	71	0.54	1.13	0.23	1.90	2.07	10.72
5128	3 yr 8 mo	OH	10	72	0.90	3.00	0.42	4.32	5.46	8.48
		MM	2	73	1.30	5.90	0.22	7.42	9.14	9.26
		RH	40	74	0.85	0.47	0.52	1.84	2.06	9.15
5126	3 yr 8 mo	OH	9	75	0.73	3.50	0.64	4.86	5.08	7.63
		MM	3	76	0.86	9.00	0.41	10.27	10.47	8.39
		RH	24	77	0.80	1.06	0.20	2.07	1.79	7.80

NOTE. OH – upper layer of oxidizing horizon of mud profile; MM – *Metallogenium* microzone; RH – reducing horizon.

The dotted columns illustrate the distribution of total iron in the same three horizons of the mud profile in the same vessels. As in the case of manganese, the amount of iron is expressed as a percentage of the dry weight.

Since the manganese and iron in the mud are mainly in the form of oxides, Table 2 shows the content of both elements in oxides converted to trivalent manganese (Mn_2O_3) and trivalent iron (Fe_2O_3). For manganese oxides we took the percentage amount of total manganese as the initial value (see Table 1, column "Total Mn").

For the muds considered here, which are distinguished by the abundant microzonal development of the manganese-iron microbe Metallogenium in radial-lobate and round-lumpy colonies and the almost complete absence of iron-oxidizing bacteria, there is a fairly regular pattern in the distribution of manganese and iron in the horizons of the diagenetic mud profile.

As regards manganese, the lowest amount was found in the reducing horizon (RH) in all vessels. In this case it consisted mainly of divalent manganese, as is clearly seen in the case of vessels 5128, 5129, 5131, 5133.

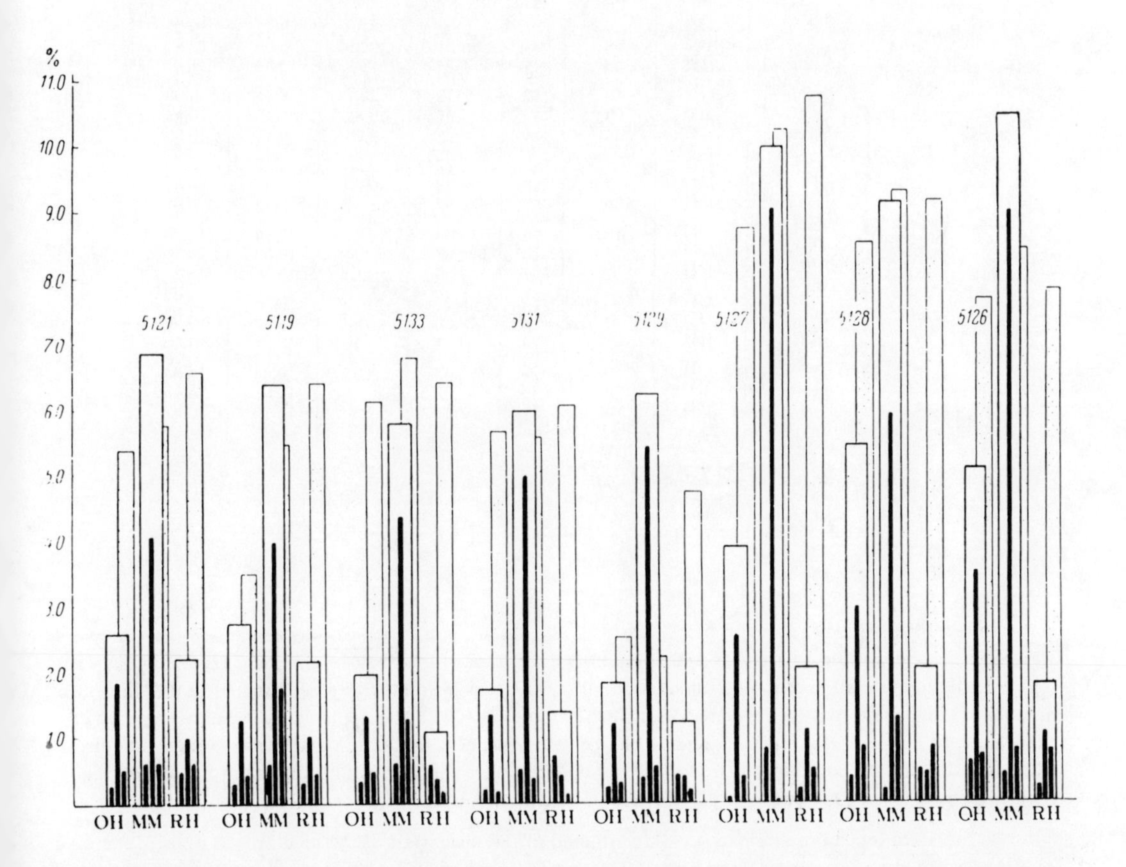

Fig. 2. Distribution of Mn and Fe in horizons of secondary microzonal mud profile from Lake Ukshezero. For each of the eight vessels with mud the columns of different height represent: total Mn from a gross determination (blank columns); amount of Mn from separate determinations (thin black columns: left – divalent, middle – trivalent, right – tetravalent); Fe content (dotted columns); the amounts of the two elements are expressed as a percentage of the dry weight of mud in the three horizons of the profile: OH – upper layer of oxidizing horizon, MM – Metallogenium microzone, RH – reducing horizon. Figures at top of columns indicate number of vessel.

TABLE 2. Amounts of Mn and Fe Oxides in Different Horizons of a Mud Profile with a Metallogenium Microzone

No. of vessel	Time of development of microzonal profile	Horizon of mud profile	Thickness of layer (mm)	No. of sample	Mn_2O_3		Fe_2O_3	
					as % of dry weight of mud	as % of dry weight of mud without oxides*	as % of dry weight of mud	as % of dry weight of mud without oxides*
5121	3 yr	OH	7	26	4.24	4.81	7.61	8.64
		MM	4	27	11.11	13.80	8.59	10.43
		RH	35	28	3.33	3.77	8.17	9.24
5119	3 yr	OH	9	29	4.83	5.37	5.19	5.76
		MM	3	30	9.57	11.57	7.66	9.25
		RH	32	31	3.05	3.30	8.95	9.68
5133	3 yr	OH	9	32	3.03	3.42	8.22	9.26
		MM	3	33	9.51	12.39	9.68	12.84
		RH	40	34	1.22	1.38	10.59	11.67
5131	3 yr	OH	10	42	2.73	3.07	8.11	9.09
		MM	3	43	8.97	10.82	8.15	9.84
		RH	34	44	2.21	2.49	9.13	10.30
5129	3 yr	OH	8.5	45	2.77	2.96	3.54	3.78
		MM	3.0	46	8.98	10.23	3.37	3.85
		RH	39	47	1.92	2.09	6.37	6.95
5127	3 yr 8 mo	OH	10	69	5.63	6.87	12.44	15.20
		MM	3	70	14.28	20.20	14.58	20.60
		RH	32	71	2.96	3.66	15.31	18.78
5128	3 yr 8 mo	OH	10	72	8.12	10.20	12.20	15.22
		MM †	2	73	13.66	18.82	13.72	18.90
		RH	40	74	3.11	3.46	12.27	14.47
5126	3 yr 8 mo	OH	9	75	7.32	8.96	10.94	13.35
		MM	3	76	15.06	20.66	12.01	16.49
		RH	24	77	2.48	2.89	11.16	12.92

* A calculation of the amount of Mn and Fe oxides as a percentage of the weight of the insoluble part of the sample illustrates more clearly the concentrating activity of microorganisms, since the latter deposit these compounds as a result of development in the form of microaccretions on the surface of the insoluble particles of mud.

† The MM horizon was loose and was not clearly demarcated from the OH horizon.

In the upper oxidized layer of mud (layer OH), in which Metallogenium was absent and the manganese was completely deposited, mainly by autoxidation, by the time of the analyses the manganese content was only a little higher than in the reducing horizon. The trivalent form clearly predominated in this case. The amount of manganese slightly increased with time (samples 69-77). The appreciably increased amount of manganese in the case of samples 72 and 75 can be attributed also to the fact that in the cores from vessels 5129 and 5128 we did not manage to separate the oxidizing horizon sufficiently well from the underlying Metallogenium microzone owing to the absence of a distinct boundary between them.

In the Metallogenium microzone (MM), situated in the lower part of the oxidizing horizon of the mud profile, the amount of manganese was greatly increased and, as can be seen from a comparison of samples taken at intervals of 8 months (samples 26-34, 42-47, and 69-77), the manganese gradually accumulated in the course of 3-4 years. Concentration of manganese in the Metallogenium microzone continued in subsequent years, too (Table 3).

The separate analysis showed that in the Metallogenium microzone the manganese was concentrated mainly in the trivalent form, whereas the amounts of di- and tetravalent forms were approximately the same as in the oxidizing horizon (OH).

TABLE 3. Concentration of Mn in the Metallogenium Microzone

No. of vessel	Mn (as % of dry weight) at different times of development of ***Metallogenium*** microzone		
	3 yr	5 yr	6 yr 6 mo
5119	6.8	8.1	—
5131	6.0	9.7	—
5129	6.2	—	9.2
5133	5.8	—	10.0

In view of the discussed results we can suggest the following mechanism of redistribution of Mn during the formation of the sediment.

In the reducing horizon of the mud profile manganese passes into the mud solution. At the low redox potential and, as we will see later, under the influence of the reducing activity of microorganisms the manganese is gradually reduced and converted into its much more soluble divalent form. The relative amount of the latter in the deposit is appreciably increased in a number of cases (see the reducing horizon in vessels 5133, 5131, 5129, and 5128 in Fig. 2).

Divalent manganese which has passed into solution in the reducing horizon apparently diffuses only in small amounts into the upper layer of mud – the oxidizing horizon (OH) – and there, being oxidized by atmospheric oxygen, is converted to a deposit. The bulk of the dissolved divalent manganese, extracted from the deposit in the reducing horizon of the mud, is intercepted by the manganese-oxidizing microbe Metallogenium which utilizes it as an energy source and deposits it mainly in the trivalent form. When highly concentrated, the manganese deposits impart an almost black color, sometimes with a metallic sheen, to the mud in the microzone of development of this microbe. As an analysis of purely biogenic deposits formed by Metallogenium in peloscopes showed (Shapiro [1964]; see also Table 4 in our paper), this microbe can oxidize manganese preferentially and, apparently, only to the trivalent state. The appearance of a large amount of iron oxides in the microaccretions indicates the simultaneous development of an iron-oxidizing microorganism, usually of the Siderococcus type (Table 4, vessel 5135), in the microzone. This is why manganese, mainly trivalent, predominates in the Metallogenium microzone in the mud profile. Thus, this element is concentrated principally in the trivalent form in the mud and mainly as a result of the vital activity of certain manganese-oxidizing microbes in the microzone of their development.

TABLE 4. Amounts of Mn of Different Valence and Fe in Biogenic Deposits Formed in Peloscopes (Mud from Lake Ukshezero)

No. of vessel	Nature of microaccretions in peloscopes	Time of development (mo)	From data of separate analyses				From data of total analysis		
			Ratio of oxides of different valence (as % of sum)			Total Mn oxides (γ)	Ratio of Mn and Fe oxides (as % of sum)		Sum of Mn and Fe (γ)
			MnO	Mn_2O_3	MnO_2		Mn_2O_3	Fe_2O_3	
5118	Peloscopes with abundant black *Metallogenium* accretions	39	14.5	85.5	0	1030	100.0	0	1214
5119	" "	21	3.2	95.4	1.4	391	89.9	10.1	668
5120	" "	30	17.9	82.1	0	647	100.0	0	669
5121	" "	21	7.0	77.7	15.3	601	81.3	18.7	690
5125	" "	35	8.9	91.1	0	481	100.0	0	774
5127	" "	35	13.3	67.0	19.7	922	67.5	32.5	1257
5133	" "	21	12.3	79.9	7.8	512	98.1	1.9	481
5129	Peloscopes with less abundant black *Metallogenium* accretions.	24	3.9	96.1	0	573	100.0	0	144
5131	" "	24	4.4	92.3	3.3	584	100.0	0	273
5135	Abundant development of *Siderococcus* along with *Metallogenium* in peloscopes	25	No analysis performed				10.8	82.2	669
							17.1	82.9	429

Formation of Manganese–Iron Layers in Mud as a Biogenic Process

As Vinogradov [1957] reported, in soils with pH 6-7.5 a large proportion of the manganese is also in the trivalent state, usually in the form of $Mn_2O_3 \cdot nH_2O$, since in a neutral medium open to oxygen Mn^{3+} is the first product of Mn^{2+} oxidation. In Mann and Quastel's opinion [1946], in the oxidation-reduction cycle of manganese in soils the $Mn^{2+} \rightleftharpoons Mn^{3+}$ transformation involves the participation of microorganisms.

Our picture of the mechanism of manganese redistribution is confirmed by observations on the mud solution, which are described in the next section of the paper. Here we will dwell briefly on the redistribution of iron in the horizons of the microzonal profile.

There is no doubt that iron, like manganese, in mud which has just been installed in glasses, is distributed fairly uniformly throughout the profile. In our mud there was rather more iron (6-10% of dry weight) than manganese (1.5 - 2.0%).

As Table 1 and Fig. 2 show, hardly any iron was concentrated either in the upper layer of the oxidizing horizon (OH) or in the Metallogenium microzone. Moreover, in these two microzones (OH and MM) the amount of iron was sometimes even a little smaller than in the reducing horizon of the mud.

The latter result can be partially attributed to the fact that in the calculation of the Fe content as a percentage of the dry weight of mud in our material we were dealing with a very uneven distribution of manganese in the horizons. But if the accumulation of the two elements was expressed as a percentage of the insoluble part of the mud, i.e., without Mn and Fe oxides (Table 2), then in the majority of vessels we found that Metallogenium had an enriching effect as regards iron, although this action was very weak. This agrees completely with the results of analyses of microaccretions of this microbe (Table 4; Shapiro [1964]).

Yet iron, like manganese, can become highly concentrated in the form of numerous thin yellowish-orange layers in the mud, but this only happens when there is a microzonal development of iron-oxidizing microbes of the Siderococcus or similar types. As an example we can cite data on the distribution of manganese and iron in the secondary microzonal profile in mud from ore-bearing Lake Valk-Yarvi (Karelian Isthmus), which is characterized by the simultaneous presence of the iron-oxidizing microbe Siderococcus and the manganese-oxidizing microbe Metallogenium (Table 5).

A similar observation is reported in Perfil'ev and Gabe's paper [1964] for Lake Gabozero in Karelia, which is also characterized by the simultaneous development of Metallogenium and iron-oxidizing microbes of the Siderococcus type in the mud.

In the above-discussed mud from Lake Ukshezero (Tables 1 and 2) no development of iron-oxidizing microbes was found in the peloscopes. Hence, there was no appreciable microzonal accumulation of iron during the formation of the secondary profile. Figure 3 shows the redistribution of Mn and Fe in the horizons during the formation of the profile of other Ukshezero mud samples, one of which showed the development of Metallogenium alone (vessels 766, 769), and the other showed Siderococcus (vessels 776, 777). While the concentration of manganese in the Metallogenium microzone in the vessels containing this microbe was similar to that observed in the previously discussed muds (Tables 1-3), then in the vessels containing Siderococcus the

TABLE 5. Distribution of Manganese and Iron Oxides in Secondary Microzonal Profile of Mud from Lake Valk-Yarvi

Horizon	No. of sample	Content (% of dry weight)			Remarks
		Mn_2O_3	Fe_2O_3	$Mn_2O_3 + Fe_2O_3$	
Oxidizing horizon	60	0.93	1.90	2.83	
Blackish-brown microzone	61	6.03	3.60	9.63	Abundant development of *Metallogenium*
Orange microzone	62	0.46	8.90	9.36	Abundant development of *Siderococcus*
Reducing horizon	63	0.33	2.71	3.04	

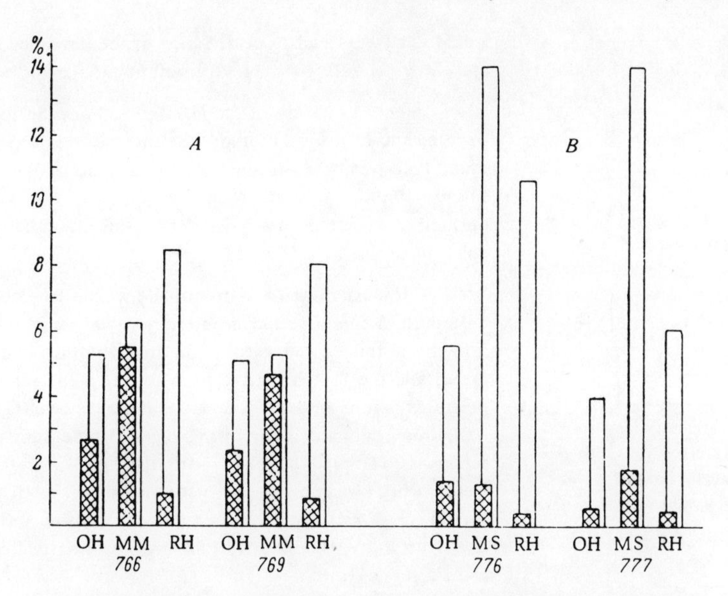

Fig. 3. Redistribution of Mn and Fe during formation of secondary microzonal mud profile (Lake Ukshezero) in relation to nature of oxidizing microflora. A) In muds containing Metallogenium; B) in muds containing the iron-oxidizing microbe Siderococcus. The Mn content of the three horizons of the mud profile is shown by the hatched columns; the Fe content in the same horizons is shown by blank columns; OH – upper layer of oxidizing horizon, MM – Metallogenium microzone, SM – Siderococcus microzone, RH – reducing horizon. The figures under the columns give the numbers of the vessels.

microzone of development of the latter contained a distinct accumulation of iron. Over a period of four years the manganese remained in the initial state, i.e., was distributed relatively uniformly throughout the horizons of the profile. The increased iron content of the reducing horizon of the mud in this case (Fig. 3) was due to the fact that the two mud samples contained large numbers of small concretions, which were displaced into the lower horizon when the mud was put into the vessels. Since the small oolites from Ukshezero consist mainly of iron, then the latter, despite the mixing of the mud sample, was distributed unevenly in the mud profile.

Passage of Manganese and Iron into Solution in the Secondary Microzonal Profile

The redistribution of manganese in the horizons during the formation of the microzonal profile with the participation of manganese-oxidizing microbes can only occur if the manganese in the reducing horizon of the mud is continuously being reduced to the divalent form and passing into solution over a long period. The same applies to iron. As Gabe and Rabinovich's paper [1964] showed, a sufficiently low redox potential to promote such a process is created in the lower horizon of mud in glasses. However, the value of the redox potential can give only a very rough idea of the concentration of Mn^{2+} and Fe^{2+} in the mud. The Mn^{2+} and Fe^{2+} content can be determined more accurately from chemical analyses of the liquid phase of the secondary microzonal mud profile.

This did not present any difficulty for bottom water; a 5-ml sample of water was taken with a graduated pipet or a medical syringe. It was much more difficult to obtain a sample of the mud solution from the reducing horizon for analysis. The generally employed methods of extracting sediment and soil solutions by compression with a powerful press or displacement with another liquid are unsuitable for this purpose. Such methods

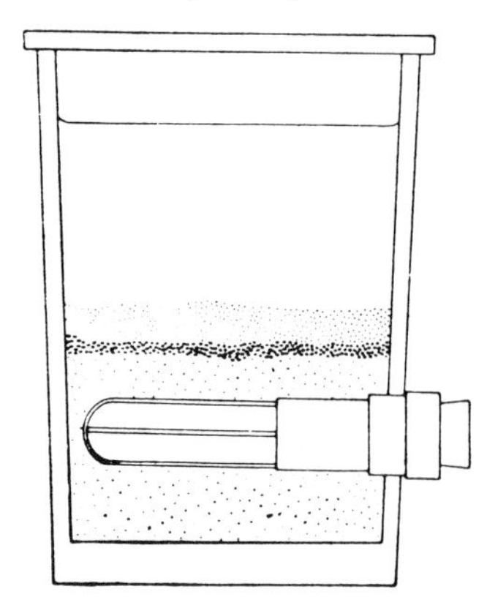

Fig. 4. Vessel with collodion chamber mounted horizontally in wall. The chamber lies in the reducing horizon of the microzonal mud profile.

would certainly lead to disturbance of the developed stratification and the vital activity of the microflora.

Hence, to obtain the mud solution from the reducing horizon we used the following method. Before the mud was put into it, a round hole was bored in the wall of the glass at the level of the future reducing horizon. A collodion chamber, consisting of a collodion sac fitted on a glass frame, was mounted in a horizontal position in this hole (Fig. 4).*

A few punctures could be made with a fine needle in the collodion chamber to speed up the penetration of the mud solution into it. In this case, however, the mud solution frequently became turbid and the sample had to be filtered for the removal of mud particles before analyses. Good results were obtained with intact collodion chambers if they were filled, immediately after each successive sample was taken, with distilled water or with botton water, which was easily done with a syringe. By diffusion of dissolved substances from the mud the water inside the collodion chambers came into equilibrium with the surrounding mud solution after a few days.

To determine divalent Mn and Fe in the mud solution and in the bottom water we used three series of glasses containing muds taken from different points in Lake Ukshezero and differing, in particular, in the manganese content of the initial samples, which was indicative of the nature of the development of the Metallogium microzone. Each series contained five glasses. The mud in glasses 765-769, which was taken directly from the ore field, was richest in manganese (manganese content about 2% of dry weight of the sample). The mud was distinguished by its brown color and contained many ore inclusions of the shot and powder type. In the formation of the secondary microzonal profile a distinct blackish-brown Metallogenium microzone developed in the lower part of the oxidizing horizon.

In the mud in glasses 770-774, which was also taken from the ore field and freed from concretions by sieving, the manganese content was much lower – a little more than 1%. The mud was pale brown and contained no microconcretions. During the formation of the secondary diagenetic profile the Metallogenium microzone developed quite well and stood out clearly as a thin blackish-brown layer against the pale brown background. Below it there was a yellowish-orange Siderococcus microzone.

The mud in glasses 775-779 was greenish grey. The Metallogenium microzone was absent, but at the lower boundary of the oxidizing horizon there appeared a yellowish-orange layer, the product of the vital activity of iron bacteria of the Siderococcus Dorff type. In this mud the manganese content was only 0.3-0.5%, while the iron content was about 30%.

In the muds of all 15 glasses we determined the manganese and iron content of the bottom water six times over a period of 3.5 years (1958-1962). The manganese and iron content of the mud solution in the reducing horizon was determined eight times.

If the mud solution became contaminated with mud particles when the sample was drawn out of the collodion chamber with a syringe, such a sample was passed immediately through a filter paper, thoroughly wetted with distilled water, before the determinations were made.

In the analysis for divalent iron 1 ml of the mud solution or 5 ml of the bottom water was put into a 50-ml measuring flask; 16 ml of buffer solution (0.4 N CH_3COOH + 0.4 N CH_3COONa) and 1 ml of 0.5% solution

*The collodion-chamber method of cultivating mud microflora in the undisturbed mud solution was suggested by Perfil'ev and described fully in Perfil'ev and Gabe's book: "Capillary Methods of Investigating Microorganisms" [1961].

of α, α'-dipyridyl was then added to the flask.* The solution in the measuring flasks was brought to the mark with distilled water and measured on a FÉK-M colorimeter.

In the analysis for manganese 1 ml of mud solution or 5 ml of bottom water was put into a 50-ml measuring flask, to which 10 ml of 10% HNO_3, 10 ml of 0.5% $AgNO_3$, and 10 ml of 20% $(NH_4)_2S_2O_8$ were added. The solution in the measuring flask was heated and boiled for 1 min. After being cooled, it was brought to the mark with distilled water containing no reductants (persulfate water) and the Mn content was determined on the FÉK-M.

The results of analysis over a period of 3.5 years are shown in Table 6, which gives the mean values from the five vessels in the series. In the first period, in the 4th-5th month after the mud was put into the vessels (time I of analyses), manganese could be found only in insignificant amounts in the water of three vessels out of 15. The manganese content of the mud solution in every glass without exception lay in the range 6-104 mg/liter.

In this initial period of formation of the microzonal profile the three series of vessels differed appreciably from one another in Mn^{2+} concentration. The most manganese (27 mg/liter on the average) was found in the mud solution of series 770-774, probably because in this mud the high Mn content (more than 1% of the dry weight) was combined with a relatively low Eh of the reducing horizon in the mud (Tables 6 and 7). The least manganese was found in the mud solution in series 775-779 (10 mg/liter on the average), the mud of which was poor in manganese (0.3-0.5%), although it was distinguished by a high rate of reducing processes (Tables 6 and 7).

Three months later (time II of analyses) the manganese content of the mud solution in all the flasks was greatly increased. Manganese appeared in the bottom water, although in much smaller amount than in the mud. The differences between the series at this time were almost levelled out. We must mention one glass (766) with an exceptionally high Mn^{2+} concentration (up to 475 mg/liter) and another (778) with a relatively low Mn^{2+} concentration (17.5 mg/liter) for the particular series at this time. In the last case the collodion chamber was located, as an exception, in the upper part of the reducing horizon, in the direct vicinity of the Metallogium microzone.

TABLE 6. Mn^{2+} and Fe^{2+} Content of Mud Solution in Reducing Horizon (Denominator) and Bottom Water (Numerator)

No. of vessels in series	Iron	Mn^{2+} and Fe^{2+} content (mg/liter) at different sampling times over 3.5 yr.					
		I	II	III	IV	V	VI
765–769	Mn^{2+} . . .	0/24.5	9/75	9/28	0/32	0/41	0.9/42
	Fe^{2+} . . .	0.2/1.9	0.3/3.2	0.5/—	0.1/1.6	0.2/1.3	1.3/7.8
770–774	Mn^{2+} . . .	0.4/27	10/61	13/28	0.2/28	0/31	0.8/66
	Fe^{2+} . . .	0/2.6	0.5/5.4	0.4/—	0.4/2.4	0/3.8	1.3/6.8
775–779	Mn^{2+} . . .	0.6/10	8/37	9/38	0/5	0/21	0.8/128
	Fe^{2+} . . .	0.1/10.7	0.4/10.0	0.1/—	0/5.4	0/11.5	1.0/6.2

*Some of the determinations of the ferrous iron content were made by the ortho-phenanthroline method (Sandell [1949]).

TABLE 7. Eh in Microzonal Profile of Muds in Vessels of Series 765-769, 770-774, and 775-779 (The numerator gives the data for bottom water, and the denominator gives the data for the reducing horizon)

No. of vessel	Eh (mV)	
	9/15/58	11/4/58
765	511/192	592/193
768	458/168	478/122
771	464/30	465/38
774	490/158	502/20
776	547/−99	460/−123
777	450/−86	436/−119

During the following year (1959) (times III and IV of analyses) the divalent manganese content of the mud solution in vessels 765-769 and 770-774 remained fairly high; in the water Mn^{2+} had almost completely disappeared by the end of the year. In series 775-779, which was distinguished by the low manganese content of the mud, the manganese content of the mud solution was much less than in the first two series. After another year, at the end of 1960 (time V), the picture was not significantly altered. The amount of manganese in the mud solution was the same as before or even a little higher. Manganese had completely disappeared from the bottom water. A year and a half later, in April 1962 (time VI), the manganese content of the mud solution in vessels 765-769 was practically unchanged (42 mg/liter on the average); the manganese content of the bottom water was very low (~0.9 mg/liter). In the vessels of the next series (770-774) the Mn^{2+} concentration in the mud was appreciably higher, almost double; traces were found in the water. Even more pronounced changes were observed in the series 775-779. The Mn^{2+} content of the mud solution was several times higher, reaching 128 mg/liter on the average. The Mn^{2+} concentration in the water did not exceed 1 mg/liter.

In the first period (July-August, 1958) iron (Fe^{2+}) was absent from the bottom water, but was found in the reducing horizon in all the glasses. Yet the amount of iron was much smaller than that of manganese, particularly in the glasses of the first two samples. In the mud of series 775-779, which was rich in iron and distinguished by intense reducing activity (Table 7), the amount of divalent iron in the mud solution was appreciably greater (10.7 mg/liter on the average), whereas in the first two series the Fe^{2+} content was only 1.9 and 2.6 mg/liter.

With the elapse of time the concentration of dissolved iron in the mud samples increased considerably and Fe^{2+} appeared even in the bottom water, although in much smaller amounts than manganese (time II). By the end of 1959 (time IV) Fe^{2+} had almost completely disappeared from the bottom water; it was still present in appreciable amounts in the mud solution. After another year (time V) the concentration of divalent iron in the mud solution had not diminished, but there was none in the bottom water. At the last time (VI) of observation, i.e., after another 1.5 yr, the Fe^{2+} concentration in the mud solution in the first two series was appreciably increased and Fe^{2+} appeared in very small amounts in the bottom water in all vessels.

Participation of Bacteria in the Reduction of Manganese and Iron in Mud

As we showed in Table 6, Mn^{2+} and Fe^{2+} ions appear in the mud solution during the formation of the secondary microzonal profile of muds containing manganese and iron oxides, and a high concentration of these ions is frequently maintained over a long period (Table 6). Periodic measurement of the Eh during the formation of the mud profile showed that a low redox potential was very rapidly created in its lower horizon (Gabe and Rabinovich [1964]). This raises the question: Do muds contain a microflora which energetically reduces manganese and iron?

The participation of microorganisms in the reduction of manganese and iron is known from the investigations of several authors, but all these works were concerned only with soil microflora.

Halvorson and Starkey [1927] found that a mixed culture of soil bacteria in a substrate containing glucose (dextrose) brought about a rapid reduction of ferric hydroxide in anaerobic conditions. When air was admitted the Fe^{2+} concentration was much lower. In a sterile medium of the same composition, even at lower pH (3.0 instead of 6.0), $Fe(OH)_3$ was not reduced at all either in anaerobic or aerobic conditions. Halvorson and Starkey showed that pure cultures of Escherichia coli and Clostridium sporogenes could reduce iron.

Roberts [1947] pointed out that the ability to reduce iron was a very specific characteristic of bacteria. Out of 265 tested cultures of soil microorganisms (yeasts, bacteria, actinomycetes) only B. polymyxa Mig. rapidly and energetically reduced iron in glucose-containing substrates. Betremieux [1951] noted in particular that glucose was essential for iron reduction.

In contradistinction to the results of Roberts [1947], Bromfield [1954a, 1954b] denied that iron-reducing bacteria were highly specialized organisms. He found that iron could be reduced not only by B. polymyxa, but also by other soil bacteria: B. circulans, E. freundii, Aerobacter, Paracolibactrum, B. megatherium, etc. The two most active species, however, were B. polymyxa and B. circulans. Bromfield found that the reducing ability of these bacteria differed on different substrates. Much more ferrous iron was formed in anaerobic conditions than in the presence of oxygen. Like the previous authors, Bromfield showed that an essential factor for the growth of iron-reducing bacteria in anaerobic culture was the presence of a carbon source in the form of a sugar in the substrate. In the case of free access of oxygen the bacteria grew on all media, except those lacking a carbon source.

Kalakutskii and Duda (Kalakutskii [1959]; Kalakutskii and Duda [1961]) found that when soil microbes were grown on Roberts medium and Bromfield medium iron-reducing ability was manifested by numerous strains of Pseudomonas sp., and also by a culture of butyric acid bacteria. In anaerobic conditions the iron-reducing activity was enhanced and the number of strains capable of reducing iron was increased.

Duda and Kalakutskii [1961] showed that iron reduction occurred directly in the cells of Pseudomonas tralucida and that the reducing activity depended on the source of ferrous iron. $Fe(OH)_3$ was reduced much less than $Fe_2(SO_4)_3$.

The mechanism of iron reduction by bacteria has still not been fully clarified. The most thorough investigations in this connection are those of Betremieux [1951] and Bromfield [1954b], particularly the latter. By cultivating a pure culture of B. circulans on his medium A, Bromfield concluded that the iron-reducing activity of bacteria is of an enzymatic nature. It depends on the presence of glucose dehydrogenase in the cells. However, as Bromfield pointed out, the dehydrogenase system alone is insufficient for the reduction of $Fe(OH)_3$, since this enzyme can mediate the reduction of the Fe^{3+} ion only if the latter is in solution. The solubility of trivalent iron in soil with a neutral or weakly acid reaction is extremely low. Hence, specific organic acids excreted by bacteria are of great importance for the iron-reduction process. With the aid of these acids the almost insoluble compounds of trivalent iron pass into solution in the form of ions or organo-mineral complexes. Unlike Betremieux [1951], Bromfield [1954b] believes that the consumption of molecular oxygen by bacteria is quite insufficient to effect the reduction of Fe^{3+}, although bacteria in anaerobic conditions use the oxygen of iron oxides in the conversion of the substrate

Bromfield found a similar dehydrogenase mechanism of iron reduction in B. megatherium and Aerobacter aerogenes, which reduce iron rather weakly. He thinks that the varying iron-reducing activities of bacteria depend also on their ability to effect the solution of $Fe(OH)_3$.

An investigation of iron-reducing microbes in mud is the subject of a special paper by one of the present authors (Troshanov [1964]). Here we will briefly discuss only the preliminary results relating to the iron- and manganese-reducing ability of enrichment cultures of microorganisms from muds of some ore-bearing lakes.

Mud with a developed secondary microzonal profile is very suitable for this purpose, since the reducing horizon in it is fairly homogeneous, can be easily demarcated visually from the distinct oxidizing microzone of biogenic deposits of Mn and Fe oxides, and is easily accessible for repeated sampling.

As a substrate we selected a slightly modified Bromfield medium A [1954a]. Its composition was: 100 ml of distilled water, 0.05 g KH_2PO_4, 0.02 g $MgSO_4$, 0.1 g $(NH_4)_2SO_4$, 0.5 g sucrose, 0.5 g $CaCO_3$, 0.5 ml of yeast autolyzate (instead of Difco yeast extract) and 6.0, 3.0, or 0.1 g of iron-manganese ore [instead of $Fe(OH)_3$, as in Bromfield's medium]. According to Bromfield, medium A is most suitable for iron-reducing bacteria.

The seeding material was taken from the reducing horizon of the secondary microzonal profile of mud from three ore-bearing lakes: Lake Ukshezero in Karelia (UO 5188, UO 720) and two lakes on the Karelian

Isthmus: Punnus-Yarvi (PY 4117) and Khepo-Yarvi (KY 085). Sample UO 5188 contained more than 2% manganese and was characterized by a very well-developed Metallogenium microzone without any growth of Siderococcus (similar to mud series 765-769 in Table 6). The sample UO 720 contained much less manganese. It had a well-developed Siderococcus microzone. The development of Metallogenium was much weaker (similar to series UO 770-774 in Table 6). The secondary profile of KY 085 was distinguished visually by intensive reduction. The reducing horizon contained a black deposit of iron hydrosulfite. Consequently, over a long period the manganese- and iron-oxidizing bacteria were displaced from the mud into the bottom water and formed iron-manganese deposits in the periphyton. In the vessel PY 4117 both microzones – the blackish-brown and the ochreous – were well developed.

The first seeding of the above muds was made in modified dilute agar (2% agar) medium A, containing 6% very finely powdered iron-manganese ore (oolites from Lake Ukshezero). Before the agar had set, the seeded medium was drawn into glass tubes, which were then sealed at both ends. Bacterial colonies developed in anaerobic conditions in the tubes. Clear zones were formed around some colonies as a result of solution of the ore particles surrounding them. The appearance of ferrous iron could be detected by a qualitative test. When reduced iron was present in the clear zone, filter paper soaked in a 0.5% solution of α, α'-dipyridyl in 10% acetic acid turned red. Bacterial colonies which did not form zones of solution did not cause reddening. The zones of solution gradually became larger and in certain tubes filled the whole canal after 20 days. The ore completely disappeared and the brown medium became colorless.

Anaerobic-culture capillaries with one rectangular canal (Perfil'ev and Gabe [1961]) are suitable for close microscopic observations of microcolonies of iron-reducing bacteria in anaerobic conditions. Through the thin flat walls of such capillaries the microcolonies on the glass surface can be examined under the high powers of the microscope, including the immersion lens. Not only the shape of the bacterial cells at the edge of the microcolony, but also the state of the microscopic particles of ore in the solution zone can be clearly seen.

Colonies which showed the ability to reduce iron consisted mainly of an accumulation of spore-forming rods (0.6 × 3-4 μ) and spores (0.7 × 1.0 μ, sometimes larger). These provided the initial material for the obtainment of enrichment cultures of manganese- and iron-reducing mud bacteria. The first subculture in liquid medium A containing 3% iron-manganese ore was made in test tubes and the second subculture was grown in 5-liter vessels. Two variants of medium A were used: in the first variant the ore content was 3% and in the second it was 0.1%. As culture vessels we used 0.5-liter milk bottles, each of which was fitted, like chemical wash bottles, with a rubber stopper carrying two glass tubes. The outer end of the short tube had a cotton-wool filter and the outer end of the long tube was fitted with a rubber tube carrying a screw clamp and terminating in a glass tip with a drawn-out and sealed point. The volume of medium A was ~ 350 ml. Anaerobic conditions, which promote more rapid reduction of manganese and iron in the cultures, were secured by sterile vegetable oil, which was introduced aseptically to form a 10- to 12-mm layer on the surface of the inoculated liquid substrate and which prevented the access of atmospheric oxygen.

From each vessel we periodically took samples, six to seven times in the course of 15 days, without contaminating the culture or altering the gas conditions in the sample. Each sample (22-25 ml) was expelled into a jar fitted with a rubber stopper carrying inlet and outlet glass tubes, a platinum electrode, and a calomel electrode. The Eh was measured with an LP-5 tube potentiometer and the pH was determined with indicator paper. The concentration of Mn^{2+} ions was determined colorimetrically (on a FÉK-M colorimeter) by the persulfate method, and the ferrous iron content by means of orthophenanthroline. The controls used for comparison were values of the pH, Eh, Mn^{2+} content, and Fe^{2+} content, determined at the same times in sterile medium A under a layer of oil in similar vessels. In addition, single determinations were made in the initial sterile medium A, which was kept in conditions allowing free access of oxygen. Two replicates usually gave similar results.

A clear illustration of the reducing activity of enrichment cultures and the variation of the pH and Eh during the experiment is given by the curves shown in Figs. 5-9.

We first discuss the cultures grown in liquid medium A with a large amount of iron-manganese ore (3%).

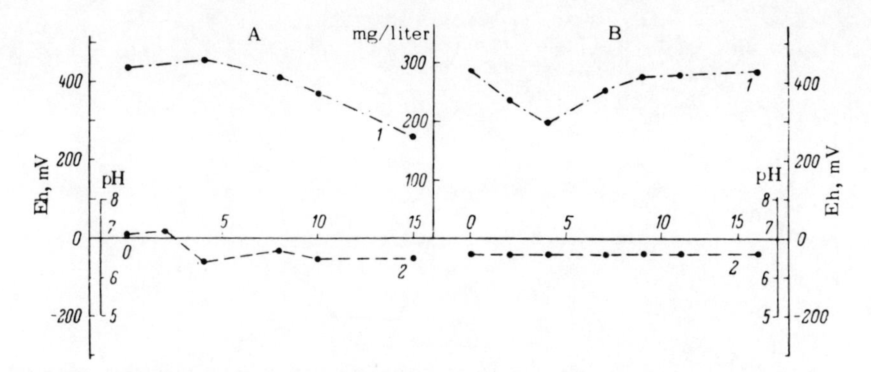

Fig. 5. State of medium in control vessels in an experimental investigation of the development of iron- and manganese-reducing bacteria in enrichment cultures. A) Liquid Bromfield medium A containing 3% iron-manganese ore; B) the same substrate with 0.1% ore. 1) Variation of Eh over 15 days (days marked on x-axis); 2) pH of medium during same time. No manganese or iron was found in solution.

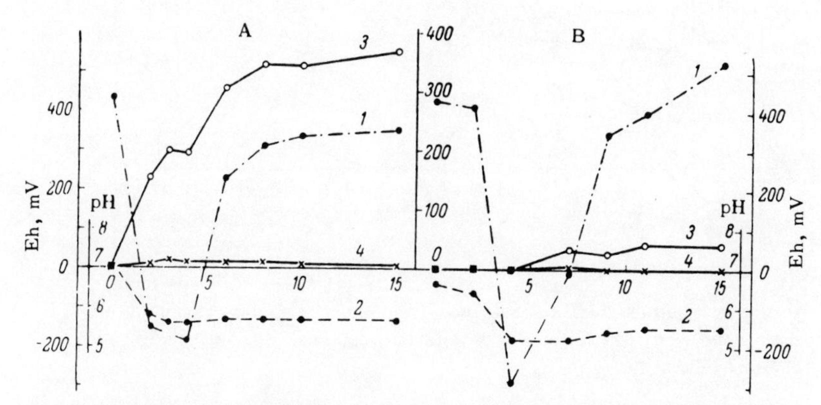

Fig. 6. Change in liquid medium A during the development of an enrichment culture of manganese-reducing bacteria isolated from a Lake Ukshezero mud sample with a manganese microzone (vessel 5188). A) Substrate with 3% iron-manganese ore; B) the same substrate with 0.1% iron-manganese ore. The determinations were made seven times during 15 days; the results are shown by the curves: 1) Eh (mV); 2) pH; 3) Mn (mg/liter); 4) Fe (mg/liter).

On the 2nd-4th days after inoculation we observed in all cases (Figs. 6-9) a pronounced drop in the Eh (by 600-700 mV) with a subsequent rapid rise. The pH varied less during the 15 days of development of the cultures: after a brief and slight drop the pH remained in the range 5.8-6.2, i.e., a little lower than in the control vessel (Fig. 5 A and B), up to the end of the experiment, i.e., over a period of 9-10 days. More reduced manganese than iron was initially formed in the culture fluid and on the 6th day the amount of Mn^{2+} in the three cultures (UO 720, KY 085, and PY 4117) was 200-250 mg/liter. Fe^{2+} appeared in the culture after some delay but also reached concentrations on the 4th-6th day: 240-270 mg/liter; i.e., it sometimes even exceeded the amount of Mn^{2+}.

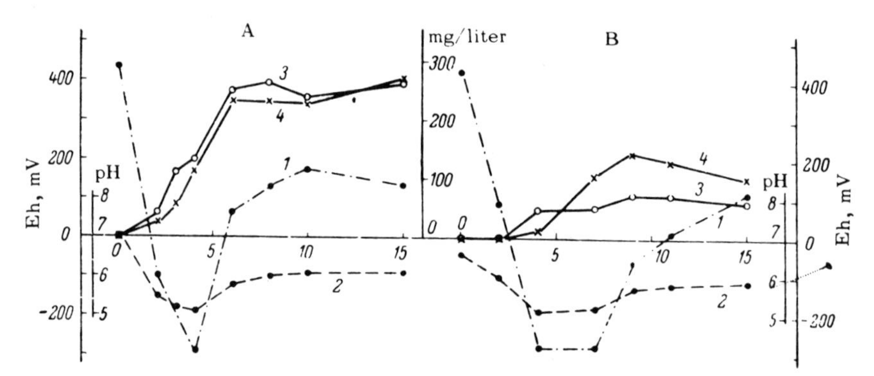

Fig. 7. Change in liquid medium A during the development of an enrichment culture of manganese- and iron-reducing bacteria isolated from a Lake Ukshezero mud sample with a double-layered manganese and iron microzone (vessel 720). Legend as in Fig. 6.

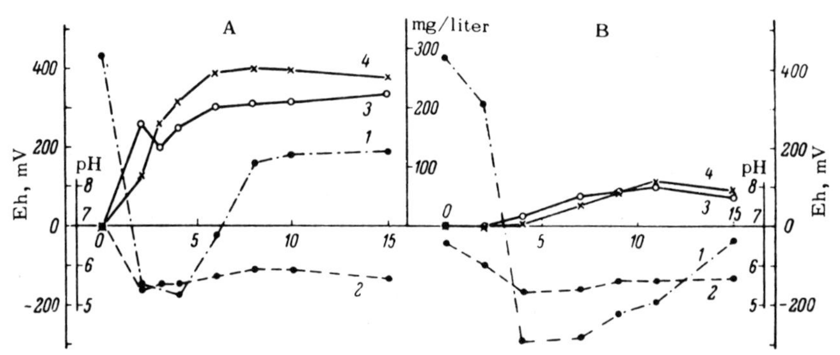

Fig. 8. Change in liquid medium A during the development of an enrichment culture of manganese- and iron-reducing bacteria isolated from mud of Lake Punnus-Yarvi (vessel 4117). Legend as in Fig. 6.

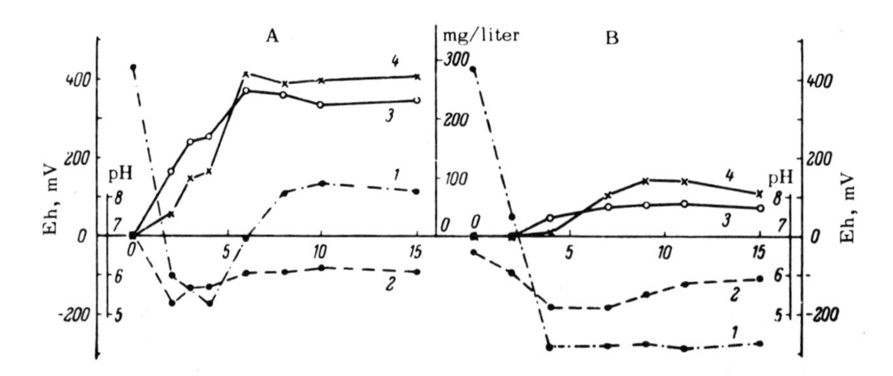

Fig. 9. Change in liquid medium A during the development of an enrichment culture of manganese- and iron-reducing bacteria isolated from bottom deposits of Lake Khepo-Yarvi (vessel 085). Legend as in Fig. 6.

An exception was the enrichment culture from the vessel UO 5188 with a well-developed Metallogenium microzone and a very weak Siderococcus microzone. In liquid medium A with 3% ore this culture reduced the greatest amount of manganese: the Mn^{2+} concentration in this case was 340-360 mg/liter at a comparatively high Eh. The amount of ferrous iron which appeared in this culture was very small, only 6-10 mg/liter; yet at least four times as much ferric oxide as manganese was introduced with the ore into the substrate.

In all the cultures on a substrate with a very low ore content (0.1%) the concentration of Mn^{2+} and Fe^{2+} ions was greatly reduced. This applied particularly to manganese, the maximum content of which was in the range 40-70 mg/liter (B in Figs. 6-9). With the exception of culture UO 5188, the Eh in this variant of the experiment was much lower than in similar vessels with a high ore content in the substrate. The reason for this is obviously that the reducing microorganisms in anaerobic culture utilize the oxygen of the Mn and Fe oxides which they reduce. Yet in this variant of the experiment the amount of oxides introduced into the substrate was 30 times less. Hence, the microorganisms also used oxygen dissolved in the medium and this led to an appreciable drop in the Eh; in certain cases the redox potential fell to $rH_2 = 0.8-1.5$ (B in Figs. 7-9). The considerable increase in the Eh on the 6th-8th days in cultures on an ore-rich substrate can probably be attributed to the fact that bacterial cells in the stationary phase excrete into the culture fluid less reducing substances than in the period of accelerated multiplication.

Our investigation of the reducing activity of the mud microflora is of a preliminary nature, since the observations were conducted on enrichment cultures and the experiment included material from a limited number of sources. We used only Bromfield medium A. The obtained results, however, indicate that muds, like soils, contain a microflora which actively reduces manganese and iron in the diagenesis of bottom deposits during the formation of the secondary microzonal mud profile and over a long period maintains a relatively high concentration of Mn^{2+} and Fe^{2+} in the mud solution of mud with a very low organic matter content; in our samples the humus content was a little more than 3%.

We observed a similarity in the rate and degree of lowering of the redox potential in mud cultures with a developing secondary microzonal profile (Gabe and Rabinovich [1964]) and the discussed enrichment cultures of reducing bacteria from these muds on a synthetic substrate.

The amount of manganese and iron reduced by the mud microflora depended not only on its reducing activity but also on the amount of manganese and iron oxides in the mud or in the synthetic substrate. A comparison of the two variants of the experiment (A and B in Figs. 6-9) shows that the Mn^{2+} and Fe^{2+} concentrations were reduced by a factor of 3-4 when the supply of oxidized compounds of these elements was much smaller, despite the fact that the Eh in this case fell by 100-150 mV.

There was no direct correspondence between the change in Eh and the reduction of Mn and Fe in any of the enrichment cultures. The considerable increase in Eh on the 6th-15th day of our experiment, presumably due to cessation of multiplication of the bacteria, did not lead to a decrease in the amount of Mn^{2+} and Fe^{2+} ions in solution. Their concentration continued to increase on the 4th-6th days and subsequently remained at the attained level without appreciable change until the end of the experiment. This agrees with Bromfield's idea [1954b] of the role of the enzymatic system of bacterial cells in the reduction of Mn and Fe.

The peculiar behavior of the enrichment culture from mud sample UO 5188, i.e., the vigorous reduction of manganese and the almost complete absence of iron reduction, probably explains why the series of vessels 5181-5190 and mud samples of similar nature from the series of vessels 765-769 (Tables 2, 3, and 6), despite the presence of a large supply of iron in the mud, had a very weakly developed iron-oxidation microzone (Siderococcus), for which there was evidently not enough Fe^{2+} in the mud solution. It is possible, however, that the comparatively high Eh typical of the mentioned muds also prevents the reduction of iron and its passage into the mud solution. This state of culture UO 5188, however, was not stable. In subsequent subcultures the enrichment culture of UO 5188 began to reduce both manganese and iron, while the enrichment culture of UO 720, which reduced Mn and Fe equally well, reduced Fe_2O_3 weakly in a subsequent subculture in one of the experiments.

Summary

1. In bottom deposits from the ore fields of Lake Ukshezero the new manganese-iron microbe Metallogenium Perf., which uses mainly manganous manganese as an energy source and deposits it in the form of oxides, greatly enriches the mud with manganese in the microzone of development of the microbe. The decisive role of the biogenic factor in ore formation is fully revealed in the case of the distinct localized development of the microbe in the profile, i.e., when it develops over a long period in a thin layer near the lower boundary of the oxidizing horizon of the mud sample.

2. The continuous accumulation of Mn oxides (mainly the trivalent form) and, to a lesser extent, Fe oxides in the mud by the manganese-iron microbe Metallogenium is ensured by the continuous influx of manganese and iron ions, formed in reducing conditions in the main mass of the mud (excluding the top, relatively thin layer), into the mud solution from the solid phase. Direct analyses of the mud solution in the reducing horizon reveal a large amount of dissolved manganese (Mn^{2+}) when the mud contains a large supply of this element in the form of ore. Fe^{2+} also occurs, but in lower concentration.

3. If there is no abundant microzonal development of iron-oxidizing microbes in the mud, iron is not concentrated in layers in the oxidizing horizon of the mud profile, despite the fact that the Eh of the upper horizon of the mud is sufficiently high to ensure almost complete precipitation of divalent iron in the mud solution.

4. From the reducing horizon of the secondary microzonal profile of mud from Lake Ukshezero and other ore-bearing lakes we isolated enrichment cultures of bacteria, mainly bacilli, which on solid sugar-containing medium (Bromfield medium A) in anaerobic conditions produced distinct zones of solution of the iron-manganese ore, and in liquid medium of the same composition brought about vigorous and rapid reduction of Mn and Fe. The concentration of Mn and Fe together reached 400-500 mg/liter.

Literature Cited

Babko, A. K., and A. T. Pilipenko. 1951. Colorimetric Analysis. Goskhimizdat, Moscow.

Betremieux, R. 1951. "Etude experimentale de l'évolution du fer et du manganese dans les sols." Ann. Agron., Vol. 2.

Bromfield, S. M. 1954a. "The reduction of iron oxide by bacteria." J. of Soil Sci. Vol. 5, No. 1.

Bromfield, S. M. 1954b. "Reduction of ferric compounds by soil bacteria." J. of Gen. Mic., Vol. 11, No. 1.

Duda, V. I., and L. V. Kalakutskii. 1961. "The role of microorganisms in reducing processes in soil. Reduction of iron by a pure culture of *Pseudomonas tralucida*." Nauchn, dokl. Vyssh. shkoly, biol. nauki, No. 2.

Gabe, D. R., and V. A. Rabinovich. 1964. "Physicochemical conditions of development of *Metallogenium personatum* in mud." In Applied Capillary Microscopy, Consultants Bureau, New York. [English Translation, 1965].

Halvorson, H. O., and R. L. Starkey. 1927. "Studies on the transformation of iron in nature. Part II. Concerning the importance of microorganisms in the solution and reduction of iron." Soil. Sci., Vol. 24.

Kalakutskii, L. V. 1959. "Role of microorganisms in iron-reduction processes in soil." Nauchn. dokl. Vyssh. shkoly, biol. nauki, No. 1.

Kalakutskii, L. V., and V. I. Duda. 1961. "Role of microorganisms in iron reduction in soil." Nauchn. dokl. Vyssh. shkoly, biol. nauki, No. 1.

Kazakov, A. V., E. I. Sokolova, and A. Z. Vainshtein. 1957. "System of equilibrium of hydroxides and oxides of iron in solutions of its chlorides and sulfates." Tr. Inst. geol. nauk Akad. Nauk SSSR, No. 152, geol. ser., No. 64.

Krotov, B. P. 1950. "Types of fresh waters and the ores formed in them." Dokl. Akad. Nauk SSSR, Vol. 71, No. 5.

Krotov, B. P. 1951. "On the genesis of marine deposits of manganese." Dokl. Akad. Nauk SSSR, Vol. 77, No. 1.

Kuznetsov, S. I. 1938. "A quantitative estimate of microflora in connection with the development of a microzonal index of muds." Mikrobiologiya, Vol. VII, No. 1.

Lavrukhina, A. K. 1949. "Determination of manganese oxides of different valence in joint occurrence." Zhurn. analitich. khimii, Vol. 4, No. 1.

Listova, L. P. 1961. Physicochemical Investigations of the Conditions of Formation of Oxide and Carbonate Ores of Manganese. Izd. Akad. Nauk SSSR, Moscow.

Perfil'ev, B. V. 1932. "The biology of therapeutic muds." In the collection: Fundamentals of Health-Resort Studies Vol. I. Gosmedizdat, Moscow.

Perfil'ev, B. V. 1937. "Absolute geochromology and biogenic ore formation." Eighteenth International Geological Congress. Abstracts of Papers. ONTI NKTP SSSR.

Perfil'ev, B. V. 1952. "Silting research and absolute geochronology." Izv. Vsesoyuzn. geogr. obshch., Vol. 84, No. 4.

Perfil'ev, B. V., and D. R. Gabe. 1961. Capillary Methods of Investigating Microorganisms. Izd. Akad. Nauk SSSR, Moscow—Leningrad.

Perfil'ev, B. V., and D. R. Gabe. 1964. "The use of the microbial-landscape method to investigate bacteria accumulating manganese and iron in bottom deposits." In Applied Capillary Microscopy, Consultants Bureau, New York. [English Translation, 1965].

Ponomarev, A. I. 1955. Methods of Chemical Analysis of Minerals and Rocks, Vol. II. Izd. AN SSSR, Moscow.

Pustovalov, L. V. 1940. Petrography of Sedimentary Rocks. Gostoptekhizdat, Moscow—Leningrad.

Rabinovich, V. A., A. M. Gal'perina, and A. A. Sapotnitskii. 1964. "The use of the polarographic method for the determination of oxygen in the microzonal profile in connection with a study of the conditions of formation of iron-manganese ores." In Applied Capillary Microscopy, Consultants Bureau, New York. [English Translation, 1965].

Rabinovich, V. A., and É. É. Sherman. 1964. "A modification of the Winkler method for the determination of dissolved oxygen in small volumes of liquid." In Applied Capillary Microscopy, Consultants Bureau, New York. [English Translation, 1965].

Roberts, J. L. 1947. "Reduction of ferric hydroxide by strains of *Bacillus polymyxa*." Soil Sci. Vol. 63.

Semenovich, N. I. 1958. "Limnological conditions of accumulation of ferruginous deposits in lakes." Tr. Labor. ozerovedeniya, Vol. VI, Izd. Akad. Nauk SSR, Moscow.

Shapiro, N. I. 1964. "The chemical composition of deposits formed by *Metallogenium* and *Siderococcus*." In Applied Capillary Microscopy, Consultants Bureau, New York. [English Translation, 1965].

Shidlovskaya-Ovchinnikova, Yu. S. 1955. "Quantitative determination of various forms of iron in natural waters." Gidrokhim. materialy, Vol. XXIV.

Sokolova, E. I. 1962. "Physicochemical Investigations of Sedimentary Iron and Manganese Ores and the Rocks Containing Them." Izd. Akad. Nauk SSSR, Moscow.

Strakhov, N. M. 1947. "Iron-ore facies and their analogs in the history of the earth." Tr. Inst. geol. Akad. Nauk SSSR, vol. 73.

Strakhov, N. M. 1954. "General scheme of sedimentation in present-day seas and lakes of low mineral content." In the book: Sedimentation in Present-day Waters. Izd. Akad. Nauk SSSR, Moscow.

Strakhov, N. M. 1956. "Some methodological errors in the investigation of chemical and biological sedimentation." Byull. MOIP, otd. geol., Vol. XXXI, No. 2.

Strakhov, N. M. 1957a. "Stages of rock formation and problems of their investigation." In the collection: Methods of Investigating Sedimentary Rocks, Vol. I., Introduction. Gosgeoltekhizdat, Moscow.

Strakhov, N. M. 1957b. "Chemical investigation of sedimentary rocks for genetic and correlational purposes." In the collection: Methods of Investigating Sedimentary Rocks, Vol. II, Pt. 3, Ch. IX. Gosgeoltekhizdat, Moscow.

Strakhov, N. M. 1960. Principles of Lithogenesis. Vol. I. Izd. Akad. Nauk SSSR, Moscow [English translation: Consultants Bureau, New York, 1965].

Troshanov, E. P. 1964. "Bacteria reducing manganese and iron in bottom deposits." In Applied Capillary Microscopy, Consultants Bureau, New York. [English Translation, 1965].

III
Weathering and High-Grade Iron Deposits

Editor's Comments on Papers 11, 12, and 13

11 Garrels and Mackenzie: *Excerpts from* Evolution of Sedimentary Rocks

12 Percival: Excerpts from *The Lateritic Iron Deposits of Conakry*

13 Dorr: *Supergene Iron Ores of Minas Gerais, Brazil* (abstract)

Among the eight most abundant elements in the earth's crust, iron is unique in that it may be oxidized and reduced in environments at and near the surface. In deep-seated plutonic rocks it is usually in the ferrous state in ferromagnesian silicate minerals. When such minerals are exposed to the air and water in the weathering sphere the iron is oxidized to one or more of the ferric oxides or oxide hydrates.

The ferric oxides are highly insoluble in the presence of oxygen, and hence they are persistent minerals in many soils, beach sands, and alluvial deposits. Their presence is easily recognized by the red, purple, yellow, or brown colors of the oxides. Where decomposition is intense, as in some tropical regions, iron may be significantly enriched in ferruginous laterites and ferricrete. Lateritic soils ("latosols") usually contain significant quantities of aluminum oxide hydrates, which also are highly insoluble products of weathering. Tropical decomposition of iron-formation or ironstone, rocks low in alumina, in which iron is present as siderite or ferrous silicate, may result in the formation of crusts of nearly pure oxide iron at the surface. The presence of gossans or rusty cappings over sulfide deposits is another well-known example of the supergene enrichment of iron oxides.

The first paper in this section (Paper 11) is an excerpt from the book *Evolution of Sedimentary Rocks* by Robert M. Garrels and Fred T. Mackenzie. It is an excellent concise summary of the behavior of iron in the weathering sphere. We noted previously that Garrels is a pioneer in the field of low-temperature geochemistry of dilute solutions. He is currently Professor at the University of Hawaii and at Northwestern University. He has also been Chairman of the Department of Geological Sciences at Harvard University, Professor at the Scripps Institution of Oceanography and he has worked in the U.S. Geological Survey. Garrels is the author of several books, including *A Textbook of Geology* and *Solutions, Minerals and Equilibria* (with C. L. Christ), and of numerous contributions to professional journals.

F. T. Mackenzie is also on the faculty of the Department of Geological Sciences at Northwestern University and he is Staff Geochemist and Trustee of the Burmuda Station for Biological Research. He received his doctorate from Lehigh University and worked as an exploration geologist for the Shell Oil Company before assuming his present position.

Many years ago the writer had the opportunity to work on the laterites of the Republic of Guinea as a geologist for Alcan Aluminum. In the course of an extensive drilling campaign for bauxite, large areas of ferruginous laterite were encountered, in which iron was enriched several times above its average crustal abundance. Similar occurrences have been described in other tropical regions. Paper 12 is about a special ferruginous laterite that is sufficiently enriched to be used as an ore of iron. The reprint is an excerpt from a paper by a distinguished British geologist, the late Frederick G.

Percival. Percival worked on iron ores and iron-rich sediments in many parts of the world and he has published widely in various professional journals on this subject. For many years he was consultant to the British Steel Corporation. One of his earlier papers with E. Spencer considered the origin of the banded hematite jaspers of Singhbum, India (Spencer and Percival, 1952). He published several review papers on the nature of the iron deposits of the world (Percival, 1955, 1972). Percival died in November 1973.

We noted previously that relatively pure bodies of iron oxide sometimes form by weathering of iron-formation and ironstone. For some of the iron ore bodies associated with iron-formations, the mode of origin is not completely clear. As we shall see in the following papers in this section, a number of investigators believe that at least some such ore bodies have been formed by hydrothermal leaching and remobilization of iron rather than by simple supergene enrichment.

The author of Paper 13, John Van N. Dorr II, spent some fourteen years in Brazil as a Geologist with the U.S. Geological Survey, and he is one of the top American authorities on iron deposits in South America (Dorr, 1973). He is presently associated with the foreign geology branch of the U.S. Geological Survey in Washington, D.C. In addition to his contributions via U.S. Geological Survey publications, Dorr published two important papers on the iron ores of the Minas Gerais district following his tenure in Brazil (Dorr, Paper 13, 1965). The first is on the supergene ores and the second on the major orebodies in the itabirite, which he considers to have been concentrated by deep-seated processes. Both papers are very thorough but unfortunately too long to be reproduced here. The abstract of the first paper on the supergene ores appears as Paper 13.

References

Dorr, J. V. N., 1965, Nature and origin of the high-grade hematite ores of Minas Gerais, Brazil: Econ. Geol., v. 60, p. 1–46.

———, 1973, Iron-formation in South America: Econ. Geol., v. 68, p. 1005–1022.

Garrels, R. M., 1951, A textbook of geology: Harper & Row, New York.

———, and Christ, C. L., 1965, Solutions, minerals and equilibria: Harper & Row, New York.

Percival, F. G., 1955, Nature and occurrence of iron deposits: *in* United Nations Dept. Economic and Social Affairs, Survey of world iron ore resources, New York, p. 335–345.

———, 1972, Iron: Economic deposits: *in* Encyclopedia of geochemistry and environmental sciences, R. W. Fairbridge, ed., Van Nostrand Reinhold Co., New York, p. 603–610.

Spencer, E., and Percival, F. G., 1952, The structure and origin of the banded hematite jaspers of Singbum, India: Econ. Geol., v. 47, p. 365–383.

11

Reprinted from *Evolution of Sedimentary Rocks,* W. W. Norton & Co., Inc., New York, 1971. pp. 149–153, by permission of the publisher.

Evolution of Sedimentary Rocks

ROBERT M. GARRELS and FRED T. MACKENZIE

* * * * * * *

INCONGRUENT SOLUTION—IRON MINERALS. The chemical weathering of iron-bearing minerals and rocks is somewhat more complex than the weathering of halite, calcium sulfate, or carbonate minerals in that most iron mineral-soil water interactions involve oxidation-reduction reactions and may also involve the formation of several residual solid phases. Most of the major iron minerals, e.g., magnetite (Fe_3O_4), siderite ($FeCO_3$), pyrite (FeS_2), pyrrhotite (FeS), and iron silicates of various compositions, weathering at the earth's surface, contain ferrous iron in their structure. These minerals

Editor's Note: A row of asterisks indicates that material has been omitted from the original article.

Table 6.3
Composite Analysis of Waters Draining a Quartzite, Sangre de Cristo Range, New Mexico[a]

Constituent	*Concentration (ppm)*
HCO_3^-	5.7
SiO_2	3.6
Ca^{2+}	1.9
SO_4^{2-}	1.8
Na^+	0.5
K^+	0.3
NO_3^-	0.1
Mg^{2+}	ca. 0.06
Cl^-	ca. 0.06

[a]Data from Miller (1961).

usually occur dispersed throughout the rock but may be in discrete bands or segregations. Ferrous and ferric iron also are found in rock minerals, other than those in which iron is a major element, substituting for ions of similar size and charge, e.g., Fe^{2+} for Mg^{2+} in dolomite and Fe^{3+} for Al^{3+} in montmorillonite.

During the course of weathering, ferrous iron is released from the minerals and oxidized by O_2 in the soil water to ferric ion which hydrolyzes to form ferric oxides. The minerals include the hydrated ferric oxide dimorphs goethite ($\alpha FeO{\cdot}OH$) and lepidocrocite ($\gamma FeO{\cdot}OH$) and the anhydrous dimorphs hematite (αFe_2O_3) and maghemite (γFe_2O_3, magnetic hematite). Because these alteration products are yellow and orange-brown to red in color, the weathering of iron-bearing rocks usually results in vividly colored soil zones that contrast sharply with the drab fresh rock from which the soils are derived. A few percent total iron in a rock is all that is necessary to impart strong reddish coloration to a soil.

The marked tendency of iron to form oxide minerals in the weathering zone and the remarkable persistence of these minerals in soils can be explained in terms of their vanishingly low solubilities under oxygenated conditions. There has been much confusion concerning the relative stabilities of the hydrous and anhydrous iron oxides in the soil environment. It now appears that hematite is the stable species, even in the presence of highly dilute soil solutions in which conditions would be most favorable for formation of a hydrate. However, all four of the oxides listed above are so extremely insoluble, and their solubility differences so small, that any one may form and persist for very long times, even from a geologic standpoint. Broadly speaking, there is a tendency for hematite to develop in the soils of warm, well-watered regions and for goethite to form elsewhere. The great range of conditions under which the iron oxides are extremely insoluble is illustrated diagramatically in Figures 6.7 and 6.8 using partial pressures of gases or Eh and pH as descriptive variables. (See Appendix B

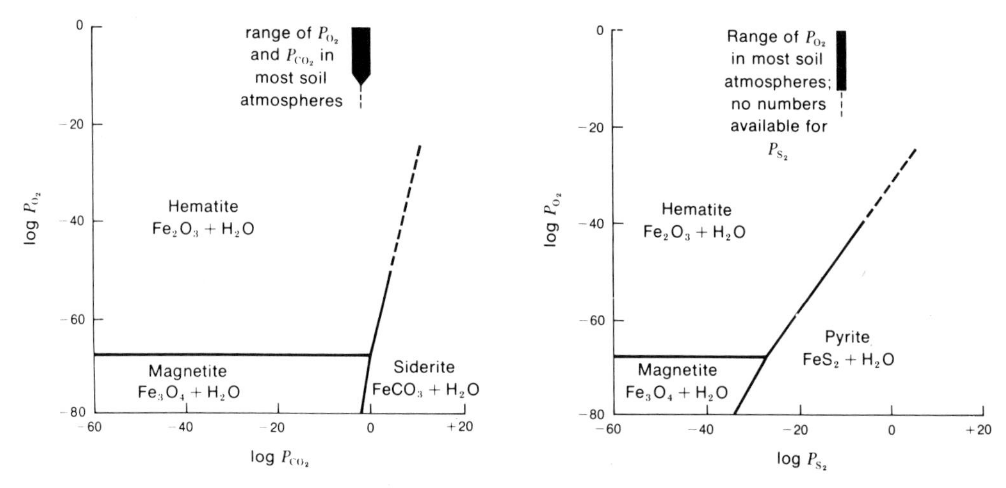

Figure 6.7 Partial pressure diagrams showing the stability of some iron minerals as functions of the partial pressure of O_2, CO_2, and S_2 (after Garrels and Christ, 1965).

for discussion of such diagrams.) On these diagrams hematite is used to represent the whole gamut of ferric oxides and iron metasilicate to represent that of the iron silicates. The differences in stabilities of the various species are so small that the relations shown are not affected by these generalizations.

Figure 6.7 shows that ferric oxide should form at the expense of magnetite, siderite, or pyrite in most soil environments, which range approximately from 10^{-1} to $10^{-3.5}$ atm of CO_2, $10^{-0.7}$ to 10^{-10} atm of O_2, and vanishingly small pressures of S_2.

Figure 6.8 shows the stability relations of a group of iron compounds as a function of oxidation potential (Eh) and pH. A number of specifications must be made about the chemical composition of the system (see the caption) in order to delineate the exact boundaries of the mineral fields, but the diagram demonstrates the general pattern of iron mineral behavior. The stippled area indicates the range of conditions found in soils; in general, the upper part of the stippled area can be considered to represent the upper, moist, aerated zone of the soil and the lower portion corresponds to conditions in the lower part of the soil zone, where the soil waters are reacting with the mineral species containing reduced iron.

Ferrous and ferric iron are the two important species of dissolved iron encountered in most natural solutions. Fe^{3+} is important only in highly oxidizing and strongly acidic environments. Fe^{2+} is present in significant concentrations ($>10^{-6}$ m) over a range of oxidizing and acidic to slightly alkaline conditions. The great stability of ferric oxide is evident from these Eh-pH diagrams, as is the relation that the numerous iron-bearing minerals containing ferrous iron are stable only under reducing, moderately acidic

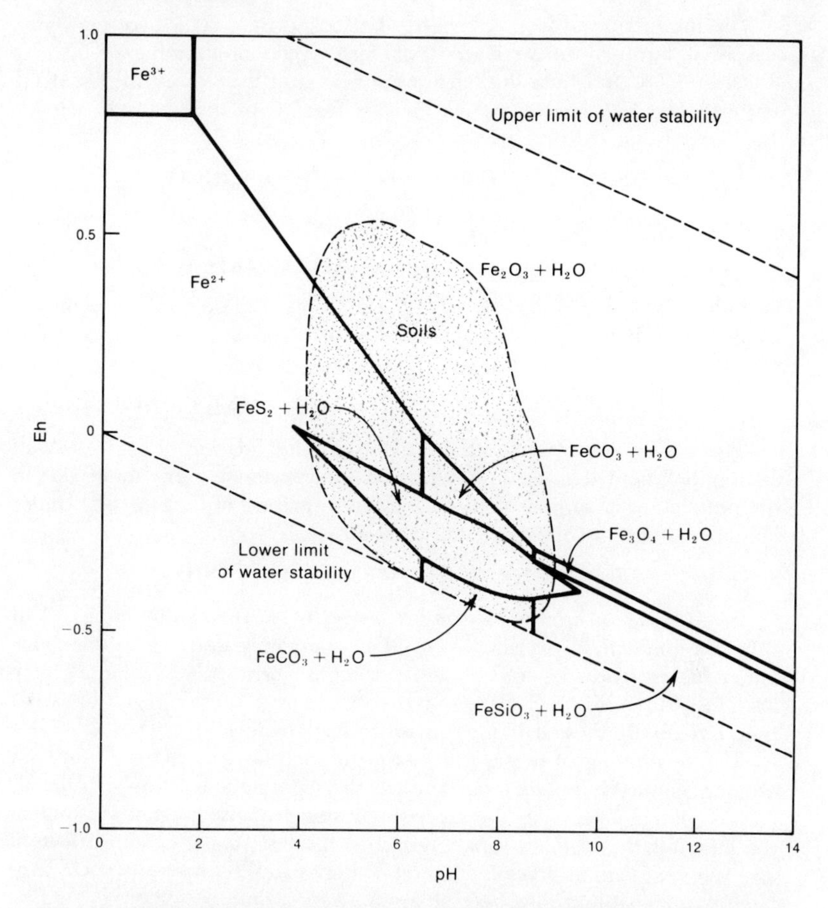

Figure 6.8 Eh-pH diagram showing the areas of dominance of dissolved iron species and stability fields of some iron minerals at 25°C and 1 atm total pressure. The fields of the dissolved species are shown where the total activity of the ions is greater than 10^{-6}. The environmental conditions are total dissolved $CO_2 = 10^0$ moles, total sulfur $= 10^{-6}$ moles, and amorphous silica present. The upper and lower dashed lines are the stability boundaries of H_2O (after Garrels and Christ, 1965).

to highly alkaline conditions. As ground waters become more concentrated in dissolved carbonate, sulfur, or silica, the stability fields of the iron minerals containing these species increase in area. In most soil-water environments, dissolved oxygen is too high, and carbonate, sulfur, or silica are too low in concentration to stabilize the primary iron-bearing minerals. Some conclusions concerning the chemical weathering of iron-rich minerals and rocks can be reached by consideration of these diagrams and some simple chemical reactions.

The production of iron oxides can be looked upon as a two-stage process. First, ferrous iron is released from ferrous-containing minerals by acid attack by CO_2, and then the released ferrous iron is oxidized by dissolved oxygen.[2] The Fe-silicates and carbonates react with the carbonic acid in the waters to yield Fe^{2+}:

$$FeSiO_3 + 2CO_2 + 3H_2O = Fe^{2+} + H_4SiO_4 + 2HCO_3^-,$$

and

$$FeCO_3 + CO_2 + H_2O = Fe^{2+} + 2HCO_3^-.$$

When the ferrous iron derived from the solution of these minerals comes in contact with dissolved oxygen, the Fe^{2+} is oxidized and precipitates as ferric oxide:

$$2Fe^{2+} + 4HCO_3^- + H_2O + 1/2O_2 = Fe_2O_3 + 4CO_2 + 3H_2O.$$

The weathering of iron sulfides involves the oxidation of sulfur as well as iron. Solutions derived from weathering of pyrite are very acidic due to the production of sulfuric acid during the formation of ferric oxide. Under humid weathering conditions, the reaction is

$$2FeS_2 + 15/2O_2 + 4H_2O = Fe_2O_3 + 4SO_4^{2-} + 8H^+.$$

In this reaction iron is oxidized from +2 to +3 and sulfur from −1 to +6. The oxidant is oxygen dissolved in the soil waters. In arid regions under highly oxidizing and acidic conditions, ferric sulfate minerals may form in addition to or in place of ferric oxides as the result of pyrite oxidation. Eventually these sulfates convert to ferric oxides.

The weathering of Fe_3O_4 (magnetite) is complicated, and the processes are not completely understood. The weathering reactions leading to the alteration of magnetite must be exceedingly slow because magnetite is one of the minerals that remains unaltered until the last stages of soil formation and is often found as a heavy mineral component of sedimentary rocks. Apparently magnetite grains become armored by a durable impermeable film of Fe_2O_3.

The above discussion and examples emphasize the point that the chemical weathering of iron-bearing minerals and rocks results in the formation of ferric oxides because of their wide range of environmental stability. Ferrous iron is the primary iron species produced in solution as a result of weathering, but it is found only at the lower part of the soil zone and is oxidized when the soil waters eventually get back to the surface. Consequently, the iron initially dissolved in slightly acid ground waters is transported in streams as discrete ferric oxide particles or as ferric oxide coatings on mineral grains rather than in solution.

[2] Conversion of ferrous compounds to ferric oxides does not require preliminary acid attack and can be accomplished by alkaline oxygenated waters. However, the usual process involves both acid attack by CO_2 and oxidation of ferrous iron by dissolved oxygen.

* * * * * * *

References

Garrels and Christ (1965) *Solutions, Minerals and Equilibria:* Harper and Row, New York.

Miller J. P. (1961) Solutes in small streams draining single rock types, Sangre de Cristo Range, New Mexico: U.S. Geol. Survey Water Supply Paper, 1535-F.

12

Reprinted from *Trans. Inst. Mining Met.*, **74,** Pt. 8, 429–433, 455–462 (1964–1965)

The Lateritic Iron Deposits of Conakry*

F. G. PERCIVAL,† O.B.E., Ph.D., MEMBER

553.317(665.3)

SYNOPSIS

The lateritic iron deposits of Conakry, Republic of Guinea, were described by Fermor in 1915, summarizing Lacroix's description, but have not been adequately discussed in English since that date, although much has been written on them in French and German publications. Blondel gave a comprehensive description in 1952, and the present paper is based on information from field exploration and mine operations since that date, with data quoted from the non-English publications referred to above.

The deposits consist of a hard lateritic carapace ('Bed A'), 7 to 10 m thick, selectively mined as iron ore with 53 per cent Fe content (dry basis), and a soft bed below the crust ('Bed C') with an iron content of about 57 per cent, varying from a few to over 100 m in thickness. Below this is an ultrabasic igneous rock (dunite) which is the source rock of the deposits. The soft bed is usually regarded as laterite, but its direct residual content is not large, and the present author prefers to consider it a mainly metasomatic replacement of the dunite, containing a minor lateritic proportion.

Both the soft bed and the carapace have inclusions of high-chrome spinel aggregates ('spinelfels') whose origin has been disputed. It is considered that they are of varied history, and the evidence is reviewed. Nickel is also a constituent affecting the value of the soft bed as an iron ore, and water (combined and free together) forms about 50 per cent of the soft bed by weight. Manganese is of minor importance.

A recent discovery is that an area of important size of the soft bed has been irregularly re-cemented by secondary goethite into hard massive 'brown ore' with less than 3·5 per cent of free moisture. An explanation of its origin is given and on this basis further areas of probable occurrence have been indicated.

The deposits are compared with laterites elsewhere and their age and duration are discussed.

THE LATERITES OF GUINEA, formerly French Guinea, were first carefully described by Lacroix in 1913[26] and, at Lacroix's request, Fermor gave a condensed summary of the publication, adding his own comments, in 1915.[14] Little more was published on these deposits, save for an article by de la Bouglise in 1936[7] and a general geographical study by de Chételat in 1938,[9] until 1950, when Einecke[13] discussed the ore rather fully, and described furnace experiments that had a bearing on the utilization of chromiferous lateritic ores. Blondel gave a much fuller description of the deposits in 1952,[4] with data largely obtained from prospecting prior to

---

*Paper received by the Institution of Mining and Metallurgy on 10th December, 1964, and published on 6th May, 1965; for discussion at a General Meeting to be arranged.

†Consulting Geologist, B.I.S.C. (Ore), Ltd.

[26]etc. See list of references at the end of the paper.

Editor's Note: A row of asterisks indicates that material has been omitted from the original article.

their development. Scheibe[40] gave a general description of them in 1954.

In recent years the deposits have been studied and described in more detail in various special aspects by Millot and Bonifas,[31] Bonifas,[6] Legoux and Percival,[27] and by Legoux,[28]; and a note was published by Bonifas and Legoux in 1957[5] on the presence of maghemite in the ore. Maignien[30] contributed a very detailed study of the 'cuirassement' of Guinean soils, containing much information of valuable application to the Conakry laterite, and a detailed mineralogical study of the ore has been made by Dr. Erich Seeliger, of the Mineralogical Institute of the Berlin Technical University, of which a brief account has been published.[41]

Much of this recent work, however, is based on specialized laboratory studies. Since Blondel's 1952 paper was published the Compagnie Minière de Conakry has acquired a large body of information from the mining faces and from some hundreds of bore-holes, many of which were continued down to the 'deck' of the mother rock from which the ore has been derived. This enables one to describe the geological setting and origin of the deposits and to give field data not previously published. Studies of many slides and polished sections have provided information on the origin of the beds and of their textures.

Lateritic formations on the scale and with the features displayed at Conakry may occur elsewhere, but have not been described in full detail. The ore is still in process of formation, and has been aptly described by Blondel as a 'living laterite'.

SITUATION AND GENERAL DESCRIPTION

The city of Conakry stands on what was formerly the small island of Tumbo, now artificially linked with the mainland, on the coast of the Guinea Republic, latitude 9° 30′ N (see Fig. 1). It is at the tip of a peninsula which continues inland as a laterite-covered ridge in a SW–NE direction for a distance of about 40 km, terminating near Mount Kakoulima, which is over 1000 m high. At about 10 km from Conakry a small eminence known as Kaloum gives its name to the peninsula. In general, the height of the peninsula does not exceed 150 m, and the width of the ridge increases from about 1 km at Conakry to 6 km near Kakoulima. The country has a tropical monsoon climate, which has been discussed in considerable detail by Blondel (*loc. cit.*). The rainy season lasts from June to the end of September, and the annual rainfall averages about $4\frac{1}{2}$ m. Most of the rain, even in the wet season, falls during the night, and mining operations can be carried on without difficulty throughout the year. There is no great annual variation in temperature, the monthly averages lying between 22 and 32° C (72 to 90° F). The peninsula is covered almost entirely with a laterite crust, which supports poor vegetation. Only limited areas of scrub forest or bush occur on the uplands, but in the valleys soil has collected sufficiently to permit some cultivation—mostly bananas and vegetables. Rice is cultivated further inland. The beaches are fringed by shallow-rooted palm trees.

The underlying rock of the peninsula is a peridotite (dunite), but it is not exposed at the surface of the ground until the vicinity of Mount Kakoulima is reached. Here there is a sequence upwards from dunite

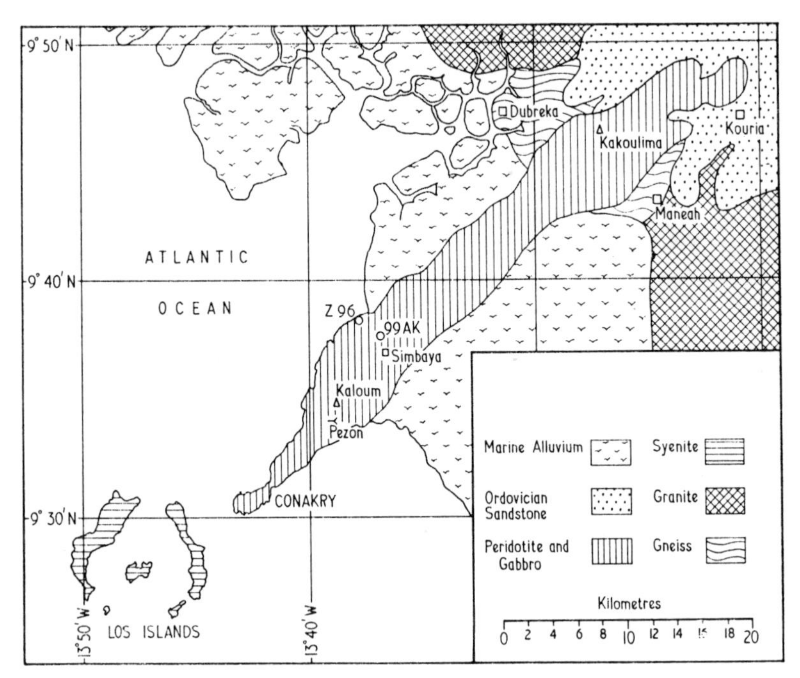

Fig. 1.—Geological map of Conakry area.

through wehrlite and troctolite to a gabbroidal rock.[3] In one of the mine borings, instead of the usual dunite a dolerite was found, but over almost the whole area of the peninsular laterite the only rock found at depth is dunite, occasionally wehrlitic through the presence of diallage, as Lacroix discovered (*loc. cit.*), and as Seeliger has recently found in samples taken from the cores of the mine bore-holes (*loc. cit.*).

Granites and gneisses crop out on both flanks of the peninsula. Near Dubreka a biotite granite has a considerable outcrop, rising to 167 m in the peak of Kambo; it is separated from the peridotite by an outcrop of muscovite gneiss. On the south flank of the peridotite, at Maneah, a similar granite is now being quarried for railway and road ballast. The gneisses are granoblastic, with both biotite and muscovite, and contain zircon. They are described by Renaud and Delaire[37] as having also apatite and garnet. The biotite granites have quartz with undulose extinction, magnetite and epidote, and also contain zircon. To the northeast and east of Mount Kakoulima almost flat-lying Ordovician sandstones rest unconformably on the older gneissic and other rocks. Their scarp edges form sub-vertical cliffs, and occasionally isolated buttes stand out from the main mass. The plateau elevation rises to about 600 m above sea-level.

Six to ten miles offshore at the tip of the peninsula lies the small archipelago of the Los Islands. There the rocks are nepheline syenites which give rise to a bauxitic crust.

In 1919–22 the Kaloum deposits were prospected by drilling 187 bore-holes, on a triangular grid of 1-km spacing, by de la Bouglise, but development was delayed for many years. In 1949 drilling was recommenced over a more limited area, with closer spacing of bore-holes, and a sample shipment was sent to Britain for blast-furnace trials. (Previous trials had been made in the Saar and Belgium in 1939.) Development of the mine was started in 1950, and shipments of ore began in 1953. Only limited high-iron low-chrome areas of the hard upper crust, about 8 m thick, are mined at present, and annual shipments have been as follows (totals are in metric tons):

1953	391 695	1959	358 374*
1954	579 618	1960	766 454
1955	674 949	1961	534 936
1956	822 413	1962	719 495
1957	1 058 028	1963	559 000
1958	372 796*	1964	701 053

Core drilling is now carried on continuously, on a hexagonal grid system, but during 1956–59 it was intensified. In 1958, for example, 372 borings were drilled with a total length of 12 660 m. The cores were sampled and analysed, largely metre by metre, for Fe, Al_2O_3, Cr, Ni and P.

The standard analysis for the ore sold is given below:

Fe	53% FeO(OH) 84·2%
Al_2O_3	9·0
SiO_2	1·5
Cr_2O_3	1·7 (Cr 1·15)
NiO	0·15 (Ni 0·12)
SO_3	0·3 (S 0·1)
P_2O_5	0·2 (P 0·085)
CaO	0·4
TiO_2	0·1
Mn	tr.
Cu, Pb and Zn	nil
BaO, MgO	nil
As and Sb	nil
H_2O combined	11·0 to 12·0

Standard opencast mining methods are employed. The rail haulage from the mine to the harbour of Conakry is by a broad-gauge track only 9 km in length. The ore is stockpiled at the port by belts and a travelling stacker, and recovered by belts from a tunnel below the stockpile to load the boats at the rate of 1000 t/h. The harbour can accommodate boats of up to 31 ft draught.

SEQUENCE OF THE BEDS

Covering practically the whole peninsula, as already indicated, there is a surface capping of dark red or mottled red and yellow material that would be recognized as laterite by anyone familiar with laterites elsewhere—

*The effect of the steel recession was very marked in these years.

in some places 'scoriaceous' at the surface, and largely vesicular. At the surface it is hard and percussion drills are necessary to drill the blast-holes. Downwards the cap gradually becomes less hard until, at a depth of 7 to 8 m, it is usually soft enough to be pierced by augur drills. (This is used to advantage in mining, the vertical, percussion-drilled blast-holes being supplemented by horizontal, augur-drilled holes driven in at the toe of the mining face.) The hard upper crust is known in the mine as Bed A. During the prospection period the lower, softer part of this crust was termed Bed B, but that distinction is little used now since most of the Bed B material is mined with Bed A. The change in hardness is, however, accompanied by chemical changes, and Bed B commonly contains less alumina than the upper part of the crust.

At a depth of about 8 to 12 m there is a further change to a soft yellow- or buff-coloured material called the *couche tendre* (soft bed) or Bed C (see Fig. 11, Plate II). The change occurs roughly at the level of the water-table, but this rises and falls seasonally. In Bed A/B the free moisture is considered rather high at 11 to 13 per cent, but in Bed C it is approximately 38 per cent. The aspect of Bed C is not at all like that of normal laterite, being fairly homogeneous in texture and free of vesicles, except where it begins to dry out at, or near, its junction with Bed B. Its thickness varies from 2 or 3 to over 100 m. It is not sticky, but feels like a compact fine silt.

Below Bed C lies the dunite. The change is generally abrupt, but there is frequently a siliceous band, largely chalcedonic, at or just above the junction, and the altered bed itself may be highly silicified locally. The silica forms occasional veins that ramify in the Bed C material for some metres above the 'deck' of the dunite.

Although Blondel (*loc. cit.*) noted that the use of the term 'bed' is not satisfactory for these rocks, its usage is now too well established to be changed.

Sporadic occurrences of a dark hard goethitic rock containing numerous glistening crystals visible to the naked eye, and recognizable with a hand lens as octahedra, are irregularly distributed at the surface of the ground and in veins in the mining faces. Owing to their high chrome content they are avoided in mining. The octahedral crystals are chrome-bearing spinels or, more rarely, simply magnetite. It is convenient to call this rock 'spinelfels'.

These spatial relationships are shown diagrammatically in Fig. 2; their time relationships are more complex and are discussed later.

* * * * * * *

GENERAL DISCUSSION

Although laterite (with its high alumina partner, bauxite) is of widespread distribution throughout the tropics, and was described and named by Buchanan as long ago as 1807,[8] certain features of its origin were disputed up to the early years of this century. Important advances in the knowledge of its formation have been made by soil geologists in the last decade, e.g. d'Hoore,[23] but despite this, occasional confusion in the use of the terms laterite, canga and limonite still persists.

Buchanan's type locality remained without further examination for over a century, but in 1936 Fox[16] collected laterites from Buchanan's chief localities, and his analyses showed that these rocks were 'vermicular lithomarge with a considerable amount of ferric hydrate present in the upper parts'. A fair amount of silica was also present as quartz.

Elsewhere in India, in the present writer's experience, there are widespread deposits of laterite without any lithomarge development. Some of these occurrences may be largely transported, showing a knife-edge contact with the underlying rocks, but not all.

Fox considered that laterite is a 'final stage' after kaolinization and Dey,[11] who re-examined Buchanan's laterite, regarded this Malabar laterite as a half-way product to be included with the material now accepted as laterite.

Gordon[19] found that much of the kaolin in the kaolinitic parts of the bauxites of Arkansas was not a half-way stage to gibbsite, but was a later kaolinization of the gibbsite.

Lacroix (*loc. cit.*) noted that the alteration from nepheline syenite to bauxite in the Los Islands, offshore from Conakry, took place within the space of a single microscope slide, but he also found occurrences where the alteration was to a plastic clay. Gordon *et al.* believe that in deposits in Arkansas derived from nepheline syenite the feldspars altered directly to microcrystalline gibbsite.

Sabot,[39] however, states that lateritization is 'almost always' preceded by an argillaceous alteration, mainly to kaolinite, forming a layer between the unaltered rock and the laterite horizon, and quotes a large number of widely distributed examples. In Guinea he refers to a passage of lithomarge in the laterite of Dabola, and surmises that Lacroix's description of a direct alteration from the mother rock to bauxite in Guinea may only apply to specimens collected at or near the ground surface. The transition from dunite to the goethitic material of Bed C is, however, quite sudden and no kaolinitic phase is normally present. As already mentioned, lenses of up to 2 m of kaolinitic material have been found in a very limited number of bore-holes, but the occurrence is generally far above the present zone of alteration. These are quite local occurrences and their origin has not yet been investigated. As a general rule there is no kaolinitic phase at Conakry at any stage between the dunite and the carapace.

The lateritization factors in these processes are those of alteration *in situ*, leading to the formation of residual laterite, with only local or internal transportation of constituents, but at the surface of the ground a lateritic carapace may become mechanically disintegrated, transported and re-deposited, in some cases intermixed with other materials such as sand grains. Fermor would have called this type 'lateritite'. An important deposit of this type occurs at Enugu in Nigeria.[21]

In the Conakry deposit the main skeletal mass of the carapace may be residual, and only minimal transportation has occurred, but there has been much re-solution and re-arrangement of the original residual material and, as indicated, the present-day carapace is mainly derived only indirectly from the dunite.

Apart from the source rock the factors in the formation of bauxite are similar to those for laterite. Gordon *et al.* suggest that optimum conditions for bauxitization include: 'A warm humid climate of continuous moisture, in which rainfall considerably exceeds evaporation most of the time'. They further state: 'An examination of stratigraphic evidence in the Arkansas bauxite region leads to the conclusion that a change from a climate of alternating wet and dry seasons to one of continuous moisture may have ushered in the period of bauxite formation; and that a return to seasonal dryness may have ended this period'.[20]

The more general opinion is that alternating wet and dry seasons favour laterite formation. The critical factor is not the amount of rainfall; laterite forms freely in parts of India with 56 in. of annual rainfall, while Conakry has an average of 180 in., and occasionally reaches 260 in. in a year. The evidence for continuous rainfall provided by Eocene deposits is naturally less positive than the evidence of present-day laterite formation in areas where alternating wet and dry seasons are now prevalent, and laterite is at the present time being formed in India and Guinea. While it may be correct that lateritic agencies are at work in present-day tropical regions with continuous rainfall, the completion of the process to the widespread formation of a hard carapace is less likely in such areas.

The possible intervention of bacteria was suggested by Holland in 1910.[22] Maignien[30] states that when the normal circulation of air of the soil is insufficient the micro-organisms are constrained to utilize other sources of oxygen, in particular those of ferric oxides, whence reduction occurs. Maignien studied the distribution of 'ferrobacteria' in the Guinean soils and tabulated counts of both reducing bacteria and bacterial 'mineralizators' of iron. He found large concentrations of the latter (but mainly in the uppermost 5 to 10 cm of the soil or 'ferralitic' crust), and concluded that if the phenomena of reduction were found to be tied in with biologic activity, the phenomena of oxidation were chiefly linked with purely chemical reactions. He notes, however, the action of certain minute algae which liberate small bubbles of oxygen on which hydrates of iron are deposited, but again these, although anaerobic, were not recorded from any significant depths. Thus while bacterial action may have played a part in the formation of the carapace, there is no evidence as yet that it has been an important agent at depth.

Laterite (as distinct from bauxite) is a comparatively short-lived rock, forming rapidly and decaying rapidly. It can be seen to form a measurable thickness over previously barren rock in a single season in India.[35] A motor-car coil has been found embedded in the surface laterite at Conakry. Alexander[1] described crown bottle tops similarly embedded in a lateritic breccia at Singapore. Its decay may be almost as rapid as its formation, for in addition to agencies of abrasion and climatic action, solution of the sesquioxides helps to break it up.

Maignien (*loc. cit.*) observes that once any vegetation secures a hold on a carapace a horizon of humus is gradually produced which has an intense solvent action on the ferruginous cement. Trees then obtain a hold, and their roots complete the disintegration of the crust.

Estimates of the life of laterite are very variable, and this uncertainty may be an indication of the relative shortness of the age of the visible carapaces. In the case of bauxites one is on surer ground. The earliest bauxites of Arkansas occur in, and are covered by, Lower Eocene rocks.[20] Bauxite resists chemical decay more than does iron-rich laterite, an obvious reason being the relative insolubility of alumina as compared with iron. Iron-rich laterite is rather rare in the geological column, except as a present-day surface occurrence, but some bauxites are as old as the Trias or even Devonian. The conditions that led to the formation of early Eocene bauxites would be equally favourable for the formation of ferruginous laterites where suitable source rocks occur, but the laterites do not appear to have persisted long enough as individuals to have been commonly covered up by later deposits. In Nigeria, however, du Preez[36] reported the occurrence of laterite in a well 'at a depth of 170 ft immediately below the base of the Chad Series' (Plio-Pleistocene), and the Grecian chromiferous lateritic iron ores are covered by Upper Cretaceous limestones.[2]

In the Sahara, within human times, the climate has been warm and humid—witness the cave drawings discovered by Lhote, and the presence of crocodiles still living in the isolated pools of Matmata in Mauritania, described by Monod.[32] Laterite was formed in these conditions. Thus at Fort Gouraud in the western Sahara of Mauritania there are thick terraces of canga on the flanks of the Kedia d'Idjil, in which the laterite cement has been preserved by the closely packed boulders of hard banded hematite quartzite. But where plain laterite without included boulders was formed on the Kedia it has decayed, and only sporadic patches a few inches thick remain—a decay that has apparently taken only a few thousand years to complete.[29]

Oertel[33] calculates that to form a crust of laterite 20 m thick in Goa, some

780-m thickness of siliceous schist must have weathered away, taking 780 000 years in the process, at an erosion rate averaging 1 mm a year. But he adds that at the same erosion rate the 20 m of laterite crust itself will weather away in 20 000 years, and consequently no particular occurrence of laterite can be more than 20 000 years old here. Thus while the process of lateritization could have been continuing perhaps since the end of the Cretaceous period, one cannot assume that any laterite carapace has necessarily persisted as an individual deposit throughout the whole of this period.

Fox[15] puts the time factor for laterite formation as at least a million years. Wilson (*loc. cit.*) writes that 'though duricrusts at the summits of the higher hills in the Sula Mountains may be in part as old as the Mesozoic era, many of them are much younger and some of them are Quaternary'.

Pallister,[34] discussing the Uganda laterites, states that 'it seems certain that the laterite of the plateau remnants was formed in mid-Tertiary times if not earlier', but 'on lower levels near the lake, artifacts found in laterite point to lower- or mid-Pleistocene age'.

Maignien (*loc. cit.*) considers that the ferralitic alteration of aluminosilicate rocks in Guinea, with intermediate stages of erosion, gives a sequence that goes back 'probably' to the Cretaceous.

Conakry lies in the zone of maximum equatorial rainfall in West Africa, but it cannot be assumed that those conditions have continued for an indefinite period. Zeuner,[46] discussing climatic phases in Africa, states that the caloric equator (the degree of latitude at which the minimum annual fluctuation of radiation occurs) has varied its position only moderately during long periods of time, but there were other periods 'during which it swung north and south repeatedly with an amplitude of as much as 10 to 16 degrees (i.e. 5 to 8 degrees N and S of the geographical equator). During these phases of violent fluctuation, the geographical belt which is now the zone of equatorial rainfall may well have come to lie sufficiently far north or south to receive only a fraction of the rainfall it enjoys at present. But such phases must have been of short duration and alternated with phases of heavier rainfall every 21 000 years. . . . Apart from earlier periods of this kind, there is one between 235 000 and 70 000 B.P., which stands out for its long duration'.

Zeuner gives these climatic interpretations as only tentative, and one need not assume that these variations in rainfall would be sufficient to inhibit, even temporarily, the formation of a laterite crust, but there may well have been little or no alteration of the dunite to form Bed C during a long dry phase.

Laterite formation below ground, and laterite degradation at the surface, must commonly be contemporaneous processes, but it does not seem too much to assume a possible net rate of formation in pluvial phases of about 1 mm a year, and with the thicknesses at Conakry this would take us back to the long dry period mentioned—a period during which degradation would be in excess of lateritization. Considering all the factors, Maignien's suggestion of a sequence that goes back probably to the Cretaceous seems an unnecessarily long period. Taking the Quaternary as covering a million years, one need not go back into the Tertiary to get all the time needed for the formation of the Conakry iron deposits, but any estimate of dates is speculative.

The poor resistance to erosive agencies and the ready solubility of its iron content explain the rarity of occurrence of laterite beds in the geological column, but one may ask what became of the iron of former deposits of the size of Conakry. There is no reason to suppose that such deposits have not been previously developed. The only essential requisites are an ample source of iron, such as an ultrabasic rock, a warm monsoon climate and possibly iron bacteria—a combination that must surely have occurred commonly throughout the earth's history and possibly frequently in Precambrian time. The erosion of these iron-containing masses would provide enough iron for large sedimentary iron deposits. This idea need not be pursued in further detail, but a Precambrian Conakry's 3 000 000 000 tons of metallic iron could have provided the iron for a sedimentary banded iron formation, with 30 per cent iron content, of the size of 10 000 000 000 tons.

Acknowledgements.—As this paper is based on a continuous association with the Conakry deposits since 1950 the author has been indebted to many more friends than can be mentioned here, but his particular thanks are due to M. Pierre Legoux, formerly Administrateur-Directeur Général of the Compagnie Minière de Conakry, who not only collected many of the statistical records used in the present paper, but shared in much of the field work, and who still continues to give greatly valued advice. Another friend whose counsel is gratefully acknowledged is M. Fernand Blondel, with whom many delightful visits and discussions were shared in earlier years at the mine and elsewhere. The present Directeur Général of the company, M. H. Saint-Maurice, maintains a similar association during visits to the mine, and his assistance in obtaining material for examination has been ably seconded by M. J. M. Holzem, Chef du département de Production at Conakry.

M. Fofana Karim, Director of Mines, Republic of Guinea, has kindly given access to material obtained in drilling for water supplies, and also assisted in a visit to the Government prospecting operations for chromite at Kouria.

Numerous quotations have been made from the work of Mme Bonifas in Guinea, and of Mackenzie Gordon in Arkansas, and the latter has also given valued personal information.

From early years of development members of the staff of the British Iron and Steel Research Association have been interested in selected aspects of investigation—mainly on Bed C—and Mr. E. W. Voice, Mr. G. E. Davies and Dr. R. Wild have given freely of their time and experience.

At the Imperial College of Science and Technology the author has had useful discussions and help from Dr. E. Cohen; Dr. G. P. L. Walker has clarified doubts on mineral identifications; and Dr. A. P. Millman has made Vickers microhardness tests on spinel crystals. Professor David Williams kindly read the paper in draft and gave valuable advice.

The author has been privileged to see some of the photographs of Bed C material obtained by the use of the Sonde Castaing apparatus at the Bureau de Recherches Géologiques et Minières, Paris, for which he is grateful. He also wishes to thank Miss R. Wittmann for assistance with somewhat involved German translations.

Finally, this paper is published by permission of the Compagnie Minière de Conakry and of the British Iron and Steel Corporation (Ore), Ltd., to both of which the author is also greatly indebted for the many opportunities they have given for interesting field work on iron ores at Conakry and elsewhere.

REFERENCES

1. ALEXANDER, F. E. S. Observations on tropical weathering: a study of the movement of iron, aluminium and silicon in weathering rocks at Singapore. *Q. J. geol. Soc., Lond.*, **115**, 1959–60, 123–42.

2. ARONIS, G. Les minerais de fer de Grèce. *Symp. sur les gisements de fer du monde. XIX Congr. géol. Int., Alger., 1952*, **II**, 223–6.

3. BARRERE, J. La presqu'île du Kaloum et le massif du Kakoulima. *Notes Serv. géol. Prospect. min Afr. occid. fr.*, 1959, 1–44.

4. BLONDEL, F. Les gisements de fer de l'Afrique occidentale française. *Symp. sur les gisements de fer du monde. XIX Congr. géol. Int., Alger., 1952*, **I**, 5–34.

5. BONIFAS, M., and LEGOUX, P. Présence de maghemite massive dans des produits d'altération latéritique. *Bull. Serv. Carte géol. Als. Lorr.*, **10**, no. 2, 1957, 7–9.

6. BONIFAS, M. Contribution à l'étude géochimique de l'altération latéritique. *Mém. Serv. Carte géol. Als. Lorr.*, no. 17, 1959, 159 p.

7. BOUGLISE, R. DE LA. Le gisement de fer de Conakry. *Chron. Mines colon.*, 1936, 116–20.

8. BUCHANAN (-HAMILTON), F. *A journey from Madras, through the countries of Mysore, Canara, and Malabar.* (London: East India Company, 1807), 3 vols.

9. CHÉTELAT, E. DE. Le modelé latéritique de l'ouest de la Guinée française. *Rev. Geogr. Phys.*, **11**, no. 1, 1938, 120 p.

10. DEB, S., and CHAKRABORTY, K. L. Origin of chromite deposits associated with the ultrabasic rocks of the eastern part of the Indian Peninsula. *Proc. natn. Inst. Sci. India*, **27**, pt. A, 1961, 508–19.

11. DEY, A. K. Observations on Buchanan's laterite of Malabar. *Trans. Min. geol. metall. Inst. India*, **47**, 1951, 129–33.

12. DUNHAM, K. C., *et al.* The chromiferous ultrabasic rocks of eastern Sierra Leone. *Overseas Geol. Miner. Resour. Bull. Supple.* no. 3, 1958, 44 p.

13. EINECKE, G. *Die Eisenerzvorräte der Welt.* (Düsseldorf: Verlag Stahleisen M.B.H., 1950), 378 p. and atlas 195 p.

14. FERMOR, L. L. The work of Professor Lacroix on the laterites of French Guinea. *Geol. Mag.*, **II**, 1915, 28–37; 77–82; and 123–9.

15. Fox, C. S. *Bauxite and aluminous laterite, 2nd ed.* (London: Crosby Lockwood, 1932), 312 p.

16. Fox, C. S. Buchanan's laterite of Malabar and Canara. *Rec. geol. Surv. India*, **69**, pt. 4, April 1936, 389–422.

17. Frasché, D. F. Origin of the Surigao iron ores. *Econ. Geol.*, **36**, 1941, 280–305.

18. Goldstein, P., and Eickworth, E. Das Verhalten von Chrom im Thomaskonverter. *Stahl und Eisen*, **78**, no. 18, Sept. 1958, 1235–46.

19. Gordon, M. Contribution to discussion in *Symp. on problems of clay and laterite genesis.* (New York: American Institute of Mining, Metallurgical and Petroleum Engineers, 1952), p. 215.

20. Gordon, M., Tracey, J. I., and Ellis, M. W. Geology of the Arkansas bauxite region. *Prof. Pap. U.S. geol. Surv.* 299, 1958, 268 p.

21. Hazell, J. R. T. The Enugu ironstone, Udi Division, Onitsha Province. *Rec. geol. Surv. Nigeria 1955*, 1958, 44–58.

22. Holland, T. H. On the constitution, origin and dehydration of laterite. *Geol. Mag.*, **10**, 1903, 59–69.

23. d'Hoore, J. L'accumulation des sesquioxides libres dans les sols tropicaux. *Publs Inst. natn. Etude agron. Congo belge*, **62**, 1954.

24. Hose, H. R. Jamaica type bauxites developed on limestones. *Econ. Geol.*, **58**, 1963, 62–9.

25. Jones, H. A. The oolitic ironstones of the Agbaja Plateau, Kabba Province. *Rec. geol. Surv. Nigeria 1955*, 1958, 20–43.

26. Lacroix, A. Les latérites de la Guinée et les produits d'altération qui leur sont associés. *Nouv. Archs. Mus. Hist. nat., Paris*, 1913, 255–356.

27. Legoux, P., and Percival, F. G. Sur la structure des cuirasses latéritiques ferrugineuses de Conakry. *C. r. hebd. Séanc. Acad. Sci.*, **248**, 1959, 2226–8.

28. Legoux, P. Les péridotites de Conakry et du Kaloum (République de Guinée) et leur serpentinisation. *Bull. Soc. geol. Fr.*, **2**, 1960, 50–63.

29. Lethbridge, R. F., and Percival, F. G. Iron deposits at Fort Gouraud, Mauritania, French West Africa. *Trans. Instn Min. Metall.*, **63**, 1953–54 (*Bull. Instn Min. Metall.*, no. 568, March 1954), 285–98.

30. Maignien, R. Le cuirassement des sols en Guinée, Afrique Occidentale. *Mém. Serv. Carte géol. Als. Lorr.*, 1958, 239 p.

31. Millot, G., and Bonifas, M. Transformations isovolumétriques dans les phénomènes de latéritisation et bauxitisation. *Bull. Serv. Carte géol. Als. Lorr.*, **8**, 1955, no. 1, 3–20.

32. Monod, T. *Méharées: explorations au vrai Sahara.* (Paris: Editions 'Je Sers', 1947), 300 p.

33. Oertel, G. Contribuição para o conhecimento das laterites de Goa. *Comunções Servs geol. Port.*, **36**, 1955, 159–98.

34. Pallister, J. W. Erosion levels and laterite in Buganda province, Uganda. *C. r. XIX Congr. géol. Int., Alger., 1952*, no. 21, 1954, 193–9.

35. Percival, F. G. The iron ores of Noamundi. *Trans. Min. geol. Inst. India*, **26**, 1931, p. 196.

36. PREEZ, J. W. DU. Notes on the occurrence of oolites and pisolites in Nigerian laterites. *C. r. XIX Congr. géol. Int., Alger., 1952,* no. 27, 1954, 163–9.

37. RENAUD, L., and DELAIRE, L. Notice explicative sur la feuille Conakry-Est. *Direction Mines A.O.F., Dakar,* 1955, 1–16.

38. RUCKMICK, J. C. The iron ores of Cerro Bolivar, Venezuela. *Econ. Geol.,* **58,** 1963, 218–36.

39. SABOT, J. Les latérites. *C. r. XIX Congr. géol. Int., Alger., 1952,* no. 21, 1954, 181–92.

40. SCHEIBE, E. A. Die Eisenerz-Lagerstätte Conakry in Französisch-Guinea (Westafrika). *Stahl und Eisen,* **74,** 1954, pt. 4, 215–9.

41. SEELIGER, E. Paragenetische Untersuchungen an C-Erzen (Weicherzen) von Conakry, Guinea. *Fortschr. Miner.,* **39,** no. I, June 1961, 139–41.

42. WEISSE, G. DE. Note sur quelques types de latérite de la Guinée Portugaise. *C. r. XIX Congr. géol. Int., Alger., 1952,* no. 21, 1954, 171–9.

43. WELD, C. M. The residual brown iron-ores of Cuba. *Trans. Amer. Inst. Min. Engrs,* **40,** 1909, 299–312.

44. WILSON, N. W., and MARMO, V. Geology, geomorphology and mineral resources of the Sula Mountains. *Bull. geol. Surv. Sierra Leone* no. 1, 1958, 103 p.

45. WOLF, W., *et al.* Betriebsversuche zur Verhüttung von Conakry Erz. *Stahl und Eisen,* **78,** 1958; 1020–7; 1100–7.

46. ZEUNER, F. E. *Dating the past, 4th ed.* (London: Methuen, 1958), 516 p.

47. CORRENS, C. W. Mineralogische Untersuchungen an Sedimentaren Eisenerzen. *Symp. sur les gisements de fer du Monde. XIX Congr. géol. Int., Alger, 1952,* **II,** 1954, p. 29.

13

Reprinted from *Econ. Geol.*, **59**(7), 1204 (1963)

Supergene Iron Ores of Minas Gerais, Brazil

JOHN VAN N. DORR II

ABSTRACT

The iron ores of Minas Gerais, Brazil, fall into two categories: (1) hypogene hematite ore averaging 66 percent or more Fe, and (2) lower-grade supergene ores. Most ore now extracted is high-grade hypogene ore; lower-grade supergene ores will be of much future value.

All supergene ores formed by weathering of itabirite, a metamorphosed oxide-facies iron formation averaging about 38 percent Fe and 44 percent SiO_2. The Cauê Itabirite crops out for about 540 linear kilometers in central Minas Gerais. Supergene ores fall into three intergradational categories: (1) enriched itabirite, averaging 49 percent Fe, easily concentratable, with reserves about 25,000 million tons; (2) intermediate grade ores, averaging perhaps 63 percent Fe, with indicated and inferred reserves more than 600 million tons; and (3) canga, averaging between 57 and 62 percent Fe, with reserves in the hundreds of millions of tons.

Disaggregation of hard and brittle itabirite by solution primarily of quartz and secondarily of other soluble constituents causes residual enrichment in iron with minor hydration of hematite. As weathering continues, most of the quartz is removed and more of the hematite is hydrated, producing intermediate grade ore. Secondary enrichment by limonite is important. The final weathering product is canga. In canga, almost all the iron is hydrated, and the rock is still further impoverished in SiO_2 and residually enriched in Al_2O_3 and P. Canga also forms by cementation of iron-rich detritus by limonite.

Four factors control the supergene ore-forming process: (1) physiography, for ores occur on ridges and plateaus; (2) climate, for seasonal rainfall is apparently needed for the formation of extensive canga blankets; (3) grain size of the original itabirite, for quartz with a grain size much greater than 0.1 millimeter is not readily soluble; and (4) composition of the iron formation.

The chemically inert and physically resistant canga blanket is essential to supergene ore formation because soft weathering products would otherwise be removed as fast as formed. Thus, canga gives time for the formation of other ore types.

Iron fixed as cementing limonite in canga and as enriching limonite in intermediate grade ore was derived by leaching and hydration of hematite from itabirite. It probably moved in the ferrous state and was precipitated as insoluble hydrous ferric oxide primarily by oxygenation of the solutions, to a lesser extent by their evaporation at or near the surface, and to a still smaller degree by pH changes.

The data show that the high-grade hematite ore, 66 percent Fe or higher, cannot have formed directly by supergene action. Geochemical processes resulting in supergene concentration of iron also concentrated alumina and phosphorus. The high-grade ore contains about the same low percentages of these materials as unweathered itabirite.

Editor's Comments on Papers 14 Through 17

14 Gruner: Excerpt from *The Mineralogy and Geology of the Taconites and Iron Ores of the Mesabi Range, Minnesota*

15 Gruner: *Hydrothermal Leaching of Iron Ores of the Lake Superior Type—A Modified Theory*

16 Dorr, Guild, and Barbosa: Excerpts from *Origin of the Brazilian Iron Ores*

17 James, Dutton, Pettijohn, and Wier: Excerpts from *Geology and Ore Deposits of the Iron River-Crystal Falls District, Iron County, Michigan*

Until the mid-1950s iron mining in the Lake Superior region was restricted to high-grade hematite-goethite ores found within the sedimentary iron-formations of the region. Subsequently, with new developments in mining and milling technology an increasing share of the total production has come from the iron-formation, or taconite, as it is called locally. While mining was centered on the enriched oxide ores, considerable geological work focused on the problem of the origin of these high-grade bodies.

On the Mesabi range of the Lake Superior district, the oxide orebodies, with 50 to 65 percent iron, occur at the surface within the Biwabik iron-formation, which contains 25 to 30 percent iron as carbonate, silicate, or magnetite. Because the known orebodies are restricted to the surface, early investigators were quick to conclude that they must represent weathering enrichments formed by the oxidation of the iron and the leaching of silica of the parent iron-formation. The fact that most orebodies exhibit slump structures, which suggest leaching of the noniron constituents from the taconite, added support to this conclusion.

The relation between the oxide orebodies and the weathering surface is not, however, equally clear in other iron-formations of the district. Some oxide orebodies occur at depths of several thousand feet and many exhibit textures suggesting that the silica of the original taconite was replaced by iron oxide. Similar deeply buried orebodies unrelated to any known erosion surface are known in the iron districts of Africa, Australia, Brazil, Canada, India, and other parts of the world. For such bodies of enriched ore the idea that oxidation and leaching took place through the action of oxygenated meteoric waters appeared unreasonable to some, and the alternative proposal that the ores were the work of hydrothermal fluids was born. The meteoric-hydrothermal controversy on the origin of enriched oxide ores within iron formation continues to this day.

J.W. Gruner was among the first to champion the hydrothermal theory for the origin of high-grade ores, and his works on this subject are still widely quoted. In a series of experiments he demonstrated the effectiveness of hot water as an agent capable of oxidizing ferrous minerals in taconite. In 1930 he published the results of these experiments and presented his view on how the Lake Superior orebodies originated through the action of hydrothermal solutions. A sharp debate followed in the literature of that day, and Gruner subsequently proposed a modified hydrothermal theory, reproduced here as Paper 15.

John W. Gruner is Professor Emeritus of the University of Minnesota, where he spent most of his professional career. Although he published on many geologic subjects, his first and continuing interest is iron-formations and iron ores. Beginning in

1922 with a paper on the origin of the Biwabik iron-formation, he contributed more than any other individual to the subject of iron geochemistry during the following three decades. The mineral minnesotaite, an iron silicate found in iron formations throughout the world, was described and named by him. An excellent field geologist, Gruner pioneered the experimental and quantitative approach to the problem of the origin of iron-formations and iron ores. His article on the mineralogy and geology of the Mesabi range, from which Paper 14 is excerpted, contains a wealth of analytical data on the Biwabik iron-formation and its members.

J. V. N. Dorr and P. W. Guild of the U.S. Geological Survey, and A.L.M. Barbosa of the Departmento Nacional da Producao Mineral, Brazil, the authors of Paper 16, each have published more comprehensive reports on the high-grade iron ores of Brazil. The present excerpt was selected because it contains a concise summary of the various ore types and a review of the ideas that have been proposed to account for the formation of the ores. In subsequent papers, both Dorr (1965) and Guild (1953, 1957) support some form of hydrothermal origin for the high-grade hard hematite ores.

In discussing the ore-forming solutions Guild (1953) concludes:

> The virtual restriction of the hematite ores to the middle group of the Minas series suggests that the iron was picked up from the itabirite formation itself and redistributed. Furthermore, the elements present in the ores are those found in the unenriched formation; no notable introduction of new elements has taken place.

Dorr (1965) similarly supports a hydrothermal origin. He states:

> The writer believes that the high-grade hematite ores of the Quadrilatero Ferrifero were caused by the synmetamorphic metasomatic replacement of quartz in the host itabirite by hematite derived from the iron-formation itself. The writer believes that the transportation of iron to and quartz from the sites of replacement was by fluids at high temperatures and pressures, probably supercritical in most cases, derived in part from the enclosing metasedimentary rocks during their metamorphism, and also from the younger granitic bodies formed and emplaced during metamorphism.

Paper 17 by H. L. James, C. E. Dutton, and K. L. Wier of the U.S. Geological Survey and by F. J. Pettijohn, Professor Emeritus of The Johns Hopkins University, contains an excellent review of the principal theories of iron ore genesis. The article is an excerpt of a monograph on the geology of the Iron River district. After a careful qualitative and quantitative analysis of the theories of ore formation, the authors propose a special version of the meteoric water theory to account for the deep ores of the district.

References

Dorr, J. V. N., II, 1965, Nature and origin of the high-grade hematite ores of Minas Gerais, Brazil: Econ. Geol., v. 60, p. 1–46.

Gruner, J. W., 1922, The origin of sedimentary iron formations: Econ. Geol., v. 17, p. 408–460.
———, 1930, Hydrothermal oxidation and leaching experiments; their bearing on the origin of Lake Superior hematite-limonite areas; Econ. Geol., v. 25, p. 697–719, 837–867.
Guild, P. W., 1953, Iron deposits of the Congonhas district, Minas Gerais, Brazil: Econ. Geol., v. 48, p. 637–676.
———, 1957, Geology and mineral resources of the Congonhas district, Minas Gerais, Brazil: U.S. Geol. Surv. Prof. Paper 290, 90 p.

14

Reprinted from *The Mineralogy and Geology of the Taconites and Iron Ores of the Mesabi Range, Minnesota,* Chap. 9, Iron Range Resources and Rehabilitation Commission, St. Paul, Minn. 1946. pp. 89–96

Hematite-Limonite Deposits

JOHN W. GRUNER

GENERAL STATEMENT

The hematite-limonite ores of the Mesabi range have been the greatest single source of iron for the last 40 to 50 years. For this reason they have received a great deal of attention in the literature of mining and metallurgy. Innumerable partial analyses of the ores, including SiO_2, Al_2O_3, P_2O_5, MnO, and moisture have been made in the course of 50 years. Texture, structure, and screen analyses have become important in the last twenty to thirty years. Several methods of improving the quality of the ores, that is, of beneficiation, as it is called, have been introduced and are used on ever increasing quantities of the crude ores. In some of this work geological science has been of relatively little help, for the ores seem very simple mineralogically and structurally. One can almost see at a glance that they are altered parts of the taconite from which SiO_2 has been leached by some natural agency. It has become possible and important, however, to correlate each kind of ore with a definite stratigraphic horizon of the Biwabik formation.

CHEMICAL COMPOSITION

Hundreds of thousands of partial analyses of the hematite-limonite ores have been made, but very few analyses are complete. One of these is shown in Table 17. It represents a large tonnage of ore from one of the pits at Hibbing. It is obvious that such small amounts of FeO and CO_2 as are shown in the Table do not influence the quality of the ore and, therefore, are usually ignored. The amounts of P, on the other hand, are of great importance and lead to the classification of the ores into Bessemer and non-Bessemer grades. The division is based on the content of P and its ratio to that of Fe. The permissible ratio is roughly 1:1100 to 1:1200. In other words, any ore containing 50% Fe, but less than .040 to .045% P would be considered Bessemer in quality. Such ore commands a slightly higher price than non-Bessemer ore. Other less important classifications are those based on manganese content, or the percentage of P in

Editor's Note: A row of asterisks indicates that material has been omitted from the original article.

non-Bessemer ore. This latter leads to "Low-Phos" and "High-Phos" non-Bessemer ores. There is practically no "High-Phos" non-Bessemer ore on the Mesabi range.

A local classification based on iron content and color (Wolff, 1917) leads to:

(1) a high grade blue or brown ore averaging, dry, 59 per cent of iron;

(2) a medium grade brown or yellow ore averaging, dry, 55 to 56 per cent of iron; and

(3) a low grade yellow or brown ore averaging, dry, about 50 per cent of iron.

The blue ore is a Bessemer ore found in the Lower Cherty division, in the Upper Cherty division, and in parts of the Lower Slaty division. The brown ore occurs in the various divisions except possibly in the Lower Cherty division. The yellow ore occurs at the top, and, in parts of the range, at the bottom of the Lower Cherty division. The ore at the top is easily recognized where it is in contact with the red Intermediate Paint rock. The yellow ore may occur also anywhere above the Paint rock, where the original rock consisted mainly of silicates.

In the early history of the Mesabi range the ores mined were mostly Bessemer and of higher grade than today because the furnaces demanded them. Since the mined tonnages were smaller, and reserves larger, there were no objections to selective mining. Furnace practices are such today that almost three times as much non-Bessemer ore is shipped as Bessemer as shown by Table 18. All ores can be and are mixed today in such a manner

TABLE 17

Complete analysis of ore (dried at 100° C) shipped during 1935 from an ore body at Hibbing.

Constituent	Per cent	Constituent	Per cent
SiO_2	8.65	CO_2	.48
Al_2O_3	1.34	P as P_2O_5	.112
Fe_2O_3	81.87	S	.012
FeO	.15	H_2O+	5.82*
MgO	.22		
CaO	.25	Total	100.25
Mn as MnO_2	1.35	Total Fe	57.25

*Ignition loss was 6.50 which would include H_2O+, S, and CO_2 and C (graphite).

TABLE 18

Average analyses and gross tons (thousands) of ore mined on the Mesabi range in 1943.

Computed from figures of Lake Superior Iron Ore Association.

	1	2	3	4	5	6	7	8*	9
	BESSEMER			NON-BESSEMER					
	Complete analyses	Analyses without MgO, CaO, Ign. Loss	Average of all Ore Assn. figures	Complete analyses	Analyses without MgO, CaO, Ign. Loss	Average of all Ore Assn. figures	Manganif-erous Assn. figures	Average of all ore in 1909	Average of all grades in 1943
Fe	59.29	60.75	59.77	57.26	58.55	58.01	53.48	58.83	58.49
as Fe_2O_3	84.78	86.87	....	81.88	83.73	....	....	84.13	....
SiO_2	8.64	7.25	8.26	8.99	6.77	7.83	9.03	6.80	7.95
Al_2O_3	.88	1.20	....	1.81	2.23	....	....	2.23	....
MgO	.19	....	....	.18	....	....	....	.32	....
CaO	.21	....	....	.20	....	....	....	.32	....
Mn	.39	.41	.39	.63	.86	.78	4.16	.82	.69
as MnO_2	.62	.65	....	1.00	1.36	....	6.58	1.30	....
P	.041	.038	.039	.067	.066	.068	.082	.062	.060
as P_2O_5	.094	.087	....	.153	.151	....	....	.158	....
S	.011	....	....	.017	....	....	....	.069	....
Loss on ignition	4.85	....	....	5.48	....	....	....	4.72	....
Total (dried at 100° C.)	100.27	96.06	....	99.71	94.24	....	....	100.05	....
Fe natural	53.65	54.54	54.04	51.17	51.12	50.93	48.14	51.61	51.79
Moisture	9.51	10.25	9.59	10.66	12.70	12.18	10.07	12.27	11.45
Gross Tons (thousands)	3,935	9,420	17,973	13,248	25,595	46,312	224	....	64,509

*Data by Van Hise and Leith (1911, p. 181).

that furnaces receive exactly the composition for which they have contracted. The average analyses of Table 18 which are representative of vast tonnages were compiled by the writer from cargo analyses published by the Lake Superior Ore Association in Cleveland.* Columns 1 and 4 contain those for which figures for MgO, CaO, S, and ignition losses were available. Columns 2 and 5 contain the ores for which these constituents were not determined. These columns may be compared with figures of the Lake Superior Iron Ore Association (columns 3, 6, and 9) which are for total tonnages shipped but which list only analyses for Fe, P, SiO_2, Mn, and moisture. Column 8 gives the average analysis for the ore of the 1909 season. As compared with 1943 (column 9) its Fe and moisture were slightly higher, but its SiO_2 was appreciably lower. The fact that ignition loss was lower in 1909 though Al_2O_3 was high would indicate that the percentage of goethite was smaller. This could be accounted for by the fact that in the last 25 to 30 years the ores of the Lower Slaty division and of the layer just below the Intermediate Paint rock which are high in goethite have contributed an increasingly larger tonnage to the yearly total.

The average analyses listed above cannot show just how much ores vary in a given vertical section in the formation. A great number of such vertical sections are in the possession of the mining companies, however. Several sections have been selected to illustrate these variations in the ores. Table 19 is a

TABLE 19

Correlation of hematite-limonite ore with the corresponding unleached taconite. Two drill holes 1000 feet apart in the vicinity of Virginia.

Drill Hole in Taconite

	Depth	Fe	P	SiO_2	Mn
	0-40	Glacial Till			
	40-46	38.40	.034	39.68	.15
	51	35.64	.031	44.90	.19
	56	42.85	.049	33.66	.27
	59	21.20	.008	67.20	.08
	64	48.08	.048	24.30	.86
	66	44.54	.053	30.44	.31
	71	42.24	.046	35.84	.11
	75	40.09	.051	37.24	.11
	78	58.60	.040	7.92	3.81
	83	31.95	.025	51.64	.45
Alg. St.	88	49.00	.051	23.66	1.47
	93	59.98	.115	6.40	.68
	98	60.67	.093	6.80	.68
	103	58.68	.041	9.08	2.58
	108	49.77	.032	25.20	.68
	113	33.79	.010	49.64	.64
	118	36.56	.009	46.60	.19
	120	37.32	.008	45.52	.11
	123	56.52	.021	17.20	.31

Drill Hole in Ore

	Depth	Fe	P	SiO_2	Mn	Al_2O_3
	0-50	Glacial Till				
	50-55	44.24	.069	25.34	.24	7.65
	60	32.29	.203	25.54	.18	17.90
	65	23.54	.098	33.90	.09	22.39
	70	22.13	.090	32.98	.11	24.44
	75	26.30	.138	30.72	.19	21.68
Va. Sl.	80	27.72	.138	27.28	1.24	22.92
	85	38.27	.215	18.46	.36	10.18
	90	48.51	.213	13.98	.50	7.70
	95	57.72	.060	7.90	.33	4.65
	100	58.43	.049	7.44	.43	4.89
	105	58.11	.053	8.48	.46	4.40
	110	59.22	.052	6.88	.39	4.74
	115	59.22	.052	6.76	.47	4.57
	120	57.96	.080	7.44	.53	4.71

*Published yearly in pamphlet form.

TABLE 19—Continued

Correlation of hematite-limonite ore with the corresponding unleached taconite. Two drill holes 1000 feet apart in the vicinity of Virginia.

Drill Hole in Taconite

Depth	Fe	P	SiO_2	Mn
128	47.92	.022	30.20	.19
133	44.85	.020	34.56	.11
138	48.38	.010	29.36	.27
141	47.00	.012	31.24	.31
143	48.86	.020	27.66	.53
148	44.79	.010	34.64	.11
153	42.95	.010	37.70	.08
158	45.03	.012	34.64	.15
163	44.49	.011	35.12	.11
168	42.35	.058	37.50	.08
173	42.65	.021	37.00	.08
178	39.32	.040	41.70	.08
183	31.55	.024	52.08	.04
188	27.92	.046	48.64	.72
193	39.17	.083	34.70	.61
198	37.55	.030	35.70	.64
203	33.01	.053	37.64	.72
208	35.94	.082	33.92	.98
213	33.55	.036	45.96	.53
218	36.01	.035	42.00	.68
223	31.86	.035	51.20	.27
228	41.33	.045	35.88	.19
233	40.17	.027	37.18	.27
238	41.33	.043	36.20	.11
243	32.32	.048	46.40	.19
248	31.69	.026	47.80	.19
253	30.86	.024	48.24	.23
258	35.55	.022	36.80	.72
263	31.69	.039	40.80	.46
268	23.09	.059	55.44	.57
273	33.32	.025	42.80	.27
278	31.09	.022	40.32	.42
283	24.40	.029	50.24	.38
288	25.86	.030	49.18	.45
293	29.86	.040	43.80	.27
298	34.82	.027	37.04	.38
303	35.35	.030	37.24	.38
308	39.65	.034	34.80	.27
313	39.32	.029	35.60	.15
318	33.64	.043	37.00	.34
323	28.72	.042	33.96	.46
328	22.90	.051	44.00	.49
333	37.63	.043	37.14	.27
338	29.18	.048	46.36	.27
343	28.64	.025	44.40	.49
348	31.64	.023	41.64	.27
353	26.57	.013	48.88	.23
358	26.88	.021	47.30	.23
363	23.27	.015	52.16	.19
Intermediate Slate				
368	18.89	.024	62.16	.34
373	33.10	.033	46.52	.11
378	26.75	.043	38.30	.80
383	26.57	.064	38.70	.68
388	27.27	.027	43.56	.57
393	24.88	.031	42.44	.64
398	27.65	.024	34.44	.64
403	24.12	.021	43.30	.72
Not Analyzed				
628-633	Algal St. and Basal Cg.			

Drill Hole in Ore

	Depth	Fe	P	SiO_2	Mn	Al_2O_3
	125	60.40	.064	5.64	.49	4.41
	130	59.37	.065	6.84	.38	4.43
	135	61.03	.071	6.04	.38	3.26
	140	60.16	.074	7.28	.53	2.15
	145	58.90	.081	7.40	1.41	1.17
	150	58.74	.092	7.12	1.05	1.57
	155	61.11	.095	4.34	.84	4.61
	160	53.07	.129	6.32	5.84	1.26
	165	54.33	.135	4.08	6.43	.89
	170	55.59	.164	4.04	3.22	1.76
	175	59.69	.135	3.64	2.67	1.22
Alg. St.	180	56.38	.098	3.90	6.62	1.62
	185	57.80	.097	4.54	3.82	2.19
	190	64.73	.048	3.12	1.00	.63
	195	63.63	.042	5.54	.96	.37
	200	64.10	.032	5.64	.51	.43
	205	64.49	.072	3.64	.33	.32
	210	64.26	.088	2.64	.47	.65
	215	64.57	.068	3.08	.28	1.11
	220	65.42	.054	2.88	.20	.61
	225	63.55	.081	3.06	.40	1.10
	230	59.06	.118	6.74	.50	1.41
	235	56.78	.095	10.50	.27	1.28
	240	56.85	.090	11.50	.27	.97
	245	61.74	.098	4.00	.27	1.57
	250	57.80	.071	11.28	.21	1.19
	255	57.01	.075	10.24	.17	2.13
	260	62.21	.062	4.42	.26	2.51
	265	61.82	.086	3.66	.34	2.34
	270	63.47	.056	2.14	.22	.80
	275	63.31	.070	2.00	.20	1.05
	280	62.05	.087	3.14	.21	1.13
	285	63.00	.069	1.90	.21	1.17
	290	62.84	.078	2.36	.25	1.02
	295	60.75	.100	2.60	.40	1.46
	300	61.74	.087	2.20	.31	.74
	305	62.37	.089	2.12	.31	.72
	310	60.51	.084	3.76	.34	1.29
	315	62.57	.080	1.94	1.24	.55
	318	60.20	.075	1.68	2.69	.49
	321	55.71	.087	8.64	.57	4.10
	326	57.04	.112	5.18	.30	2.68
	331	57.71	.132	4.64	.42	2.41
	336	58.62	.121	3.30	.67	1.67
	341	54.03	.179	5.34	1.54	3.62
	346	51.74	.149	8.48	.87	5.67
	351	52.93	.140	6.56	2.56	3.51
	356	53.80	.108	6.16	1.80	4.51
	361	50.72	.154	5.08	.59	6.34
	Intermediate Slate					
	366	57.04	.093	6.08	.43	3.98
	371	61.30	.066	2.40	1.61	.52
	376	63.99	.056	2.56	.42	2.09
	381	64.62	.039	3.84	.19	.33
	386	64.30	.028	4.84	.09	.75
	391	64.22	.019	4.60	.08	1.17
	396	59.88	.038	8.44	.17	1.12
	401	56.88	.041	11.24	.18	1.77
	406	59.72	.032	10.64	.12	.33
	409	62.57	.040	6.60	.24	.42
	414	Taconite				
	417	57.19	.045	12.04	.19	.67
	419	56.88	.036	15.72	.14	.17
	420	58.93	.043	11.68	.16	.92
	420-460	Taconite				
	465	53.31	.041	19.60	.10	.81
	470	57.98	.032	13.86	.13	.69
	475	59.88	.026	11.70	.23	1.01
	480	53.56	.023	20.56	.26	1.04
	480-533	Taconite				
	533-538	Quartzite				

TABLE 20

Comparison of taconite with ore derived from it based on analyses of two drill holes of Table 19. It is assumed that the bulk density of the ore is very similar to that of the taconite (3.45). Under these conditions units of chemical analyses can be compared directly.

	Taconite	Iron Ore	Ratio
Fe units	1900.11	1969.57	100:104
Fe average analyses	35.85	59.68	
P units	1.72	3.11	100:182
P average analyses	.032	.094	
SiO_2 units	2141.33	156.76	100: 7.3
SiO_2 average analyses	40.40	4.75	
Mn units	17.68	19.67	100:111
Mn average analyses	.33	.60	
Al_2O_3	58.3 *	62.10	100:107
Al_2O_3 average analyses	1.1 *	1.88	
Total thickness	255 feet	161 feet	
No. of analyses	53	33	
Total slump		94 feet	

*Based on average of Al_2O_3 for all available taconite analyses.

record of analyses of samples from a deep drill hole in one of the richest and largest ore bodies near Virginia. This ore has been mined out. The drill hole is particularly interesting as it penetrates all divisions, though about 90 feet of the Lower Cherty division are still taconite and therefore have not been analyzed. The first six analyses are of decomposed Virginia Slate as shown by their very high Al_2O_3. Algal structures occur at 180 feet. The bottom of the Intermediate Paint rock is at 361 feet. Leaching of SiO_2 and corresponding concentration of Fe has been unusually thorough in these beds. Al_2O_3 is probably more erratic in this area than in most places. It is particularly high in the Intermediate Paint rock, a condition met all over the range. The content of P is much too high for Bessemer ore except in 35 feet of the Lower Cherty ore. Concentration of Mn is conspicuous near the Algal structures and was observed in this horizon at other places in this ore body.

COMPARISON OF ORE AND THE TACONITE FROM WHICH IT WAS DERIVED

One thousand feet west of the drill hole just described is another which cuts taconite. It penetrates almost all of the formation except about 100 feet of the Upper Slaty division. This is one of the very few taconite holes of great depth which has been analyzed for Fe, P, SiO_2, and Mn. Unfortunately Al_2O_3 was omitted. Algal structures are found at 88 feet, and the bottom of the Paint rock is at 363 feet. The basal conglomerate was observed at 633 feet.

There has been some oxidation and a little leaching of SiO_2 in this taconite but no slumping below 108 feet. It is, therefore, possible to set these taconite analyses along side those of the corresponding ore and compare the layers between the Algal structures and Intermediate Slate (or Paint rock) with one another (Table 19). As these two holes are 1000 feet apart allowance must be made for some chemical differences, even though the main beds are persistent. With this reservation it may be assumed that the taconite from 108 to 363 corresponds to the ore from 200 to 361 feet. Therefore, the total units of Fe, P, SiO_2, Mn, and Al_2O_3 in the two holes can be compared with one another provided the bulk densities of the taconite and ore are approximately the same. As discussed elsewhere in this report the density is about 3.4 for each. Table 20 shows comparisons of the total units and their ratios. In the case of the undetermined Al_2O_3 of the taconite hole, the average content for all taconite, that is, 1.1%, was substituted.

It is readily seen that the ratios of Fe and Al_2O_3 have not changed materially, in accord with early data given by Van Hise and Leith in 1911 (p. 181). On the other hand, there is almost twice as much P in ore as in taconite, which could mean that P is introduced locally. It is well known that it has a tendency to be high where Al_2O_3 is high in the ores, but there are striking exceptions to this where high alumina ores may be almost Bessemer in quality. In the unaltered taconite P is not necessarily associated with any horizons high in Al_2O_3. Its occurrence has not been associated with any particular kind of taconite as can also be shown in Table 19. How thorough the leaching of SiO_2 may be is seen from the ratio of 100:7.3 (Table 20). The slump is correspondingly large, namely 94 ft.

It would be a mistake to project comparisons like the above to beds which represent a relatively small thickness of the total formation. Local differences in the original composition may lead to conspicuous discrepancies. For example, Table 21 gives data for 126 feet of taconite and its corresponding 80 feet of ore at a distance of 700 feet away near Hibbing. These layers occur in the upper part of the Lower Cherty division directly under the Paint rock where leaching was more pronounced than in most of the other horizons. Total units of Al_2O_3 have apparently decreased to one-half while those of P have remained constant in these beds.

TABLE 21

Correlation of hematite-limonite ore with the corresponding unleached taconite. Two drill holes 700 feet apart near Hibbing. Lower Cherty Division.

Drill hole in taconite 21 samples of 6 feet each Total 126 feet					Drill hole in ore 16 samples of 5 feet each Total 80 feet				
Fe	P	SiO_2	Mn	Al_2O_3	Fe	P	SiO_2	Mn	Al_2O_3
35.62	.030	40.88	.38	.23	60.29	.085	3.98	.26	.31
29.93	.010	40.86	1.83	.20	60.96	.037	2.71	.24	.42
33.80	.027	38.00	1.53	.28	60.81	.035	2.92	.15	.53
33.72	.025	43.80	.61	.44	59.62	.044	3.76	.59	.66
37.91	.056	35.39	.94	1.78	59.10	.050	3.59	1.06	.43
39.92	.034	33.54	.57	.56	60.14	.079	2.67	.44	.48
36.78	.039	36.75	.55	.88	60.29	.089	3.52	.26	.41
35.85	.039	36.08	.68	2.14	60.29	.056	6.67	.19	.61
34.86	.040	38.21	.64	.84	60.46	.056	7.27	.17	.21
31.69	.032	41.85	.48	.59	58.74	.041	11.58	.15	.20
37.27	.028	33.75	.50	.60	53.23	.026	20.35	.17	.26
38.62	.032	34.84	.48	.60	52.78	.026	20.46	.15	.36
34.96	.022	41.82	.28	.39	58.30	.020	13.66	.15	.31
32.77	.024	45.03	.30	.51	60.68	.026	9.10	.21	.56
29.34	.022	44.30	.43	.26	58.37	.035	11.65	.28	.86
34.61	.025	43.00	.34	.28	58.30	.064	10.64	.35	1.04
29.85	.026	48.69	.45	.28					
30.61	.024	47.55	.47	.57					
34.43	.028	41.70	.31	.54					
30.92	.033	46.90	.39	.63					
26.56	.030	51.54	.41	.99					
UNITS									
852.02*	.751*	1037.38*	15.08*	16.30*	942.36	.769	134.53	4.82	7.65
AVERAGE ANALYSES									
33.81	.030	41.16	.60	.65	58.90	.048	8.41	.30	.48

*Since the taconite samples are 6 ft. samples and are to be compared with 5 ft. ore samples, their sums are multiplied by the factor 6/5.

Mn frequently is leached from some of the layers to be reprecipitated and even concentrated in others higher up immediately under or in the Paint rock. MgO and CaO are largely removed except for 10 to 20% of the original amounts. These are about the only generalizations that may be made safely with regard to the migration of the important chemical constituents in the process of leaching of taconite.

* * * * * * *

References

Van Hise, C. R., and Leith, C. K. (1911). The geology of the Lake Superior region: U.S. Geol. Surv. Mon. 52.

Wolff, J. F. (1917). Recent geologic developments on the Mesabi iron range, Minnesota: Proc. Lake Superior Mining Inst., vol. 21, pp. 229–257; Am. Inst. Min. Eng. Trans., vol. 56, pp. 142–69.

15

Reprinted from *Econ. Geol.,* **32**(2), 121–130 (1937)

HYDROTHERMAL LEACHING OF IRON ORES OF THE LAKE SUPERIOR TYPE—A MODIFIED THEORY.

JOHN W. GRUNER.*

INTRODUCTION.

A HYPOTHESIS for the oxidation and leaching of iron formations chiefly by hot magmatic waters was advanced by the author ten years and six years ago, respectively.[1] The many discussions favorable and unfavorable which followed helped him greatly in formulating the modified hypothesis presented in these pages. The recently published, highly detailed investigations by Allen and Day [2] on the hot springs of Yellowstone Park provided the writer with excellent data that makes it possible to elevate the hypothesis to the rank of a theory, it is believed. It differs from the old ideas chiefly in laying more stress on heated *meteoric* waters than was done before, especially in the case of the soft Mesabi ores to which it will be specifically applied in the following pages. No modification of the original hydrothermal hypothesis would have been necessary for the hard Vermilion and Marquette ores in which replacement of quartz by hematite has

* Published by permission of the Director of the Minnesota Geological Survey.

1 Gruner, J. W.: The Soudan formation and a new suggestion as to the origin of the Vermilon iron ores. ECON. GEOL., vol 21, pp. 629–644, 1926.

Gruner, J. W.: Hydrothermal oxidation and leaching experiments; their bearing on the origin of Lake Superior hematite-limonite ores. ECON. GEOL., vol. 25, pp. 697–719; 837–867, 1930.

Gruner, J. W.: Additional notes on secondary concentration of Lake Superior iron ores. ECON. GEOL., vol. 27, pp. 189–205, 1932.

2 Allen, E. T., and Day, A. L.: Hot springs of the Yellowstone National Park. Carnegie Inst. of Washington, Pub. 466, 1935.

been an important process. But here, too, heated meteoric waters probably have been a significant factor in the leaching of silica. Lack of space does not permit a review of the papers of 1930 and 1932, with which the student will need to be acquainted to some degree in order to follow this discussion closely.

FACTORS OPPOSED TO WEATHERING PROCESSES.

Restatement of factors which led to the abandonment of the weathering hypothesis for the Mesabi ores.[3]

1. Large ore bodies extend to a known depth of 905 feet.
2. No change in the quality and physical condition of the ore is recognizable with depth.
3. Solution of quartz and not only of silicates on a vast scale.
4. Complete oxidation of ferrous iron and especially of magnetite to martite.
5. Complete lack of leaching of silica unless accompanied or preceded by oxidation.
6. No apparent leaching of silica today as shown by mine water and other water analyses.
7. Probability that cold meteoric waters entering the iron formation were already saturated with respect to silica (for that temperature) due to previous contact with silicates in the soil and in other formations.
8. Probability that the leaching of the ore bodies was practically completed in pre-Cambrian time.
9. Lack of synclinal structures under the ore bodies to guide the flow of meteoric waters.

[3] Econ. Geol., vol. 25, pp. 850–858. Econ. Geol., vol. 27, p. 203.

The geology of the Mesabi range is simple. The Upper Huronian Biwabik iron formation overlies Pokegama quartzite and underlies Virginia slate conformably. The dip of the formations is southward and averages about 10 degrees. Taconite which makes up the iron formation, is a banded ferruginous quartz and greenalite rock containing some slaty phases of which the "intermediate slate (paintrock)" is the most prominent. The most common iron mineral in the taconite is fine-grained magnetite. Next in abundance are greenalite, siderite and hematite. The ore bodies are troughs in shape. The troughs are due to slumping of the ore layers after leaching out of the silica.

10. Absence of important impervious layers in the iron formation under which artesian waters might have circulated.

11. The axes of elongation of ore bodies in the majority of cases are not in positions which would be expected if the leaching solutions had flowed down the dip of the formation.

12. Many ore bodies do not extend up the dip to the surface but appear to be cut off. If circulation had followed the bedding planes down the dip the portions of the formation between the surface and the ore bodies should have been leached first.

13. Steep and sharp walls of many ore bodies indicate rapid circulation in well defined zones.

14. Notwithstanding the lack of structures controlling cold ground water circulation, ore bodies are confined to a limited number of areas. The iron formation between these places is unattacked.

15. The slumping of the ore bodies from wall to wall for as much as 250 ft. vertically was caused by leaching of silica from the bottom of ore bodies *upward*. If leaching had started at the top the porous ores could have been eroded as rapidly as they formed. Besides, there would have been no reason why the groundwaters should have descended from a porous zone into a dense unleached rock with their load of silica. On the other hand, if leaching started from below, the deposition of silica as sinter at the surface would have protected the ore bodies from erosion for extended periods.

16. During the leaching period the then existing erosion surface was at least 150 to 250 feet higher in the neighborhood of the large ore bodies than it is today (Fig. 2). This is proved by the fact that the top layers of the large ore bodies have slumped that distance. This also means that at least some of the ore bodies were covered partially by Virginia slate when leaching occurred. As a matter of fact, patches of this highly altered and bleached slate have been found on top of at least two ore bodies.

17. Existence of large Keweenawan intrusives under the iron formation as proved by diabase intrusions in the iron formation at least as far west as Keewatin. West of this town leaching is

incomplete and " wash ores " are the result, indicating that the solutions were less potent, in other words, not as hot as farther east.

18. Lack of ore bodies on the East Mesabi and Gunflint ranges where the intrusives (Duluth gabbro) came to rest above the iron formation making *any* kind of circulation impossible.

19. Occurrence of very large magnetite crystals in cavities in conglomerate ore between Mountain Iron and Kinney.[4]

FACTORS OPPOSED TO HYDROTHERMAL LEACHING.

Factors which seem to argue against leaching by magmatic waters.

(*a*) Magmatic waters should have been nearly saturated with silica when they entered the iron formations unless they passed through the gaseous phase on the way up and condensed on reaching the iron formation, a change conceivable if the temperature on mingling with ground water dropped sufficiently for the existing pressure.

(*b*) Some ore bodies bottom in the iron formation some distance above the Pokegama quartzite. Apparently there is not much leaching under them. If the magmatic emanations rose essentially in a vertical direction this lack of leaching may be explained by the existence of the emanations in the gaseous state before reaching the site of the ore body.

(*c*) Minerals commonly thought to be associated with magmatic waters are rare. However, as pointed out previously [5] on account of the simple composition of the iron formations interaction with them could not have produced very complex minerals, even if the temperatures had exceeded 200° C on the Mesabi range.

(*d*) Limonite (goethite) is present in relatively large amounts. It is an alteration product of the iron silicates and siderite. There has been considerable discussion as to the upper limit of

[4] Gruner, J. W.: Magnetite cementing certain ore conglomerates of the Mesabi Range. ECON. GEOL., vol. 29, pp. 757–760, 1934.

[5] ECON. GEOL., vol. 27, p. 196, 1932.

stability of goethite [6] which is supposed to be at about 140° C. Goethite has been reported, however, lately from bore-holes in the Yellowstone Park geyser basins [7] at depths to almost 400 feet. The measured temperature where the goethite was found was as high as 175° to 180° C. It is conceivable that it even exists at somewhat higher temperatures since field observations were not carried beyond this temperature. The petrographic descriptions by Fenner suggest to the writer that the temperature of *formation* of this goethite may have been higher than the measured temperature. Be this as it may, this occurrence proves that goethite (limonite) exists at temperatures close to 180° C.

HEATING OF METEORIC WATERS BY MAGMATIC EMANATIONS.

The belief that water issuing from hot springs is heated by igneous intrusions, chiefly by coming in contact with the hot rocks, is of long standing. It has been applied almost universally to geyser waters. More recently geologists have also given credit to hot gases escaping from a magma as media for heating meteoric ground waters. Lately Allen and Day [8] have come to the conclusion that the large quantities of geyser water in Yellowstone Park do not receive their heat from any igneous rock with which they are in direct contact. It is inconceivable that igneous rock, which is a poor conductor, could lose such enormous quantities of heat as rapidly as is required by the amounts of run-off observed and over a period of many thousands of years. The chilled contacts would soon become good heat insulators. Therefore, the heat must be supplied by some other means not subject to these limitations. Hot emanations rising from a deeper source, chiefly as gases, seem to be ideal for these processes. They possess high mobility, great heat capacity, and are of a large enough order of magnitude. Steam would be the chief con-

[6] Tunell, G., and Posnjak, E.: The stability relations of goethite and hematite. Econ. Geol., vol. 26, p. 337, 1931.

Gruner, J. W.: Econ. Geol., vol. 26, p. 442, 1931.

[7] Fenner, C. N.: Bore-hole investigations in Yellowstone Park. Jour. Geol., vol. 44, no. 2, part 2, p. 237 and 270, 1936.

[8] *Op. cit.*, p. 214.

stituent. It would, of course, condense if brought in contact with sufficient amounts of meteoric water. Even at this late stage of activity in Yellowstone Park, heat sufficient to melt three tons of ice every second is imparted to about 109 cu. ft. of water per second, according to Allen and Day.[9] This water carries away in solution about 390 tons of material in 24 hours according to the same authors,[10] of which a considerable part is SiO_2.

Oxidation and Leaching of Iron Ores.

It is a relatively simple matter to apply the above mentioned facts and ideas to the oxidation and leaching of the Lake Superior iron ores and especially to those of the Mesabi range where the magmatic water hypothesis had met with the objections enumerated under points *a* to *d*. The iron formations are much jointed and fractured due to their brittleness, permitting easy access of groundwaters along these openings. In some areas where basic intrusions of Keweenawan age approached the Biwabik formation from below more closely than in others, this fracturing may have been even more pronounced. It may be assumed that groundwater saturated the iron formation. It has been suggested by Leith[11] that the Lake Superior region was semi-arid, a very low water table presumably being necessary for oxidation and leaching to 3000 and 4000 feet depth in a "mountainous region." The relative attitudes of ore bodies and surrounding structural features have remained essentially unchanged since the beginning of formation of the ore bodies. It is, therefore, difficult to expect any aid from such assumed conditions for the hypothesis of cold water circulation either with regard to quantity or depth. It is much more likely that there was plenty of water available for leaching of silica at the same time as oxidation occurred, for field study has shown these two processes most intimately connected. They began to operate on a grand scale when hot gaseous emanations broke through and in their upward

9 *Op. cit.*, p. 55.

10 *Op. cit.*, p. 128.

11 Leith, C. K.: Secondary concentration of Lake Superior iron ores. Econ. Geol., vol. 26, p. 286, 1931.

rush heated and deflected the ground waters toward the surface (Fig. 1). The path of least resistance was upward. Even if the ground water had lacked any appreciable head due to topographic conditions it could not have "backed up" on account of greater friction laterally.

It is, of course, impossible to estimate the amount of magmatic water of the emanations that condensed and mingled with the meteoric water. The amount of silica that was carried in solution may have been of similar magnitude as in Yellowstone Park where some waters contain as much as 800 parts per million. This silica was largely deposited on the surface. Besides protecting the underlying ore from erosion temporarily, this capping had another function. It frequently sealed off early channels and caused spreading of the leaching laterally and up and down the dip (Figs. 1 and 2). As the water and gases were expelled, ground water would enter laterally and down the dip. This could occur, of course at *any* horizon in the iron formation depending upon local conditions. Such behavior explains the sudden ending of ore bodies in the taconite either laterally or vertically at depth. These points are really the places where the meteoric waters first came in contact with the hot emanations and acquired their leaching power. Genetically they are the beginnings, not the ends, of the ore bodies.[12] This interpretation

[12] On the Gogebic range where in places as many as six ore bodies occur at six different elevations one above the other, the new theory is able to explain such stacking almost perfectly. On the Cuyuna range known ore bodies reach to a depth of almost 900 ft. They follow steeply dipping beds downward and bottom in iron formation commonly. This at first rather puzzling fact finds its explanation now. The emanations and meteoric waters met at these depths and rose together. The "hanging ore bodies" of the Marquette and Menominee district (ECON. GEOL., vol. 25, p. 841 and 847, 1930) find a logical interpretation as to their attitude for the first time. The positions of the soft ores of the Marquette range are also readily explained.

One is not dependent, therefore, on ancient erosion surfaces in the iron formations as Mr. Stephen Royce believes (ECON. GEOL., vol. 27, pp. 487–491, 1932 and ECON. GEOL., vol. 28, p. 293, 1933). He makes it a point to show that in the Brotherton-Sunday Lake properties of the Gogebic range a Keweenawan erosion surface reached the iron formation and that an ore body was formed at that place due to surface oxidation and leaching. Iron ore pebble conglomerate lies between the ore and the

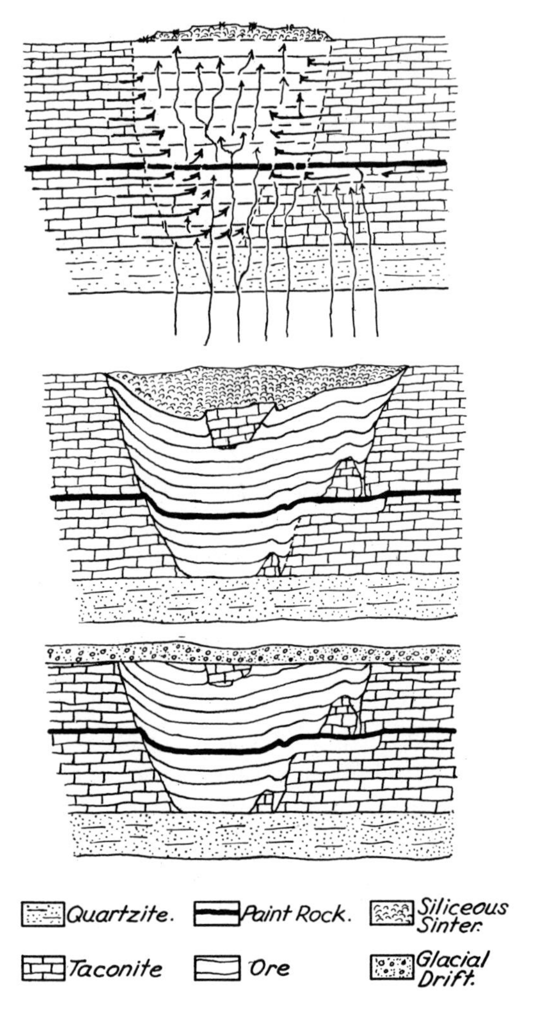

FIG. 1. First stage in the development of Mesabi ore body. Rising emanations mingle with meteoric waters entering at different horizons of iron formation.

FIG. 2. Final stage of leaching. Due to the capping of sinter the ore body has spread laterally.

FIG. 3. Ore body after erosion of capping and deposition of glacial drift. The vertical sections are parallel to the strike of the formation.

also furnishes a ready answer to the common question: "Where did the silica go to?"

The axes of the ore bodies followed those fissures which gave egress to the largest quantities of solution. The underlying quartzite was less jointed. As it contained no ferrous minerals (as did the iron formation) which on oxidation disintegrated the rock and facilitated circulation, it was attacked relatively little. Where the temperature and emanations decreased before leaching was fairly complete (or were lower to begin with), wash ores high in loose quartz grains resulted. No cold water hypothesis can explain why leaching activity shows a *gradual* decline from Hibbing westward for 40 miles. A fading of igneous activity westward offers an easy explanation, on the other hand. The occurrence of these "sugary" quartz phases in the iron ores which can be removed by washing are not confined to the Mesabi range but seem to occur in practically all ores of the Lake Superior type though in quite different proportions. They have even been described lately from the Minas Geraes ores by Sanders [13] where they occur in enormous quantities.

Keweenawan sediments. He fails to mention that the ore body is intimately associated with a diabase dike upon which it is found. In this respect (and probably therefore in origin) it is like the great majority of the Gogebic ore bodies which were *not* formed on an ancient erosion surface between the Tyler slate and iron formation. The conglomerate was formed when later erosion cut into the ore layers.

Attention is called once more to the fact that intrusive activity immediately preceded the formation of ore bodies and as far as known lasted until after the ore bodies were completed. This applies especially to the Gogebic and Marquette ranges. One does not receive that impression for the Marquette range, however, when reading the guide book of the International Geological Congress (Guidebook 27, Lake Superior Region, 1933, p. 16). C. O. Swanson does not mention there the earlier intrusives, which arrived before Upper Huronian time in the Negaunee iron formation according to Van Hise, Bailey and Leith. The writer thinks them responsible for the hard ores, that is the heat which came from the larger masses of the same magma. The soft ores were caused by the heat from the Keweenawan magmas. This statement is a departure from his earlier ideas (ECON. GEOL., vol. 25, p. 865, 1930) that all the Marquette ores might have been of one period of concentration.

[13] Sanders, B. H.: Iron ores at Itabira, Brazil. Inst. Min. and Met., Bull. 346, July, 1933.

CONCLUSIONS.

A modified theory of hydrothermal oxidation and leaching of the Lake Superior iron ores, especially of the Mesabi ores, is advanced. It is proposed that the chief source of the hot waters was meteoric. The waters mingled with gaseous emanations that rose from large intrusives. Ordinarily nearly stagnant, these ground waters when heated became active solvents of silica. They were deflected upward and with the emanations issued at the surface depositing their silica load as sinter on the ore. The sinters formed a temporary protection against erosion of the soft ores. The emanations probably were largely superheated steam and as such were able to heat large quantities of meteoric water by the heat of condensation alone. Expulsion of hot water and influx of new ground water from all sides was a process that continued as long as emanations stimulated circulation. The action may be compared to that taking place in the hot springs region of Yellowstone Park today. Close study shows that practically all former difficulties encountered in adhering strictly either to the weathering or the magmatic water hypothesis disappear. The new theory is applicable to all iron ores of the Lake Superior type. The chief differences are probably only in type, temperature, and quantities of the emanations. Variations in compositions of the formations and their attitudes with respect to dikes, faults and more or less impervious beds could readily account for some of the differences that one sees in the field. Although the subject is a very tempting one it is beyond the scope of this paper to apply the theory to pre-Cambrian iron ores of other continents.

University of Minnesota,
Minneapolis, Minnesota,
January 24, 1937.

16

Reprinted from *Symp. Gisements Fer Monde, Internat. Geol. Congr., Algiers,* 1952, pp. 286, 293–297, 306–310

CHAPTER II

ORIGIN OF THE BRAZILIAN IRON ORES [1]

JOHN VAN N. DORR II

PHILIP W. GUILD
U. S. Geological Survey.

A. L. M. BARBOSA
Departamento Nacional da Produção Mineral

I. — PRELIMINARY STATEMENT AND DEFINITIONS

In a paper of the length permissible for this symposium, it is obviously impossible to cite all the authors who have contributed ideas on the origin of Brazilian iron ore or to give an adequate discussion of the various theories advanced. More than fifty papers were studied in the preparation of this paper; it is hoped that omission of many ideas and citations will be understood and excused. Our special debt to L.-J. de Moraes, O.-H. Leonardos, O. Barbosa, B.-H. Sanders and B. von Freyberg should, however, be acknowledged. The authors' own field and laboratory studies on the subject are incomplete; the lack of definite conclusions on various points may be explained thus and by the lack of definite data on which to base conclusions. Because mining and development are now proceeding rapidly, making more and better data available, within a few years much more definite statements will be possible.

By defining various terms used in this discussion, the ambiguity which some of the technical words have acquired in the literature may be avoided.

Hard Ore : Material averaging 66 % Fe or more, which gives a metallic ring when struck by a hammer and produces little powder on breaking. Mostly hematite. (Similar in part to the 'massive ore' of India).

Soft Ore : Pulverulent hematite averaging 66 % Fe or more. (Similar in part to the 'blue dust' of India).

Intermediate Ore : Material intermediate in physical character between hard and soft, averaging 66 % Fe or more. In part mixed hard and soft, often quite schistose.

Itabirite : A laminated metamorphic rock, dominantly and often entirely composed of granular quartz and iron oxide. (Similar in part to the quartz-hematite rock of India, the itabirite of Venezuela, and to some of the laminated ferruginous rocks of the Sahara).

Canga : A surficial cap on other rocks, ranging from Hard Ore fragments cemented by limonite (67 % Fe) to earthy material cemented by limonite (35 % Fe). Similar in part to 'laterite' of India and to canga of Venezuela).

Jacutinga : This much abused word, which has been so loosely used in the past that it has lost all specific meaning, should be abandoned as a scientific term.

In the following discussion, the various types of iron ores will be taken up in the order of increasing complexity of origin with ores of possible igneous origin discussed last.

---

1. Published with the permission of the Directors of the Departamento Nacional da Produção Mineral, Ministério da Agricultura, and the Geological Survey, U. S. Department of Interior.

Editor's Note: A row of asterisks indicates that material has been omitted from the original article.

* * * * * * *

e) THE ORE DEPOSITS

At the present time, the only ores, properly speaking, are the *hard pure hematite* which is mined for *export* (68.5 % Fe +), the *soft pure hematite* which is locally sintered for *domestic blast furnace use*, "*chapinha*" (weathered itabirite in which plates of rather pure hematite remain when the disaggregated granular silica is screened out), and several varieties of *canga* (50-66 % Fe), which are used in *domestic charcoal blast furnaces*. Within a few years, the richer and softer itabirites will become ore, as economic and transportation conditions change, but they will be excluded from the following discussion.

Canga, present in hundreds of millions of tons in the area, is a secondary product of the *leaching* of silica from itabirite and of the *hydration* and the shallow concentration of iron by ground water and by gravity, and it need not concern us further, except as an illustration of the great relative solubility of silica under the semi-tropical and tropical environment of Brazil. Similarly, the *chapinha* is a weathering product of itabirite.

The export ores are extraordinarily pure. Shipments of 384,867 tons in 1948 from one mine averaged 68.7 % Fe, 0,036 % P, 0.52 % SiO_2, 0.63 % Al_2O_3, 0.08 % Mn, and 0.78 % H_2O, buyers analyses. Shipments in 1950 were higher grade and lower in phosphorus. One shipload lot averaged 69.9 % Fe. This ore is not concentrated.

The pure ores occur in lenses and "beds" ranging from less than a centimeter to over 100 meters in thickness, and are always associated with and nearly always enclosed in itabirite. The lenses vary up to more than a kilometer in length. Although the outcrops usually show only hard ores, soft and intermediate ores have been found in every sizable bedrock deposit which has been opened by mining or prospecting. The percentages of such materiel vary greatly from deposit to deposit.

On surfaces etched by weathering, it is often possible to see that the hard pure ore is crumpled, twisted, isoclinally folded, and otherwise deformed in a manner and with a texture entirely similar to that so strikingly shown by many itabirite exposures. It is possible to see this on freshly broken faces only in those cases where the rock is strongly laminated. Soft and intermediate ores show similar structures. Locally, breccia textures are not uncommon.

All the pure ores are formed of blue to steely gray *hematite*, except as noted below. The size of the individual crystals forming the ore varies considerably, but is generally quite fine (-110 mesh). In the western part of the Central Minas area, the ore tends to be finer grained, more granular, and less specular, reflecting the lower grade of metamorphism. Sporadic small (0.6-0.2 cm) crystals of *martite* and *magnetite* scattered at randon in the hematite are not uncommon; they are often encased in a thin selvage of *talc* (?) [1]. Rarely nests several meters across of coarsely crystalline (up to 3-4 cm.) martite and magnetite in a matrix of ordinary hematite are encountered. Concentrations of these minerals are also found along certain dikes cutting the ores. Small pockets and smears of talc (?) are common in some pure ore deposits and are found in almost all of them : this is the principal visible gangue mineral of the purer ores, although it rarely amounts to more than one percent by weight, and is usually much less. *Tourmaline* is reported in the literature [2] to occur in

1. Talc (?) is a mineral, not yet certainly identified, which is said by some authorities to be sericite, by others to be talc. Chemical analyses by the Institute de Tecnologia Industrial de Minas Gerais for the writers and microscopic work by the writers indicate it to be probably talc. X-ray examination, not yet completed, indicates the material to be a mixture of talc and chrysotile, according to a preliminary report by Dr. TAVORA of the D.N.P.M.

2. SANDERS, B. H., *Iron Ores at Itabira (Minas Gerais) Brazil; Inst. Min. Met. Bulls.* 346 and 349 (discussion). London. 1933-34.

one hard ore body, but the writers have never seen this mineral in the ores. Empty spaces left by the solution of some acicular mineral, possibly monoclinic, are sometimes encountered in the hard ore.

The ore deposits locally contain very minor seams of white clay on joints as well as stringers of coarse platy green and tan talc. The pure ores are rarely cut by quartz veins, although these are common in the itabirites and other rocks of the Minas Series. The writers know of only one small pod of vein quartz in pure ore.

Some ore bodies are cut by post hard ore dikes, now completely altered to a rotten talc (?) schist, which contain tourmaline and many inclusions of hematite. These dikes exercize no structural control over ore occurence.

The texture of the hard ore is quite variable within the same orebody. It can be massive, with no visible variations in grain size, foliation, or porosity; it can have streaks of black powdery hematite and small pores, with most irregular walls lined with the black powdery hematite; it can have distinct variation in grain size between laminae. These are the most important varieties; other exist. The soft ores also vary considerably in texture, some being black, with fragments of hard ore, others blue homogeneous specularite.

ORIGIN OF THE SOFT ORE

It is clear that the soft ores formed at the expense of the hard ore and that *originally the soft ore was hard.*

This is proved by the fact that joints locally form the soft ore-hard ore boundary, by the fact that joints are sometimes preserved in the soft ore (material that is now too plastic to form joints under stress), by the facts that the soft ore is often equally contorted and in the same manner as the hard ore and that the complex minor structures run from the soft into the hard with no change or interruption, by the fact that residual fragments of hard ore are found in the soft, conformable in structure, and by the fact that the hard ore often grades into soft ore and back into hard ore within the same large joint block.

It is very probable but cannot be proved at this point that the disaggregation is caused by *supergene water* which *leached out* small quantities of hematite at the corners of the interlocking grains (solubility increases with stress), thereby disaggregating the whole. The Indian "blue dust", similar to much of the Brazilian soft ore, was observed by the senior author at the Noamundi mine to have formed by supergene leaching of pure hard hematite along bedding planes.

It is not impossible that the formation of some of the soft ore is related to the *hydrothermal gold-pyrite mineralization* mentioned below, although it does not seem probable from the evidence at hand.

Some soft ore undoubtedly is of *tectonic origin*, being the results of crushing, mylonization, or recrystallization into coarse hematite schist of the hard ore along slip planes, but quantitatively this process does not seem to be important.

ORIGIN OF THE HARD ORE

It is certain that some of the hard pure ore was formed by the *metasomatic replacement* of the silica in itabirite by hematite; it seems probable that the larger bodies were formed by such replacement. The major alternative to this replacement theory is the hypothesis that the pure ores were formed by *original sedimentation* of pure iron oxide; this is the hypothesis hitherto in vogue to explain the Brazilian deposits, most explicitly stated by HARDER and CHAMBERLAIN [1], and by FREYBERG [2]. The replacement theory is not original with the writers; SANDERS [3] in his outstanding paper on Itabira clearly implies this.

1. HARDER, E. C. and CHAMBERLAIN, R. T., *The Geology of Central Minas Gerais. Journal of Geology*, Vol. XXIII, Nos. 4 and 5, Chicago. 1915.
2. FREYBERG, B. VON, *Ergebnisse geologischer Forschungen in Minas Gerais (Brasilien). Neus Jahr. Min. Geol. Pal.* Sonderband II. Stuttgart. 1932.
3. SANDERS, B. H. *op. cit.*

In many localities it is possible to demonstrate, without question, replacement on a small scale. On Cauê Peak, Itabira, numerous examples can be cited, including folds one side of which will be hard ore, the other side itabirite, with a sharp contact across the bedding but continuous structures across the contact; stockworks in itabirite with hard ore normal and parallel to the bedding and foliation of the itabirite and relict structures continuous through the hard ore; blocks of hard ore with unreplaced itabirite within them. In Conceição the same features can be observed. In the itabirite in Esmeril can be seen low angle fractures with very minor displacement with hard ore formed along the fractures (evidently channel ways) and irregularly grading into the itabirite.

There can be no doubt that replacement is an effective agent for forming hard ore. There is difficulty in proving that large bodies, containing tens of millions of tons of pure hematite, had this origin largely because replacement, in the writers' view, has gone to completion and destroyed most evidence of the nature of the original rock. Post-ore metamorphism also confuses the picture.

Indirect evidence which is indicative, though not conclusive, must be relied on to prove large scale replacement. Perhaps most important is the fact that itabirite and what is now pure hematite show in detail *the same type of failure under stress.* It does not seem probable that a laminated bimineralic rock, with distinct differences in physical properties between the iron-rich bands and the silica bands, would deform in the same manner as a homogeneous monomineralic rock. The quartzites and the dolomites certainly deformed differently than the itabirites. Therefore it seems probable that the pure ore had not formed at the time of the main deformation of the itabirite. More evidence in this direction is that, in the conglomerates of the overlying Itacolumi Series, cobbles of itabirite, often somewhat folded, are common. The writers know of not a single cobble of hard pure ore in proved Itacolumi. Yet today cobbles of hard ore are abundant in all streams draining the iron area, whether or not large hard ore bodies are present, for the material is far more durable than itabirite and probably more durable than vein quartz.

Another line of evidence is the *structural setting* of the hard ore bodies. In this part of Minas Gerais the most striking and one of the most important of the structural features is the pronounced lineation in all the rocks of the Minas Series and in many of the other rocks. This lineation, reflecting parallelism of fold axes and mineral orientation in the rocks, generally strikes within 45° of East and dips between 10°-35° East. It is post-Itacolumi in age, and controls the attitudes of some of the gold ore bodies and also those of some of the iron deposits.

In the case of the Casa de Pedra, Pico de Itabira (near Itabirito), and the Jangada hard ore bodies (the last two evidently rather cigar-shaped), the dip of the lineation is far steeper than normal, locally being vertical. It seems probable that these localities may well have been stress foci. It is thought from such evidence and from the fact that hard pure ore often forms on the axes, and on the flanks near the axes, of folds in itabirite (both on large and small scale) that *the solubility of silica relative to hematite is greatly increased under stress conditions.* Pure iron ore bodies seem to favor high-stress zones in itabirite. Were the deposits of sedimentary origin, this fact would be difficult to explain. (It should be stated clearly that at this time not all the pure ore deposits are known to be in high-stress zones. Further work may permit a wider generalization).

In the pure ore itself, the lamination which is locally apparent and the variation in grain size, often systematic and layered, are thought to represent original hematite (recrystallized into larger grains) and replaced silica (the smaller hematite grains). In some specimens this seems obvious; in most, recrystallization has gone so far that only a homogeneous rock is left. In the Itabira district, in those places where a few grains of silica remain, they tend to be in the finer-grained ore.

Like most replacement bodies in sedimentary rocks, the pure iron ores tend to follow particular horizons. Locally they have very regular and conformable contacts for a hundred meters or more with the under-or overlying itabirite. (This is the strongest argument for the sedimentary theory). Often, as indicated in the accompanying measured stratigraphic sections, which start within 10 meters of each other, no detailed correlation is possible even over very short distances.

Often, too, the contact of the hard ore lenses is transgressive, sometimes very abruptly so, in relation to the itabirite.

The lack of vein quartz in the pure hard ore is, to the writers' minds, most significant. The authors also have never seen a quartz vein in pure soft ore. (The nomenclature used in the literature is so imprecise that it is not possible to affirm that the auriferous quartz veins which are reported in "jacutinga" and "itabirite" *are* or *are not* in pure soft ore, because both those terms have been used both for itabirite as defined herein as well as for soft ore as defined herein). The lack of vein quartz in the pure ore seems significant because vein quartz is common in all other rocks in the area, including itabirite, and very probably was once present in the rock that is now pure hematite. This quartz must have been *removed* at the same time that the silica of the original itabirite was removed. It is difficult to envision any reason why the quartz veins would not have been formed in the hematite, when they definitely were formed in itabirite running up to 60 % Fe.

The *nature* of the replacing solutions and the *source* of the replacing material must be explained. This is of course the most difficult part of the replacement theory and the one which at this time is weakest. It is hoped that future work will throw more light on the subject. Geologic literature discusses many large ore bodies of various metals and minerals which are almost universally recognized as replacement bodies, the source and depositional mechanisms of which are not clearly understood. Therefore the writers are unwilling to abandon the replacement theory because present limitations of their knowledge do not permit a complete explanation. The fact of replacement can be proved, even thought the mechanism is hazy. If replacement can operate on a small scale to form pure ore, there is no reason apparent to the writers why it cannot do the same on a large scale.

It is noteworthy that many small (1-10 cm thick) hard pure hematite lenses in itabirite are closely associated with and clearly related to minor quartz veins, indicating the passage of *hot waters* or *gases* which could mobilize both the iron and silica.

The abundant *talc* (?) in the ore might indicate that replacement occurred above ordinary temperature. The importance of stress in localizing ore bodies also points in this direction, as stresses producing the type and grade of metamorphism found in the country rock and the neatness of schistosity in the ore bodies, which trangresses primary structural features, do not commonly occur near the surface. Whether the replacing solutions were supergene, heated at depth, or whether the source of the solutions is to be looked for in the abundant post-Minas intrusives is not yet clear.

Similarly, the source of the replacing iron is not clear. Certainly the itabirite adjacent to the pure ore bodies has not been leached of iron; it has been in part enriched. Iron may have been mobilized from the formation as a whole and deposited at favorably situated structural sites after large scale intraformational migration. The iron thus mobilized would have been only a small fraction of the total iron in the formation and the impoverishment of the formation in general would hardly be detectable.

The *time of formation* of the pure ores is not yet known. It must have been post-Itacolumi, for no hard ore is found in the Itacolumi conglomerates. It must have been before the gold mineralization of the area, for soft ore had begun to form at the time of that mineralization, which is thought to have been Caledonian by D. Guimaraes (unless indeed, the hydrothermal solutions causing gold-pyrite mineralization over an area even learger than that in which the pure ores occur had some part in forming the pure ore deposits. This hardly seems probable, owing to the low sulfur content of the pure ore).

There is one other possible mode of origin which should be discussed. It will be remembered that in the section on physiographic development as related to the ores, it was pointed out that the *iron formation was subject to local sub-aerial erosion and possible supergene enrichment* during pre-Itacolumi time and for long periods during later ages.

This enrichment could have been a *residual* enrichment such as is the origin of the Noamundi slump ores in India and, possibly, of the Mesabi ores in the United States, or it could have been a *metasomatic* replacement of silica by hematite under supergene conditions such as can also be observed at the Noamundi [1] mine. Had it been residual enrichment by the removal of silica, slump and breccia-structures should be common, particulary in the wall rocks. Had the enrichment been by replacement, such textures would not be expected. As a matter of fact, they are not found in the wall rocks.

Assuming supergene replacement to have taken place in pre-Itacolumi time, the pure material would have been soft during the erosion of the Minas Series which supplied the cobbles of itabirite to the Itacolumi conglomerates. Therefore hard ore cobbles would not to be expected in the Itacolomi. They are not found in that formation. During the various post-Itacolomi metamorphisms, the soft material could be expected to assume its present hard and foliated state.

This rather attractive hypothesis has several weaknesses. An important one is the fact that the itabirite cobbles in the Itacolumi conglomerates, although deformed, are not twisted and isoclinally folded like the structures in the ore and itabirite today. Cobbles of twisted and isoclinally folded itabirite are found in modern alluvial deposits. The pre-Itacolumi deformation must have been a relatively gentle one. This leaves us with the same difficulty we met before in explaining the similar types of failure under stress of dissimilar materials. The seeming localization of ore bodies at or near stress foci would also not be explained. Most important, it would indeed be stretching the long arm of coincidence to postulate, as one would have to, that the pre-Itacolumi replacement zone coincided so neatly with the present day erosion surface, for one could expect that such replacement would have taken place over a limited vertical range.

It might be argued that enrichment had taken place during Paleozoic or post-Paleozoic time. The metamorphic grade of the ores would necessitate a pre-Caledonian concentration, for after that epoch, no further strong metamorphic action is known. Whether the formation was subject to post-Itacolumi and pre-Caledonian sub-aerial erosion is a matter of speculation.

It is hoped that, during the next decade, enough concrete evidence can be gathered to definitely settle these questions. On the basis of present evidence, the writers do not think that the pure ores were caused by supergene enrichment under sub-aerial conditions, but that the replacement took place at considerable depths and at elevated temperature.

* * * * * * *

1. Jones, H. Cecil, *Iron Ore Deposits of Bihar and Orissa*. *Mem. Geol. Surv. India*. Vol. LXIII, Pt. 2. Calcutta. 1934.

CHAPTER V

PRINCIPAL BIBLIOGRAPHY

DOLORES IGLÉSIAS

MARIA DE LOURDES MENEGHEZZI

Départamento Nacional da Produção Mineral

ALMEIDA, FERNANDO FLAVIO MARQUES DE, *Origem dos minérios de ferro e manganês de Urucum (Corumbá, Estado de Mato Grosso) : Brasil, Divi. Geol. Mineralogia, Boletim* n. 191, 58 p., est., map., Rio de Janeiro. 1946.

ALMEIDA, FRANCISCO ANTONIO DE, *Noticias sôbre as minas de ferro de Jacupiranguinha. Bases de um projecto de exploração,* (Memori apresentada a sua Excia. o Sr. Visconde do Rio Branco.) 40 p., Rio de Janeiro.

ARAUJO, M. ALVES DE, *Fabrica de ferro de São João de Ipanema.* (Extracto do relatorio apresentado á assembléa geral pelo Ministro e Secretario dos Negocios da Agricultura, etc.) : *Auxiliador Ind. Nac.*, v. L, p. 138, Rio de Janeiro. 1882.

BARBOSA, ALUIZIO LICINIO DE MIRANDA, *Reservas brasileiras de minerio de ferro : O Observ. Econ. Financeiro,* Ano XV. n. 176, p. 70-77, ilus., Rio de Janeiro. 1950.

BARBOSA, OCTAVIO, *Reservas de minério de ferro em Santa Catarina : Mineração e Metalurgia,* v. V, n. 25, p. 21-24, Rio de Janeiro. 1940.

— *Minério de ferro no Brasil : Mineração Metalurgia,* v. XIV, n. 82, p. 100-101, Rio de Janeiro. 1949.

— *Contribuição á Geologia do Centro de Minas Gerais. Mineração e Metalurgia,* vol. XIV, n. 79, p. 3-19 Rio de Janeiro. 1949.

BAUER, HENRIQUE E., *As minas de ferro de Jacupiranguinha : Revista de Engenharia,* n. 170, IX, p. 213, Rio de Janeiro, 28 de setembro de 1887.

BELLO, JOSAPHAT, *Official report on the Minas Iron Deposits : Brazilian Min. Review,* I, p. 219-220, Rio de Janeiro. 1904.

BIRKINBINE, JOHN, *Iron ores of Brazil : U. S. Geol. Survey, Ann. Report* 16th, 1894-1895, Part III, p. 67-69, Washington. 1895.

BRANDT, FRIEDRICH, *Ein neuer Typ von Eisen-Tonerdephosphat. Vorkommen (Maranhão, Nord-Brazilien) : Chemie der Erde,* Bd. 7, t. 3, p. 383-425, 16 est., Jena. 1932.

CAMPOS, LUIZ FELIPE GONZAGA DE, *Fisiografia da zona ferrifera de Minas Gerais : Mineração e Metalurgia,* v. VII, n. 38, p. 65-68, map., Rio de Janeiro. 1943.

* The data for 1951 are only from January 1rst to September 30th.

CAMPOS, LUIZ FELIPE GONZAGA DE, *Geologia da zona ferrifera do Centro de Minas Gerais : Mineração e Metalurgia*, v. 7, n. 40, p. 187-193, map. Rio de Janeiro. 1943.
— *Jazidas ferríferas da Serra da Piedade, Minas Gerais : Mineração e Metalurgia*, v. VII, n. 41, p. 285-288, maps., Rio de Janeiro. 1943.
— (Terceira parte do relatório inédito *Minerios de ferro da região Central do Estado de Minas Gerais* apresentado em 1911 ao Dr. ORVILLE A. DERBY).
— *Jazidas ferriferas de Pitanguí e São Luiz, Minas Gerais : Mineraçãoe Metalurgia*, v. XII, n. 71, p. 225-227, map., Rio de Janeiro. 1948.
CARNEIRO, ARTHUR, *Ferro e Carvão*, 136 p. *Imprensa Naval*, Rio de Janeiro. 1921.
CORRÊA JUNIOR, FRANCISCO DE ASSIS BARCELLOS, (GROASSE, E.) *O minerio de ferro da Fazenda Fábrica, da Companhia de Mineração de Ferro e Carvão, S. A., distrito de Sao Julião municipio de Ouro Preto, Estado de Minas Gerais : Mineração e Metalurgia*, v. XI, n. 65, p. 267-272, ilus., perfis, Rio de Janeiro. 1946.
CURVELLO, WALTER S., *Metallographie study of the Cratheús iron : Museu Nacional, Boletim, N. Ser., Geologia*, n. 10, 4 p., 4 est, Rio de Janeiro. 1950.
DERBY, ORVILLE A., *Origem sedimentaria dos minerios de ferro : Revista industrial de Minas Geraes*, anno I, n. 7, p. 155-159, Ouro Preto. 1894.
— *On the occurence of monazite in iron ore and graphite : American Journal of Science*, 4th Series, v. XIII, p. 211-122, New Haven. 1902.
— *Os minerios de ferro do Brasil : Jornal do Commercio do Rio de Janeiro*, 25 de agosto. 1909.
— *Almanach Garnier* para 1911, p. 279-289.
— *Brasil, Minister. Agr., Ind., Commercio, Boletim*, Anno II, jan.-fevr. 1913, p. 88-97, Rio de Janeiro. 1913.
— *Early Iron Making in Brazil : Eng. Min. Journal*, v. 88, n. 23, p. 1112, n. 26, p. 1258-1259. New York. 1909.
— *The Iron Ore Resources of the World : International Geol. Congr.* 11e, p. 813-822, ilus., 2 maps., Stockholm. 1909.
— *The iron ores of Brazil : The Times*, dec. 28, p. 56, London. 1909.
DINIZ GONSALVES, ALPHEU, *Ferro no Brasil : Brasil, Serv. Geol. Mineralogico, Boletim* n. 61, XI-150 p., ilus., maps., Rio de Janeiro. 1932.
— *O Ferro. A produção mundial e importação do Brasil : Rev. O Economista*, n. 168, Rio de Janeiro, março, 1934.
— *O Ferro na economia nacional : Brasil, Minister. Agr., Direct. Estatis. Produçao*, 153 p., ilus., Rio de Janeiro. 1937.
DORR, JOHN VAN II, *Manganese and iron deposits of Morro do Urucum, Matto Grosso, Brazil : U. S. Geol. Survey, Bulletin* 946-A, 47 p., est., 6 maps. in bolso, Washington. 1945.
— *Depositos de manganês e ferro do Morro do Urucum.* Mato Grosso, Brasil. (Tradução do Eng. EUGENIO BOURDOT DUTRA) : *Brasil, Div. Fom. Prod. Mineral, Boletim* n. 76, 76 p., est., 6 maps. in bolso, Rio de Janeiro. 1946.
— (GUILD. PHILIP W.), *Notes on the iron ores of Central Minas Gerais, Brazil : Geol. Soc. America, Bulletin* v. 60, n. 12, Pte. 2, p. 1883, New York. 1949.
— *How much iron ore in Brazil? : The Iron Age*, v. 166, n. 7, p. 81-84; n. 8, p. 79-82, map., diagr., New York. 1950.
— (WHITEHEAD, GILBERT), *Ores and mining in the Itabira iron district, Brazil : Economic Geology*, v. 45, n. 4, p. 389-390, Lancaster, Pa. 1950.
— *The Iron ores of Central Minas Gerais, Brazil : Mineração e Metalurgia*, v. XVI, n. 92, p. 95-100, ilus., map., Rio de Janeiro. 1951.
DUPRÉ JUNIOR, LEANDRO, *Memoria sobre a fabrica de ferro de São João de Ipanema : Ouro Preto, Escola de Minas*, Annaes n. 4, p. 59-90, Ouro Preto. 1885.
— *Revista de Engenharia*, n. 148, p. 230-234; n. 149, p. 245-247, Rio de Janeiro. 1886.
DUTRA DE MORAES, GERALDO, *Jazidas de ferro do Brasil : O Observ. Econ. Financeiro*, Ano VIII, n. 93, p. 155-162, Rio de Janeiro. 1943.
ERICHSEN, ALBERTO ILDEFONSO, *Nota preliminar sobre as jazidas de ferro dos municipios de Joinville e S. Francisco. Estado de Santa Catharina : Brasil, Serv. Geol. Mineralogico, Boletim* n. 13, p. 87-99, ilus., 2 maps., Rio de Janeiro. 1925.
— *Os minerios de ferro do Municipio de Joinville, Estados de Santa Catharina : Minerio, Combustivel e Transporte*, Ano 1, n. 1, p. 25-27, Rio de Janeiro. 1928.
FEIJÓ, JOÃO DA SILVA, *Memoria sobre os mineraes de ferro de Cantagy de Xorò, na Capitania de Ceará, escripta no anno de 1814 : Brasil, Minister. Agr., Ind. Commercio, Rel. do Ministro*, Annexo, 8 p., Rio de Janeiro. 1864.
— *Publicado em parte na Chorographia da Provincia do Ceará por* JOSÉ POMPEU DE A. CALVANTI, p. 64-66, Rio de Janeiro. 1888.
FERRAND, PAUL, *Formas dos deposittos de ferro em Minas : Revista de Engenharia*, n. 250, p. XIII, 345, Rio de Janeiro 1890.
FERREIRA, BENEDICTO ALVES, *Contribuições sobre a composição de algunas ocorrencias de minerio de ferro no Estado, de São Paulo : O I. G. G. (Inst. Geogr. Geol.)* Ano I, v. II, n. 2 ,p. 143-152, Sao Paulo. 1944.
FRANTZ, HARRY W., *As grandes reservas de minério de ferro do Brasil : Revista Mineira de Engenharia*, Ano 1, n. 4, p. 57, Belo Horizonte. 1938.
FRASER, H. J., (NEWBERRY, A.-W.), *Current iron & steel situation in Brazil : Pan Amer. Inst. of Min. Eng. and Geology, U. S. Section, Technical Paper*, n. 3, 19 p., ilus., maps., New York, s /d.

FREYBERG, B. VON., *Ergbnisse geologischer Forrschungen in Minas Geraes, (Brasilien) : Neues Jb. Min. Geol. u. Paleon.* Sonderband II, XI, p. 401, ests., tab. maps. Stuttgart. 1932.
— *Die Bodenschätze des Staates Minas Geraes, Brasilien.* XII, 453 p., 73 est., 37 pls. *Schweizerbart'sche verlagabuchhandlung,* Sttutgart. 1934.
GEISSEL, HENRY, *The Problem of Mining Brazilian Iron Ore : Eng. and Mining Journal,* v. 112, n. 19, p. 729, New York. 1921.
GROSSE, E, (CORRÊA Junior, FRANCISCO DE ASSIS BARCELLOS). *O Minério de ferro da Fazenda Fabrica, da Companhia de Mineração de Ferro e Carvão S. A., distrito de São Julião, municipio de Ouro Preto, Estado de Minas Gerais : Mineração e Metalurgia,* v. XI, n. 64, p. 267-272, ilus., perfis, Rio de Janeiro. 1946.
— (MELLO, AFFONSO VAZ DE). *O minério de ferro da fazenda Fábrica da Companhia de Mineração de Ferro e Carvão S. A., distrito de São Julião municipio de Ouro Preto, Estado de Minas Gerais : Mineração e Metalurgia,* v. XI, n. 62, p. 105-115, ilus, Rio de Janeiro. 1946.
GUILD, PHILIP W., (DORR, JOHN VAN II). *Notes on the iron ores of Central Minas Gerais, Brazil : Geol. Soc. America, Bulletin,* v. 60, n. 12, pte 2, p. 1883, New York. 1949.
GUIMARÁES DJALMA, *Contribuição á geologia do Estado de Minas Gerais : Brasil, Serv. Geol. Mineralogico.* 1931.
— *Metalogênese nas formaões árqueo-proterozóicas do Brasil. Instituto de Tecnologia Industrial. Bol.* n. 4, p. 65, Belo-Horizonte. 1947.
— *O estilo da evolução geodinãmica do estudo brasilero e sua influencia nos processos metalogeneticos. Ass. Bras. Metais. Bol.* 6, n. 20, p. 205-223, São Paulo. 1950.
— *Contribuição ao estudo da origem dos depositos de minerio de ferro e manganez de Centro de Minas Geraes : Brasil, Serv. Fom. Prod. Mineral, Boletim* n. 8, 70 p., maps., Rio de Janeiro. 1935.
HARDER, E. C., (LEIH, C.-K.) *Hematite Ores of Brazil and a comparison with hematite ores of Lake Superior : Economic Geol.,* v. VI, p. 670-686, map., Urbana. 1911.
HARDER, E. C., CHAMBERLIN, R. T., *The Geology of Central Minas Geraes, Brazil : Journal of Geol.,* v. XXIII, n. 4, p. 341-378, n. 5, p. 385-424, ilus., map. Chicago. 1915.
— *Minerios de ferro do Brasil comparados com os do Lago Superior : Brasil, Minister, Agr. Ind. Comercio, Boletim,* Anno II, n. 4, p. 113-125, Rio de Janeiro. 1913.
HUSSAK, E., *Uber das Vorkommen von Palladium und Platin in Brasilien : (Konigliche) Akad. der Wissens. Math. Naturhist. Classe Sitzungsberichten,* B. CXIII, Abh. I. Wien. Juli. 1904.
— Relatório; Part. I. *Sôbre a estrutura geológica da região do Estado de Goyaz,* examinada pela Comissão Exploradora do Planalto Central. Part. II. *Ocorrência de mineras valiosos, mineros,* etc., na região explorada. Anexo, n. 5, p. 281-319. (Em português e francês). H. Lamberts et Cia.; Rio de Janeiro. 1894.
JAMES, PRESTON E., *Itabira Iron : Quart. Journal Inter. Amer. Rel.,* v. 1, p. 37-48, Washington. 1939.
KAUSEL, ERNESTO, *Mineria e industria del fierro en el Estado de Minas Geraes, Brazil : Ipimigeo, (Inst. Pan. Ing. Minas y Geol.)* Año II, 1-2 trim. 1947, p. 23-24, Santiago de Chile. 1947.
KEGEL. WILHELM, *Mineração do ferro em Minas : O Observ. Econ. Financeiro,* v. 5, n. 28, p. 20-24, ilus, Rio de Janeiro. 1938.
— *Minerios de ferro.* (Conferencia realisada na Escola Politécnica da Univ. de São Paulo.) : *Revista Politécnica,* Ano XXXIV, n. 128, p. 235-242, São Paulo. 1938.
KNECHT, THEODORO, *As ocorrencias de minérios de ferro e pirita no Estado de São Paulo : S. Paulo, Inst. Geogr. Geol., Boletim* n. 25, 90 p., ilus., map. Sao Paulo. 1939.
— *Relatórios sôbre minério de ferro nos arredores do Morro do Vacanga, no municipio de Parnaiba: O. I. G. G. (Inst. Geogr. Geol.)* Ano I, v. II, n. 2, p. 118-128, ilus., perfis geol. Sao Paulo. 1944.
LACOURT, FERNANDO, *Ferro em Ouro Preto e Mariana, Minas Gerais : Mineração Metalurgia,* v. III, n. 15, p. 181-182, ilus., perfis., Rio de Janeiro. 1938.
LEINZ, VIKTOR, *Eisenerz-Vorkommen in Paraná, Brasilien : Zeitschrift für praktische Geologie,* 1938, 46 Jahr., h. 1, 5 p., 4 est Halle (Saale). 1938.
LEITH, C. K., (HARDER, E.-C.) *Hematite Ores of Brazil and a comparison with hematite ores of Lake Superior : Economic Geol.,* v. VI, p. 670-686, map., Urbana. 1911.
— *Minerios de ferro do Brasil comparados com os do Lago Superior : Brasil, Minister. Agr. Ind. Comercio, Boletim,* Anno II, n. 4, p. 113-125, Rio de Janeiro. 1913.
— *Iron ores of the Americas : Soc. Pan American Sci., Congr., Proceedings,* v. 8, p. 954-959, Washington. 1917.
LEONARDOS, OTHON HENRY, *Ferro no Estado da Bahia : Mineração e Metalurgia,* v. 2, n. 7, p. 51-57, ilus., perfis., Rio Janeiro. 1937.
— *Brasil, Serv. Fom. Prod. Mineral, Avulso* n. 21, p. 1-14, ilus.,Rio de Janeiro. 1937.
— *Ferro no Paraná : Brasil, Minister. Agricultura, Boletim,* Ano 26, ns. 7-9, p. 39-77, maps, Rio de Janeiro. 1937.
— *Brasil, Serv. Fom. Prod. Mineral, Boletin* n. 25, pte. I, 49 p., 10 ests., 4 fls., Rio de Janeiro. 1938.
— *Depósito de minério de ferro do pico de Itabirito, Minas Gerais : Mineração e Metalurgia,* v. 2, n. 13 p. 2-8, ilus., Rio de Janeiro. 1938.
— *Brasil, Serv. Fom. Prod. Mineral, Avulso* n. 28, 14 p., ilus., Rio de Janeiro. 1938.
— *Nota sôbre as ocorrencias de minerio de ferro no Estado do Ceará : Brasil, Minister. Agricultura, Boletim,* Anno 27, p. 79-85, Rio de Janeiro. 1938.
— *Minério de ferro en Pernambuco : Mineração e Metalurgia,* v. IV, n. 20, p. 90-91, Rio de Janeiro. 1939.
LISBOA, MIGUEL ARROJADO RIBEIRO, *Relatório preliminar sôbre as jazidas de minérios de manganês e de ferro do Urucum (Mato Grosso-Brasil) : Brasil, Div. Fom. Prod. Mineral, Boletim* n. 62, pte. II, p. 31-81, Rio de Janeiro. 1944.

MALOZENOFF, A., *The United Nation's newest source of iron : Eng. Min. Journal*, v. 142, n. 12, p. 55-59, New York. 1942.

MELLO, AFFONSO VAZ DE, (GROASSE, E.)., *O minério de ferro da fazenda Fabrica da Companhia de Mineração de Ferro e Carvão S. A., distrito de São Julião municipio de Ouro Preto, Estado de Minas Gerais : Mineração e Metalurgia*, v. XI, n. 62, p. 105-115, ilus., Rio de Janeiro. 1946.

MELLO JUNIOR, JOSÉ LINO DE, *Jazidas de minério de ferro de Jequié : Brasil, Div. Fom. Prod. Mineral, Boletim* n. 39 pte. I, p. 13-45, maps. Rio de Janeiro. 1940.

— *Revista Brasileira de Chimica*, v. IX, n. 54, p. 219-255; v. X, n. 55, p. 21-27., São Paulo. 1940.

MENEZES, FRANCISCO XAVIER OLIVEIRA DE, *Relatorio que acompanha a planta topographica e geologica das minas de ferro do Jacupiranguinha e Turvo na Comarca de Iguape, da Provincia de S. Paulo, das quaes é concessionario o Snr. Joaquim Ignacio Silveira da Motta por Dec. n. 5152, de 27 de Novembro de 1872.* - Typ. Carioca, Rio de Janeiro. 1889.

(Empresa Brasil Metallurgico, Analyse e considerações sobre as minas de Jacupiranguinha, etc. p. 31-37.)

MORAES, L. J., *Jazidas de ouro dos Districtos de Caeté e Santa Barbara : Brasil, Div. Fom. Prod. Mineral, Boletim*. n. 38, part. I, p. 20-150, ests., maps. Rio de Janeiro. 1939.

— *Importancia dos recursos minerais do Estado. (Minas Gerais) : Rev. Mineira Eng.*, Ano, II, ns. 16-17. Belo-Horizonte. 1940.

— *Jazidas de magnetita de Morro do Ferro, Município de Oliveira, Minas Gerais. Mineração e Metalurgia*, vol. XII, n. 71, p. 223-224. Rio de Janeiro. 1948.

MORAES REGO, LUIZ FLORES DE, *As jazidas de ferro do Centro de Minas Gerais*, 81 p., 1 map. Imp. Oficial. Belo Horizonte. 1933.

MOURA, PEDRO DE, OLIVEIRA, AVELINO IGNACIO DE, *Geologia da região de Corumbá e minerios de manganês e ferro do Urucum, Mato Grosso : Mineração e Metalurgia*, v. VII, n. 42, p. 335-345, ilus., maps., perfis geol., Rio de Janeiro. 1944.

— *Brasil, Div. Fom. Prod. Mineral, Boletim* n. 62, pte. I, p. 13-29, ilus. maps., perfis geol., Rio de Janeiro. 1944.

NEWBERRY, A.-W., (FRASER, H.-J.) *Current iron & steel situation in Brazil : Pan Amer. Inst. Min. Eng. and Geology, U. S. Section, Technical Paper*, n. 3, 19 p., ilus., maps., New York, s /d.

NUNES, JANARY GENTIL, *Histórico das negociações para aproveitamento das jazidas de ferro do Territorio Federal do Amapá : Mineração e Metalurgia*, v. X, n. 59, p. 203-208, ilus., Rio de Janeiro. 1946.

OLIVEIRA, AVELINO IGNACIO DE, MOURA, PEDRO DE, *Geologia da região de Corumbá e minérios de manganê e ferro do Urucum, Mato Grosso : Mineração e Metallurgia*, v. VII, n. 42. p. 235-345, ilus., maps., perfis geol. Rio de Janeiro. 1944.

— *Brasil, Div. Fom. Prod. Mineral, Boletim*, n. 62, pte. I, p. 13-29, ilus., maps., perfis geol. Rio de Janeiro, 1944.

OLIVEIRA, EUZEBIO PAULO DE, *Minerios de ferro e a industria siderurgica.* (Conferencia feita na Soc. do Geographia do Rio de Janeiro, em maio de 1930) : *Jornal do Commercio do Rio de Janeiro*, 6 de junho. 1930.

— Separata : *Brasil, Serv. Geol. Mineralogico*, 13 p., Rio de Janeiro. 1930.

— *A Politica do ferro : Gazeta da Tarde*, 24 de novembro de 1933, Rio de Janeiro. 1933.

— *Brasil, Serv. Geol. Mineralogico, Notas preliminares e estudos*, n. 9, p. 10-12, Rio de Janeiro. 1937.

OLIVEIRA, PAULO JOSÉ DE, *Relatorio sobre as minas de carvão de pedra e ferro da ilha de Itamaricá : Brasil, Minister. Agr. Ind. e Commercio, Rel.*, Anexo 36 p., Rio de Janeiro. 1864.

— *Exploração de mineraes : Brasil, Minister. Agr. Ind. e Commercio, Rel.*, Anexo, 19 p., Rio de Janeiro. 1865.

PAES LEME, LUIZ BETIM, *Carvão e ferro no Brasil.* (Conferencia realizada no Club de Engenharia, em 28 de agosto de 1919) : 24 p. Typ. *Gomes Brandão Marcondes & Cia.*, Rio de Janeiro. 1919.

PAIVA FILHO, JOSÉ ELIAS DE, *Fabrica de ferro de Ipanema : Brasil, Direct. Material Bellico, Relatorio.* 32 p., Ipanema, São Paulo, s /d.

PARDEE, FRANKLIN G., *Outlook for iron from Brazil : Eng. & Mining Journal*, v. 144, n. 10, p. 75-77, ilus., New York. 1943.

PIMENTA, DERMEVAL JOSÉ, *Exportação de minério de ferro pelo vale do Rio Doce : Geologia e Metalurgia* (*publicacão do Centro Morães Rego*), *Boletim* n. 7, p. 62-85; 86-101, São Paulo. 1949.

PINTO, MARIO DA SILVA, *Composição e gênese dos minérios de ferro de Jequié : Mineraçáo e Metalurgia*, v. IV, n. 22, p. 207-210, qd., Rio de Janeiro. 1939.

— *Brasil, Div. Fom. Prod. Mineral, Boletim* n. 39, p. 46-56, Rio de Janeiro. 1940.

— *Rev. Bras. Chimica*, v. IX, n. 54, p. 219-225; v. X, n. 55, p. 21-27, Sao Paulo. 1940.

ROSA, WENCESLAU, *O Ferro brasileiro e suas possibilidades economicas : Mineração e Metalurgia*, v. XV, n. 87, p. 90.

SANDERS, BERNARD H., *Iron ores at Itabira (Minas Geraes), Brazil : Inst. Min. Metal. Bulletin*, n. 346, 23, p. 9, ests., 9 pls. (incl. map. 1 : 40.000). Jul. 1933. *Discussion : Bulletin* n. 349, p. 1-8, n. 351. p. 29-32, n. 352, p. 27-28, London. 1933-1934.

ROXO, MATHIAS GONÇALVES DE OLIVEIRA, *Nota preliminar sobre a região ferrifera de Jequié, no Estado da Bahia : Brasil, Serv. Geol. Mineralogico, Rel. An. do Directoor*, 1931, p. 83-85, Rio de Janeiro. 1932.

— *Jornal do Commercio do Rio de Janeiro*, 25 de novembro de 1934.

— *Brasil, Minister. Trab. Ind. e Comercio, Boletim* n. 4, p. 150-163, Rio de Janeiro. 1934.

— *Brasil. Distr. Fed., Direct. Eng. da Prefeitura, Revista*, Anno IV, n. 17, p. 444-453, Rio de Janeiro. 1935.

— *Minerios de ferro do Brasil : Brasil, Serv. Geol. Mineralogico, Notas preliminares e estudios*, n. 14, p. 1-8, Rio de Janeiro. 1937.

SANDERS, BERNARD H., *Iron ores at Itabira (Minas Geraes), Brazil : Inst. Mining & Metallurgy, Bulletin* n. 346, 23 p., 9 figs., 9 ests. (incl. mapa) Jul. 1933. *Discussion : Bulletin* n. 349, 8 p.; n. 351, p. 29-32; n. 352, p. 27-28, London. 1933-34.

SCHMIDT, F., *Carvão de pedra e ferro.* (*São João de Ipanema*) *: Revista Polytechnica* (en português e alemão, redigida por F. SCHMIDT). Anno I, n. 11, nov. 1853, p. 287-293, Hamburgo. 1853.

SCOTT, HERBERT KILBURN, *The iron ores of Brazil : Jour. of. Iron & Steel Inst.*, London. 1902.

— *Separata.* 20 p., ilus., 1 maps., parcial mostrando a zona de ferro, London. 1902.

— *Brazilian Eng. Min. Review*, v. 11, n. 8, p. 117-124, ilus., 2 maps., Rio de Janeiro. 1905.

— *Iron ores of Brazil : Eng. Min. Journal*, v. 74, p. 750, New York. 1902.

— *The Principal Iron ore deposits of the World : Cleveland Inst, of Engineers, Proceedings*, Session 1922-23. n. 3, p. 69-117. Cleveland. 1922.

SENA, JOAQUIM CANDIDO DA COSTA, *Minerios de ferro no Brasil princip almente no Estado de Minas. Consederações sobre a industria do ferro. Influencia que sobre ella exercera o Brasil em futuro nao remoto. Memoria apresentada ao Congresso Scientifico Latino Americano : Ouro Preto, Escola de Minas, Annaes*, n. 10, p. 3-17, Ouro Preto. 1908.

— *Industria*, Anno I, n. 3, p. 12-19, Rio de Janeiro. 1912.

— *Minerios de ferro no Brasil principalmente no Estado de Minas Geraes : Ouro Preto, Escola de Minas*, Annaes, n. 10, p. 19-34, Ouro Preto. 1908.

SOUZA, HENRIQUE CAPPER ALVES DE, *Exportação de minério de ferro : Mineração e Metallurgia*, v. III, n. 13, p. 33, ilus., Rio de Janeiro. 1938.

— *Ferro do Chaval, Ceará : Mineração e Metalurgia*, v. IV, n. 21, p. 139-147, ilus., perf., qd., Rio de Janeiro. 1939.

— *Ferro e ametista em Sento Sé : Brasil, Div. Fom. Prod. Mineral, Boletim* n. 69, 32 p., est., map., Rio de Janeiro. 1945.

TEIXEIRA, EMILIO ALVES, *The Iron ore resources of Brazil and their economic importance : Eng. Min. Journal.* v. 124, p. 730-735, New York. 1927.

— *As fontes de minerios de ferro no Brasil e seu valor economico : Rev. Bras. Engenharial*, Anno VIII, t. XV, ns. 1 e 2, pp. 14-17, 57-61, Rio de Janeiro. 1928.

— *Brasil. Exceptional reserves of iron, manganese, and nickel promise the development of a vast mineral industry : Eng. & Min. Journal*, v. 143, n. 8, p. 89-93, ilus., map., New York. 1942.

VAZ, TEODORO AMALIO DA FONSECA, *Jazida de minério de ferro de Taquaril : Mineração e Metallurgia*, v. II, n. 14, p. 97-100, ilus., perfis., Rio de Janeiro. 1938.

VIERA JUNIOR, A. RODRIGUES, *Jazida de minerio de ferro de Sapatú, valle do rio Ribiera, Estado de São Paulo Brasil, Minister., Agr., Ind. e Commercio, Boletim* v. 1, anno XVII, n. 4, p. 501-505, Rio de Janeiro. 1928,

WANKER, R. G., *Brazilien iron ore ressources : Blast Furnace & Steel Plant.* v. 39, n. 3, p. 337-338, Pittsburgh. 1951.

WHITEHEAD, GILBERT, (DORR, JOHN VAN). *Ores and mining in the Itabira iron district. Brasil : Economic Geology*, v. 45, n. 4, p. 389-390, Lancaster, Pa. 1950.

17

Reprinted from *Geology and Ore Deposits of the Iron River-Crystal Falls District, Iron County, Michigan,* (U.S. Geol. Survey Prof. Paper 570), 1968, pp. 115, 118–124, 127–130

Geology and Ore Deposits of the Iron River-Crystal Falls District, Iron County, Michigan

H. L. JAMES, C. E. DUTTON. F. J. PETTIJOHN, and K. L. WIER

ORIGIN OF THE ORES

Although it can be stated at the outset that the question of origin of the ores remains virtually unsolved, the range of concepts that can profitably be considered is tightly restricted by the array of facts and reasonable inferences that can be assembled. These facts and inferences are organized as follows:

General

1. The ores occur only in iron-formation, which in its preore state consisted mainly of interbedded chert and siderite.
   The concept of a preore conversion of chert and siderite to metamorphic silicates as a requisite step in the ore-forming process (Tyler, 1949; Mann, 1953) is wholly without support in the Iron River–Crystal Falls district, as it is in the Mesabi district (White, 1954, p. 82). Indeed, there is a negative correlation between preore abundance of silicates and the occurrence of ore.
2. The ores are of Precambrian age and probably formed during the interval from 650 to 1,100 million years ago.
   Neither limit is certainly established. The lower limit of 1,100 million years is set only by an inferred relation to the Mesabi district.
3. The amount of oxidized iron-formation and ore per unit area of iron-formation for the district as a whole is greatest at the surface and decreases progressively with depth.
   The actual distribution of oxidation is not regular, however. Unoxidized iron-formation is at the present surface in places where immediately adjacent iron-formation is oxidized to depths of a thousand feet or more. Also, in several large areas the iron-formation is wholly unoxidized at the surface; these tracts may represent areas topographically high during the epoch of deep oxidation and from which the oxidized rock has since been eroded.
4. Ore bodies are most numerous and largest in areas where the iron-formation is most extensively oxidized, and all ore bodies grade laterally into oxidized iron-formation.
5. Most ore bodies connect to the surface in some dimension, though often indirectly or in diminished size.
   For some small ore bodies, exploration has not been adequate to demonstrate an extension to the surface, but certainly all connect to the surface via oxidized iron-formation if not by ore.
6. Many large ore bodies reach their maximum dimensions at depths of 500–1,500 feet.
   The two largest ore bodies known in the district—the Hiawatha No. 2 ore body and the ore body on the south flank of Mineral Hills—have far greater size at depth than they do at the surface.
7. Oxidized iron-formation and ore bodies extend to a known depth of half a mile.
   Extensive and complete oxidation is known to extend to depth of half a mile in at least four places in the district, and a reasonable assumption is that locally at least it may extend to 3,000 feet.

Structural

1. The ore bodies were formed in their present structural position.
   In many places, the form of the ore body bears a delicate relation to overturning of the beds; an ore body in a syncline will extend for some distance up the flattened limb but will terminate abruptly on the overhanging limb. Furthermore, ore in which color banding reflects the original layering

Editor's Note: A row of asterisks indicates that material has been omitted from the original article.

is contorted typically into tight crumples and drag-folds—structures that could not possibly form in material of the present composition. Local zones of rubbly or breccialike aspect can be attributed to slumping during the ore-forming process.

2. Most of the ore bodies that have a definable structural position are in upward-facing structures, generally synclines.

   A few ore bodies are related to faults or to dikes that become one side of a structural trough. In general, the faults have been barriers to circulation rather than channels for it.

3. The ore bodies typically rest on a well-defined footwall of less permeable (or at least less readily altered) rock.

   The footwall for most ore bodies is pyritic graphitic slate; locally, in the eastern part of the district, it is a slaty unit within the iron-formation. The oxidation characteristically fades out abruptly in the footwall unit—within a few feet under major ore bodies in the western part of the district—whereas the oxidation is likely to extend to the surface in the hanging-wall rocks.

4. Ore bodies occur on very few major anticlinal structures.

   The relation between oxidation and structure is less clear. Many major anticlinal areas are deeply oxidized, but there is a suggestion in the map patterns that this is true mainly in areas of steep plunge. In the Crystal Falls–Alpha belt of folded iron-formation, in which the folds plunge to the northwest at 40°–50°, unoxidized iron-formation is more common in the anticlinal areas than in the synclinal parts of the folds.

5. Some very large bodies of ore attain their maximum size at depth in the lowest parts of tight doubly plunging synclines.

   The best example of ore in a doubly plunging synclinal structure is in the Buck mine. (See fig. 62.) In terms of a possible circulation system, structural basins of this sort would tend to be stagnant, yet clearly they have been favorable loci for the formation of ore.

Mineralogical and chemical

1. The ores are porous very fine grained mixtures of (dominantly) hematite and goethite.

   Hematite and goethite vary in proportions within short distances. No relation of proportion to depth has been noted. Interlayering of goethite-rich and hematite-rich layers suggests some control by original layer-to-layer compositional differences in the iron-formation.

2. The ores have formed by oxidation of original siderite and by at least partial replacement of chert layers by iron oxides.

   The replacement of chert layers by iron oxides is obvious in hand specimens and is further indicated by the fact that the stratigraphic thickness of the formation does not change measurably in the passage from unoxidized iron-formation to oxidized iron-formatioh to ore.

3. Gangue minerals are of microscopic dimensions and consist mainly of relict chert, clay mica (illite), and kaolinite dispersed through the iron oxides.

4. The stable mineral assemblage is goethite, hematite, illite, kaolinite, gypsum, and apatite(?).

   The quartz identified in the ores is assumed to be relict from incomplete replacement of chert. The deficiency of many ores in calcium suggests that the phosphate may be present, at least in part, as vivianite or some other comparable hydrous phosphate, such as dufrenite.

5. The ore-forming process resulted in separation of the iron and manganese.

   The iron ores are noticeably deficient in manganese relative to the original iron-formation. Local concentrations of manganese, chiefly as hausmannite, postdate the iron ores.

Regional

1. Ores of the "Lake Superior" type are virtually restricted to iron-formation of low metamorphic grade.

   This stricture is true not only for the Michigan iron districts (James, 1955) but also for the Mesabi and Cuyuna districts of Minnesota and the Labrador trough of Canada. Presumably the metamorphic increase in grain size of the quartz of the chert layers inhibits leaching and replacement.

2. A period of very deep chemical weathering preceded deposition of Cambrian strata on the Canadian Shield.

   Baker (1939) has found widespread evidence to indicate an important epoch of deep chemical weathering in late Precambrian time. In most places, the weathered rocks were stripped before deposition of basal Paleozoic strata, or have since been eroded. In New York, caverns were formed in marble of the Grenville Series to a depth of a thousand feet prior to deposition of the Potsdam Sandstone (A. E. J. Engel, oral commun.). In Dickinson County, a short distance east of the Iron River–Crystal Falls district, gneisses and schists bordering the overlapping sandstone of Cambrian age locally are altered to clay minerals to a depth of several hundred feet (James, Clark, and others, 1961, p. 76–77). The patches of silcrete in the southwestern part of the district (see p. 72–75) and elsewhere in the region (Leith, 1925) may be relicts of a duricrust formed during a cycle of aridity and deep weathering.

CRITICAL REVIEW OF CURRENT THEORIES [2]

Three theories of origin of iron ores of the Lake Superior type have current status: (1) action of meteoric waters—essentially deep weathering (as stated by Van Hise and Leith (1911, p. 544), "The agents of alteration are surface waters carrying oxygen and carbon dioxide from the atmosphere"); (2) action of hydrothermal solutions derived from magmatic sources at depth (Gruner, 1930); and (3) action of waters dominantly meteoric in origin but added to and activated by fluids from magmatic sources (Gruner, 1937). These three theories will be referred to respectively as meteoric, hydrothermal, and modified hydrothermal.

METEORIC THEORY

The meteoric theory of Van Hise and Leith is supported by many of the facts presented in the preceding section. The mineral assemblage is one that is stable only under highly oxygenated, primarily atmospheric conditions, and the ore bodies bear an evident relation to the surface. The formation of the ores required the addition of large volumes of oxygen, for which the atmosphere is the only adequate source.

Two major objections can be raised to the meteoric theory: the removal of silica on a large scale and the apparent inadequacy of any reasonable ground-water system to circulate to the great depths required.

The solubility of quartz is not easily established. Some natural waters contain as much as several hundred parts per million SiO_2 (Krauskopf, 1956), but most contain far less. The true solubility of quartz in water is low, 6 ppm at 25°C and 100 ppm at 136°C according to Morey, Fournier, and Rowe (1962), but these same investigators obtained concentrations of nearly 400 ppm at 25°C by tumbling crushed quartz in water for a period of about a year. The great increase in amount of quartz in solution is not attributed to abrasion; rather, it is believed to be a supersaturation due to excess solution from high-energy surfaces formed during the grinding of the quartz. The role of tumbling is to permit more rapid removal of dissolved silica (presumably as $Si(OH)_4$) from surfaces of the grains. Morey, Fournier, and Rowe (1962, p. 1040) noted that the rate and amount of supersaturation is dependent upon several factors, among them time and the grain size of the quartz. The grain size of quartz used in the experiments was about 0.15 mm. In comparison, the quartz of the chert layers is about an order of magnitude less (0.01–0.03 mm), which means the surface area of individual grains is about 100 times greater. It does not seem unreasonable to assume an effective solubility of SiO_2 of 100 ppm for this fine-grained quartz during the ore-forming process, even at normal ground-water temperatures. Whether this degree of solubility is adequate to account for the large-scale removal would depend on the volume of solution passing through the rock being altered.

A rough estimate of the volume of water necessary to form the ore can be obtained from the oxygen requirement. The absorption coefficient for oxygen in water at 20°C is 0.031 cc(g) per cc H_2O at $P_{O_2}=760$ mm (volume of the gas reduced to 0°C, 760 mm). At present atmospheric concentration, water saturated with O_2 would contain 0.0065 cc(g) per cc H_2O, or about 9.3×10^{-6}g. Each cubic centimeter of average ore (table 18) contains about 2.5g Fe_2O_3. The iron, whether in the form of siderite or in solution, originally was in the ferrous state, yielding ferric oxide according to the reaction

$$2FeO+1/2(O_2)=Fe_2O_3$$

Each mole (160 g) Fe_2O_3 requires ½ mole (16 g) of O_2. Formation of the ore, therefore, required addition of 10 percent oxygen by weight for each unit of ferric oxide, or 0.25 g of O_2 per cc of ore. If the dissolved oxygen content of the water was 9.3×10^{-6}g cc, then each cubic centimeter of ore required the passage of 2.7×10^4 cc of water, assuming that all the oxygen was extracted. Now, assuming silica to be dissolved to the extent of 100 ppm (1×10^{-4}g per cc), each gram extracted would require the passage of 10^4 cc of water. From table 18 it is seen that the formation of each cubic centimeter of ore involved a loss of 0.8 g SiO_2. This would require the passage of 8×10^3 cc H_2O per cc of ore at 100 ppm solubility for SiO_2, or a third of that required to transmit the necessary amount of oxygen in solution. This calculation cannot, of course, be taken to indicate anything more than order-of-magnitude, but it does suggest that the two major aspects of ore formation—removal of silica and oxidation of iron—are not seriously in imbalance in a postulated ground-water system.

The second major doubt concerning the meteoric theory is with respect to the adequacy of a normal ground-water system to circulate the required volumes of water. Two extreme situations may be visualized, one in which the flow of water was in an unconfined system,

[2] In preparing this section, use has been made of a U.S. Geological Survey file report by C. V. Theis, entitled "The nature of the hydraulic system involved in the enrichment of iron ore near Iron River, Michigan," dated June 1945.

with an outlet at levels below the ore bodies, and the other in which the flow was confined; in the latter the ore bodies represent zones of greatest permeability in an aquifer—that is, the iron-formation. In the western part of the district, the ore bodies typically are floored by impermeable graphitic slate, and the geometry of many of the structures precludes an outlet below that of the ore bodies; an unconfined system therefore is improbable. An artesian system, on the other hand, is theoretically possible, even though the beds overlying the iron-formation are by no means impermeable and the flow would therefore not be strictly confined, at least with respect to the upper surface of the aquifer.

If the typical system is assumed to be artesian and if the variations in degree of confinement are ignored, the rate of water movement would depend chiefly on the relative difference in elevation of inlet and outlet and the permeability of the aquifer. Mathematical solution of the problem, however, is difficult unless further large and possibly fatal simplifying assumptions are made. The oxidized iron-formation, with its contained ore bodies, is now an aquifer, but it is so because of oxidation of the original rock, which was relatively impermeable. The permeability, therefore, was a constantly changing factor in time and space. The hydraulic gradient is also dependent on relative elevations of inlet and outlet; these were continually changing with time as a result of erosion. Thermal gradients then existing are not known; they would affect not only the movement of the water but also the solubility of oxygen and silica.

Bearing these major uncertainties in mind, we may arrive at an arithmetic solution of a highly simplified system. Consider an ore-bearing bed folded into a U-shape with a cross-sectional length of 2,000 meters, one arm of the U reaching to a higher level topographically. Within this consider a parallelepiped of ore having a cross-sectional area of 1 cm^2. The volume of the parallelepiped would be 2×10^5 cm^3. From the previous estimate of oxygen requirements (2.7×10^4 cc H_2O per cc of ore), the total volume (Q) of water necessary for conversion to ore would be

$$Q=(2.7\times10^4)\ (2\times10^5)=5.4\times10^9 \text{ cc } H_2O.$$

The velocity of flow can be approximated from Darcy's law, expressed here as

$$V=K \sin\theta$$

where

V = velocity of flow
K = coefficient of permeability
θ = slope of pressure surface.

The permeability coefficient (K) cannot be determined satisfactorily on specimens because most of the water moves through fractures and larger spaces. The only in situ value available is that made for the Spies-Johnson ore body, where the value is estimated to be about 2 gallons per day per square foot (Stuart and others, 1948, p. 45), or approximately 110 millidarcys. The permeability of unoxidized iron-formation in place has not been determined. In specimen it is very low (on the order of 1×10^{-3} millidarcys), and although it doubtless is somewhat larger in situ, it still can be considered practically as zero. Let us assume a logarithmic mean value of about 10 millidarcys for the iron-formation during its conversion to ore. Let us further assume that the pressure surface between inlet and outlet maintains a slope of 0.5°. Then,

$$\begin{aligned} V &= K \sin\theta \\ &= 10\times0.009 \text{ millidarcys} \\ &= 9\times10^{-5} \text{ darcys.} \end{aligned}$$

The time (t) required for passage of the required volume (Q) of unit viscosity at the estimated velocity (V) per unit of cross section (A) is

$$\begin{aligned} t &= \frac{Q}{VA} \\ &= \frac{5.4\times10^9 \text{ cm}^3}{9\times10^{-5} \text{ cm/sec}\times1 \text{ cm}^2} \\ &= 6\times10^{13} \text{ sec} \\ &\cong 2\times10^6 \text{ yr} \end{aligned}$$

The conditions postulated are not unreasonable and the amount of time required on this basis is within the realm of possibility. In a very general way, therefore, it can be concluded that the concept of artesian circulation has a gross quantitative adequacy. Nevertheless, some serious objections remain.

The principal objection is based on the actual distribution of ore in a trough of the type just discussed. The ore is not evenly distributed in the iron-formation. The major loci are along the axial zones of minor synclines or structural terraces on the flanks of the trough and, if the trough is not excessively deep, along the keel of the main structure. Water at many of these positions would be relatively stagnant. The steep limbs of the folds, where circulation would have been most vigorous, are not favorable loci for development of ore. Nor in an aquifer would there seem any particular reason for the ore to select, as it does, a position on the footwall. Furthermore, it is common in such a structure for the hanging-wall strata to be thoroughly oxidized and otherwise altered, which indicates that the ground water was not necessarily confined with respect to the upper surface.

HYDROTHERMAL THEORY

The possibility that the ores were formed in a hydrothermal system of the classic type—that is, one in which the fluids are of magmatic derivation—has little to commend it. The stable mineral assemblage is a fine-grained porous mixture of goethite, hematite, clay mica, kaolinite, and gypsum. Although these minerals are known to occur individually in magmatic hydrothermal ores, the assemblage as a whole certainly bears little resemblance to those of true hydrothermal character, and all the minerals in the ore, including the clay mica, are compatible with a low temperature origin (illitic mica has been synthesized by Henin (1956) at temperatures as low as 20°C).

The confinement of ores to original iron-formation, the absence of ore in downward-facing structures, the evident relation to the surface, the absence of sulfides except as minor postore fillings, and the inverse relation to igneous activity and metamorphism all are potent objections to the hydrothermal theory. One of the major aspects—introduction of oxygen on a large scale—would, at even modest hydrothermal temperatures, require passage of enormous volumes of solution; yet, the rock beneath ore bodies is unaltered.

MODIFIED HYDROTHERMAL THEORY

The theory of origin by hot magmatic fluids proposed by Gruner (1930) was vigorously attacked by Leith (1931) and others. Later, Gruner (1937) proposed a modified hydrothermal theory, based on analogy with the hot spring activity of Yellowstone Park. According to this theory, the ores were formed in waters dominantly of meteoric origin but added to and heated by fluids of magmatic derivation. As expressed by Gruner (1937, p. 125–126):

> Hot emanations rising from a deeper source, chiefly as gases, seem to be ideal for these processes. They possess high mobility, great heat capacity, and are of a large enough order of magnitude. Steam would be the chief constituent. It would, of course, condense if brought in contact with sufficient amounts of meteoric water.

The theory is an attractive one. The high oxygen requirement would be satisfied by the meteoric water, the increase in temperature would increase greatly the solubility of silica and provide a driving force for deep circulation and expulsion of fluids, and the activated system would bear the requisite type of relation to upward-facing structures and to the surface. Quantitative evaluation of the system is not worthwhile since most intensity factors of the magmatically derived component could be increased or decreased at will, but there is little doubt that reasonable conditions could be postulated that would be adequate.

Despite the fact that the modified hydrothermal theory would meet many of the principal geologic criteria and probably is quantitatively adequate, several serious objections can be raised. The first objection is the complete lack of evidence indicating passage of magmatically derived fluids into the meteoric system—that is, into the structures now occupied by ore. In many of the mines, workings have been developed in the footwall below large ore bodies, which in some mines, such as the Buck, is beneath the keels of ore-filled synclines. The footwall rock typically is oxidized for a few feet below the ore but otherwise is unaltered. It is almost inconceivable that hot fluids of the volumes required could pass through without a trace. Faults intersected in the mines away from or below ore bodies are not bounded by altered rock, which certainly would be true if these faults had acted as conduits (as they do in most "hydrothermal" districts).

The second objection is geological. In proposing the theory, Gruner used the Yellowstone Park hot-spring activity as the prime example of the process in action. In contrast to the Yellowstone area, which is one of long-continued igneous and volcanic activity abundantly reflected in the rocks, the Iron River-Crystal Falls district shows no evidence of such a volcanic epoch. Except for the one dike of Keweenawan age in the northern part of the Iron River area, the igneous rocks predate the metamorphism and are much older than the ore.

The third objection is mineralogical. Though probably most of the minerals of the ores are not incompatible with moderately elevated temperatures (100°–250°C), the absence of more characteristic hydrothermal minerals is striking. Noticeably absent are albite, adularia, calcite, barite, zeolites, and sulfides. Whereas, in most areas of hydrothermal activity, quartz and chalcedonic silica are abundant as depositional products, they are wholly absent in the ores except as a relict and probably unstable phase. The only minerals of hydrothermal aspect have been shown to be postore in age.

To the present authors, at least, these objections seem insuperable and constitute refutation of the hydrothermal theory, even in its modified form.

PREFERRED THEORY OF ORIGIN

None of the current theories of origin seems adequate to encompass the known facts regarding the iron ores and their environs. All are unsatisfactory in some major respect. The same is true, at least to some degree, of the eclectic theory here presented.

The key postulate of the preferred theory is that of a long period of extraordinarily deep water table during later Precambrian time, an epoch possibly unmatched in later history of the earth. During this epoch of aridity, the iron-formation was irregularly oxidized to great depths in the zone of aeration and suspended (vadose) water, above the permanent water table. The great addition of oxygen and loss of carbon dioxide involved in the change of siderite to iron oxides, therefore, would not require long-continued circulation of oxygen-bearing waters; it would be accomplished principally by exchange with "soil air," perhaps through the medium of ephemeral water.

The pattern of this oxidation would be controlled by local topography, structure, and the vagaries of movement of vadose water, but it would be irregular, particularly at depth. Once oxidation began at a particular site, the rock would become more permeable, further local oxidation would be speeded up, and original chance irregularities would be accentuated. Axial zones of synclines, marked as they are by more crumpled rock and floored by less permeable strata, would be natural loci for deeper oxidation. This process would result in irregular zones of highly permeable rock, which would serve as aquifers during periods of greater inflow. The end product, it is to be noted, is oxidized iron-formation, not ore.

During wetter cycles in this epoch, water would accumulate in upward-facing traps. These traps could be synclines or other structural troughs, or they could be simply oxidized zones in the iron-formation bottomed by unoxidized rock. They could be at any elevation, down to the limits of oxidation. The water accumulating in these stagnant pools would be charged with carbon dioxide from breakdown of siderite and would contain ferrous salts to the limit of solubility. Under stagnant conditions, silica would dissolve to the limits permitted by the presence of quartz as aggregates of very fine grains of irregular shape and great surface area. Some replacement of the chert by secondary siderite probably would occur as a result of gradual loss of carbon dioxide by evaporation.

The next step in development of ore would be periodic expulsion of the silica-saturated waters from these stagnant basins. In places this could be accomplished or aided by the addition of magmatic fluids as proposed in Gruner's modified hydrothermal theory, but more likely the expulsion would be in imperfectly confined artesian systems of brief duration.

A typical situation may be visualized as follows: A trough of oxidized iron-formation is floored by a relatively impermeable unit—graphitic slate, slaty iron-formation, or even unoxidized iron-formation—and overlain by partly to completely oxidized iron-formation, slate, or graywacke, all of varying degrees of permeability. The impermeable unit reaches a higher elevation on one side of the trough than the other but does not necessarily reach the surface. Eventually, the iron-formation in the troughs is saturated with water that enters both from updip positions of the permeable iron-formation and from the irregularly permeable overlying rocks. After complete saturation, water will move laterally down any hydraulic gradient that may exist. The system as a whole might be classed as unconfined, but with respect to deeper parts of the principal aquifer (that is, the oxidized iron-formation), the circulation will be semiartesian, with water moving downward to the lower part of the structure, migrating upward on one flank, and leaving the structure at an elevation relatively higher than that of the keel.

During this semiartesian cycle, any secondary siderite in the troughs would be oxidized. In reference to the previous calculations of volume and time of circulation in an artesian system, it can be pointed out that the permeability would have a much higher value, the oxygen requirement would be practically eliminated, and degree of supersaturation by silica could be much greater. This process of stagnation and periodic expulsion, repeated many times, would result in elimination of silica, and in addition of iron, both by formation and later oxidation of secondary siderite and by infiltration of colloidal iron oxides from higher levels; the ultimate product is iron ore. In a very real sense, the ore bodies would "grow from the bottom up," in contrast to the initial oxidation, which was from the top down.

As previously stated, the key postulate is that of a period of aridity of extraordinary intensity and duration, perhaps hundreds of millions of years, during which the permanent water table was at a minimum depth of 3,000 feet and probably considerably more. The concept of such a period of aridity may appear to do violence to the doctrine of uniformitarianism, which has proved as an invaluable a control on geologic thinking as have the laws of thermodynamics in physics and chemistry. Woolnough (1928; 1937; written commun., Aug. 24, 1951) has pointed out, however, that the ideas of what constitutes uniformitarianism have been formulated mainly from experience with the geology of the Northern Hemisphere and with observations of processes operating in temperate climates. By analogy with Australia, he stressed the possible great importance, during long periods of geologic time, of deep chemical weathering of an intensity not now recognized on the present surface of the earth.

Even under present-day conditions in Australia, artesian water is obtained in arid areas from aquifers at depths of more than 4,000 feet; single wells yield more than a million gallons a day (Meinzer, 1923, p. 45). Widespread remnants of siliceous duricrust (silcrete), mantling bedrock altered to unknown depths, testify to the existence of an earlier epoch of chemical weathering under arid conditions (Williamson, 1957).

The conditions leading to the formation of the iron ores are conceived to be somewhat comparable to those of the desert regions of Australia of the present and relatively recent past, but of greater intensity and longer duration.

Independent evidence bearing on the postulated epoch of aridity in the Lake Superior region is almost completely lacking. The geologic record of the last 500 million years of Precambrian history—that is, of the time between the Keweenawan and the Cambrian—is virtually a blank. The only evidence remaining is that of indications of widespread deep weathering of the Precambrian surface, as previously noted, and of a few patches of possible duricrust. It is tempting to use the deep oxidation itself as evidence, but the argument of course is circular. Because of the almost complete absence of independent factual support, the concept of origin presented must be considered as only plausible speculation until some new critical data are obtained or some other means can be devised to test it. In its favor, however, is the fact that once the main postulate is granted, the predictable results fit all the known facts regarding the ores.

* * * * * * *

SELECTED REFERENCES

Aldrich, L. T., Davis, G. L., and James, H. L., 1965, Age of minerals from metamorphic and igneous rocks near Iron Mountain, Michigan: Jour. Petrology, v. 6, no. 3, p. 445–472.

Allen, R. C., 1910, The Iron River iron-bearing district of Michigan: Michigan Geol. and Biol. Survey Pub. 3, Geol. Ser. 2, 151 p.

Allen, R. C., 1912–1920, Mineral resources of Michigan: Michigan Geol. and Biol. Survey—1912, for 1910 and prior years, Pub. 8, Geol. Ser. 6, 465 p.; 1914, for 1912 and prior years, Pub. 16, Geol. Ser. 13, 150 p.; 1915, for 1914 and prior years, Pub. 19, Geol. Ser. 16, 359 p.; 1916, for 1915 and prior years, Pub. 21, Geol. Ser. 17, 402 p.; 1917, for 1916 and prior years, Pub. 24, Geol. Ser. 20, 291 p.; 1918, for 1917 and prior years, Pub. 27, Geol. Ser. 22, 225 p.; 1920, for 1918 and prior years, Pub. 29, Geol. Ser. 24, 214 p.

Allen, R. C., and Barrett, L. P., 1915, Contributions to the pre-Cambrian geology of northern Michigan and Wisconsin: Michigan Geol. and Biol. Survey Pub. 18, Geol. Ser. 15, 189 p.

Ayres, V. L., 1940, Mineral notes from the Michigan iron country: Am. Mineralogist, v. 25, no. 6, p. 432–434.

Bacon, L. O., and Wyble, D. O., 1952, Gravity investigations in the Iron River–Crystal Falls mining district of Michigan: Am. Inst. Mining Metall. Engineers Trans., v. 193, Tech. Paper 3383L, p. 973–979.

Bailey, S. W., and Tyler, S. A., 1960, Clay minerals associated with the Lake Superior iron ores: Econ. Geology, v. 55, no. 1, p. 150–175.

Baker, M. B., 1939, The floor of the Paleozoic in Canada: Royal Soc. Canada Trans., 3d ser., v. 33, sec. 4, p. 11–18.

Balsley, J. R., James, H. L., and Wier, K. L., 1949, Aeromagnetic survey of parts of Baraga, Iron, and Houghton Counties, Michigan, with preliminary geologic interpretation: U.S. Geol. Survey Geophys. Inv. Prelim. Rept.

Barrett, L. P., and James, H. L., 1953, The occurrence and sampling of radioactive zones in the Sherwood mine, Iron River district, Michigan: Memorandum report to the Atomic Energy Comm., 9 p., 4 pl.

Barrett, L. P., Pardee, F. G., and Osgood, Wayland, 1929, Geological map of Iron County [Mich.]: Michigan Dept. Conserv., Geol. Survey Div.

Bath, G. D., 1951, Magnetic base stations in Lake Superior iron districts: U.S. Bur. Mines Rept. Inv. 4804.

Bayley, R. W., 1959, Geology of the Lake Mary quadrangle, Iron County, Michigan: U.S. Geol. Survey Bull. 1077, 112 p.

Bayley, R. W., Dutton, C. E., and Lamey, C. A., 1966, Geology of the Menominee iron-bearing district, Dickinson County, Michigan, Florence and Marinette Counties, Wisconsin, *with a chapter on* The Carney Lake Gneiss, by S. B. Treves: U.S. Geol. Survey Prof. Paper 513, 96 p.

Bergquist, S. G., 1932, Glacial geology of Iron County, Michigan: Michigan Acad. Sci. Papers, v. 16, p. 363–372.

——— 1935, Valley-train deposits in the Northern Peninsula of Michigan: Michigan Acad. Sci. Papers, v. 20, p. 439–447.

——— 1941, The distribution of drumlins in Michigan: Michigan Acad. Sci. Papers, v. 27, p. 451–464.

Borchert, Hermann, 1960, Genesis of marine sedimentary iron ores: Inst. Mining and Metallurgy Trans., v. 69 [Bull. 640], p. 261–279.

Brindley, G. W., ed., 1951, X-ray identification and crystal structures of clay minerals: London, Mineralog. Soc., 345 p.

Clements, J. M., and Smyth, H. L., 1899, The Crystal Falls iron-bearing district of Michigan: U.S. Geol. Survey Mon. 36, 512 p.

Correns, C. W., 1952, Mineralogische Untersuchungen an sedimentären Eisenerzen, *in* Gisements de fer du monde: Internat. Geol. Cong., 19th, Algiers 1952, Symposium, v. 2, p. 28–30.

Dutton, C. E., 1949, Geology of the central part of the Iron River district, Iron County, Michigan: U.S. Geol. Survey Circ. 43, 9 p.

——— 1968, Geologic and magnetic data for central Iron River area, Michigan: Michigan Rept. Inv. 5 (in press).

Dutton, C. E., Park, C. F., and Balsley, J. R., 1945, General character and succession of tentative divisions in the stratigraphy of the Mineral Hills district, Iron River, Iron County, Michigan: U.S. Geol. Survey Prelim. Rept., 4 p.

Foster, Z. C., Veatch, J. O., and Schoenman, L. R., 1937, Soil survey of Iron County, Michigan: U.S. Dept. Agriculture, Bur. Chemistry and Soils, Ser. 1936, no. 46.

Frankel, J. J., 1952, Silcrete near Albertina, Cape Province: South African Jour. Sci., v. 49, p. 173–182.

Frankel, J. J., and Kent, L. E., 1938, Grahamstown surface quartzites (silcretes): South Africa Geol. Soc. Trans., v. 40, p. 1–42.

Gair, J. E., and Wier, K. L., 1956, Geology of the Kiernan quadrangle, Iron County, Michigan: U.S. Geol. Survey Bull. 1044, 88 p.

Goldich, S. S., Nier, A. O., Baadsgaard, Halfdan, Hoffman, J. H., and Krueger, H. W., 1961, The Precambrian geology and geochronology of Minnesota: Minnesota Geol. Survey Bull. 41, 193 p.

Good, S. E., and Pettijohn, F. J., 1949, Magnetic survey and geology of the Stager area, Iron County, Michigan: U.S. Geol. Survey Circ. 55, 4 p.

Gruner, J. W., 1930, Hydrothermal oxidation and leaching experiments; their bearing on the origin of Lake Superior hematite-limonite ores: Econ. Geology, v. 25, no. 7, p. 697–719; no. 8, p. 837–867.

——— 1937, Hydrothermal leaching of iron ores of the Lake Superior type—a modified theory: Econ. Geology, v. 32, no. 2, p. 121–130.

——— 1946, The mineralogy and geology of the taconites and iron ores of the Mesabi range, Minnesota: St. Paul, Minn., Iron Range Resources and Rehabilitation Comm., 127 p.

Hamblin, W. K., 1958, The Cambrian sandstones of northern Michigan: Michigan Dept. Conserv., Geol. Survey Div. Pub. 51, 146 p.

Hénin, S., 1956, Synthesis of clay minerals at low temperatures, *in* Swineford, Ada, ed., Clays and clay minerals: Natl. Research Council Pub. 456, p. 54–60.

Holland, H. D., 1962, Model for the evolution of the earth's atmosphere, *in* Engel, A. E. J., James, H. L., and Leonard, B. F., eds., Petrologic studies (Buddington volume): Geol. Soc. America, p. 569–598.

Hough, J. L., 1958, Fresh-water environment of deposition of Precambrian banded iron formations: Jour. Sed. Petrology, v. 28, no. 4, p. 414–430.

Hutton, C. O., 1956, Further data on the stilpnomelane mineral group [Calif.]: Am. Mineralogist, v. 41, nos. 7–8, p. 608–615.

James, H. L., 1948, Field comparisons of some magnetic instruments, with analysis of Superdip performance: Am. Inst. Mining Metall. Engineers Trans., v. 178, Tech. Pub. 2293, p. 490–500.

——— 1951, Iron formation and associated rocks in the Iron River district, Michigan: Geol. Soc. America Bull., v. 62, no. 3, p. 251–266.

——— 1954, Sedimentary facies of iron-formation: Econ. Geology, v. 49, no. 3, p. 235–293.

——— 1955, Zones of regional metamorphism in the Precambrian of northern Michigan: Geol. Soc. America Bull., v. 66, no. 12, pt. 1, p. 1455–1488.

James, H. L., 1958, Stratigraphy of pre-Keweenawan rocks in parts of northern Michigan: U.S. Geol. Survey Prof. Paper 314–C, p. 27–44.

——— 1966, Chemistry of the iron-rich sedimentary rocks: U.S. Geol. Survey Prof. Paper 440–W, p. W1–W61.

James, H. L., Clark, L. D., Lamey, C. A., and Pettijohn, F. J., 1961, Geology of central Dickinson County, Michigan: U.S. Geol. Survey Prof. Paper 310, 176 p.

James, H. L., Clark, L. D., and Smith, L. E., 1947, Magnetic survey and geology of the Ice Lake-Chicagon Creek area, Iron County, Michigan: U.S. Geol. Survey Strategic Minerals Inv. Prelim. Map 3–213.

James, H. L., and Clayton, R. N., 1962, Oxygen isotope fractionation in metamorphosed iron formations of the Lake Superior region and in other iron-rich rocks, *in* Engel, A. E. J., James, H. L., and Leonard, B. F., eds., Petrologic studies (Buddington volume): Geol. Soc. America, p. 217–239.

James, H. L., and Dutton, C. E., 1951, Geology of the northern part of the Iron River district, Iron County, Michigan: U.S. Geol. Survey Circ. 120, 12 p.

James, H. L., Dutton, C. E., Pettijohn, F. J., and Wier, K. L., 1959, Geologic map of the Iron River-Crystal Falls district, Iron County, Michigan: U.S. Geol. Survey Mineral Inv. Map MF–225 [1960].

James, H. L., Dutton, C. E., and Wier, K. L., 1968, Geologic and magnetic data in northern Iron River area, Michigan: Michigan Geol. Survey Rept. Inv. 4.

James, H. L., Pettijohn, F. J., and Clark, L. C., 1968, Geologic and magnetic data for area between Iron River and Crystal Falls, Michigan: Michigan Geol. Survey Rept. Inv. 7 (in press).

James, H. L., and Wier, K. L., 1948, Magnetic survey and geology of the eastern and southeastern parts of the Iron River district, Iron County, Michigan: U.S. Geol. Survey Circ. 26, 18 p.

——— 1968, Geologic and magnetic data for southeastern Iron River area, Michigan: Michigan Geol. Survey Rept. Inv. 6 (in press).

Kraus, E. H., Seaman, W. A., and Slawson, C. B., 1930, Seamanite, a new manganese phospho-borate from Iron County, Michigan: Am. Mineralogist, v. 15, no. 6, p. 220–225.

Krauskopf, K. B., 1956. Dissolution and precipitation of silica at low temperatures: Geochim. et Cosmochim. Acta, v. 10, nos. 1–2, p. 1–26.

——— 1957, Separation of manganese from iron in sedimentary processes: Geochim. et Cosmochim. Acta, v. 12, nos. 1–2, p. 61–84.

Kulp, J. L., Eckelmann, W. R., Owen, H. R., and Bate, G. L., 1953, Studies of the lead method of age determination, Pt. 1: U.S. Atomic Energy Comm. NYO–6199, issued by Tech. Inf. Service, Oak Ridge, Tenn., 19 p.

Lake Superior Iron Ore Association, 1938, Lake Superior iron ores: Cleveland, Ohio, 364 p.

——— 1952, Lake Superior iron ores [2d ed.]: Cleveland, Ohio, 334 p.

Leith, C. K., 1925, Silicification of erosion surfaces: Econ. Geology, v. 20, no. 6, p. 513–523.

——— 1931, Secondary concentration of Lake Superior iron ores: Econ. Geology, v. 26, no. 3, p. 274–288.

Leith, C. K., Lund, R. J., and Leith, Andrew, 1935, Pre-Cambrian rocks of the Lake Superior region: U.S. Geol. Survey Prof. Paper 184, 34 p.

Leverett, Frank, 1911, Surface geology of the Northern Peninsula of Michigan * * *: Michigan Geol. and Biol. Survey Pub. 7, Geol. Ser. 5, 91 p.

——— 1929, Moraines and shore lines of the Lake Superior region: U.S. Geol. Survey Prof. Paper 154, p. 1–72.

Mann, V. I., 1953, Relation of oxidation to the origin of soft iron ores of Michigan: Econ. Geology, v. 48, p. 251–281.

Martin, H. M., compiler, 1936, The centennial geological map of the Northern Peninsula of Michigan: Michigan Dept. Conserv., Geol. Survey Div. Pub. 39, Geol. Ser. 33.

——— 1957, Map of surface formations of the Northern Peninsula of Michigan [pt. 2]: Michigan Dept. Conserv., Geol. Survey Div. Pub. 49.

Meinzer, O. E., 1923, The occurrence of ground water in the United States: U.S. Geol. Survey Water-Supply Paper 489, 321 p.

Michigan Department of Conservation, Geological Survey Division, 1951–61 [Reports, variously titled, on general statistics covering costs and production of Michigan iron mines]: Lansing, Mich., mimeographed repts.

Michigan Department of Mineral Statistics, 1879–1909 [Reports of Commissioner of Mineral Statistics; variously titled—Annual reports, Mineral resources, Mines and mineral statistics; volumes issued for 1877–78, 1880, 1881, 1882, 1883, 1885, 1886, 1887, 1888, 1889, 1890–91, 1895, 1897, 1900, 1901, 1901–2, 1906–7, 1907, each including coverage for previous years]: Menominee, Herald-Leader Co.

Morey, G. W., Fournier, R. O., and Rowe, J. J., 1962, The solubility of quartz in water in the temperature interval from 25° to 300°C: Geochim. et Cosmochim. Acta, v. 26, p. 1029–1044.

Mountain, E. D., 1952, The origin of silcretes: South African Jour. Sci., v. 48, p. 201–204.

Oana, Shinya, and Deevey, E. S., Jr., 1960, Carbon 13 in lake waters, and its possible bearing on paleolimnology: Am. Jour. Sci., v. 258–A (Bradley volume), p. 253–272.

Oftedahl, Christoffer, 1958, A theory of exhalative-sedimentary ores: Geol. Fören. Stockholm Förh., v. 80, no. 1, p. 1–19.

Pettijohn, F. J., 1948, Magnetic and geological data of parts of the Crystal Falls-Alpha iron district, Iron County, Michigan: Michigan Dept. Conserv., Geol. Survey Div., geol. maps, magnetic anomalies.

——— 1952, Geology of the northern Crystal Falls area, Iron County, Michigan: U.S. Geol. Survey Circ. 153, 17 p.

——— 1957, Sedimentary rocks [2d ed.]; New York, Harper & Bros., 718 p.

——— 1968, Geologic and magnetic data for northern Crystal Falls area, Michigan: Michigan Geol. Survey Rept. Inv. 8 (in press).

——— 1968, Geologic and magnetic data for southern Crystal Falls area, Michigan: Michigan Geol. Survey Rept. Inv. 9 (in press).

Pettijohn, F. J., and Clark, L. D., 1946, Geology of the Crystal Falls-Alpha iron-bearing district, Iron County, Michigan: U.S. Geol. Survey Strategic Minerals Inv. Prelim. Map 3–181.

Pettijohn, F. J., Gair, J. E., Wier, K. L., and Prinz, W. C., 1968, Geologic and magnetic data for Alpha-Brule River and Panola Plains areas, Michigan: Michigan Geol. Survey Rept. Inv. 10 (in press).

Royce, Stephen, 1936, Geology of the Lake Superior iron deposits: Lake Superior Mining Inst. Proc., v. 29, p. 68–107; Mining Cong. Jour., v. 22, no. 3, p. 16–30.

Royce, Stephen, 1942, Iron ranges of the Lake Superior district, *in* Newhouse, W. H., ed., Ore deposits as related to structural features: Princeton Univ. Press, p. 54–63.

Rubey, W. W., 1951, The geologic history of sea water: Geol. Soc. America Bull., v. 62, no. 9, p. 1111–1147.

——— 1955, Development of the hydrosphere and atmosphere, with special reference to probable composition of the early atmosphere, *in* Poldervaart, Arie, ed., Crust of the earth: Geol. Soc. America Spec. Paper 62, p. 631–650.

Russell, I. C., 1907, The surface geology of portions of Menominee, Dickinson, and Iron Counties, Michigan: Michigan Geol. and Biol. Survey Ann. Rept., 1906, p. 7–91.

Shapiro, Leonard, and Brannock, W. W., 1956, Rapid analysis of silicate rocks: U.S. Geol. Survey Bull. 1036–C, p. 19–56.

Slawson, C. B., 1934, Sussexite from Iron County, Michigan: Am. Mineralogist, v. 19, no. 12, p. 575–578.

Smith, R. A., 1922, 1924–1929, Mineral resources of Michigan: Michigan Geol. and Biol. Survey—1922, for 1920 and prior years, Pub. 32, Geol. Ser. 26, 145 p.; 1924, for 1922 and prior years, Pub. 34, Geol. Ser. 28, 146 p.; 1925, for 1923 and prior years, Pub. 35, Geol. Ser. 29, 115 p.; 1929, for 1924, 1925, 1926 and prior years, Pub. 37, Geol. Ser. 31, 321 p.

Smith, R. A., and Martin, H.M., 1923, Mineral resources of Michigan * * * for 1921 and prior years: Michigan Geol. and Biol. Survey Pub. 33, Geol. Ser. 27, 138 p.

Stockdale, P. B., 1922, Stylolites—their nature and origin: Indiana Univ. Studies, v. 9, p. 1–97.

——— 1943, Stylolites—primary or secondary: Jour. Sed. Petrology, v. 13, p. 3–12.

Strakhov, N. M., 1959, Schéma de la diagènese des depots marine: Eclogae geol. Helvetiae, v. 51, p. 761–767.

Stuart, W. T., Theis, C. V., and Stanley, G. M., 1948, Ground-water problems of the Iron River district [Mich.]: Michigan Dept. Conserv., Geol. Survey Div. Tech. Rept. 2, 59 p.

Theis, C. V., 1945, The nature of the hydraulic system involved in the enrichment of iron ore near Iron River, Michigan: U.S. Geol. Survey open file report, June 1945.

Twenhofel, W. H., 1950, Principles of sedimentation [2d ed.]: New York, McGraw-Hill Book Co., 673 p.

Tyler, S. A., 1949, Development of Lake Superior soft iron ores from metamorphosed iron formation: Geol. Soc. America Bull., v. 60, no. 7, p. 1101–1124.

Tyler, S. A., Barghoorn, E. S., and Barrett, L. P., 1957, Anthracitic coal from Precambrian upper Huronian black shale of the Iron River district, northern Michigan: Geol Soc. America Bull., v. 68, no. 10, p. 1293–1304.

Tyler, S. A., and Twenhofel, W. H., 1952, Sedimentation and stratigraphy of the Huronian of Upper Michigan; Am. Jour. Sci., v. 250, pt. 1, no. 1, p. 1–27; v. 250, pt. 2, no. 2, p. 118–151.

Tyrrell, G. W., 1926, Principles of petrology: New York, Dutton and Company, 349 p.

Urey, H. C., 1959, The atmosphere of the planets: Handbuch der Physik, v. 52, p. 363–418.

U.S. Department of Agriculture, 1941, Climate and man: U.S. 77th Cong., House Doc. 27, 1st sess., Dept. Agriculture Yearbook, 1941, 1248 p.

Van Hise, C. R., and Leith, C. K., 1911, The geology of the Lake Superior region: U.S. Geol. Survey Mon. 52, 641 p.

Vickers, R. C., 1956a, Origin and occurrence of uranium in northern Michigan [abs.]: Geol. Soc. America Bull., v. 67, no. 12, pt. 2, p. 1741.

——— 1956b, Origin and occurrence of uranium in northern Michigan: U.S. Geol. Survey open-file report, 76 p.

Weaver, C. E., 1958, Origin and significance of clay minerals in sedimentary rocks, Pt. 1 *of* Geologic interpretation of argillaceous sediments: Am. Assoc. Petroleum Geologists, v. 42, no. 2, p. 254–271.

White, D. A., 1954, The stratigraphy and structure of the Mesabi Range, Minnesota: Minnesota Geol. Survey Bull. 38, 92 p.

White, W. S., 1949, Cleavage in east-central Vermont: Am. Geophys. Union Trans., v. 30, no. 4, p. 587–594.

Wier, K. L., 1950, Comparisons of some aeromagnetic profiles with ground magnetic profiles: Am. Geophys. Union Trans., v. 31, no. 2, pt. 1, p. 191–195.

——— 1967, Geology of the Kelso Junction quadrangle, Michigan: U.S. Geol. Survey Bull. 1226, 47 p.

——— 1968, Geologic and magnetic data for northeastern Crystal Falls area, Michigan: Michigan Geol. Survey Rept. Inv. 11 (in press).

Williamson, W. O., 1957, Silicified sedimentary rocks in Australia: Am. Jour. Sci., v. 255, no. 1, p. 23–42.

Winchell, A. H., and Winchell, Horace, 1951, Description of minerals, Pt. 2 *of* Elements of optical mineralogy—an introduction to microscopic petrography [4th ed.]: New York, John Wiley & Sons, 551 p.

Woolnough, W. G., 1928, Presidential address: Royal Soc. New South Wales, Jour. and Proc., 1927, v. 61, p. 1–53.

——— 1937, Sedimentation in barred basins, and source rocks of oil: Am. Assoc. Petroleum Geologists Bull., v. 21, no. 9, p. 1101–1157.

Yoder, H. S., and Eugster, H. P., 1955, Synthetic and natural muscovites: Geochim. et Cosmochim. Acta, v. 8, nos. 5–6, p. 225–280.

Zinn, Justin, 1933, Correlation of the Upper Huronian of the Marquette and Crystal Falls districts: Michigan Acad. Sci. Papers, v. 18, p. 437–456.

Zinner, Paul, Holmberg, C. L., and Terry, O. W., 1949, Investigation of the iron-bearing formation of Iron County, Michigan, using geophysical and other methods: U.S. Bur. Mines Rept. Inv. 4583, 40 p.

IV
Iron-Rich Sedimentary Rocks

Editor's Comments on Papers 18, 19, and 20

The papers in this section were selected to provide some descriptive information and additional analytical data on the two principal types of iron-rich sediments: cherty Precambrian iron-formations and oolitic younger ironstones. Because the focus in this volume is on the behavior of iron in the surface cycle, it was not feasible to cover in detail all the lithologies and associations exhibited by these rocks. Neither was there space to examine the equilibrium relations among iron minerals under varying conditions of metamorphism as reported by French (1968), Klein (1966), Mueller (1960), and others.

Although most Precambrian iron-formations consist chiefly of chert and one or more iron minerals they differ materially in texture, structure, and associations. Many are delicately banded, whereas others exhibit granule, oolitic, or other textures. Some show characteristics of clastic sediments (Mengel, 1963), whereas others are slaty, and still others exhibit wavy, crinkly banding characteristic of some lime rocks. La Berge (1973) interprets minute spherical structures in iron-formations of the Lake Superior region as being of biologic origin. In spite of these physical differences, iron-formations are remarkably uniform in such chemical attributes as tenor of iron, low content of alumina and phosphorus, and the practical absence of trace elements.

G. A. Gross (1965) notes that in Canada the siliceous iron-formations are frequently divided into two main types: Algoma Type, cherty iron-formations usually of limited extent that are associated with volcanic rocks and/or graywackes in eugeosynclinal belts; and Lake Superior Type, usually more extensive iron-formations associated with quartzites, lime rocks, or black shales in shelf-type environments. Although this classification is based on lithology and associations, it turns out that most Algoma-type formations are found in early Precambrian rocks. The early Precambrian iron-formations are also frequently called Keewatin type.

Paper 18 is a portion of a paper by A. M. Goodwin on one of the classic early Precambrian iron districts, the Michipicoten area of Ontario. Although classic in the sense that the iron-formations of this area have been studied by many distinguished geologists since the turn of the century, the iron-formations of the Michipicoten area are not typical of Keewatin-type iron-formations. They are unique in that the carbonate and sulfide facies are more fully developed than normal.

A. M. Goodwin is a graduate of Queens University and the University of Wisconsin. He was employed for eight years as a research geologist by the Algoma Steel Corporation, the principal operators in the Michipicoten region. Subsequently, he spent another eight years as a field geologist with the Ontario Department of Mines and the Geological Survey of Canada. He joined the University of Toronto in 1964 as Professor of Geology. Goodwin has published many papers, particularly on early Precambrian iron-formations and volcanic rocks and on the evolution of the Precambrian crust.

Paper 19, by A. F. Trendall of Australia, compares three major areas of middle Precambrian iron sedimentation. A. F. Trendall is a member of the Geological Survey of Western Australia. In addition to being involved in research on the iron-formations of Australia (Trendall and Blockley, 1970), he has traveled extensively and visited most of the major areas of iron-formation in other parts of the world. He was a participant and contributor at the International Symposium on the Geology and Genesis of Precambrian Iron and Manganese Deposits held in Kiev (1970), and he reported on the iron-formations of Australia at the Symposium on Precambrian Iron-Formations of the World held in Duluth in 1972 (Trendall, 1973).

Paper 20, by Harold L. James, is an excerpt from a real classic. This paper by James is referred to in practically every subsequent publication on iron-formations or ironstones. In this study of iron-formations in the Lake Superior district, James recognized four facies (oxide, carbonate, silicate, and sulfide) on the basis of the dominant iron mineral. He, moreover, interpreted these facies to reflect differences in the chemical parameters of the depositional environment, and he related the environments to stages of geosynclinal development. The facies principle has since been applied in mapping and interpreting iron-formations and ironstones throughout the world. It is of interest to note that in the unreproduced portion of this paper, James attributes the differences between Precambrian and younger rocks to more intense weathering in the Precambrian rather than to any differences in atmospheric composition. In several later papers, however, he relates the formation of Precambrian iron-formations to a higher partial pressure of CO_2 in the atmosphere (Papers 2, 17, 21, and 32).

References

French, B. M., 1968, Progressive contact metamorphism of the Biwabik iron-formation, Mesabi range, Minnesota: Minnesota Geol. Surv. Bull. 45, 103 p.

Gross, G. A., 1965, Geology of iron deposits in Canada, vol. I. General geology and evaluation of iron deposits: Canada Geol. Surv. Econ. Geol. Rept. 22, 181 p.

Klein, C., 1966, Mineralogy and petrology of the metamorphosed Wabush iron formation, southwestern Labrador: Jour. Petrology, v. 7, p. 246–305.

LaBerge, G. L., 1973, Possible biologic origin of Precambrian iron-formations, Econ. Geol., 68, p. 1098–1109.

Mengel, J. T. Jr., 1963, The cherts of the Lake Superior iron-bearing formations: unpubl. Ph.D. thesis, Univ. Wisconsin.

Mueller, R. F., 1960, Compositional characteristics and equilibrium relations in mineral assemblages of a metamorphosed iron formation: Amer. Jour. Sci., v. 258, p. 449–497.

Trendall, A. F., 1973, Precambrian iron-formations of Australia: Econ. Geol., v. 68, p. 1023–1034.

Trendall, A. F., and J. G. Blockley, 1970, The iron formations of the Hammersley Group, Western Australia: Western Australia Geol. Surv. Bull. 119, 353 p.

18

Reprinted from *Geol. Soc. America Bull.,* **73,** 561, 573–580, 585 (May 1962)

A. M. GOODWIN *Ontario Dept. Mines, Parliament Buildings, Toronto, Ontario, Canada*

Structure, Stratigraphy, and Origin of Iron Formations, Michipicoten Area, Algoma District, Ontario, Canada

Abstract: The Michipicoten group, of Precambrian age, comprises flows and pyroclastic rocks of the andesite-rhyolite association together with conformable zones of clastic sediments and banded iron formations. Volcanic rocks display great heterogeneity, typically exhibiting marked variation in lithology, structure, and thickness over short intervals. The typical volcanic cycle progressed from (1) widespread and prolonged outpouring of andesite-basalt flows and pyroclastic material, through (2) brief but violent expulsion of rhyolite-dacite pyroclastic rocks, to (3) large-scale hot-spring and fumarolic activity. Clastic sediments are interpreted as products of contemporaneous erosion of expanding volcanic piles. Development of the Michipicoten group is viewed as a continuous process which, once initiated, proceeded through explosive, erosional, and chemical phases to produce a complex volcanic-sedimentary family group in which the members, although each possessing unique characteristics, are related by common volcanic heritage.

Volcanic divisions are described in terms of distribution, lithology, relationship to adjacent formations, and environment of deposition. Average chemical analyses of volcanic rocks are presented. In contrast to the typical andesite-rhyolite suite, Michipicoten volcanic rocks are deficient in CaO, Na_2O, K_2O, and SiO_2, and enriched in Fe, MnO, and CO_2.

Banded iron formations contain two mutually gradational facies associated respectively with sedimentary and volcanic rocks. The latter type contains large bodies of siderite and pyrite. Banded iron formations are ascribed genetically to large-scale hot-spring and fumarolic activity. Iron carbonate and sulfur components appear to be of subvolcanic, presumably magnatic, derivation, whereas silica was largely derived by chemical leaching of the volcanic rocks. Average chemical compositions of banded chert, pyrite, and carbonate members of the iron formation are presented.

The clastic sediments are like true volcanic sediments in that rock and mineral components have their counterparts in subjacent volcanic rocks in either extrusive or intrusive form and appear to have been derived from them by rapid, contemporaneous erosion. Granite detritus in coarse clastic sediments is inferred to reflect contemporaneous erosion of near-surface granite stocks and apophyses emplaced under conditions of high geothermal gradient.

Michipicoten rocks have been folded about east-west-trending primary axes, themselves cross-folded about northwest-trending axes. As a result, fold axes describe undulating patterns in longitudinal and cross sections. Prominent, northerly striking vertical faults with left-hand horizontal components of displacement have sliced the area into large parallel blocks.

* * * * * * *

Editor's Note: A row of asterisks indicates that material has been omitted from the original article.

Iron Formation

INTRODUCTION: The term iron formation as applied to the Michipicoten area refers to a banded rock composed of chert and one or more of the iron minerals siderite, pyrite, pyrrhotite, magnetite, and hematite. An "iron range" is a band of iron formation extending several thousands of feet along strike. Iron formation zones contain either thick, extensive bands or thin, discontinuous lenses of iron formation.

The association of Michipicoten iron formations with a thick assemblage of volcanic and sedimentary rocks is typical of many Keewatin-type areas of the world. Michipicoten iron formations, however, contain two mutually gradational and contrasting facies associated respectively with sedimentary and volcanic rocks. Michipicoten iron formation of sedimentary association is typically composed of alternating layers of chert and siliceous magnetite or hematite; it closely resembles standard Keewatin-type iron formations. Michipicoten iron formation of volcanic association, on the other hand, appears to differ in the following respects: (1) The iron formation where fully developed consists of three members (Fig. 7): (a) an upper or banded silica member of alternating layers of chert, siliceous carbonate, and sulfides that grades down into (b) the pyrite member which contains some pyrrhotite and other sulfides. The pyrite member in turn grades down into (c) a carbonate member composed mainly of siderite with minor quantities of ankerite, dolomite, and calcite. The three members are usually well developed on the major iron ranges, whereas on the smaller ranges, the carbonate and pyrite members are commonly poorly developed or lacking. The banded silica member is subordinate in some ranges to the pyrite and carbonate members and is absent in others. (2) Felsic volcanic rocks commonly underlie the iron formation, whereas intermediate to mafic volcanic rocks commonly overlie it. (3) The chert of the banded silica member is usually sugary and of coarser grain than the associated siderite.

DISTRIBUTION: Two main zones of iron formation exist in each of the three stratigraphic blocks of the Michipicoten area (Figs. 3, 4); in addition, small, isolated lenses and patches occur locally throughout the volcanic series. In the Helen-Magpie block, the upper zone, referred to as the Helen iron formation, is the thicker and more persistent of the two. In the Goudreau block, the lower zone, the Goudreau iron formation, is the more prominent. In the Kabenung block, on the other hand, both iron formations are of comparable thickness. Correlation of iron formation zones between individual blocks is uncertain.

In the Helen-Magpie block, faulted segments of the once-continuous Helen iron formation, extending from Michipicoten Harbour to Hawk Junction, include the north-facing Mildred, Helen, Johnson, Eleanor, Lucy, Ruth, Josephine, Bartlett, and East Brooks ranges (Fig. 2). These ranges lie on the south limb of the South range syncline. The southwest-facing Sheldon-Big Lake and Centre Brooks ranges, located 2 miles north of the East Brooks and Bartlett ranges respectively, lie on the faulted north limb of the South range syncline. The southwest-facing West Brooks, Reynolds, and Godon ranges, which extend northwest of the Centre Brooks range, lie on the south limb and nose of the Centre anticline. A sharp flexure north of Godon Lake carries the South Evans range eastward 3 miles to the Magpie River. A parallel band of iron formation 1 mile north, the North Evans range, may represent the folded extension of the South Evans range. East of the Magpie River, thin, north-facing, faulted segments of iron formation extend across the top of the map area to the McVeigh Creek fault. To the west, south-facing iron formation, which includes the Brant range, extends westward from Evans Creek toward Kabenung Lake. At the west edge of the Helen-Magpie block, the east-facing Dore River range, extending 9 miles from the vicinity of Kabenung Lake southeastward toward Catfish Lake, lies on the west limb of the Josephine-Kabenung cross-syncline.

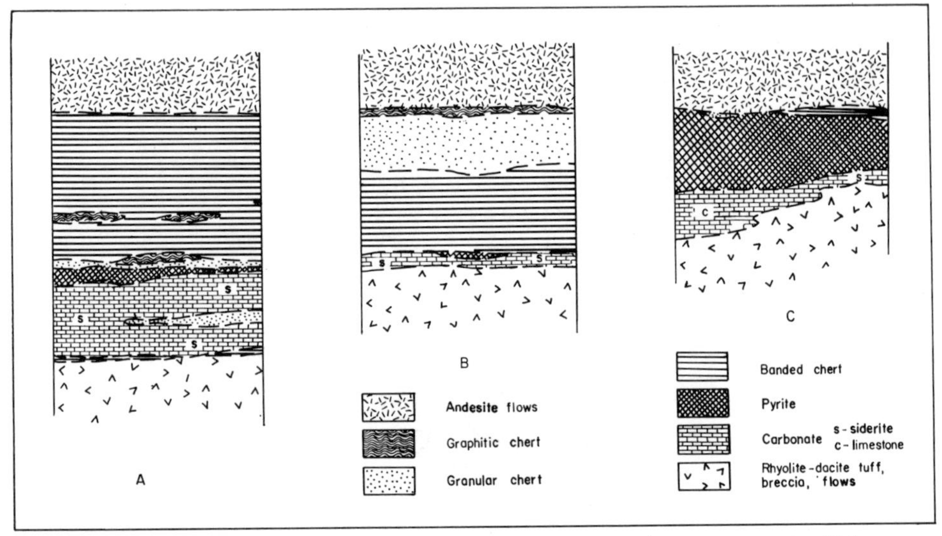

Figure 7. Diagrammatic cross sections of typical iron formations, Michipicoten area: A—Helen range, B—Godon range, C—Goudreau range. Shows stratigraphic arrangements and relationship to adjacent volcanic rocks

Discontinuous bands of iron formation, which lie 3000–10,000 feet stratigraphically below the main Helen iron formation, include segments near Firesand River, Loonskin Lake, Eccles Lake, Cedar Falls, the old Magpie mine, and possibly the Rand No. 2 deposit.

In the Goudreau block, three north-facing iron formations extend east of the McVeigh Creek fault at Alden, Goudreau, and Dreany Lake respectively. The Goudreau iron formation includes the Rand No. 1, "C", "A" Bear, Morrison 3, and Morrison 1 deposits. Both the

Alden range to the south and the Dreany range to the north consist of thin, discontinuous segments. The Goudreau and Dreany iron formations both appear to lie on the north limb of the Centre anticline; according to this interpretation the Goudreau iron formation underlies the Dreany iron formation. The Alden formation, on the other hand, apparently lies on the south limb of the South range syncline.

In the Kabenung block, the lower iron formation, extending from the north shore of Kabenung Lake on the east to Iron Lake on the west, includes the Magnetic Point, Morse Mountain, and Iron Lake ranges. The upper iron formation, which lies near the southeast shore of Kabenung Lake, includes the Elmo, Pine Point, and Betty Lake ranges; this iron formation may represent the west extension of the Brant range of the Helen-Magpie block. The north-facing Jimmy Kash range 4 miles southwest of Kabenung Lake may lie on the south limb of the North range syncline.

IRON FORMATION OF VOLCANIC ASSOCIATION: The uppermost or banded silica member is the most persistent and usually the thickest member of the iron formation. Its maximum thickness is 800 feet in the Helen range but it is commonly less than 200 feet thick. The rock consists of bands or layers of white to gray chert which alternate with bands of pale-brown, siliceous carbonate. Individual bands range in thickness from barely perceptible laminae to 3 inches. The banding usually lacks regularity in that individual bands commonly swell, contract, terminate abruptly, or unite with other bands. The contact between adjacent chert and carbonate bands is typically gradational. On the Helen range, banding is commonly made up of white chert, brown siliceous siderite, and dark-gray carbonaceous chert; the three types are locally arranged in rhythmical succession, carbonaceous layers separating overlying chert from underlying siderite layers.

Locally the chert is massive and devoid of bedding. This is common in the Goudreau iron formation where the banded chert member is thin to absent. On the Reynolds and Godon ranges the banded silica member contains an upper zone of structureless, coarse-grained chert 50–75 feet thick which grades down into a banded chert zone 75–125 feet thick (Fig. 7B). The massive, structureless variety of chert appears to have been derived from normal banded chert by leaching of carbonate content, thereby leaving a loose framework of sugary chert grains. The end stage of this process is complete freeing of chert grains to form loose silica sand found on the upper surface of some iron formations.

Chert bands are composed of quartz grains ranging in diameter from less than 0.4 mm to about 0.8 mm with the average nearer the coarser limit. The quartz grains lack dust rims, rounding, or other evidence of clastic origin. The chert commonly has a pronounced sugary texture. Grain size may vary considerably in adjacent bands.

Siliceous carbonate layers are normally composed of variable proportions of siderite and quartz with minor quantities of magnetite, pyrite, chlorite, and white mica. The quartz grains are appreciably smaller (approximately 0.02 mm) than those of the chert layers.

Brecciation is a comparatively common local feature confined to individual beds, lenses, or irregular zones up to 30 feet thick. Within the breccia zones, platy or rectangular fragments of chert ranging up to 3 inches thick and 1 foot long are distributed either chaotically or in subparallel fashion in a matrix of siliceous siderite; they are clearly related in thickness to original chert layers. Single brecciated chert layers commonly lie between undisturbed chert layers. Voids or vuggy cavities between fragments are absent. The nature and disposition of fragments and matrix suggest that brecciation developed during or shortly after deposition of the chert layers, possibly as a result of wave and current action or slumping.

The banded chert member contains layers and lenses of thin-bedded, black carbonaceous shale ranging up to 30 feet thick and several hundred feet long. The rock is composed largely of fine-grained chert, amorphous carbon, and variable sulfides; pyrite and pyrrhotite occur as thin discontinuous layers and lenses less than one-eighth of an inch thick, as scattered grains, and as concretions; thin concordant streaks of chalcopyrite and sphalerite occur locally in the Helen chert member. On the Reynolds and Godon ranges, persistent carbonaceous zones 5–15 feet thick lie at the top of the chert member (Fig. 7B). A sample from the Reynolds range contained 12.8 per cent free carbon. On the Helen range, several carbonaceous zones occur toward the base and center of the chert member (Fig. 7A); in addition, relict patches of carbonaceous chert of varying size are scattered throughout the chert member, suggesting greater original distribution of carbon than is now apparent. The association of carbonaceous-sulfide material suggests accumulation of organic material in a reducing environment. An organic origin is supported by carbon isotope ratios in Helen material (Goodwin, 1960, p. 41).

The average chemical composition of the banded chert member of the Reynolds, Godon, South Evans, and North Evans ranges (Table 3), which is based on 2500 feet of drilling and 1000 feet of surface sampling, represents the member as a whole in the central portion of the Helen-Magpie block. Columns 1–5 of Table 3 list partial composition of the individual ranges. The results demonstrate the uniform chemical composition of the member along strike. The average composition of the banded chert member on the Helen range (Table 3, column 1) was determined by sampling across the full width of 620 feet in an old adit at the midlength of the range.

TABLE 3. CHEMICAL COMPOSITION OF BANDED CHERT MEMBER OF THE HELEN, REYNOLDS, GODON, SOUTH EVANS, AND NORTH EVANS RANGES, MICHIPICOTEN AREA, ALGOMA DISTRICT, ONTARIO, CANADA

	1	2	3	4	5	6
Total Fe	17.7	12.6	17.5	14.9	16.5	16.0
SiO_2	57.7	59.7	55.7	58.5	63.6	60.1
Al_2O_3	2.07	..	..	..	..	..
S	1.25	..	..	..	..	1.6
MnO	0.66	..	..	..	..	0.7
CaO	0.85	..	..	..	..	..
MgO	1.95	..	..	..	..	..
Loss on ignition	11.5	..	..	..	..	..

1. Helen range—average of 61 samples taken along "old" adit; analyst, J. H. Dann, Wawa, Ont.
2. Reynolds range—average of 50 representative samples; analyst, E. Herbert, Sault Ste. Marie, Ont.
3. Godon Lake range—average of 114 representative samples; analyst, E. Herbert, Sault Ste. Marie, Ont.
4. South Evans range—average of 46 representative samples; analyst, E. Herbert, Sault Ste. Marie, Ont.
5. North Evans range—average of 115 representative samples; analyst, E. Herbert, Sault Ste. Marie, Ont.
6. Average of sample nos. 2–5

	Reynolds-Godon ranges		*Helen range*	
	Total Fe	SiO_2	Total Fe	SiO_2
Top of chert member	10	80	10	80
Base of chert member	25	40	30	22

In contrast to uniform composition along strike, the banded chert member varies uniformly in chemical composition across strike. Iron content increases from top to bottom, reaching a maximum at, or close to, the base of the member. The silica content varies inversely. Table 3 lists typical iron and silica contents at the base and top of the Reynolds, Godon, and Helen ranges respectively.

The banded chert member in proximity to younger intrusive rocks contains more or less magnetite in place of siderite. In addition, conformable zones containing coarse-grained magnetite are present in the Helen banded chert. Secondary silicates such as actinolite and grunerite are present locally.

The pyrite member of the iron formation is conformable to and grades upward into the banded silica member and downward into the carbonate member. It shows a rudimentary development on some ranges but is usually present as a well formed unit (Fig. 7). It varies greatly in thickness from range to range and from place to place in one range. On the Helen range the pyrite member is 60 feet thick at the west end and thins gradually to 5–10 feet thick at the east end. The member reaches a maximum thickness of 120 feet on the Goudreau range.

The pyrite commonly has a well-developed granular texture. Grains range up to 0.8 mm in diameter. Veins and bands of dense, fine-grained pyrite commonly occur with the granular variety. The rock is composed of pyrite with variable proportions of pyrrhotite, siderite, magnetite, and silica. Chert and siderite occur in disseminated form in the massive sulfides and as beds and lenses in the leaner. The pyrite member in the Goudreau area contains persistent traces of nickel, arsenic, and gold (Collins and Quirke, 1924, p. 62–63).

The lowermost or carbonate member of the iron formation is best developed on the Helen range where a tabular body of siderite reaches a maximum thickness of 350 feet and extends more than 6000 feet along strike (Figs. 6, 7). The carbonate members on the Eleanor, Lucy, Ruth, Josephine, Bartlett, Magpie mine, and Betty Lake ranges consist of tabular bodies and lenses of siderite which range up to 200 feet in thickness. Elsewhere the carbonate member is present either in rudimentary form or is absent altogether.

The siderite ranges from light gray to brown. It is usually dense and structureless in appearance. Individual grains range in diameter from less than 0.003 to 0.07 mm with the average about 0.022 mm. Siderite is locally banded in contrasting shades of gray and brown. Local zones of banded siderite contain breccialike siderite fragments set in a dense siderite matrix of contrasting color. Banding and fragments within both the siderite member and the overlying banded chert member are essentially similar in dimension and appearance; they may be related by replacement of banded chert by siderite.

TABLE 4. CHEMICAL COMPOSITION OF CARBONATE AND PYRITE MEMBERS FROM THE HELEN, ELEANOR, LUCY, RUTH, BARTLETT, BIG LAKE, RAND NO. 2, AND BETTY LAKE RANGES, THE MAGPIE MINE, AND THE GOUDREAU A DEPOSIT, MICHIPICOTEN AREA, ALGOMA DISTRICT, ONTARIO, CANADA

	1	2	3	4	5	6	7	8	9	10
SiO_2	10.18	8.59	13.20	6.97	3.60	3.24	3.40	3.40	9.5	4.69
Al_2O_3	1.53	1.74	..	0.57	0.87	..	..	..	..	0.56
S	4.89	2.30	0.21	6.11	2.97	..	0.73	..	1.2	32.6
FeO	45.6	43.65	39.80	44.90	51.75	46.50	40.00	44.59	53.17	54.1
MnO	2.55	2.72	3.08	2.26	3.33	3.84	9.83	2.84	2.96	1.28
CaO	2.60	3.38	2.57	3.55	1.57	1.65	3.11	5.48	..	3.87
MgO	5.54	4.64	5.61	4.32	3.68	6.52	4.73	5.51	1.22	1.90
CO_2	..	..	34.27	..	..	39.41	37.64	32.24	..	..
Loss on ignition	26.22	26.67	..	26.54	24.59	..	..	..	26.00	..

1. Helen range—weighted average of 49 complete intersections, Helen-Victoria-MacLeod mines (includes silica waste bands); analyst, J. H. Dann, Wawa, Ont.
2. Eleanor range—Sir James mine, average of 6 complete intersections; analyst, J. H. Dann, Wawa, Ont.
3. Lucy range—analysis no. R-15 *in* D. H. Richter (M.Sc. thesis, Queens Univ., Kingston, Ont.)
4. Ruth range—from Moore and Armstrong (1946, p. 72)
5. Bartlett range—average of 7 complete intersections; analyst, E. Herbert, Sault Ste. Marie, Ont.
6. Rand no. 2 range—analysis no. R-7 *in* D. H. Richter (M.Sc. thesis, Queens Univ., Kingston, Ont.)
7. Big Lake range—analysis no. R-4 *in* D. H. Richter (M.Sc. thesis, Queens Univ., Kingston, Ont.)
8. Magpie mine—sample of raw siderite ore; analysis No. II *in* Collings and Quirke (1926, p. 64)
9. Betty Lake range—average of 3 intersections; analyst, E. Herbert, Sault Ste. Marie, Ont.
10. Goudreau A deposit—average of 3 intersections; analyst, J. H. Dann, Wawa, Ont.

The carbonate ore bodies are largely composed of fine-grained siderite associated with variable quantities of ankerite, quartz, sulfides, magnetite, chlorite, and iron sulfides. In the McPhail and "A" deposits in the Goudreau block and locally on the Dore River range to the west, the member is composed mainly of white, crystalline calcite. Where siderite is the dominant mineral the rock tends to be massive and essentially devoid of bedding. Bedding becomes more distinct as the quantity of either chert or sulfides increases. Lenses and layers of banded silica lie at the base of the siderite member on the Helen, Eleanor, and Lucy ranges. Also, a central zone of coarse-grained, structureless chert devoid of bedding, which ranges up to 40 feet thick, is present in the Helen carbonate member toward the east end of the range (Fig. 7A).

Table 4 presents average analyses of carbonate from the Helen, Eleanor, Lucy, Ruth, Bartlett, Big Lake, Rand No. 2, Magpie mine, and Betty Lake ranges; they demonstrate the wide range in relative proportions of iron, magnesium, calcium, and manganese components in the carbonate. It is inferred that variations in carbonate composition reflect local variations in chemical environment, particularly ph, Eh, and salinity, during the period of carbonate deposition.

Chert remnants ranging from small isolated clusters of grains to large segments many feet long are common throughout the carbonate member. Where the pyrite member is thin or absent the carbonate member grades upward by gradual increase in chert lenses, layers, and fragments to the overlying banded chert member. Banded chert may be seen in various stages of replacement by the carbonate (Tanton, 1948, p. 425).

Fragments and layers of tuffaceous rock are also present in the carbonate member. Pyritiferous shale 1–3 feet thick overlies banded chert at the base of the Helen carbonate member; angular felsic pyroclastic fragments up to 6 inches in diameter are enclosed in siderite near Sayer Lake at the west end of the Helen range; and thin zones of dark-gray, dense, tuffaceous rock extend along the center of the carbonate member on the Eleanor range and on adjacent ranges to the east. In addition, shreds and patches of microscopic dimension are present throughout the member (Collins and Quirke, 1926, p. 64–66). The total tuffaceous content, however, is generally small as indicated by low average Al_2O_3 content (Table 4).

IRON FORMATION OF SEDIMENTARY ASSOCIATION: Iron formations of sedimentary association, which range up to 1000 feet thick and 3 miles long, are commonly 200–300 feet thick and 1000–3000 feet long. Iron formation zones commonly contain several parallel bands each 5 to 100 feet thick and separated by 50–200 feet of shale and graywacke. Individual bands are particularly lensy in distribution; they pinch, swell, and bifurcate abruptly along strike, and commonly terminate in a few feet of black, siliceous, pyritiferous shale.

Iron formations of sedimentary association are typically composed of alternating layers of chert, siliceous magnetite, and jasper associated with variable quantities of siderite, pyrite, and shaly material. Individual layers of the banded iron formation range from one-quarter of an inch to 2 inches thick and normally persist along strike for 10–30 feet. The chert is typically fine-grained; grains on the Iron Lake range measure 0.03–0.04 mm in diameter. Individual magnetite grains are 0.01–0.15 mm in diameter. The contacts between chert- and iron-bearing layers are normally sharp and well defined, in contrast to gradational contacts prevailing in iron formations of volcanic association. In the western part of the area, near Iron Lake in particular, brilliantly banded jasper iron formation is common in which white, black, and maroon layers indicate chert, magnetite, and hematite constituents respectively. Iron formations of sedimentary association are of relatively uniform chemical composition across strike, differing in this respect from banded chert members in iron formations of volcanic association wherein iron content increases toward the base.

RELATIONSHIP TO ADJACENT FORMATIONS: Iron formations of volcanic association are in sharp contact with overlying volcanic rocks. The upper contact of banded chert with pillowed flows typically lacks evidence of erosion or structural disturbance, indicating that the chert was sufficiently indurated to resist scouring or defacement by flowing lava. On the Goudreau, Reynolds, and Godon ranges, the topmost few feet of chert have been locally rendered loose, sugary, and incohesive; this may reflect postdepositional chemical leaching of flat-lying iron formation. The lower contact of the carbonate member with underlying volcanic rocks ranges from abrupt, in which case a thin, banded chert unit intervenes, to gradational over 1–5 feet, in which case basal carbonate layers contain shreds and patches of volcanic rock, and the underlying 2–3 feet of volcanic rocks contains veinlets and lenses of siderite and pyrite.

Iron formations of sedimentary association are typically gradational along and across strike to argillite and graywacke, the former with delicate laminations, the latter with graded bedding; the iron formations were apparently deposited in moderately deep water as integral syngenetic units.

The transition from iron formation of volcanic association to iron formation of sedimentary association is marked by the following features: (1) the iron formation gradually assumes a lensy, discontinuous distribution along strike, dividing into two or more parallel bands; (2) internal banding becomes more regular, pronounced, and persistent along strike; (3) chert becomes finer-grained, losing its course, sugary texture; (4) basal iron concentration dwindles, the iron formation attaining uniform chemical composition across strike; and (5) magnetite and hematite content increases, in place of siderite. The two types of iron formation are normally transitional along strike intervals of several miles. Typical transitions are displayed between Godon range (volcanic type) and South Evans range (sedimentary type), near Kabenung Lake between Betty Lake range (volcanic type) and Pine Point range (sedimentary type), and on a larger scale between the Helen-Magpie block (volcanic type) and the Kabenung block (sedimentary type).

ENVIRONMENT OF DEPOSITION: In general, Michipicoten iron formations have the aspects of moderately deep-water deposits; this is suggested by broad stratigraphic distribution, pillow structures, graded bedding, and delicate laminations in intimately associated rocks, as well as by absence of shallow-water features such as wave and ripple marks, channelling, and cross bedding.

Iron formations of volcanic association were apparently deposited upon a volcanic terrain dominated by broad, shieldlike, pyroclastic domes of considerable relief. The relative purity of the iron formations suggests rapid chemical deposition during a period of extrusive quiescence. Some idea of the nature of the terrain at the time of deposition may be gained by viewing the iron formations as continuous marker horizons. As the rocks have been tilted, the present erosion surface represents a suitable cross section for this purpose. The Helen iron formation, when viewed in prefaulted position in the interval from Michipicoten Harbour northeastward to Hawk Junction, presents a sinuous pattern with concavities centering at the Helen and Josephine ranges; at both locations, iron formation changes strike from southwest to southeast when passing from west to east. We may reasonably infer that the concavities represent topographic highs formed of pyroclastic accumulations; this suggests local relief of many hundreds of feet during deposition of iron formation.

ORIGIN: Coleman and Willmott (1902) noted the intimate relationship of iron formation to volcanic rocks and proposed that iron formations represent chemical sediments deposited during a period of volcanic quiescence. Collins and Quirke (1926) suggested that iron formations resulted from the action of Keewatin volcanic hot springs rising from depth and charged with iron, sulfur, and carbon dioxide; accordingly, pyrite and carbonate members represent a portion of the volcanic complex transformed by chemical replacement, whereas the banded silica member was deposited on land and in local bodies of water as a precipitate from outflowing hot springs charged with silica leached from the underlying volcanic rocks.

Grout (1926), noting the presence of pyrrhotite, that suggested high temperature-pressure environment, proposed that the banded silica was deposited on surface and buried to considerable depth before deposition of carbonate and sulfides by waters of higher temperature and pressure. Moore (1931) agreed with Grout's modification of prereplacement burial and suggested that deeply buried, flat-lying, banded silica formed a barrier that helped impound rising, carbonate-bearing hot waters from the still hot lavas. Bruce (1940) suggested that both siderite and pyrite represent replacements of volcanic rocks underlying the banded silica after these rocks had been deposited and tilted to their present position.

Hawley (1942) noted many lenslike inclusions of pyritized, schistose volcanics in the Rand No. 2 iron formation as well as finely laminated chert identical in structure to partially carbonatized and silicified tuffs, which indicated to him a replacement rather than sedimentary origin for the chert as well as for the carbonate and sulfides. Tanton (1948, p. 424) ascribed the distinctively banded structure of the Helen iron formation to "successive replacement of a foliated host rock" and the siderite ore body to replacement by hot, ascending mineralizing solutions of magmatic origin.

W. L. Young (1954, Ph.D. thesis, McGill Univ., Montreal, P. Q.), noting the large aerial extent of carbonate and sulfide members and the presence in the Lucy ore body of many tuffaceous zones, suggested that all members of the iron formation were formed by chemical sedimentation. D. H. Richter (1952, M. Sc. thesis, Queen's Univ., Kingston, Ontario) concluded that banded silica was formed by chemical sedimentation and that the carbonate and sulfide members were formed by replacement of felsic fragmental rocks after they had been buried to considerable depth but were still flat-lying.

Evidence pertaining to origin of Michipicoten iron formations is considered to favor the hypothesis of chemical sedimentation of banded chert, pyrite, and carbonate members in a subaqueous volcanic environment (Goodwin, 1960). We may reasonably infer that (1) Michipicoten iron formations represent integral genetic units of specific andesite-rhyolite volcanic cycles, (2) the dominant volcanic-topographic features at the time of deposition of banded iron formation were broad, shield-like, rhyolite-andesite breccia masses, (3) the period of highly explosive volcanic activity that produced this environment was followed by one of chemical volcanic activity on a correspondingly grand scale during which hot springs and fumaroles poured forth large quantities of siliceous bicarbonate and sulfur-bearing solutions and gases, (4) iron carbonate and sulfur constituents in the iron formations were of subvolcanic, presumably magmatic, derivation, whereas silica was largely derived by chemical leaching of volcanic rocks through which carbonate-sulfur-bearing solutions passed and that (5) the local type of iron formation reflects the local environment during the period of deposition and lithification.

* * * * * * *

REFERENCES CITED

Bruce, E. L., 1940, Geology of the Goudreau-Lochalsh area: Ont. Dept. Mines 49th Ann. Rept., pt. 3, 47 p.

Coleman, A. P., and Willmott, A. B., 1902, The Michipicoten iron ranges: Univ. Toronto Studies, Geol. ser., no. 2, 83 p.

Collins, W. H., and Quirke, T. T., 1926, Michipicoten iron ranges: Geol. Survey Canada Mem. 147, 170 p.

Cooke, H. C., 1937, Structure of the Dore Series, Michipicoten district, Ontario: Royal Soc. Canada Trans., 3d ser., v. 31, p. 69–80

Cross, W., and Larsen, E. S., 1935, A brief review of the geology of the San Juan region of southwestern Colorado: U.S. Geol. Survey Bull. 843, 138 p.

Fisher, R. V., 1960, Classification of volcanic breccias: Geol. Soc. America Bull., v. 71, p. 973–982

Frohberg, M. H., 1935, The ore deposits of the Michipicoten area: Ont. Dept. Mines 44th Ann. Rept., pt. 8, p. 39–83

Gledhill, T. L., 1927, Michipicoten gold area, District of Algoma: Ont. Dept. Mines 36th Ann. Rept., pt. 2, p. 1–49

Goodwin, A. M., 1960, Genetic aspects of Michipicoten iron formation: Canadian Inst. Mining and Metallurgy Trans., v. 64, p. 32–36

Grout, F. F., 1926, Michipicoten iron ranges: Econ. Geology, v. 21, p. 813

Hawley, J. E., 1942, Origin of some siderite, pyrite, chert deposits, Michipicoten district, Ontario: Royal Soc. Canada Trans., v. 36, sec. 4, p. 79–87

Logan, W. E., 1863, Geology of Canada: Geol. Survey Canada, Rept. Progress to 1863, p. 53–55

Moore, E. S., 1931, Goudreau and Michipicoten gold areas: Ont. Dept. Mines 40th Ann. Rept., pt. 4, p. 1–54

—— 1948, Structure of the Michipicoten-Goudreau area, p. 414–419 *in* Structural geology of Canadian ore deposits: Canadian Inst. Mining and Metallurgy, 948 p.

Moore, E. S., and Armstrong, H. S., 1946, Iron deposits in the District of Algoma: Ont. Dept. Mines 55th Ann. Rept., pt. 4, p. 1–118

Nockolds, S. R., 1954, Average chemical compositions of some igneous rocks: Geol. Soc. America Bull., v. 65, no. 10, p. 1007–1032

Smith, R. L., 1960, Ash flows: Geol. Soc. America Bull., v. 71, p. 795–842

Tanton, T. L., 1948, New Helen mine, p. 422–429 *in* Structural geology of Canadian ore deposits: Canadian Inst. Mining and Metallurgy, 948 p.

Turner, F. J., and Verhoogen, J., 1951, Igneous and metamorphic petrology: New York, McGraw-Hill Book Co. Inc., 602 p.

Williams, H., 1927, The geology of Snowdon (North Wales): Geol. Soc. Quart. Jour., v. 83, pt. 3, p. 346–431

—— 1932, Geology of the Lassen Volcanic National Park, California: Univ. Calif., Dept. Geol. Sci. Bull., v. 21, no. 8, p. 195–385

19

Reprinted from *Geol. Soc. America Bull.,* **79,** 1527–1544 (Nov. 1968)

A. F. TRENDALL *Geological Survey of Western Australia, Perth, Western Australia*

Three Great Basins of Precambrian Banded Iron Formation Deposition: A Systematic Comparison

Abstract: The origin of Precambrian banded iron formations is controversial. One type of evidence is a comparison of different occurrences. Three of the best-preserved basins of Precambrian iron formation deposition are here defined and compared systematically: the Hamersley Basin of Western Australia, the Animikie Basin of North America, and the Transvaal System Basin of South Africa. After a brief summary of the broad structural and stratigraphic evolution of each basin, their differences and similarities are reviewed. They differ mainly in: major stratigraphic sequence, thickness of iron formation, thickness variation, stratigraphic continuity, lithology of iron formation, nature of sedimentary structures, conspicuousness of varves (microbanding), clastic association, and abundance of diagenetic riebeckite. With some reservations, they resemble each other in: age, basin size, chemistry and mineralogy, broad time-structural evolution of basin, precedence of chert, volcanic association, and in the restricted, medial and transitional stratigraphic status of the main iron formation. It is concluded that the Western Australian and South African iron formations are very closely similar, but that both differ markedly from the Animikie iron formations of the Lake Superior area. However, all three are more closely similar in chemistry than is required by the fact that their definition is chemical. Quantitative geochemical argument indicates a direct volcanic contribution of iron to the Hamersley Basin; it is possible that such vulcanicity is restricted to a limited medial part of basin development in a particular kind of basin-forming process.

CONTENTS

INTRODUCTION

It is widely accepted that banded iron formations are chemically deposited sedimentary rocks and are mostly Precambrian in age. But there is still strong disagreement on their depositional chemistry, their paleogeographic and paleoclimatic significance, and the immediate source of their constituent material, especially the iron.

Among the main published work of the last two decades relevant to this last point, Sakamoto (1950), James (1951; 1954; 1966), White (1954), Alexandrov (1955), Hough (1958),

Huber (1959), Cilliers and Genis (1964), Lepp and Goldich (1964), and Govett (1966), believed that surface processes were adequate to extract, transport, and concentrate iron from adjacent chemically unexceptional land. On the other hand, Tanton (1950), Guild (1953; 1957), Goodwin (1956; 1961; 1962), Oftedahl (1958), Harder (1963), Trendall (1965a), and LaBerge (1966a; 1966b) either emphasized the common association of vulcanicity and iron formation, or saw direct or indirect volcanic contribution of iron as a main source of this element, either in a particular iron formation or in iron formations in general. Oftedahl (1958) aptly labeled these two views the "from-above" and "from-below" theories. Judgment between them is largely subjective: Tyler and Twenhofel (1952, p. 136) disagreed on the issue even in a joint presentation of a good deal of relevant data. Borchert (1960) stands almost alone as the protagonist of a different type of "from-above" hypothesis involving intra-marine redistribution ("from-within").

From older work, it is noteworthy that, although Gruner (1922) was the first to challenge the basically "from-below" ideas of Van Hise and Leith (1911), he was later reconciled to them (James, 1966, p. 47). Gross (1965, p. 106–110) recently reviewed the evidence impartially, and concluded that more was needed, a view also emphasized by Trendall (1965a, p. 1069).

Evidence about iron formation, like that about any other rock, may be of three kinds: it may be abstract and remote from the rock, based on broad theory or experimental data; it may be based on detailed work within, and concern one single body of the rock; or it may be based on comparative features of a number of separate bodies. The frequent appeal to a common volcanic association of some sort to support a volcanic origin is of this third type. Such evidence is difficult to assess objectively; many important features of Precambrian iron formation needed for comparison are either unknown, unpublished, or obscured by metamorphism.

In 1966 I was able, after some years of work on the iron formation of Western Australia, to spend consecutive months in the field in three of the world's best-preserved basins of Precambrian iron formation deposition: the Hamersley area of Western Australia, the Lake Superior area of North America, and the Cape Province-Transvaal area of South Africa. The location of each is indicated in Figure 1. I was impressed by several differences and resemblances between them; the purpose of this paper is to review these in a systematic way. Such comparison is not easily made from the literature; indeed, the Brockman Iron Formation of the Hamersley Basin, possibly the least altered, least deformed, least oxidized, thickest, most areally extensive, and best-exposed Precambrian iron formation—and certainly that whose internal stratigraphy is best known —is not mentioned by James (1966), so rapid

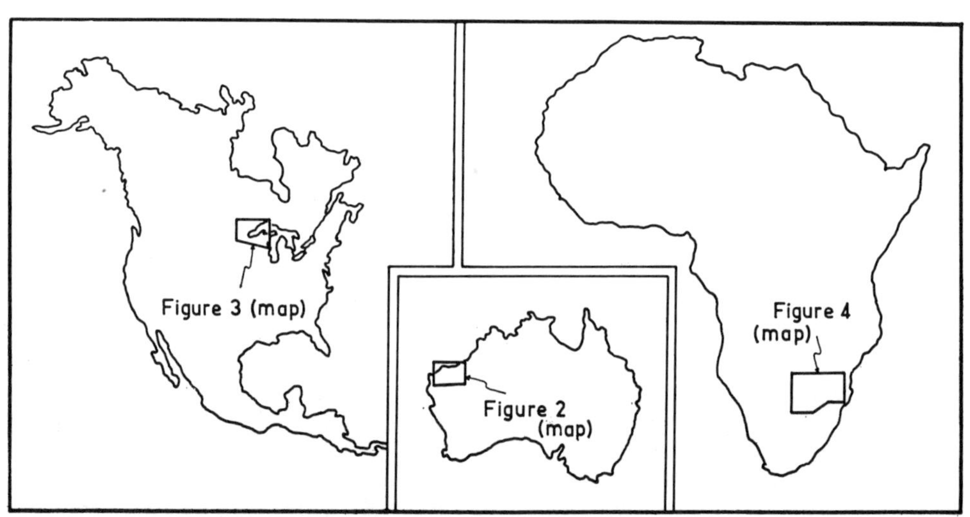

Figure 1. Location of Figures 2, 3, and 4 in the Australian, North American, and African continents, respectively. Scale throughout is 1:140,000,000.

has been the progress of its recent study. In restricting the comparison to three basins, this paper is necessarily an early draft of what iron formation geologists must have as one ultimate aim: the compilation of a complete comparative catalogue of the world's iron formations. Only in this way will it be seen which features are common (and genetically required), and which are incidental.

In the following pages, each of the three chosen basins is first defined, and its broad structural and stratigraphic evolution summarized. Differences and similarities are then listed, and tentative suggestions of the significance of the comparison are finally made.

ACKNOWLEDGMENTS

It is a pleasure to acknowledge the help given by mining companies and government organizations during my tour of North America and South Africa; I am indebted in this respect to geologists of the United States Geological Survey, the Minnesota Geological Survey, the Geological Survey of Canada, the Ontario Department of Mines, the Cleveland-Cliffs Iron Company, the Hanna Mining Company, the Inland Steel Corporation, the Iron-Ore Company of Canada, Pickands Mather and Company International, the Geological Survey of South Africa, Asbestos Investments (Pty) Ltd., Cape Asbestos South Africa (Pty) Ltd., the General Mining and Finance Corporation Ltd., and the South African Iron and Steel Industrial Corporation Ltd. (ISCOR). Although it is unfair to select individuals from these organizations, special tribute must be paid to the co-operation of Dr. H. L. James and Dr. J. E. Gair in Michigan, Dr. P. K. Sims in Minnesota, Dr. G. A. Gross in Ottawa, and Dr. J. J. Le R. Cilliers and L. N. Kuyper in Johannesburg. Dr. P. R. de Villiers, of ISCOR, kindly translated for me part of his Ph.D. dissertation from Afrikaans, and drew my attention to the paper by Engelbrecht (1962). Dr. A. E. Cockbain drew my attention to Nordeng's work (1963) on algae, and carefully read the text; errors and ambiguities remaining are mine. The permission of the Director of the Geological Survey of Western Australia to submit this paper for publication is gratefully acknowledged.

THE HAMERSLEY BASIN

The term Hamersley Basin is here applied to the depositional basin of the Hamersley Group of Western Australia (MacLeod and others, 1963; MacLeod, 1966). The outcrop of this group is shown on Figure 2, which also illustrates the remainder of this brief summary. The group is defined by the presence of iron formation, which forms some 3000 feet of its total thickness of 8000 feet. The Hamersley Group conformably overlies the Fortescue Group (Kriewaldt, 1964), a mainly volcanic and pyroclastic succession varying between 4000 and 14,000 feet in thickness. The Fortescue Group rests with marked angular unconformity on the granites, metasediments, and metavolcanics of the older Precambrian Pilbara block (Ryan, 1964); these have a probable age in the range 2800 to 3000 m.y. (Leggo and others, 1965). The Wyloo Group, a sequence of mainly clastic sediments with a thick dolomite and basalt (Halligan and Daniels, 1964), overlies the Hamersley Group with equivocal, locally variable, but broadly conformable relationship; it is intruded by granites (Daniels, 1965) about 1700 m.y. old. The Fortescue, Hamersley, and Wyloo Groups together constitute the Mt. Bruce Supergroup, which represents a single major depositional sequence of more than 40,000 feet of sediment; its age is discussed later, under the appropriate heading. The younger Precambrian Bresnahan and Bangemall Groups unconformably overlie the Mt. Bruce Supergroup and the granites intruding it.

Structurally the Fortescue Group dips gently southward off the older Pilbara block. Farther south, it becomes steadily more disturbed and is tightly folded with the Hamersley and Wyloo Groups where they pass below the younger Precambrian groups; these are comparatively slightly folded. Only the Wyloo Group has been seriously affected by regional metamorphism.

Ryan and Blockley (1965) have shown from isopachs that the Hamersley Basin was probably closed, and had the general dimensions of the outcrop area.

THE ANIMIKIE BASIN

Figure 3, which illustrates this summary, is adapted from the map of Leith and others (1935). The iron formations with which this paper is concerned are those of the Animikie Series (James, 1958) or Group (Goldich and others, 1961). The probable age of this succession lies in the range 2500 to 1600 m.y.; the evidence for this is discussed later.

Folding, and an extensive cover of Pleistocene drift, together account for the fact that the Animikie iron formations are now restricted in

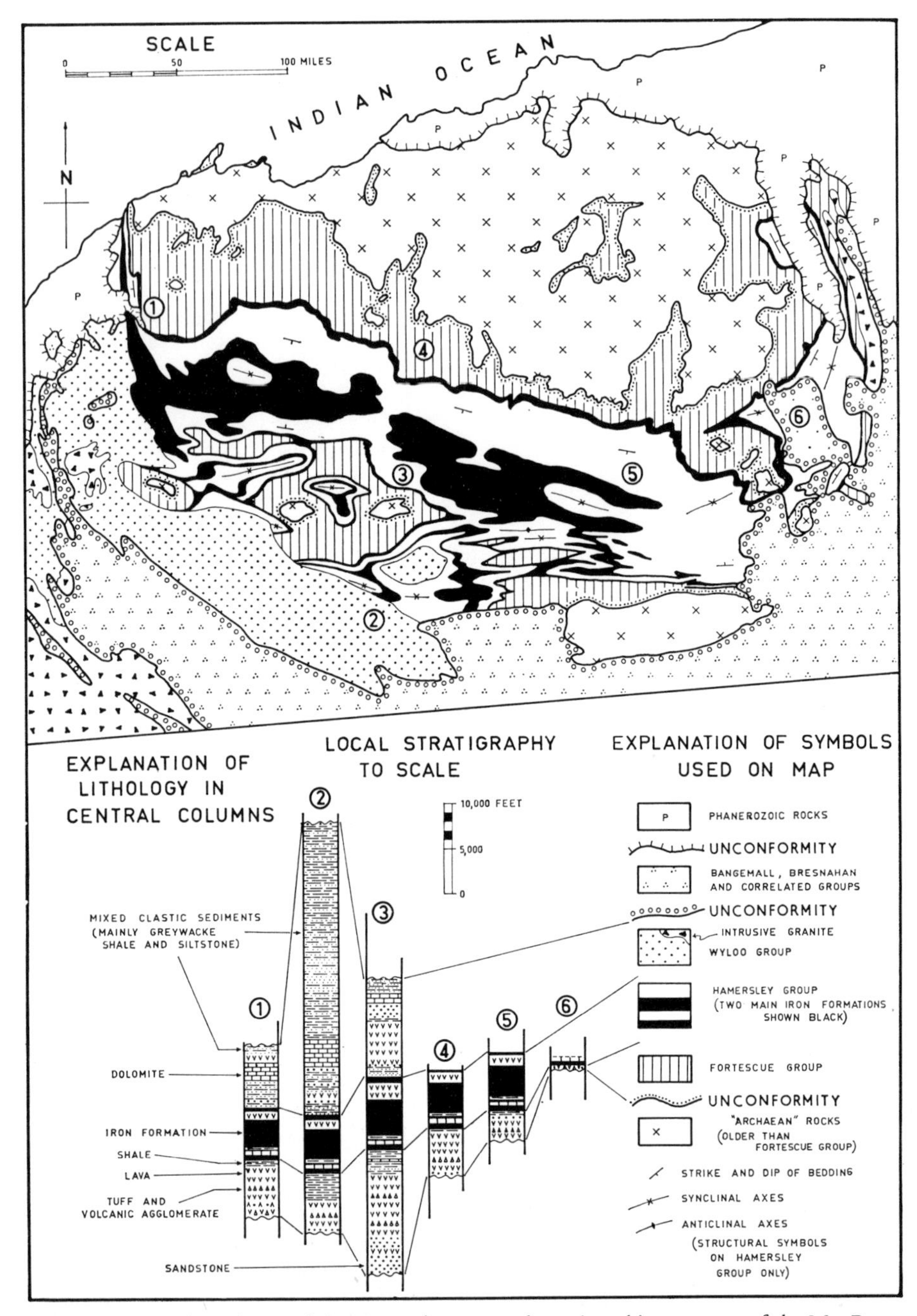

Figure 2. Geological map of the Hamersley area and stratigraphic summary of the Mt. Bruce Supergroup (includes Fortescue, Hamersley, and Wyloo Groups). Map based on those of Horwitz (1966) and MacLeod (1966), with some modifications. Some faulted boundaries continuous with unconformities are shown as unconformities for clarity. Numbers refer to 1:250,000 map sheets of the Geological Survey of Western Australia: 1 = Yarraloola (Williams, 1965); 2 = Turee Creek (Daniels, 1967); 3 = Mt. Bruce (de la Hunty 1965); 4 = Pyramid (Kriewaldt and Ryan, 1965); 5 = Roy Hill (MacLeod and de la Hunty, 1966); 6 = Balfour Downs (de la Hunty, 1964). As far as possible symbols used are equivalent to those of Figures 3 and 4, but it is not implied that the main unconformities are exactly time-equivalent.

outcrop to a number of separate "iron ranges." Although continuity between ranges cannot be mapped, there are marked resemblances in their stratigraphic sequences. In general (Fig. 2), a basal quartzite-dolomite group (for example, Chocolay Group of eastern ranges) is succeeded with local unconformity by a group including the main iron formation (for example, Menominee Group of eastern ranges), which is in turn followed, again with local unconformity, by a mainly fine-grained clastic group (for example, Baraga Group of eastern ranges). The Animikie Series was deposited unconformably on the older granite, gneiss, metavolcanic, and metasedimentary rocks (including iron formations) of the Canadian Shield. Post-Animikie folding, accompanied by metamorphism (James, 1955) and local granite intrusion, took place most strongly in the eastern ranges—the Penokean orogeny or metamorphic event (Aldrich and others, 1965; Goldich and others, 1961). The main subsequent event in the Lake Superior area was the depression of the Keeweenawan Basin, roughly beneath the present site of Lake Superior to receive some 50,000 feet of lavas and mainly pyroclastic sediments, into which the Duluth Gabbro was intruded. These rocks overlie the Animikie Series unconformably and are of the order of 1000 m.y. old.

Two problems make a clear definition of the Animikie Basin more difficult than a definition of the Hamersley Basin: first, the extent to which the Lake Superior area formed part of a more or less continuous girdle of coeval iron formation deposition encircling what is now the Superior Province of the Canadian Shield; and, second, the extent to which, within the Lake Superior area, the iron formation of each range was laid down locally in a trough restricted to the general vicinity of the range itself.

James (1966, p. 34) has drawn attention to the former concept, which may be followed most clearly on the map compiled by Gross (1965). Certainly there is remarkable clockwise continuity along the line Belcher Islands—Cape Smith—Wakeham Bay—Labrador Trough—Lake Albanel, encircling the "Ungava stable area" of Bergeron and others (1962), but it is damaging to the simplicity of the larger picture that between Lake Albanel and the Lake Superior ranges lies the type area of the Huronian. No satisfying lithological correlation between the Animikie and the Huronian can be made; James (1958, p. 33–35) described the uncertainties involved and noted some support for the younger age of the Huronian. Later evidence (van Schmus, 1965) shows that the problem remains unresolved. I suggest that the discontinuity in the continental-scale iron formation girdle created by the Huronian area, the clustered arrangement of the Lake Superior ranges, and their obvious mutual stratigraphic resemblance makes it at least possible that the Animikie iron formations accumulated in a structurally discrete basin covering much the present area of the ranges.

This raises the second problem: to what extent can it be supposed that the obvious "correlation" of formations between ranges indicates their former physical continuity? At present there seems to be too little evidence for definite judgment. James and Pettijohn (*in* James and others, 1961, p. 45–46) have argued for the deposition of at least some Animikie iron formations in small restricted basins on the grounds that: (1) detailed stratigraphic correlation within the "same" iron formation of adjacent ranges is not possible, and (2) restricted basins are necessary for the deposition of sulfides and ferrous carbonate (James, 1954). A further type of evidence needed here is that of isopachs. White (1954, p. 41–47) has used thickness with other environmental factors to interpret the Biwabik Formation of the Mesabi Range as a near-shore deposit. In the Marquette Range, the current detailed mapping of J. E. Gair (1966, personal commun.) has confirmed the view of Tyler and Twenhofel (1952, p. 131) that the extreme thickness variations of the Negaunee Formation, known for many years (Van Hise and Bayley, 1897, p. 335–336), are largely primary depositional differences, and Gair believes that the axial syncline of this range follows the approximate course of a local depositional, possibly fault, trough. On the other hand the virtually continuous outcrop of the Gunflint-Biwabik iron formation over a strike length of some 250 miles gives at least one minimum dimension for continuous Animikie iron formation deposition. It also seems likely simply from outcrop that the uppermost thick pelites of most ranges (Rove-Virginia-Tyler-Michigamme) accumulated in a single basin, although Schmidt (1963, p. 40) has drawn attention to dissimilarities between the Rabbit Lake Formation of the Cuyuna Range and the Virginia Slate of the Mesabi Range.

Although the evidence is not conclusive, it therefore appears that, although a broad depositional basin probably existed in Animikie time in much the same position as the later Keeweenawan depression, its southeastern

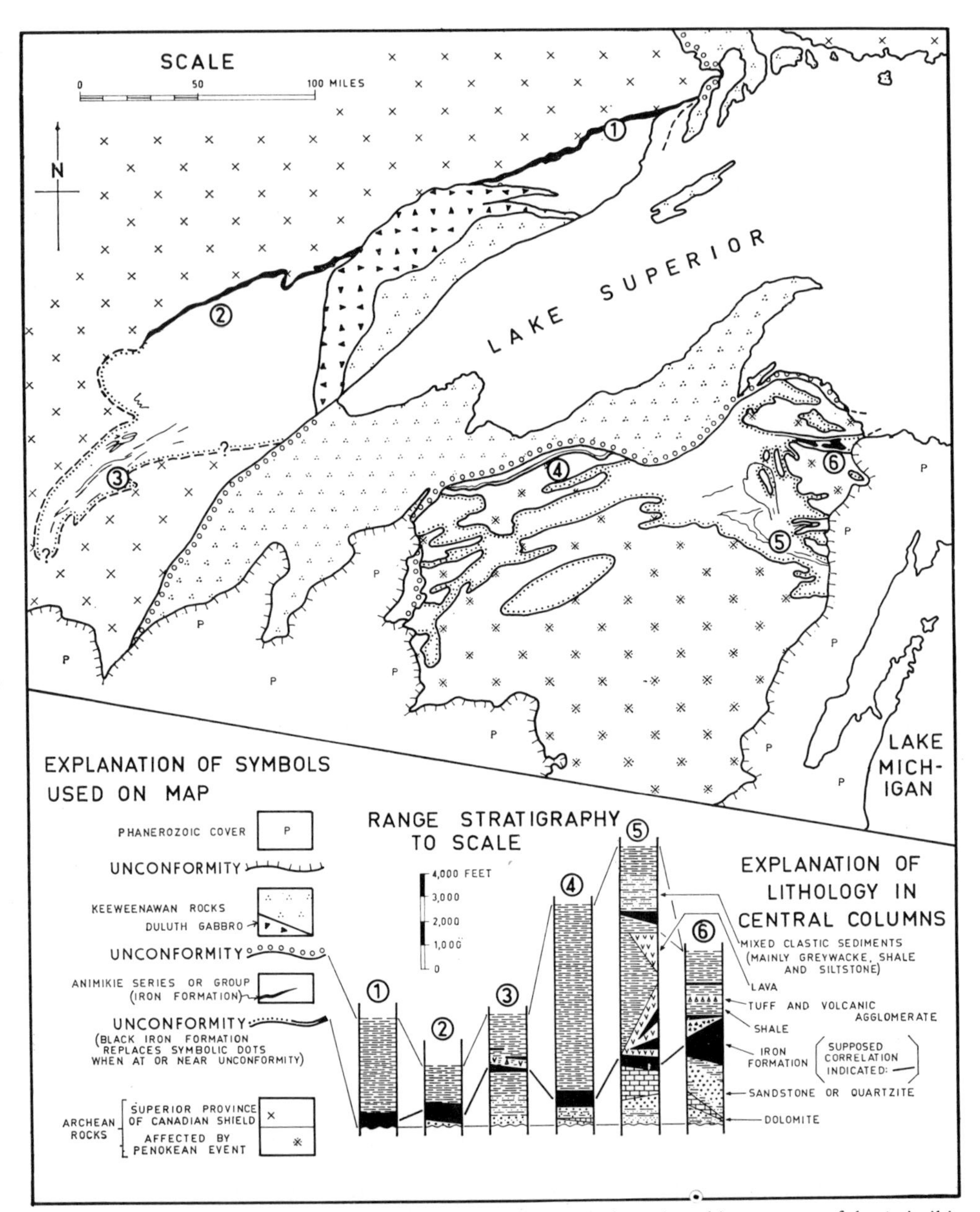

Figure 3. Geological map of the western Lake Superior area and stratigraphic summary of the Animikie series or group. Map based on that of Leith and others (1935), with a hypothetical edge of the Cuyuna synclinorium modified and extended after Schmidt (1963). Numbers refer to iron ranges, with authorities for stratigraphy as follows: 1 = Gunflint Range (Goodwin, 1960; Moorhouse, 1960); 2 = Mesabi Range (White, 1954); 3 = Cuyuna Range (Schmidt, 1963); 4 = Gogebic Range (Aldrich, 1929); 5 = Crystal Falls-Iron Mountain-Felch-Menominee area (James, 1958; James et al., 1961); 6 = Marquette Range (Tyler & Twenhofel, 1952; Boyum, 1964). Note that the vertical scale of the stratigraphic columns is expanded two and a half times compared with that of Figure 2. As far as possible symbols used are equivalent to those of Figures 2 and 4, but it is not implied that the main unconformities are exactly time-equivalent.

margin, at least, was complicated by local troughs and lagoons, some of which may have been isolated from the main basin.

THE TRANSVAAL SYSTEM BASIN

In South Africa, banded iron formations of probably similar age (*see* later discussion) to those of the Hamersley and Lake Superior areas, occur within the Transvaal System. The two main outcrop areas of this, shown in Figure 4 with a stratigraphic summary, are: (1) an ovoid in the Transvaal itself, in which dips are moderate and inward toward the central Bushveld complex, and (2) an area of northern Cape Province, where dips are low and generally westward. These two parts are separated by a mainly sand-covered area of Botswana (formerly Bechuanaland); the stratigraphic succession in each was at first independently described and named (Du Toit, 1945, p. 125–126), but the gradual assumption of various correlations between them has led to a fusion of nomenclature which conceals the fact that there is no unequivocal evidence for either their contemporaneity or their former physical continuity. Although on a different scale, it is a problem of the same type as that of interrelating the Lake Superior ranges.

Cullen (1963) based his preferred correlation on a regional tectonic interpretation of the depositional environment, and supposed that the depositional basin of the Transvaal System embraced both parts of, and spread some distance beyond, its existing outcrop. Earlier, Cullen (1956, p. 460) had emphasized the depositional continuity of both areas and represented this as contrary to Du Toit's beliefs. This was a misinterpretation: Du Toit (1945, p. 126–127) stated specifically that "much of what is now South Africa must during the Transvaal epoch have subsided beneath the ocean," and his description of two "basins" clearly had existing structural, not depositional, significance. Haughton (1963, p. 121) emphasized this belief, held, before and after Cullen's observations, by many South African geologists. Correlations between the two "halves" of the Transvaal System are currently in a state of reappraisal, involving even transfer of some rocks previously thought to belong to younger systems into the upper part of the Transvaal System (P. R. de Villiers, 1966, personal commun.). These problems are not discussed further in this paper.

The Transvaal System was deposited on a fairly even (Haughton, 1963) surface of older Precambrian rocks. In addition to granites, gneisses, metasediments, and metavolcanics of similar age and appearance to those beneath the Hamersley and Animikie Basins, these older rocks included the Witwatersrand and Ventersdorp Systems, sedimentary and volcanic sequences of an age apparently not represented elsewhere. In the Transvaal, the Transvaal System was intruded by the great Bushveld Complex, and is overlain by younger Precambrian sediments (Waterberg and Loskop Systems) which may be correlative with the Matsap System of the Cape Province. Later Karroo sediments and a veneer of Kalahari sand and limestone now obscure parts of the outcrop.

Most of the Transvaal System is not metamorphosed, but thermal effects extend below Bushveld Complex to a variable degree.

CONTRASTS BETWEEN THE THREE BASINS

Major Stratigraphic Sequence

In these basins iron formation does not consistently follow or precede any other sediment type. The succession in the Hamersley Basin starts with thick volcanics, in the Transvaal System with thick carbonates overlying thin mixed clastics, and in the Animikie Basin with a locally variable but mostly thin clastic-carbonate sequence. The overlying rocks are equally variable (Figs. 2 to 4).

Total Iron Formation Thickness

Of the 8000 feet of the Hamersley Group, at least 3000 feet is of iron formation with total Fe above 20 percent. A single formation of the group, the Brockman Iron Formation, has a thickness of more than 2000 feet (MacLeod, 1966).

The main Animikie iron formations of the Lake Superior ranges have thickness of the following orders: 450 to 550 feet (Gunflint Range: Goodwin, 1960, p. 48), 350 to 800 feet (Mesabi Range: White, 1954, p. 22), 0 to 450 feet (Cuyuna Range: Schmidt, 1963, Pl. 6), 650 feet (Gogebic Range: Aldrich, 1929, p. 93), 300 to 500 feet (Felch Mountain district: C. A. Lamey *in* James and others, 1961, p. 131), and 650 feet (Menominee Range: Bayley, 1904, p. 361). The Negaunee Iron Formation of the Marquette Range is more than 2000 feet in the vicinity of Ishpeming (Boyum, 1964); this is by far the thickest development of the whole basin. Iron formations above the Menominee

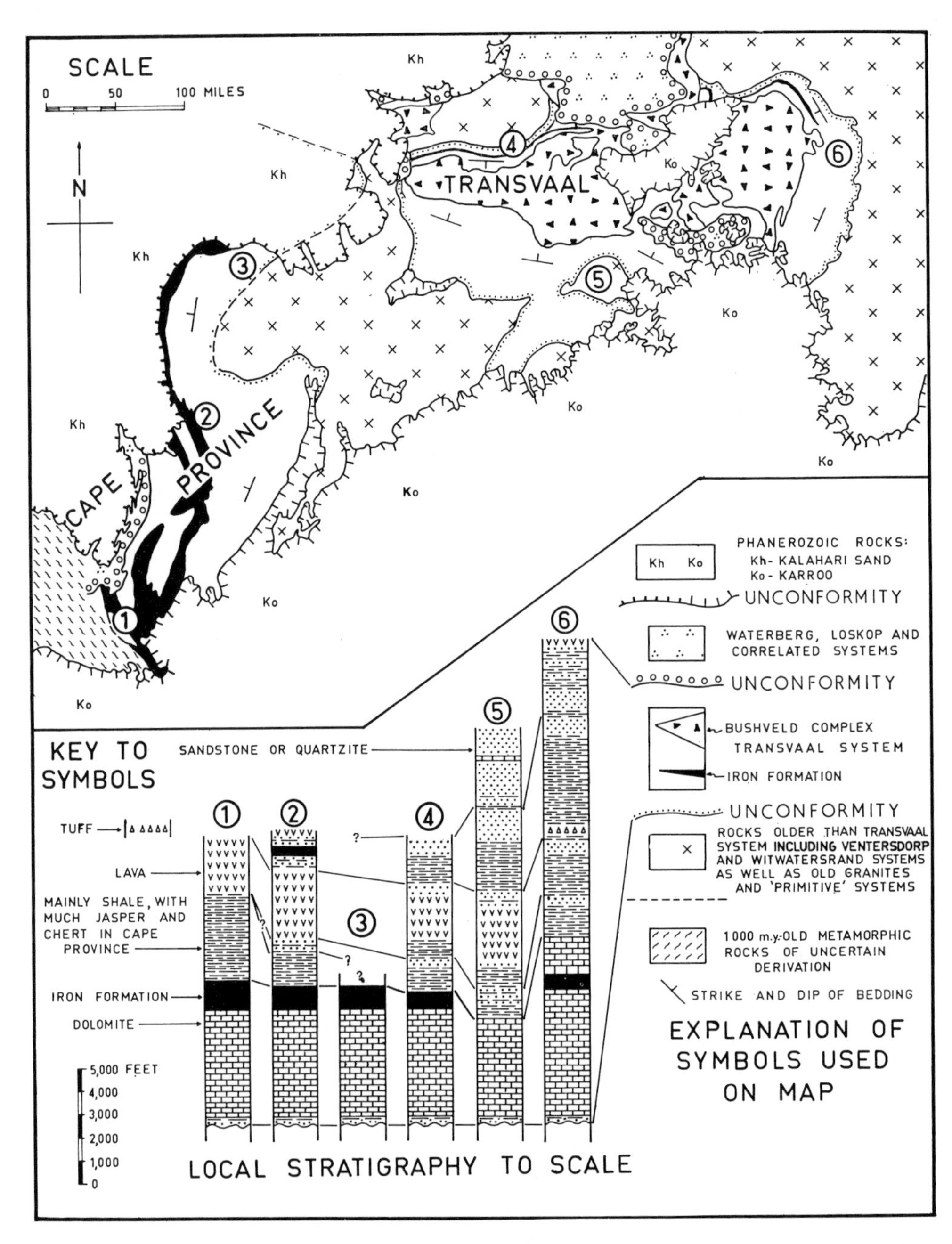

Figure 4. Geological map of part of the Republic of South Africa and stratigraphic summary of the Transvaal System. Map based on that of Du Toit (1954), with modifications after de Villiers (1966), Genis (1961), and Nicolaysen and Burger (1965). Stratigraphic columns compiled from Du Toit (1954), Cilliers and Genis (1961), and de Villiers (1966): 1 = Koegas; 2 = Kuruman; 3 = Pomfret; 4 = Thabazimbi; 5 = Pretoria; 6 = eastern Transvaal. The northern (Botswana) extension of the basal unconformity of the Transvaal System is based on very scattered outcrop. Vertical scale of the columns is the same as that of Figure 3. As far as possible symbols used are equivalent to those of Figures 2 and 3, but it is not implied that the main unconformities are exactly time-equivalent.

Group in the eastern part of the Lake Superior area have thicknesses of 500 feet (Mansfield iron-bearing slate member of the Hemlock Formation: James, 1958, p. 36), 300 feet (Bird iron-bearing member of the Hemlock Formation: James, 1958, p. 36), 1500 feet (Amasa Formation: James, 1958, p. 37) and 600 feet (Riverton Iron Formation: James, 1958, p. 38). However, in most of these there is an unknown admixed thickness of rocks other than iron formation.

In the Cape Province, the thickness of the Lower Griquatown Stage is reported by Cilliers and Genis (1964, p. 549–550) to vary in thickness from less than 1000 feet in the northern end of the outcrop to about 5000 feet at the southern end. However, only about 1500 feet of this consists of iron formation, and this is probably the best maximum thickness estimate. Although the Upper Griquatown Stage is 5000 feet thick (Du Toit, 1954, p. 162) only 500 feet consist of iron formation (P. R. de Villiers, 1967, written commun.). In the Transvaal, the iron formation of the Dolomite Series locally reaches a thickness of 700 to 800 feet (Du Toit, 1954, p. 133).

Thickness Variation

In the Hamersley Group the average thickness change of the Dales Gorge Member of the Brockman Iron Formation (Trendall, 1965b; Trendall and Blockley, 1968; Trendall and Blockley, in press) is about 100 feet over 25 miles; since the total thickness is about 450 feet, this represents a gradient of about 1 foot per 100 feet thickness per lateral mile. The steepest continuous gradient for the Dales Gorge Member over a distance of 25 miles within the basin is about twice this. Although no comparably accurate data are available for the full thickness of the Hamersley Group, scattered estimates suggest that a similar order of variation would be found.

Gradients in the Lake Superior area are more variable. The highest recorded are those of the Trommald Formation of the Cuyuna Range (0 to 450 feet within less than 5 miles laterally: Schmidt, 1963, Pl. 6) and the Negaunee Formation of the Marquette Range (500 to 2000 feet over 100,000 feet laterally: Boyum, 1964, Fig. 7). On the other hand there is a total thickness range of only 450 to 800 feet over the 250 miles strike length of the combined Mesabi-Gunflint Ranges.

In the Cape Province, the Lower Griquatown Stage varies from 1000 feet to 5000 feet from north to south. This represents an average of about 13 feet per mile over 300 miles, a similar order of gradient to that of the Hamersley Basin. The variation of 0 to 800 feet of the Transvaal iron formation takes place across 200 miles (straight-line, not along strike). There is insufficient published information to say what internal variation exists within these distances, but most accounts emphasize the evenness of the stratification.

Stratigraphic Continuity

In the Hamersley Group any chosen part of the 466-foot type section of the Dales Gorge Member of the Brockman Iron Formation (Trendall and Blockley, 1968) is potentially correlatable, at mesoband scale (about 1 inch), over some 20,000 square miles. Within selected correlated chert mesobands, internal correlations of varves have been made on a microscopic scale over 185 miles.

No stratigraphic continuity on anything approaching this scale has been demonstrated in the Animikie iron formation, and it is a reasonable assumption (*see* "Sedimentary Structures," below) that it does not exist. The greatest continuity known is that within the Biwabik Formation of the Mesabi Range. A general idea of continuity here is given by White's (1954) Plate 1 and Gundersen and Schwartz's inserted Plate (1962), from which it can be seen that their I submember, the upper algal horizon, with an average thickness of 5 feet, can be followed over 50 miles.

In the Transvaal System of the Transvaal, internal subdivisions of the iron formation are not well enough known for comparison. Stilpnomelane bands a few inches thick can be identified in boreholes 40 miles apart in the central part of the Cape Province belt (personal observation, by courtesy of Kuruman Cape Blue Asbestos [Pty] Ltd.), and this seems likely to be an index of potential correlatability throughout the 1500 feet of the Lower Griquatown Stage here. Engelbrecht (1962, p. 72) has noted the persistence of markers from less than 1 foot to 3 feet thick over at least 100 and possibly over 250 miles.

Lithology of Iron Formation

Trendall (1965b, p. 62–64) gave a preliminary account (expanded in Trendall and Blockley, in press) of the petrography of fresh core material from the Brockman Iron Formation of the Hamersley Group. Previous accounts (for example, Miles, 1942, p. 11–15) were based on surface material and cannot now be related to recently defined stratigraphy. In essence, the Hamersley Basin iron formations consist of alternating bands (mesobands) between 0.25 and 2 inches thick which are probably continuous over the entire depositional basin. The more silica-rich mesobands with a quartz mosaic of average grain diameter 10 to 30 μ, are called chert, and are sharply divided from the intervening and intergradational magnetite and "quartz-iron oxide (QIO)" mesobands. Mesobands consisting mainly of carbonate, stilpnomelane, and riebeckite form a smaller proportion of the total. The lithology of the Transvaal System iron formations (Cilliers and Genis, 1964; author's observation) is very close to that of the Western Australian rocks, although Trendall's (1965b) chert types are not so clearly differentiable, and the application of this nomenclature to South Africa in its entirety would be inappropriate.

For the Animikie iron formation there are, in addition to the classic descriptions of Van Hise and Leith (1911), more recent lithological accounts of the following iron formations: Gunflint (Moorhouse, 1960, p. 23–36); Biwabik (Mesabi Range: Gruner, 1946; Gundersen and Schwartz, 1962, p. 19–68); Trommald (Cuyuna Range: Schmidt, 1963, p. 19–26); Ironwood (Gogebic Range: Aldrich, 1929, p. 136–143); Riverton (Iron River district: James, 1951, p. 255–259); and Vulcan (of Felch and Calumet areas: James and Pettijohn *in* James and others, 1961, p. 39–46). From these accounts and from personal observation, it is clear that, although banded iron formation closely similar to that of the Hamersley and Cape Province-Transvaal areas does occur (for example, James, 1951, Pl. 1, Fig. 2; Schmidt, 1963, Fig. 2), granule iron formation, with its characteristic wavy bedding (Aldrich, 1929, p. 138) is a lithological type abundant in the Lake Superior ranges, especially in the west, but either absent or extremely rare in the other two areas.

Sedimentary Structures

The stratification of both the Hamersley Basin and the Transvaal System Basin is notably even on a range of scales, and depositional structures such as cross-bedding have not been reported. Trendall (1966b) has described structures defined by discontinuities of thin cherts; these early postdepositional structures represent the greatest degree of bedding irregularity known in the banded iron formations of the Hamersley Group.

Mengel (1965) has recorded the existence of graded bedding and cross-bedding in Lake Superior taconites. The existence of, in particular, coarse cross-bedding in Mesabi Range taconite is known to numerous local geologists, but has apparently not previously been recorded in print: publication of a fully illustrated descriptive study would be of great interest.

Varves

Although Alexandrov (1955), Hough (1958), and Sakamoto (1950) suggested that the banding of banded iron formation was caused by seasonal weathering processes, they did not relate this suggestion to the actual petrography of a particular iron formation. Cullen (1963, p. 390) was the first to suggest specifically that the finest laminae of Transvaal System iron formation were seasonal, the coarser banding within which they occurred being caused by periodic uplift of the adjacent land. Trendall (1965b, p. 64) independently suggested that the finest banding of the Brockman Iron Formation of the Hamersley Group represented seasonal stratification, and applied the term microbanding to it; however, he suggested that the wider bands (mesobands) within which it occurred arose through diagenetic differentiation of originally homogeneous material, a hypothesis which was later developed and related to other features of the rocks (Trendall, 1966b, p. 84–87). Trendall (1966a) drew attention to the close parallelism between his 1965 estimate of the depositional rate, longevity of basin, and basin size for the Brockman Iron Formation and the only other closed basin with varved sediments for which similar data were available—the Eocene Green River Basin (Bradley, 1929).

Microbanding, whatever its origin, is a common and conspicuous feature of chert mesobands in both the Western Australian and South African iron formations. Although it is locally present in Animikie iron formations (for example, the "second order laminae" described by Tyler and Twenhofel, 1952, p. 129; *see* Van Hise and Leith, 1911, Pl. XXXIIB), it is uncommon and rarely conspicuous (personal observation).

Clastic Association

In the Lake Superior area clastic material is interbedded with the Trommald Formation of the Cuyuna Range (Schmidt, 1963, p. 24–26) and the Negaunee Formation of the Marquette Range (Tyler and Twenhofel, 1952, p. 130; Gair, 1967). Mengel (1965) notes scattered clastic quartz grains in Lake Superior taconite.

Such an association has not been reported for the banded iron formations of either Western Australia or South Africa.

Riebeckite

The local abundance of riebeckite in both massive and fibrous (crocidolite) bands in iron formations of the Hamersley Basin was described by Miles (1942). Ryan and Blockley (1965) and Trendall (1965b; 1966b) gave details of the distribution of both types both areally and vertically, and showed that both were products of diagenesis.

The similarly occurring riebeckite in the Lower Griquatown iron formations of the Cape Province was described from various viewpoints by Hall (1918; 1930), Du Toit (1945), and Cilliers and Genis (1964). In the Transvaal System of the Transvaal riebeckite is present but much less abundant (Hall, 1930).

Crocidolite is known from the Labrador Trough (Neal, 1949, p. 31–32), but in the Animikie iron formation of the Lake Superior area, the only published occurrence of riebeckite is that described as a contact metasomatic product by White (1954, p. 64–66). My own examination of this material in a sample kindly supplied by Dr. H. T. Hall, Minnesota Geological Survey, suggests that it is texturally unlike riebeckite of the Hamersley area, and could therefore well have the somewhat different origin suggested by White. Riebeckite occurs in the Negaunee Formation of the Empire Mine, Palmer, Michigan (Marquette Range), with an abundance and distribution in relation to the banding closely similar to that of the Hamersley and Cape Province areas, although metamorphically recrystallized (personal observation, by courtesy of Cleveland-Cliffs Iron Company). Tsu-Ming Han (1953 unpublished report of Cleveland-Cliffs Iron Company) identified and described this riebeckite. The uniqueness of the occurrence emphasizes the general absence of riebeckite from the Animikie iron formation.

RESEMBLANCES BETWEEN THE THREE BASINS

Age

The age of iron formation cannot be directly determined by currently available methods; the iron formations under discussion must therefore be dated either by the age of other conformably associated sediments or lavas, by later igneous or metamorphic events (minimum age), or by unconformably underlying rocks (maximum age).

Only in the Hamersley Group have interstratified lavas been dated. Leggo and others (1965) interpreted an isochron age of about 2100 m.y. from Rb-Sr data for five total-rock samples from the Woongarra Volcanics, a 1500-foot sequence of extrusive acid volcanics near the top of the Hamersley Group. P. A. Arriens has subsequently analyzed 46 further samples collected serially through three of the constituent flows and a preliminary interpretation of the data suggests an age of high accuracy close to 2000 m.y. (1967, personal commun.). Other unpublished Rb-Sr isochron ages (P. A. Arriens, 1967, personal commun.) suggest an age of the order of 2200 m.y. for the lower part of the Fortescue Group, which is entirely consistent with Trendall's (1965b) estimate of 2000 years per compacted foot of Hamersley Group iron formation. The Hamersley Basin is the best dated of the three; ages of rocks above and below are not of direct significance for the age of the iron formation, and were noted above.

Data relevant to the age of Animikie sedimentation have been given by Wasserburg and, others (1956), Goldich and others (1961), Hurley and others (1961), Stockwell (1964), Aldrich and others (1965, summarizing work reported previously by Aldrich and others, 1958, 1959, 1960, 1961), and by Davis and others, 1960), Peterman (1966), and by Kovach and Faure (1967). The final synthesis of all this work is disappointingly reliant on interpretation.

Stockwell's range (1964, p. 5) of 2730 to 2230 m.y. for the Kenoran orogeny of the Superior Province of the Canadian Shield provides a safe maximum age which embraces Goldich and others' estimate (1961, p. xix) of 2600 m.y. for the equivalent Laurentian orogeny, Hurley and others' K-Ar age (1961, p. 491) of 2570 $\pm$ 75 m.y. for biotite in granite unconformably underlying the Gunflint formation, and Aldrich and others' zircon-forming event (1965, p. 459) at 2700 m.y. in pre-Animikie Michigan gneisses.

It is in distinguishing between depositional Animikie ages and subsequent Penokean metamorphic ages that the evidence is less satisfactory. Kovach and Faure (1967) point out that their total-rock Rb-Sr isochron age of 1597 $\pm$ 21 m.y. for the Gunflint and Rove Formation of Ontario is close to the age of 1570 m.y. obtained by Peterman by the application of the same method to the Rove,

Virginia, and Thomson argillites of Minnesota, and also to the K-Ar age of about 1600 m.y. obtained by Hurley and others (1961) from Gunflint argillites. They follow Peterman in interpreting this figure as a minimum age reflecting loss of radiogenic strontium during regional metamorphism related to the Penokean orogeny, although Hurley and others (1961, p. 491) believed, from the mineralogy, that their argillites from the same area had suffered virtually no metamorphism. Goldich and others (1961) placed the Penokean orogeny in the range 1800 to 1650 m.y. from the ages of granites and gneisses in southwest Minnesota, and regarded ages of 1700 to 1600 m.y. from Animikie sediments as Penokean. Aldrich and others (1965), from Michigan evidence, put the Penokean orogeny in the interval 1900 to 1700 m.y., and took the older figure as a minimum depositional age for Animikie sediments.

It may have been too readily assumed in discussion of this problem that Animikie sedimentation and Penokean metamorphism were separate and successive happenings, rather than penecontemporaneous and closely related phases of a single event. Taking the "average rate" of sedimentation from the top of the Cambrian to the top of the Cretaceous as about 700 feet per million years (Hudson, 1964, Fig. 1), the deposition of the comparatively thin (*compare* Figs. 2 and 3) Animikie rocks may reasonably have occupied only 15 m.y.; Trendall's estimated (1965b) depositional rate for iron formation of 500 feet per million years is of the same order. There may, therefore, be no need to suppose that the Canadian Gunflint rocks were up-dated by a Penokean orogeny with such slight apparent effect, and the figure of 1600 m.y. may well be close to a true depositional age, making the Animikie Basin a surface buckle toward the latter part of a sequence of deep events which were in continuous progress during a 200 m.y. period. Gair's suggestion (1967) that important faulting took place during Animikie sedimentation in the Marquette area is entirely consistent with such a concept.

In South Africa, as in the Lake Superior area, there is no direct evidence for the age of strata conformable with the iron formations. A minimum age for the Transvaal System is given by the age of the Bushveld Complex (1920 ± 130 m.y.: Schreiner, 1958; 1950 ± 150: Nicolaysen and others, 1958). Nicolaysen (1962, p. 578–579) discussed the age of the conformably underlying Witwatersrand System and gave as a preferred interpretation of the equivocal data that Witwatersrand or Ventersdorp deposition took place at approximately 2100 m.y. ago. Van Niekerk and Burger's later determination (1964) of an age of 2300 ± 100 m.y. for zircon microphenocrysts from Ventersdorp lava makes a depositional age of the Transvaal System in the approximate range 2200 to 2000 m.y. likely.

This Transvaal System range includes the known 2000 m.y. age of part of the Hamersley Group, but the Animikie rocks could be much younger. In view of the relatively rapid deposition of the Hamersley Group, if microbands are varves, it is not known whether iron formation deposition overlapped in time between the two southern hemisphere basins. All three seem to be covered by about the same 600 m.y. of Precambrian time, but more work is needed before a closer limit can be set.

Basin Size

As defined above, the Hamersley Basin was ovoid, with a long axis of about 300 miles and a short axis probably about 150 miles, giving an area of about 50,000 square miles. The Animikie Basin could well have had identical dimensions, if its long axis is assumed to have been parallel to, and over the present western part of, Lake Superior (Fig. 3).

The difficulty of interpreting Transvaal System paleogeography has already been discussed. Isopach maps for all divisions of the system are a prerequisite for solving the problem. Should the two outcrop areas represent separate depositional basins then each would be very closely similar in shape and size to the Hamersley and Animikie Basins.

Chemistry and Mineralogy

The best estimate of the bulk composition of iron formation from any of the three basins is that of the Biwabik Formation of the Mesabi Range by Lepp (1966, p. 248). This is shown in Table 1 together with a previously unpublished analysis of part of the Dales Gorge Member from Western Australia and an analysis of banded magnetite-chert from the Lower Griquatown Stage given by Genis (1961, Table 8, G7M). The close resemblance is remarkable in view of the differences between the lithology of the Biwabik iron formation and those of Western Australia and South Africa. Trendall (1965a) drew attention to the danger in placing chemical limits on the definition of a rock and then pointing out its chemical identity, but the general similarity in constituents other than iron (for example, Al_2O_3,

TABLE 1. CHEMICAL COMPOSITIONS OF THE BIWABIK FORMATION AND OF SAMPLES OF IRON FORMATION FROM WESTERN AUSTRALIA AND SOUTH AFRICA

	1	2	3
SiO_2	46.12	55.1	46.86
Al_2O_3	0.86	0.10	0.43
Fe_2O_3	19.47	13.3	24.68
FeO	19.26	13.79	17.19
MnO	0.66	0.18	—
MgO	2.88	2.50	2.58
CaO	1.79	3.1	1.49
Na_2O	0.05	0.33	0.16
K_2O	0.14	0.25	0.10
Ignition	1.68	0.21	0.57
P_2O_5	0.07	.01	0.25
TiO_2	0.04	0.12	0.05
CO_2	6.79	7.80	5.81
C	0.20	—	—
TOTAL	100.01	96.79	100.17
TOTAL Fe	28.59	20.02	30.60

1. Biwabik Formation, average composition (Lepp, 1966, p. 248)
2. Drill core from Lower Griquatown banded magnetite-chert at Heuningvlei, Cape Province, South Africa (Genis, 1961, Table 8, G7M). Analyst, J. H. Genis
3. Drill core from Dales Gorge Member banded iron formation at Wittenoom, Western Australia. DDH 28, 587′5″ to 589′11″. Analyst, J. R. Gamble, Western Australian Government Chemical Laboratories

MgO, CaO) is quite beyond the requirements of definition in the analyses of Table 1.

As may be expected from the close chemical resemblance between all three basins, the mineral compositions of each are closely similar in spite of other contrasts of the basins. Quartz, magnetite, carbonates, hematite, and stilpnomelane, in that order of abundance, are the dominant minerals of the unmetamorphosed and unoxidized iron formation.

Evolution of Basins

The three basins have the following common characters associated with the broad crustal evolution of their areas: (1) each basin was initiated on a fairly smooth erosion surface cut across "Archean" (3000 to 2500 m.y.) granites and metamorphic rocks (in South Africa the Witwatersrand and Ventersdorp Systems were also eroded); (2) some time after the completion of deposition, part of the basin was folded or metamorphosed, while the remainder still rests in virtually its original position; and (3) a younger sequence of Precambrian sedimentary rocks partially overlies each basin (Bresnahan-Bangemall in the Hamersley Basin; Keeweenawan in North America; Matsap-Loskop-Waterberg in South Africa).

Precedence of Chert

In the Hamersley Group, beds of chert are common in the Mt. McRae Shale, immediately beneath the Brockman Iron Formation, as well as in the Jeerinah Formation, immediately underlying the basal Marra Mamba Iron Formation (MacLeod, 1966). In the Transvaal System chert is frequently abundant in the lower dolomite, and in the Cape Province is increasingly abundant in the higher part of the dolomite (Du Toit, 1954, p. 133). In the Kona Dolomite of the Marquette range Gair and others (1961, p. 79) described chert layers which they believed to be primary. Thus, of the two main iron formation constituents (silica and iron oxide), there is an indication from all three basins of the local deposition of silica before the onset of iron formation deposition.

Volcanic Association

The Hamersley Group iron formations are underlain by the volcanic Fortescue Group and are interbedded with the 1500-foot-thick acid lavas of the Woongarra Volcanics (MacLeod and others, 1963). LaBerge (1966a) noted the existence of shards within the Brockman Iron Formation. In the Animikie Basin, the volcanic association of the Gunflint Iron Formation is plain (Goodwin, 1956; 1960). Volcanic rocks are interstratified with the Ironwood Iron Formation in the eastern part of the Gogebic Range, and were suggested by Irving and Van Hise (1892, p. 377–381) and by Allen and Barrett (1915, p. 47–48) to be partly extrusive.

On all the ranges, volcanic rocks appear somewhere in the succession. In the Cape Province of South Africa, the Lower Griquatown iron formations are overlain by the 3600-foot-thick Ongeluk Volcanics (Du Toit, 1954, p. 161). LaBerge (1966b) recorded volcanic material from these iron formations closely similar to that of the Brockman Iron Formation.

This volcanic association is highly variable, and it is doubtful whether Precambrian basins lacking iron formation differ in this respect. Vulcanicity is a common event in basin development, and it is unreasonable to argue that rocks associated with volcanics must themselves be volcanic in origin.

Stratigraphic Status of Iron Formation

With the possible exception of the Iron River area of the Lake Superior area, the iron formation in all these basins has the following common characteristics.

(1) *It is concentrated.* That is, iron formation is restricted to one section of the stratigraphic column, rather than being evenly scattered throughout in small thicknesses.

(2) *It is medial.* The concentration of iron formation is normally central in the stratigraphic column; part of the Gunflint Range is exceptional here, in that the iron formation rests directly on the older Precambrian.

(3) *It is transitional.* The medial iron formation in all three basins marks a change in type of sedimentation (*compare*, Figs. 2, 3, and 4).

DISCUSSION

Although some of the contrasted characters of the basins genuinely differ between all three, many differ only between the Animikie iron formations and those of the two other basins taken together: for example, lateral thickness variation, sedimentary structures, lithology of iron formation, conspicuousness of varves, clastic association, and the abundance of riebeckite. The question arises whether there existed, in this span of the Precambrian, two distinct types of iron formation basin: an Animikie, or northern, type, and a Hamersley-Transvaal, or southern, type. Such a distinction is certainly valid among these three basins, and is clearly related to some basic properties of stability and paleogeography; but the sample size of three is too small for definite conclusions, and an assumption that the two-fold distinction is of general applicability would be premature. However, it does seem from this comparison that Gross's distinction (1965, p. 90–92) between Algoma Type and Superior Type iron formations needs modification; the granules and oölites described by Gross as typical of Superior Type iron formations are absent from both the Hamersley and Transvaal System Basins, although both these extend for hundreds of miles (Superior Type) rather than for just a few miles (Algoma Type).

The characters chosen for comparison on this survey do not include all important features. Two estimates of the paleolatitude of the Animikie Group, using different criteria, were recently published independently (Nordeng, 1963; Symons, 1966), and a current paleomagnetic study of the Brockman Iron Formation (H. Porath, Australian National University) should ultimately allow a comparison, but there is a wide divergence in the two Animikie estimates, and a useful comparison is not yet possible here. More information is badly needed also on bulk composition and volume, not only of the iron formations, but of the total infilling material of the basins. I argued (Trendall, 1965a) that the Fe/Al proportions in the Brockman Iron Formation, and the total quantity of iron, together preclude a weathering hypothesis for its origin. This argument still stands, but there is greater uncertainty in much of the data needed for equivalent estimates in the other basins.

The main purpose of this paper is to marshal and juxtapose the available data for three Precambrian iron formation basins so that gaps in evidence required for a solution of their various associated problems may be shown up. The emphasis is therefore on facts, but there rests a final responsibility to suggest an interpretation of the facts reviewed. As a hypothesis I accept the "from-below" theory because there is better evidence for it in the Hamersley Basin than there is for either theory in any other basin. This assumed, it seems that in all these basins, the early depression took place with little compensating elevation of the surrounding areas, leading to the accumulation of non-clastic material (carbonates or volcanics). The submarine expulsion of vast quantities of iron and silica took place in the middle stage of development. Atmospheric and basinal chemistry was such that this material was distributed and precipitated (?biochemically) evenly, rather than deposited close to its entry point. Subsequent basin development was more normal, with erosion of the rising basin edges to fill the centre.

REFERENCES CITED

Aldrich, H. R., 1929, The Geology of the Gogebic Iron Range of Wisconsin: Wisconsin Geol. and Nat. History Survey Bull. 71, 279 p.

Aldrich, L. T., Wetherill, G. W., Tilton, G. R., and Davis, G. L., 1958, Age Patterns in Zones of Regional Metamorphism: Carnegie Inst. Washington Year Book 57, p. 115–117.

Aldrich, L. T., Wetherill, G. W., Bass, M. N., Compston, W., Davis, G. L., and Tilton, G. R., 1959, Mineral Age Measurements (Michigan): Carnegie Inst. Washington Year Book 58, p. 242–245.

Aldrich, L. T., Wetherill, G. W., Bass, M. N., Tilton, G. R., and Davis, G. L., 1960, Mineral Age Measurements and Earth History (Northern Michigan): Carnegie Inst. Washington Year Book 59, p. 209–212.

Aldrich, L. T., Hart, S. R., Wetherill, G. W., Davis, G. L., Tilton, G. R., and Doe, B., 1961, Radioactive Ages of Rocks (North Michigan summary): Carnegie Inst. Washington Year Book 60, p. 251–253.

Aldrich, L. T., Davis, G. L., and James, H. L., 1965, Ages of Minerals from Metamorphic and Igneous Rocks near Iron Mountain, Michigan: Jour. Petrology, v. 6, p. 445–472.

Alexandrov, E. A., 1955, Contribution to studies of origin of Precambrian banded iron ores: Econ. Geology, v. 50, p. 459–468.

Allen, R. C., and Barrett, L. P., 1915, Contributions to the Precambrian Geology of Northern Michigan and Wisconsin: Michigan Geol. Survey Biol. Pub. 18, p. 13–64.

Bayley, W. S., 1904, The Menominee iron-bearing district of Michigan: U.S. Geol. Survey Monogr. 46, 513 p.

Bergeron, R., Berard, J., and Gelinas, L., 1962, Tectonics of regions bordering the Ungava stable area: Royal Soc. Canada Spec. Pub. 4, p. 144–148.

Borchert, H., 1960, Genesis of marine sedimentary iron ore: Inst. Mining and Metallurgy Trans. 640, v. 79, p. 261–279.

Boyum, B. H., 1964, The Marquette Mineral District, Michigan: Conference on Lake Superior Geology: National Science Foundation Summer Conference sponsored by Michigan Technological University. Published by the Cleveland-Cliffs Iron Company, Ishpeming, Michigan, 21 p.

Bradley, W. H., 1929, The varves and climate of the Green River epoch: U.S. Geol. Survey Prof. Paper 158-E, 110 p.

Cilliers, J. J. LeR., and Genis, J. H., 1964, Crocidolite Asbestos in the Cape Province: *in* The Geology of some Ore Deposits of Southern Africa, vol. II; published by the Geol. Soc. South Africa, p. 543–570.

Cullen, D. J., 1956, Pretoria Series formations near Kanye in the Bechuanaland Protectorate: Geol. Mag., v. 93, p. 456–464.

—— 1963, Tectonic implications of banded ironstone formations: Jour. Sed. Petrology, v. 33, p. 387–392.

Daniels, J. L., 1965, Proterozoic granites of the Ashburton region, North-West Division: Western Australia Geol. Survey Annual Rept. for 1964, p. 31–34.

—— 1967, Turee Creek, Western Australia: Western Australia Geol. Survey, Record No. 1967/7 (unpublished open file report). Also in press in published Explanatory Notes series.

Davis, G. L., Tilton, G. R., Aldrich, L. T., Wetherill, G. W., and Bass, M. N., 1960, The Ages of Rocks and Minerals (The Ages of Minerals from Metamorphic Zones in Northern Michigan): Carnegie Inst. Washington Year Book 59, p. 152–154.

de la Hunty, L. E., 1964, Balfour Downs, Western Australia: Western Australia Geol. Survey, Explanatory Notes, 23 p.

—— 1965, Mount Bruce, Western Australia: Western Australia Geol. Survey, Explanatory Notes, 28 p.

Du Toit, A. L., 1945, The origin of the amphibole asbestos deposits of South Africa: Geol. Soc. South Africa Trans., v. 48, p. 161–206.

—— 1954, Geology of South Africa (3rd Ed.): Edinburgh and London, Oliver and Boyd, 611 p.

Engelbrecht, L. N. J., 1962, Markers in the Lower Griquatown Stage near Kuruman, Cape Province: South Africa Geol. Survey Annals, v. 1, p. 71–80.

Gair, J. E., 1967, Influence of faulting on deposition of clastic interbeds in Negaunee Iron-Formation near Palmer, Michigan (Abstract): Program, 13th Annual Conference, Institute of Lake Superior Geology, Michigan State University, May 1–2, 1967.

Gair, J. E., Thaden, R. E., and Jones, B. F., 1961, Silicification of the Kona Dolomite in the Eastern Part of the Marquette Iron Range, Michigan: U.S. Geol. Survey Prof. Paper 424-C, p. 78–80.

Genis, J. H., 1961, The genesis of the blue amphibole asbestos of the Union of South Africa: Ph.D. dissert., University of Cape Town, Union of South Africa, 146 p.

Goldich, S. S., Nier, A. O., Baadsgaard, H., Hoffman, J. H., and Krueger, H. W., 1961, The Precambrian Geology and Geochronology of Minnesota: Minnesota Geol. Survey Bull. 41, 193 p.

Goodwin, A. M., 1956, Facies relations in the Gunflint iron formation: Econ. Geology, v. 51, p. 565–595.

—— 1960, Gunflint Iron Formation of the Whitefish Lake Area, District of Thunder Bay: Ontario Dept. of Mines Annual Rept., v. 69, p. 41–63.

—— 1961, Genetic aspects of Michipicoten Iron-Formations: Canadian Mining Inst. Trans., v. 64, p. 32–36.

—— 1962, Structure, stratigraphy, and origin of iron-formations, Michipicoten area, Algoma district, Ontario: Geol. Soc. America Bull., v. 73, p. 561–586.

Govett, G. J. S., 1966, Origin of Banded Iron Formations: Geol. Soc. America Bull., v. 77, p. 1191–1212.

Gross, G. A., 1965, Geology of Iron Deposits in Canada. Volume 1: General Geology and Evaluation of Deposits: Canada Geol. Survey Econ. Geology Report No. 22, 181 p.

Gruner, J. W., 1922, Organic matter and the origin of the Biwabik iron-bearing formation of the Mesabi Range: Econ. Geology, v. 17, p. 407–460.

—— 1946, The mineralogy and geology of the taconites and iron ores of the Mesabi range, Minnesota: St. Paul, Minnesota, Iron Range Resources and Rehabilitation Comm. and Minnesota Geol. Survey, 127 p.

Guild, P. W., 1953, Iron deposits of the Congonhas District, Minas Gerais, Brazil: Econ. Geology, v. 48, p. 639–676.

—— 1957, Geology and mineral resources of the Congonhas district, Minas Gerais, Brazil: U.S. Geol. Survey Prof. Paper 290, 90 p.

Gundersen, J. N., and Schwartz, G. M., 1962, The Geology of the Metamorphosed Biwabik Iron-Formation, Eastern Mesabi District, Minnesota: Minnesota Geol. Survey Bull. 43, 139 p.

Hall, A. L., 1918, Asbestos in the Union of South Africa: Union of South Africa Geol. Survey Mem. 12, 152 p.

—— 1930, Asbestos in the Union of South Africa (2nd ed.): Union of South Africa Geol. Survey Mem. 12, 324 p.

Halligan, R., and Daniels, J. L., 1964, Precambrian geology of the Ashburton valley region, North-West Division: Western Australia Geol. Survey Annual Rept. for 1963, p. 38–46.

Harder, H., 1963, Zur Diskussion über die Entstehung der Quarzbandererze (Itabirite): Neues Jahrb. Geologie u. Paläontologie Monatsh. 12, p. 303–314.

Haughton, S. H., 1963, The stratigraphic history of Africa south of the Sahara: London and Edinburgh, Oliver and Boyd, 365 p.

Horwitz, R. C. (compiler), 1966, Geological map of Western Australia: Western Australia Geol. Survey.

Hough, J. L., 1958, Fresh-water environment of deposition of Precambrian banded iron-formations: Jour. Sed. Petrology, v. 28, p. 414–430.

Huber, N. K., 1959, Some aspects of the origin of the Ironwood iron-formation of Michigan and Wisconsin: Econ. Geology, v. 54, p. 82–118.

Hudson, J. D., 1964, Sedimentation rates in relation to the Phanerozoic time-scale, p. 37–42: Geol. Soc. London Quart. Jour., v. 120S, 458 p.

Hurley, P. M., Fairbairn, H. W., Pinson, W. H., and Hower, J., 1961, Unmetamorphosed minerals in the Gunflint Formation used to test the age of the Animikie: Jour. Geology, v. 70, p. 489–492.

Irving, R. D., and Van Hise, C. R., 1892, The Penokee iron-bearing series of Michigan and Wisconsin: U.S. Geol. Survey Monogr. 19, 534 p.

James, H. L., 1951, Iron formation and associated rocks in the Iron River district, Michigan: Geol. Soc. America Bull., v. 62, p. 251–266.

—— 1954, Sedimentary facies of iron-formation: Econ. Geology, v. 49, p. 235–291.

—— 1955, Zones of regional metamorphism in the Precambrian of northern Michigan: Geol. Soc. America Bull., v. 66, p. 1455–1488.

—— 1958, Stratigraphy of Pre-Keeweenawan Rocks in Parts of Northern Michigan: U.S. Geol. Survey Prof. Paper 314-C, 44 p.

—— 1966, Data of Geochemistry, 6th Edition. Chapter W. Chemistry of the Iron-rich Sedimentary Rocks: U.S. Geol. Survey Prof. Paper 440-W, 61 p.

James, H. L., Clark, L. D., Lamey, C. A., and Pettijohn, F. J., 1961, Geology of central Dickinson County, Michigan: U.S. Geol. Survey Prof. Paper 310, 176 p.

Kovach, J. and Faure, G., 1967, Whole-Rock Rb-Sr Age of the Gunflint Formation, Ontario, Canada (Abstract): Program, 1st Annual Meeting, North-Central Section, Geol. Soc. America, Indiana University, Bloomington, April 19–22, 1967, p. 16.

Kriewaldt, M., 1964, The Fortescue Group of the Roebourne region, North-West Division: Western Australia Geol. Survey Annual Rept. for 1963, p. 30–34.

Kriewaldt, M., and Ryan, G. R., 1965, Pyramid, Western Australia: Western Australia Geol. Survey Record No. 1965–13 (unpublished open file report). Also in press in published Explanatory Notes series.

LaBerge, G. L., 1966a, Altered pyroclastic rocks in iron-formation in the Hamersley Range, Western Australia: Econ. Geology, v. 61, p. 147–161.

—— 1966b, Altered pyroclastic rocks in South African iron-formation: Econ. Geology, v. 61, p. 572–581.

Leggo, P. J., Compston, W., and Trendall, A. F., 1965, Radiometric ages of some Precambrian rocks from the North-West Division of Western Australia: Adelaide Geol. Soc. Australia Jour., v. 12, p. 53–66.

Leith, C. K., Lund, R. J., and Leith, A., 1935, Precambrian rocks of the Lake Superior Region: U.S. Geol. Survey Prof. Paper 184, 34 p.

Lepp, H., 1966, Chemical composition of the Biwabik iron formation, Minnesota: Econ. Geology, v. 61, p. 243–250.

Lepp, H. and Goldich, S. S., 1964, Origin of the Precambrian iron formations: Econ. Geology, v. 59, p. 1025–1060.

MacLeod, W. N., 1966, The geology and iron deposits of the Hamersley Range area, Western Australia: Western Australia Geol. Survey Bull. 117, 170 p.

MacLeod, W. N., and de la Hunty, L. E., 1966, Roy Hill, Western Australia: Western Australia Geol. Survey, Explanatory Notes, 27 p.

MacLeod, W. N., de la Hunty, L. E., Jones, W. R., and Halligan, R., 1963, A preliminary report on the Hamersley Iron Province, North-West Division: Western Australia Geol. Survey Annual Rept. for 1962, p. 44–54.

Mengel, J. T. Jr., 1965, Precambrian Taconite Iron Formation: A special Type of Sandstone: Geol. Soc. America, Program for 1965 Annual Meetings. Nov. 4–6, 1965. Kansas City, Missouri, Abstracts, p. 106.

Miles, K. R., 1942, The blue asbestos bearing banded iron formation of the Hamersley Range, Western Australia: Western Australia Geol. Survey Bull. 100, 37 p.

Moorhouse, W. W., 1960, Gunflint Iron Range in the Vicinity of Port Arthur: Ontario Dept. Mines Annual Rept., v. 69, p. 1–40.

Neal, H. E., 1949, The geology of the Hook Lake area, New Quebec, with special reference to the iron formation: M.A. thesis, University of Toronto, Canada.

Nicolaysen, L. O., 1962, Stratigraphic Interpretation of Age Measurements in Southern Africa: Geol. Soc. America, Buddington volume, p. 569–598.

Nicolaysen, L. O., and Burger, A. J., 1965, Note on an extensive zone of 1000 million-year old metamorphic and igneous rocks in Southern Africa: Nancy, Sciences de la Terre, v. 10, p. 497–516.

Nicolaysen, L. O., de Villiers, J. W. L., Burger, A. J., and Strelow, F. W. E., 1958, New measurements relating to the absolute age of the Transvaal System and of the Bushveld Igneous Complex: Geol. Soc. South Africa Trans., v. 48, p. 161–206.

Nordeng, S. C., 1963, Precambrian stromatolites as indicators of polar shift: Society of Economic Paleontologists and Mineralogists, Special Publication No. 10, p. 131–139. Soc. Econ. Paleontologists and Mineralogists Spec. Pub., Tulsa, Oklahoma, 10: p. 131–139.

Oftedahl, C., 1958, A theory of exhalative-sedimentary ores: Geol. Fören. Stockholm Förh., v. 8, p. 1–19.

Peterman, Z. E., 1966, Rb-Sr Dating of Middle Precambrian Metasedimentary Rocks of Minnesota: Geol. Soc. America Bull., v. 77, p. 1031–1044.

Ryan, G. R., 1964, A reappraisal of the Archaean of the Pilbara Block: Western Australia Geol. Survey Annual Rept. for 1963, p. 25–28.

Ryan, G. R., and Blockley, J. G., 1965, Progress report on the Hamersley blue asbestos survey: Western Australia Geol. Survey Record No. 1965/32, (unpublished open file report).

Sakamoto, T., 1950, The origin of the Precambrian banded iron ores: Am. Jour. Sci., v. 248, p. 449–474.

Schmidt, R. G., 1963, Geology and ore deposits of the Cuyuna North Range, Minnesota: U.S. Geol. Survey Prof. Paper 407, 96 p.

Schreiner, G. D. L., 1958, Comparison of the ^{87}Rb-^{87}Sr ages of the red granite of the Bushveld complex from measurements on the total rock and separated mineral fractions: Royal Soc. [London] Proc., ser. A, v. 245, p. 112–117.

Stockwell, C. H., 1964, Fourth report on structural provinces, orogenies, and time-classifications of the Canadian Precambrian Shield; *in* Age determinations and geological studies: Geol. Survey Canada Paper 64–17, pt. II, p. 1–21.

Symons, D. T. A., 1966, A paleomagnetic study on the Gunflint, Mesabi, and Cuyana iron ranges in the Lake Superior region: Econ. Geology, v. 61, p. 1336–1361.

Tanton, T. L., 1950, Origin of iron range rocks: Royal Soc. Canada Trans., v. 44, ser. 3.

Trendall, A. F., 1965a, Origin of Precambrian iron formations (Discussion): Econ. Geology, v. 60, p. 1065–1070.

—— 1965b, Progress report on the Brockman Iron Formation in the Wittenoom-Yampire area: Western Australia Geol. Survey Annual Rept. for 1964, p. 55–65.

—— 1966a, Second progress report on the Brockman Iron Formation in the Wittenoom-Yampire area: Western Australia Geol. Survey Record No. 1966/1 (unpublished open file report).

—— 1966b, Second progress report on the Brockman Iron Formation in the Wittenoom-Yampire area: Western Australia Geol. Survey Annual Rept. for 1965, p. 75–87.

Trendall, A. F., and Blockley, J. G., 1968, Stratigraphy of the Dales Gorge Member of the Brockman Iron Formation in the Precambrian Hamersley Group of Western Australia: Western Australia Geol. Survey Annual Rept. for 1967, p. 48–53.

—— in press 1968, Iron formations of the Precambrian Hamersley Group of Western Australia, with special reference to crocidolite: Western Australia Geol. Survey Bull. 119.

Tyler, S. A., and Twenhofel, W. H., 1952, Sedimentation and stratigraphy of the Huronian of Upper Michigan: Am. Jour. Sci., v. 250, p. 1–27 and 118–151.

Van Hise, C. R., and Bayley, W. S., 1897, The Marquette iron-bearing district of Michigan: U.S. Geol. Survey Monogr. 28, 608 p.

Van Hise, C. R., and Leith, C. K., 1911, The geology of the Lake Superior region: U.S. Geol. Survey Monogr. 52, 641 p.

van Niekerk, C. B., and Burger, A. J., 1964, The Age of the Ventersdorp System: Union of South Africa Geol. Survey Annals, v. 3, p. 75–86.

van Schmus, R., 1965, The geochronology of the Blind River-Bruce Mines area, Ontario, Canada: Jour. Geology, v. 73, p. 755–780.

Wasserburg, G. J., Hayden, R. J., and Jensen, K. J., 1956, A^{40}-K^{40} dating of igneous rocks and sediments: Geochim. et Cosmochim. Acta, v. 27, p. 525–546.

White, D. A., 1954, The stratigraphy and structure of the Mesabi range, Minnesota: Minnesota Geol. Survey Bull. 38, 92 p.

Williams, I. R., 1965, Yarraloola, Western Australia: Western Australia Geol. Survey, Record No. 1965/29 (unpublished open file report). Also in press in published Explanatory Notes series.

20

Reprinted from *Econ. Geol.,* **49**(3), 236–240, 246–249, 272–275, 281–284 (1954)

Sedimentary Facies of Iron-Formation

HAROLD L. JAMES

ABSTRACT

The sedimentary iron-formations of Precambrian age in the Lake Superior region can be divided on the basis of the dominant original iron mineral into four principal facies: sulfide, carbonate, oxide, and silicate. As chemical sediments, these rocks reflect certain aspects of the chemistry of the depositional environments. The major control, at least for the sulfide, carbonate, and oxide types, probably was the oxidation potential. The evidence indicates that deposition took place in restricted basins, which were separated from the open sea by thresholds that inhibited free circulation and permitted development of abnormalities in oxidation potential and water composition.

The sporadic distribution of metamorphism and of later oxidation permits description of the primary facies on the basis of unoxidized, essentially unmetamorphosed material. The *sulfide facies* is represented by black slates in which pyrite may make up as much as 40 percent of the rock. The free-carbon content of these rocks typically ranges from 5 to 15 percent, indicating that ultra-stagnant conditions prevailed during deposition. Locally, the pyritic rocks contain layers of iron-rich carbonate. The *carbonate facies* consists, in its purer form, of interbedded iron-rich carbonate and chert. It is a product of an environment in which oxygen concentration was sufficiently high to destroy most of the organic material but not high enough to permit formation of ferric compounds. The *oxide facies* is found as two principal types, one characterized by magnetite and the other by hematite. Both minerals appear to be of primary origin. The magnetite-banded rock is one of the dominant lithologies in the region; it consists typically of magnetite interlayered with chert, carbonate, or iron silicate, or combinations of the three. Its mineralogy and association suggest origin under weakly oxidizing to moderately reducing conditions, but the mode of precipitation of magnetite is not clearly understood. The hematite-banded rocks consist of finely crystalline hematite interlayered with chert or jasper. Oolitic structure is common. This facies doubtless accumulated in a strongly oxidizing, probably near-shore, environment similar to that in which younger hematitic ironstones such as the Clinton oolite were deposited. The *silicate facies* contains one or more of the hydrous ferrous silicates (greenalite, minnesotaite, stilpnomelane, chlorite) as a major constituent. Granule

Editor's Note: A row of asterisks indicates that material has been omitted from the original article.

structure, similar to that of glauconite, is typical of some varieties; others are nongranular and finely laminated. The most common association of the silicate rocks is with either carbonate- or magnetite-bearing rocks, which suggests that the optimum conditions for deposition ranged from slightly oxidizing to slightly reducing.

The relationship between the iron-rich rocks and volcanism, stressed by many authors, is considered by the writer to be structural, not chemical: in the Lake Superior region both iron-deposition and volcanism are believed to be related to geosynclinal development during Huronian time. In Michigan, the lower Huronian rocks are iron-poor quartzite and dolomite—typical "stable-shelf" deposits; much of the upper Huronian consists of iron-poor graywacke and slate with associated volcanic rocks —a typical "geosynclinal" assemblage. Thus the iron-rich beds of the middle Huronian and lower part of the upper Huronian were deposited during a transitional stage in structural history. The major environmental requirement for deposition of iron-formation is the closed or restricted basin; this requirement coincides in time with what would be a normal stage in evolution of the geosyncline: namely, structural development of offshore buckles or swells that subsequently develop into island arcs characterized by volcanism.

INTRODUCTION

The term "iron-bearing formation"—or more commonly "iron-formation"—is applied in the Lake Superior region to a wide variety of rocks in which the only common denominator is a high content of primary (sedimentary) iron. In both written discussions and field mapping, the all-inclusive nature of the term has tended to mask the real differences that are present. Actually, iron-formation is a term for a large class of rocks of strongly differing original characteristics and degrees of metamorphism. Widespread and deep oxidation increases further the range in possible character of the rock. These secondary processes—metamorphism and oxidation—greatly complicate the task of determining primary lithologies; yet knowledge of original material is essential to the construction of rational patterns of distribution that, in turn, are required for intelligent exploration and development of the iron-rich beds.

According to the classic view, developed by Van Hise, Leith, and others who took part in the first comprehensive study of the region by the U. S. Geological Survey, the primary iron-formation consisted chiefly of chemically precipitated iron-carbonate and chert, with abundant greenalite (an iron silicate similar to glauconite) in some areas. This view is stated in its most complete form in Monograph 52 (Van Hise and Leith, 95).[1] Volcanism was considered to play an important part in the origin of the rocks, by contributing iron to sea water through reaction between submarine lavas and sea water and by direct contribution through gaseous and liquid emanations.

In a recent report (50) the writer suggested that the primary iron-rich rocks can be divided into four major sedimentary facies—sulfide, carbonate, silicate, and oxide—depending upon the dominant original iron mineral in the sediment. In this paper these facies of iron-formation are further described, and the relationship of the iron-rich rocks to volcanism and geosynclinal de-

[1] Numbers in parentheses refer to Bibliography at end of paper.

velopment is discussed. It must be emphasized that definition of iron-formation facies is in terms of original sedimentary features, insofar as these features can be determined; every attempt has been made to separate primary characteristics from characteristics that are due to later metamorphism or oxidation. Many of the iron-rich rocks now composed dominantly of silicates doubtless owe their origin to metamorphic reactions such as described by Tyler (91), and, of course, much of the rock characterized by iron oxides is due to later oxidation. But recognition of these processes and products in no way negates the proposition that iron-rich rocks characterized by silicates and by oxides also were primary sedimentary types; the later processes simply have increased

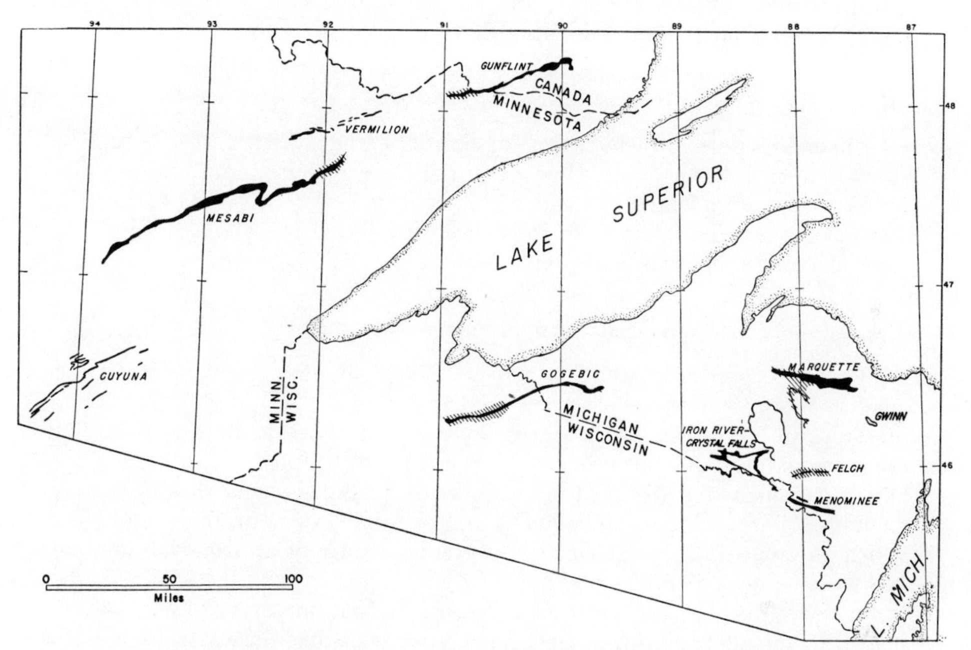

FIG. 1. Distribution of the major iron districts of the Lake Superior region. Areas of moderate- to high-grade metamorphism indicated by cross-hatching.

the difficulty of determination. Fortunately, the metamorphism of the Huronian iron-formations, though widespread, has a considerable range in intensity from place to place. Gradients are relatively steep, and in the Marquette and Gogebic ranges of Michigan and the Mesabi range of Minnesota the metamorphic gradients parallel the strike so that the progressive metamorphism can be observed for definite stratigraphic units of iron-rich rock. The distribution of the iron-formations in relation to generalized areas of moderate to high-grade metamorphism is shown in Figure 1. The grade of metamorphism of the iron-formation can be established by reference to minerals such as chlorites, micas, amphiboles, and garnet, but is most readily determined by the grain size of the "chert." (The term "chert" is used in the Lake Superior region for the silica that forms thin layers alternating with iron-rich layers in the iron-formation. The material is certainly chemical in origin—that is, nonclastic—but with a few exceptions is now entirely crystalline quartz.) The grains have a range from about 0.01 mm average diameter in low-grade metamorphic zones such as the Iron River district to 1 mm or more average diameter in the high-grade metamorphic zones such as the west end of the Marquette range. Though this criterion must be used with caution—the associated materials have a strong modifying influence—it does provide an exceedingly delicate indicator of metamorphic grade. The features of iron-formation believed to be of primary origin are described in terms of rocks from the areas of lowest metamorphic grade, as determined by the criteria of metamorphic index minerals and chert grain size.

ACKNOWLEDGMENTS

The field studies on which this paper is based have been part of a regional study by the U. S. Geological Survey of the Lake Superior iron ranges. The writer is deeply indebted to many of his colleagues for field data and critical discussion, and for laboratory assistance such as chemical analyses, X-ray identification of minerals, and preparation of photomicrographs.

THE TERM "IRON-FORMATION"

The term "iron-formation" as a rock name is one that gradually has gained general acceptance as a field term among geologists and engineers. In the literature the term has been used without definition or has been avoided, and the more cumbersome "iron-bearing formation" substituted. In the Lake Superior region the term is used in reference to a banded iron-rich rock of sedimentary origin. The rock commonly contains thin layers or laminae of chert, which alternate with layers consisting predominantly of an iron-rich mineral; and to some geologists the presence of chert is considered a necessary feature of the definition. However, in many areas—indeed, in parts of the iron-bearing strata in all areas—iron-rich rock is present that does not contain the characteristic chert layers. Commonly such rock is called "slaty iron-formation," "carbonate slate," or "ferruginous slate" and included with the iron-formation proper. In the Cuyuna district of Minnesota a considerable part of the rock that makes up the iron-formation is lacking in chert. The iron contained in iron-formation may be in the form of magnetite, martite, specularite, soft red hematite, "limonite," siderite, chlorite, greenalite, minnesotaite, stilpnomelane, grunerite, fayalite, or pyrite. It appears clear, therefore, that neither the presence of chert nor the mineralogy of the iron can enter into the definition, although both may be incorporated as modifying adjectives.

The basic feature remaining to the definition of iron-formation is the high content of primary (sedimentary) iron. A second feature, to the writer's knowledge always present, is thin-bedded or laminated structure. In this paper, therefore, iron-formation is defined as follows: *a chemical sediment, typically thin-bedded or laminated, containing 15 percent or more iron of sedi-*

mentary origin, commonly but not necessarily containing layers of chert. This is admittedly a very general definition, yet a more restricted definition would exclude some rocks now referred to as iron-formation. It encompasses the "itabirite" of South America, the "quartz-banded ores" of Sweden, the "banded hematite quartzites" of India, and the "banded ironstones" of South Africa, all of which typically consist of interlayered chert (crystalline quartz) and iron oxides. The definition does not provide a sharp distinction with the noncherty iron-rich strata of younger age; indeed, insofar as the mineralogy and content of iron is concerned, there is no real difference. In the present paper, the term is extended to include rock that normally would not be called iron-formation, such as graphitic pyritic slate, because of facies relationships to more typical varieties of iron-formation.

* * * * * * *

THE FACIES OF IRON-FORMATION

General

As might be expected, the lithologies encountered in the field are more complex than those suggested by generalized theoretical considerations. Four clearly defined end members—sulfide, carbonate, silicate, and oxide—make up a large part of the iron-formations. But many of the rocks were deposited in fluctuating environments, with resultant interlayering and modification of contrasting materials; others were strongly modified by diagenesis under chemical environments much different from those existing during deposition; still others owe some of their properties to clastic additions during chemical sedimentation. These factors make pigeon-hole classification of the present rock units a difficult task, but at the same time the preserved record furnishes valuable evidence with respect to relative stabilities of the minerals and the nature of the depositional and burial environments.

The sulfide, carbonate, and oxide (hematite) facies stand in well-defined theoretical and field relationships to one another. The analysis by Krumbein and Garrels (57) shows that there is little or no overlap of stability fields. This is borne out by field evidence; except for diagenetic modifications—to be discussed later in this report—pyrite, carbonate, and hematite are mutually exclusive within a given layer of iron-formation. Also, since the chemistry of depositional environments does not change radically within short periods of time, interbedding, if present, is between adjacent types—that is, between sulfide and carbonate or between carbonate and oxide—rarely if ever between sulfide and oxide.

The silicate facies does not appear to occupy a fixed position in terms of Eh, the major environmental control. Iron silicate apparently of primary origin is present as interstitial material or as discrete layers in rocks composed dominantly of sulfide, carbonate, or oxide. However, it occurs most abundantly in rocks with layers that contain either oxide or carbonate. This association suggests that the optimum environment for its deposition is one that lies, with respect to Eh, near the boundary zone between oxidizing and reducing. But other factors, such as addition of clastic material, probably are involved in the formation of the silicate rocks. Several fairly distinct types can be recognized, but the susceptibility of primary silicate rocks to metamorphism and the development of secondary silicate rocks through metamorphic reactions in carbonate iron-formation are serious obstacles to reconstruction of original characteristics and environments of deposition.

Iron-formation that contains iron chiefly in the form of magnetite is a major rock type in the Lake Superior region. Much of this rock is believed by the writer to be of primary origin and is classed as a variety of the oxide facies. This facies—or subfacies—is not predicted by the Eh-pH diagram of Krumbein and Garrels (57), in which the only oxide indicated is hematite. Although almost certainly some magnetite in the iron-formation is formed by metamorphic reactions such as breakdown of iron carbonate or primary iron silicate, this explanation seems quite inadequate to account for some of the magnetite-banded rocks. The principal lines of reasoning that appear to support a concept of primary origin for these rocks are as follows:

1. The amount of magnetite (plus martite formed by surficial oxidation of magnetite) in most types of iron-formation bears relatively little systematic relation to the degree of metamorphism. This is noted in descriptions of the Gunflint range in Minnesota by Broderick (6, p. 440), who states: "For instance, the magnetite-rich rock of the Lower Slaty horizon were sampled in Sec. 28, where the (Duluth) gabbro is close by, and in Sec. 22, where it is further away. . . . The two samples had the same percentage of magnetite within the limits of sampling error." Concerning the Biwabik iron-formation of the Mesabi, Broderick writes: "Thus, drill cores of the unoxidized Biwabik formation, far from any igneous intrusives, show that the chief iron-bearing mineral is magnetite."

2. Layers composed almost entirely of magnetite are found interbedded with layers of iron silicate or of iron carbonate. Intimate association with these two minerals in layers less than a millimeter thick would seem to rule out the possibility of derivation by metamorphism from either constituent. Derivation by metamorphism of hematite likewise seems improbable in view of the fact that in areas of intense metamorphism such as the Republic district of Michigan, hematite remains a major constituent—much of the banded specularite-jasper rock there contains virtually no magnetite.

3. Textural relations to be described later show that at least some of the magnetite is diagenetic in origin. Doubtless the diagenetic environments differ considerably from the depositional environments in terms of Eh, pH, and composition of the liquid phase, yet the occurrence of magnetite as a diagenetic mineral indicates that its field of stability is within reach of ordinary temperatures and pressures.

4. The magnetite-banded rocks are typically associated with silicate iron-formation, the principal varieties of which, as stated previously, appear to have been formed in an Eh environment intermediate between the oxide—that is, hematite—and carbonate zones. Such an environment might also be favorable for formation of a ferrous-ferric oxide mineral under certain conditions.

The principal features of the sedimentary facies of iron-formation are summarized in Table 1 and are described in greater detail in the pages that follow.

* * * * * * *

SUMMARY OF THE FACIES CHARACTERISTICS AND RELATIONSHIPS TO DEPOSITIONAL ENVIRONMENT

The conclusions regarding general characteristics and relationships of the four sedimentary facies of iron-formation are summarized below:

The *sulfide* facies is represented in the Lake Superior region by pyritic black slates. The rock originated as a black organic mud in sea water abnormally rich in iron. The depositional environment was characterized by poor bottom ventilation, with oxygen not being sufficiently abundant to destroy the organic material showered down from the more highly aerated upper zones. Iron in solution in the sea water is precipitated as sulfide by the H_2S that is generated by bacterial action on the organic material. In part the sulfur is derived from organic proteins, but the major contribution is almost certainly derived by bacterial reduction of sulfates in the sea water.

The *carbonate* facies consists of interbedded chert and iron-rich carbonate in roughly equal proportions. This rock was deposited as a chemical precipitate under reducing conditions in which oxygen was abundant enough to remove most of the organic material, yet not sufficiently abundant to cause oxidation of the ferrous compounds. The carbonate lacks oolitic or granular structure; it appears to have accumulated as a fine mud below the level of wave action. The carbonate is a molecular mixture of four components—$FeCO_3$, $MgCO_3$, $MnCO_3$, and $CaCO_3$—with $FeCO_3$ normally accounting for 70 percent or more of the total.

The *oxide* facies contains two principal types: hematite-banded and magnetite-banded. The *hematite-banded* rocks consist of interbedded hematite and chert or jasper. The hematite is now crystalline to a degree dependent upon the metamorphism undergone; in areas of low-grade metamorphism it is now fine-grained, gray or bluish specularite. The hematite is believed to have been deposited as hydrated ferric oxide in shallow, well-aerated waters. Oolitic structure is present in many layers, the ooliths consisting of thin skins of hematite and silica in all proportions ranging from a mere film of hematite around a chert core to a solid granule of hematite. The ooliths are believed to originate by the rolling action of waves and currents on chemically deposited

TABLE 1

PRINCIPAL FEATURES OF THE IRON–FORMATION FACIES

	Sulfide	Carbonate	Silicate		Oxide	
			Nongranular	Granular	Magnetite-banded	Hematite-banded
Lithology	Laminated to thin-banded black pyritic carbonaceous slate. Chert rare	Thin-bedded to laminated rock consisting of alternating layers of gray chert and carbonate	Laminated light-green to greenish-black rock. Chert rare	Massive dark-green rock with irregular bedding marked by layers of chert and magnetite	Dark, thin-bedded to irregularly bedded rock consisting of layers of magnetite alternating with layers of dark chert, green silicates, or silicates plus carbonate	Thin-bedded to irregularly bedded rock consisting of alternate layers of crystalline hematite and gray chert or reddish jasper
Principal iron mineral	Pyrite	Iron-rich carbonate	Iron silicate (minnesotaite, stilpnomelane, chlorite)	Iron silicate (greenalite, minnesotaite, stilpnomelane)	Magnetite	Crystalline hematite
Subsidiary iron minerals (rarer minerals in parenthesis)	Carbonate (Greenalite)	Pyrite Stilpnomelane Minnesotaite Magnetite (Hematite)	Carbonate Magnetite	Magnetite Carbonate Hematite	Greenalite Minnesotaite Stilpnomelane Carbonate Hematite (Pyrite)	Magnetite (Carbonate)
Typical range in content of metallic iron, in percent	15–25	20–35	20–30	20–30	25–35	30–40
Distinctive features	"Graphitic"	Stylolites common	Laminated structure	Granule-bearing	Strongly magnetic	Commonly oolitic
Environment of origin	Strongly reducing, anaerobic	Reducing	Variable, but typically mildly reducing	Mildly oxidizing to mildly reducing	Mildly oxidizing to mildly reducing	Strongly oxidizing

material. Mechanical transport of ooliths prior to final entrapment accounts for the lack of homogeneity and composition of the ooliths; in many respects the oolitic rocks possess definite affinities with clastic deposits.

The *magnetite-banded* rocks consist of layers of magnetite alternating with layers that contain varying proportions of iron silicates, carbonate, and chert. On the basis of associated minerals such as carbonate and hematite, the conclusion that the rock originated in an environment that ranged from mildly oxidizing to mildly reducing seems valid. The magnetite may have been formed by the settling of ferric oxide that was precipitated in upper well-oxygenated layers of the water into bottom environments in which the oxidation potential was too low to permit the stable existence of hematite. The abundance of post-depositional magnetite and carbonate in these rocks suggests also that diagenetic activity was strong.

The *silicate* facies comprises two major types, granular and nongranular. Both commonly, though by no means invariably, contain abundant magnetite and carbonate. The silicate may be greenalite, minnesotaite, stilpnomelane, or chlorite; of these, only greenalite appears to be definitely primary. The low content of alumina and potash indicates that neither glauconite nor chamosite, typical minerals of younger ironstones, were important primary constituents. In the Mesabi and Gunflint ranges, the silicates are commonly in the form of rounded to irregularly shaped granules. The granules differ from hematite ooliths in not possessing concentric rings; they more closely resemble glauconite granules.

Iron silicate, apparently either of primary origin or derived from a pre-existing silicate, is found in association with minerals as contrasting as pyrite and hematite, so it is evidently a stable mineral over a wide range of oxidation-reduction environments. However, the optimum conditions for precipitation of the silicates, to judge from the associated minerals, are in the range from mildly oxidizing to mildly reducing. The conditions that would permit precipitation of iron and silica as a single mineral rather than as separate phases are not clear, although mutual precipitation of two colloids (in contrast to separate precipitation of two minerals from solution) is an obvious possibility.

THE PROBLEM OF THE CHERT

The problems related to the origin of the chert in the iron-formation rocks can be touched upon only briefly in this paper. The literature dealing with chert is extensive and suggests that chert may be formed in a variety of ways. The evidence seems to indicate that the chert of the iron-formation is a primary precipitate rather than a product of diagenesis or later replacement. The more important lines of evidence that lead to this conclusion are tabulated as follows:

1. The amount of chert in a given bed of iron-formation remains almost constant over wide areas. Post-consolidation replacements would yield a much more irregular pattern of distribution.
2. The amount of chert in a given type of iron-formation is reasonably constant. For example, the amount of chert in carbonate iron-forma-

tion is 30 to 35 percent, whereas that in oxide iron-formation is about 40 percent. It seems, therefore, that the chert must be related to the primary process of sedimentation.

3. As shown in an earlier paper (50), veinlets of chert are cut by stylolites that were formed before the beds were structurally disturbed. The veinlets quite reasonably may be considered diagenetic in origin, but they cut—with sharp-walled contacts—finer-grained layers of chert.
4. Slump structures, almost certainly formed before lithification, have been observed by the author in many of the rocks (50). These slumps involve thin bands of chert, therefore the chert is pre-lithification in origin. Similarly, intraformational breccia contains sharp-edged fragments of banded chert.

The abundance of chert in the Precambrian iron-formations is a highly distinctive feature, and although it has been shown by Hayes (46), and more recently by Kelley (55), that chert is present as interstitial material in some of the younger oolitic ironstones, the banded chert appears to be virtually limited to iron-rich strata of the Precambrian. Sakamoto (78) postulates that seasonal changes will account for alternating deposition of iron and silica. According to this theory, iron is transported in acidic solutions during wet seasons and precipitated when these solutions are neutralized, whereas silica is transported in alkaline solutions and precipitated in an acid environment. The theory is an attractive one, although, as pointed out by Tyler and Twenhofel (93), it does not explain the limitation of banded cherty iron-formation to the Precambrian.

DIAGENETIC MODIFICATIONS

The term diagenesis encompasses those changes produced in a rock after deposition and prior to lithification (90, p. 108). A very large number of modifications of the original sediment properly are to be ascribed to diagenesis. For example, it is probable that the pyrite in the pyritic slates originally was in another form, and that the hematite in the oxide rocks was originally a hydrous oxide. For the sake of brevity this discussion is limited to those changes that involve replacement of one iron mineral by another of different type.

As has been pointed out, the major factor in formation of the iron minerals is the oxidation-reduction potential (redox potential); and in general the burial environment of fine-grained sediments appears to possess a lower redox potential than the depositional environment. This is attributable chiefly to the decomposition of mechanically included organic material and to the fact that the sediment is more or less isolated from the oxygen-bearing sea water. A present-day example of profound diagenesis is described by Brujewicz (8, 9), who studied bottom conditions in the Barents Sea, off the north shore of western Russia; he reports that the water is well oxygenated from surface to bottom and that oxides of iron and manganese accumulate in brown deposits containing a considerable amount of organic material but no carbonate. Below the depositional interface, the brown layer grades into gray mud, much higher in ferrous iron and lower in organic carbon. The amount of mechanically included organic material in the original deposit is apparently more than adequate, upon decomposition, to entirely reduce the oxides contained in the muds. Zobell (100) found that negative redox potentials are typical in the finer grained bottom sediments off the coast of California and Lower California; he also attributes the low potential chiefly to included organic matter. Emery and Rittenberg (24), in their study of drill cores in modern sediments of California, show that in addition to a lowering of Eh with depth, a slight increase in pH is evident.

In most fine-grained sediments of normal composition, the amount of organic matter included appears adequate to reduce all or practically all of the iron from the ferric state. However, it must be remembered that in an ordinary sediment the amount of reducible material—chiefly oxides of iron and manganese—is relatively small. Zobell (100, p. 484) points out that both the intensity and capacity factors of a system must be considered. He states: "It should be emphasized that the redox potential is an intensity factor in the same sense that temperature and pH are intensity factors. The redox potential does not indicate the reducing or oxidizing capacity of a system any more than the temperature of a system indicates how many calories of heat it may contain. . . ." The iron-formation, containing 5 to 10 times the amount of iron of a normal sediment, should show the effects of a lower redox potential during diagenesis, but the total effect ordinarily would not be large because of the bulk of reducible material present.

The observed modifications of the iron-formations that may be reasonably attributed to diagenesis are of a nature and extent that would be expected. Primary oxide rocks and associated silicate show some replacement by carbonate; carbonate rocks show comparable replacement by pyrite. In magnetite-banded rocks from the Gogebic range, some layers contain ooliths that apparently were originally hematite. These ooliths have been replaced by magnetite and carbonate in such a fashion as to largely destroy the oolith, the outlines of which either may be preserved by disconnected areas of hematite, or, as shown in Figure 33, may be almost completely lost. Figure 21 shows a dark graphitic phase of carbonate iron-formation from the Crystal Falls district; it illustrates typical diagenetic replacement by pyrite. The pyrite is rather coarse grained; it occurs as replacements around chert nodules and lenses, as paper-thin laminae, and as clusters of grains. Whether deposition of pyrite on the borders of the chert is due to greater susceptibility of the chert to replacement or whether this surface simply represents a structural discontinuity along which solutions could move is not clear. Inasmuch as Emery and Rittenberg (24) have shown that increase of pH with depth of burial is common, it seems likely both factors are operative; the presence of conditions more alkaline than the depositional environment would favor replacement of the silica, and the structural discontinuity would permit passage of solutions.

In general the diagenetic minerals are considerably coarser in grain than the primary materials. Distribution is irregular, and the minerals typically form clots and veinlets.

* * * * * * *

BIBLIOGRAPHY

1. Aldrich, H. R., 1929, The geology of the Gogebic iron range of Wisconsin: Wisconsin Geol. and Nat. History Survey, Econ. ser. 24, Bull. 71, 279 p.
2. Alling, H. L., 1947, Diagenesis of the Clinton hematite ores of New York: Geol. Soc. America Bull., vol. 58, p. 991–1017.
3. Ayres, V. L., 1940, Mineral notes from the Michigan iron country: Am. Mineralogist, vol. 25, p. 432–434.
4. Bayley, W. S., 1904, The Menominee iron-bearing district of Michigan: U. S. Geol. Survey Mon. 46, 513 p.
5. Berz, K. C., 1922, Uber Magneteisen in marinen Ablagerungen: Centralbl. fur Mineralogie, Geologie, and Palaontologie, p. 569–577.
6. Broderick, T. M., 1920, Economic geology and stratigraphy of the Gunflint iron district, Minnesota: ECON. GEOL., vol. 15, p. 422–452.
7. Brown, J. S., 1943, Supergene magnetite: ECON. GEOL., vol. 38, p. 137–148.
8. Brujewicz, S. W., 1938, Oxidation-reduction potentials and pH of sea bottom deposits: Verh. der Internat. Vereiningung fur theoretische und angewandte limnologie, bd. 8, p. 35–49.
9. ——,1938, Oxidation-reduction potential and the pH of sediments of the Barentz and Kara seas: Comptes rendus (Doklady) de l'Acad. des Sci. de l'URSS, vol. 19, no. 8, p. 637–640.
10. Cady, W. M., McKelvey, V. E., and Wells, F. G., 1950, Geotectonic relationships of mineral deposits (abs.): Geol. Soc. America Bull. vol. 61, pt. 2, p. 1447.
11. Castaño, J. R., and Garrels, R. M., 1950, Experiments on the deposition of iron with special reference to the Clinton iron ore deposits: ECON. GEOL., vol. 45, no. 8, p. 755–770.
12. Cayeux, L., 1909, Les Minerais de fer oölithique de France, I. Minerais de fer primaires: Minist. Trav. Publics, Etudes gites minéraux de la France.
13. ——, 1916, Introduction à l'étude pétrographique des roches sedimentaires, Paris.
14. ——, 1922, Les Minerais de fer oölithique de France, II. Minerais de fer secondaires: Minist. Trav. Publics, Etudes gites minéraux de la France.
15. Collins, W. H., Quirke, T. T., and Thomson, Ellis, 1926, Michipicoten iron ranges: Canada Geol. Survey Mem. 147, p. 1–141.
16. Déverin, L., 1945, Etude pétrographique des minerais de fer oölithiques du Dogger des Alpes suisses: Betröge zur Geologie der Schweiz, Geotech. ser., Lf. 13, bd. 2, 115 p.
17. Dewey, H., and Flett, J. S., 1911, Some British pillow lavas and the rocks associated with them: Geol. Mag., vol. 8, p. 202–209 and 241–248.
18. Dorr, J. V. N., 2d., 1945, Manganese and iron deposits of Morro do Urucum, Mato Grosso, Brazil: U. S. Geol. Survey Bull. 946–A, 47 p.
19. Dunn, J. A., 1935, The origin of iron-ores in Singhbhum, India: ECON. GEOL., vol. 30, p. 643–654.
20. ——, 1937, The mineral deposits of eastern Singhbhum and surrounding areas: India Geol. Survey Mem., vol. 69, pt. 1, 279 p.
21. du Preez, J. W., 1945, The structural geology of the area east of Thabazimbi and the genesis of the associated iron ores: Stellenbosch Univ. Annals, vol. 22, sec. A, no. 1–14, p. 263–360.
22. Dutton, C. E., 1949, Geology of the central part of the Iron River district, Iron County, Michigan: U. S. Geol. Survey Circ. 43, 9 p.
23. Edwards, A. B., 1936, The iron ores of the Middleback ranges, South Australia: Australasian Inst. Min. Metallurgy Proc., vol. 102, p. 155–207.
24. Emery, K. O., and Rittenberg, S. C., 1952, Early diagenesis of California basin sediments in relation to origin of oil: Am. Assoc. Petroleum Geologists Bull. 36, p. 735–806.
25. Eskola, Pentti, 1920, The mineral facies of rocks: Norsk geol. tidsskr., vol. 6, p. 143–194.
26. ——, Vuoristo, Urho, and Rankama, Kalervo, 1937, An experimental illustration of the spilite reaction: Comm. geol. Finlande Bull. 119, p. 61–68.
27. Galliher, E. W., 1933, The sulfur cycle in sediments: Jour. Sed. Petrology, vol. 3, p. 51–63.
28. Geijer, Per, 1938, Stripa Odalfälts Geologi: Sveriges geol. undersökning, vol. 28, ser. Ca.

29. Gill, J. E., 1926, Gunflint iron-bearing formation, Ontario: Canada Geol. Survey, Summary Rept. for 1924, pt. C., p. 28–88.
30. ——, 1927, Origin of the Gunflint iron-bearing formation: Econ. Geol., vol. 22, p. 687–728.
31. Grout, F. F., 1919, Nature and origin of the Biwabik iron-bearing formation of the Mesabi range, Minnesota: Econ. Geol., vol. 14, p. 452–464.
32. Grout, F. F., and Thiel, G. A., 1924, Notes on stilpnomelane: Am. Mineralogist, vol. 9, p. 228–231.
33. Gruner, J. W., 1922, The origin of the sedimentary iron-formations; the Biwabik formation of the Mesabi range: Econ. Geol., vol. 17, p. 407–460.
34. ——, 1924, Contributions to the geology of the Mesabi range, with special reference to the magnetites of the iron-bearing formation west of Mesaba: Minnesota Geol. Survey Bull. 19, 71 p.
35. ——, 1936, The structure and chemical composition of greenalite: Am. Mineralogist, vol. 21, p. 449–455.
36. ——, 1937, Composition and structure of stilpnomelane: Am. Mineralogist, vol. 22, p. 912–925.
37. ——, 1944, The structure of stilpnomelane reexamined: Am. Mineralogist, vol. 29, p. 291–298.
38. ——, 1944, The composition and structure of minnesotaite, a common iron silicate in iron formations: Am. Mineralogist, vol. 29, p. 363–372.
39. ——, 1946, The mineralogy and geology of the taconites and iron ores of the Mesabi range, Minnesota: Iron Range Resources and Rehabilitation, St. Paul, Minn., 127 p.
40. Hallimond, A. F., 1925, Iron ores: Bedded ores of England and Wales: Great Britain Spec. Rept. Min. Resources, Petrography and Chemistry, vol. 29.
41. ——, Dunham, K. C., Hemingway, J. E., Taylor, J. H., Davies, W., Dixie, R. J. M., and Bannister, F. A., 1951, The constitution and origin of sedimentary iron ores: a symposium: Yorkshire Geol. Soc. Proc., vol. 28, pt. 2, p. 61–101.
42. Harder, E. C., 1919, Iron-depositing bacteria and their geologic relations: U. S. Geol. Survey Prof. Paper 113, 89 p.
43. ——, and Johnston, A. W., 1918, Preliminary report on the geology of east central Minnesota, including the Cuyuna iron-ore district: Minnesota Geol. Survey Bull. 15, 178 p.
44. Harker, A., 1908, Petrology for Students, Cambridge University Press.
45. Hawley, J. E., 1942, Origin of some siderite, pyrite, and chert deposits, Michipicoten district, Ontario: Royal Soc. Canada Trans., 3rd ser., vol. 36, sec. 4, p. 79–87.
46. Hayes, A. O., 1915, Wabana iron ore of Newfoundland: Canada Geol. Survey Mem. 78, 163 p.
47. Hotchkiss, W. O., 1919, Geology of the Gogebic range and its relation to recent mining developments: Eng. and Min. Jour., vol. 108, p. 443–452, 501–507, 537–541, 577–582.
48. Hutton, C. O., 1938, The stilpnomelane group of minerals: Mineralog. Mag., vol. 25, p. 172–206.
49. Irving, R. D., and Van Hise, C. R., 1892, The Penokee iron-bearing series of Michigan and Wisconsin: U. S. Geol. Survey Mon. 19, 534 p.
50. James, H. L., 1951, Iron formation and associated rocks in the Iron River district, Michigan: Geol. Soc. America Bull. 62, p. 251–266.
51. ——, and Dutton, C. E., 1951, Geology of the northern part of the Iron River district, Iron County, Michigan: U. S. Geol. Survey Circ. 120, 12 p.
52. ——, Clark, L. D., and Smith, L. E., 1947, Magnetic survey and geology of the Ice Lake-Chicagon Creek area, Iron County, Michigan: U. S. Geol. Survey Strategic Min. Inv. Prelim. Rept. 3–213, 11 p.
53. ——, and Wier, K. L., 1948, Magnetic survey and geology of the eastern and southeastern parts of the Iron River district, Iron County, Michigan: U. S. Geol. Survey Circ. 26, 18 p.
54. Jolliffe, F. J., 1935, A study of greenalite: Am. Mineralogist, vol. 20, p. 405–425.
55. Kelley, V. C., 1951, Oolitic iron deposits of New Mexico: Am. Assoc. Petroleum Geologists Bull. 35, p. 2199–2228.
56. Krotov, B. P., 1940, On the occurrence in the Khalilovo iron ore deposits (Urals, Russia) of magnetite formed from solutions of superficial origin at a low temperature: Acad. Sci. URSS, C.R. (Dokl.) v. 26, no. 8, p. 801–803.
57. Krumbein, W. C., and Garrels, R. M., 1952, Origin and classification of chemical sediments in terms of pH and oxidation-reduction potentials: Jour. Geology, vol. 60, p. 1–33.
58. Kulp, J. L., Kent, P., and Kerr, P. F., 1951, Thermal study of Ca-Mg-Fe carbonate minerals: Am. Mineralogist, vol. 36, p. 643–670.

59. Lake Superior Iron Ore Association, 1938, The, Lake Superior Iron Ores.
60. Landergren, Sture, 1948, On the geochemistry of Swedish iron ores and associated rocks: Sveriges geol. undersökning, Arsbok 42, no. 5, ser. C, no. 496.
61. Leith, C. K., 1903, The Mesabi iron-bearing district of Minnesota: U. S. Geol. Survey Mon. 43, p. 316.
62. ——, 1934, The pre-Cambrian: Geol. Soc. America Proc. for 1933, p. 151–180.
63. MacGregor, A. M., 1927, The problem of the Precambrian atmosphere: South African Jour. Sci., vol. 24, p. 155–172.
64. Miles, K. R., 1941, Magnetite-hematite relations in the banded iron-formations of Western Australia: Australasian Inst. Min. Metallurgy Proc., no. 124, p. 193–201.
65. Moore, E. S., 1946, Origin of iron deposits of the "Lake Superior" type: New York Acad. Sci. Trans., Ser. 2, vol. 9, no. 2, p. 43–51.
66. ——, and Armstrong, H. S., 1948, Iron deposits in the district of Algoma: Ontario Dept. Mines Ann. Rept., 1946, vol. 55, pt. 4, p. 1–118.
67. ——, and Maynard, J. E., 1929, The solution, transportation, and precipitation of iron and silica: Econ. Geol., vol. 24, p. 272–303, 365–402, 506–527.
68. Nanz, R. H. Jr., 1953, Chemical composition of pre-Cambrian slates with notes on the geochemical composition of lutites: Jour. Geol., vol. 61, p. 51–64.
69. Palmqvist, Sven, 1935, Geochemical studies on the iron-bearing Liassic series in southern Sweden: Lunds Geologisk-Mineralogiska Institution, Meddelanden, ser. 2, no. 60.
70. Park, C. F., Jr., 1946, The spilite and manganese problems of the Olympic peninsula, Washington: Am. Jour. Sci., vol. 244, p. 305–323.
71. Percival, F. G., 1931, The iron-ores of Noamundi: India Min. Geol. Inst. Trans., vol. 26, pt. 3, p. 169–276.
72. Pettijohn, F. J., 1943, Archean sedimentation: Geol. Soc. America Bull. 54, p. 925–972.
73. ——, 1947, Geology of the Crystal Falls-Alpha iron-bearing district, Iron County, Michigan: U. S. Geol. Survey Min. Inv. Prelim. Map 3–181.
74. ——, 1952, Geology of the northern Crystal Falls area, Iron County, Michigan: U. S. Geol. Survey Circ. 153, 17 p.
75. Royce, Stephen, 1936, Geology of the Lake Superior iron deposits: Lake Superior Min. Inst. Proc., vol. 29, p. 68–107.
76. ——, 1938, Geology of the iron ranges: the influence of geological conditions on mining practice, *in* Lake Superior Iron Ores, The Lake Superior Iron Ore Association, Cleveland, p. 27–61.
77. Rubey, W. W., 1951, The geologic history of sea water: Geol. Soc. America Bull. 62, p. 1111–1147.
78. Sakamoto, Takao, 1950, The origin of the pre-Cambrian banded iron ores: Am. Jour. Sci., vol. 248, p. 449–474.
79. Sampson, Edward, 1923, The ferruginous chert formations of Notre Dame Bay, Newfoundland: Jour. Geol., vol. 23, p. 571–598.
80. Smyth, C. H., 1892, On the Clinton iron ore: Am. Jour. Sci., 3rd ser., vol. 43, p. 487–496.
81. ——, 1894, Die Hämatite von Clinton in den Ostlichen Vereinigten Staaten: Zeitschr. prakt. Geologie, p. 304–313.
82. ——, 1911, The Clinton type of iron-ore deposits: *In* Types of Ore Deposits, p. 33–52. Edited by H. F. Bain.
83. Spencer, E., and Percival, F. G., 1952, The structure and origin of the banded hematite jaspers of Singhbhum, India: Econ. Geol., vol. 47, p. 365–383.
84. Spiroff, Kiril, 1938, Magnetite crystals from meteoric solutions: Econ. Geol., vol. 33, p. 818–828.
85. Spurr, J. E., 1894, The iron-bearing rocks of the Mesabi range in Minnesota: Minnesota Geol. and Nat. History Survey Bull. 10, 268 p.
86. Taylor, J. H., 1949, Petrology of the Northampton sand ironstone formation: Great Britain Geol. Survey Mem.
87. Thiel, G. A., 1924, Iron sulfides in magnetic belts near the Cuyuna range: Econ. Geol., vol. 19, p. 466–472.
88. Turner, F. J., 1935, Contribution to the interpretation of mineral facies in metamorphic rocks: Am. Jour. Sci., 5th ser., vol. 29, p. 409–421.
89. ——, and Hutton, C. O., 1935, Stilpnomelane and related minerals as constituents of schists from western Otago, New Zealand: Geol. Mag., vol. 72, p. 1–8.
90. Twenhofel, W. H., 1932, Treatise on sedimentation (2d ed.): The Williams & Wilkins Co., Baltimore, 926 p.
91. Tyler, S. A., 1949, Development of Lake Superior soft iron ores from metamorphosed iron formation: Geol. Soc. America Bull. 60, p. 1101–1124.

92. ——, 1950, Sedimentary iron deposits, *in* Applied Sedimentation, John Wiley & Sons, Inc., p. 506–523.
93. ——, and Twenhofel, W. H., Sedimentation and stratigraphy of the Huronian of Upper Michigan: Am. Jour. Sci., vol. 250, p. 1–27 and 118–151.
94. Van Hise, C. R., and Bayley, W. S., 1897, The Marquette iron-bearing district of Michigan: U. S. Geol. Survey Mon. 28, 608 p.
95. ——, and Leith, C. K., 1911, Geology of the Lake Superior region: U. S. Geol. Survey Mon. 52, 641 p.
96. Wagner, P. A., 1928, The iron deposits of the Union of South Africa: South Africa Geol. Survey Mem., vol. 26.
97. Woolnough, W. G., 1928, Presidential address: New South Wales Royal Soc. Jour. and Proc. for 1927, vol. 61, p. 1–53.
98. ——, 1937, Sedimentation in barred basins, and source rocks of oil: Am. Assoc. Petroleum Geologists Bull. 21, p. 1101–1157.
99. ——, 1941, Origin of banded iron deposits—a suggestion: Econ. Geol., vol. 36, p. 465–489.
100. ZoBell, C. E., 1946, Studies on redox potential of marine sediments: Am. Assoc. Petroleum Geologists Bull. vol. 30, no. 4, p. 477–513.

Editor's Comments on Papers 21 Through 24

The following papers in this section were chosen to present additional information on the chemistry of iron-formations and to contrast these older rocks with the younger ironstones. That there is a difference between these two main kinds of iron-rich sediments has not always been clear. Moore and Maynard (1929), for example, state:

> Further, the work of various investigators already cited indicates that some of the largest Paleozoic and Mesozoic sedimentary iron deposits such as those of France, England, Newfoundland and the eastern United States have been formed by processes of sedimentation without the direct aid of magmatic waters. These processes of solution, transport, and deposition apparently operated under special topographic and climatic conditions and probably special conditions for the development of low forms of life. The great similarity between some of these iron formations and the Animikie formations of Minnesota, Ontario and the Hudson's Bay region lead one to conclude that they might have formed in the same manner.

In the same paper, however, the senior author concludes:

> The condition of formation of these banded formations must be peculiar to the pre-Cambrian era since no deposits exactly similar have been formed in later eras, although they were deposited on every continent in that era. The only thing approaching such highly siliceous deposits forming today is found around hot springs and in association with igneous rocks.

There are indeed similarities between iron-formations and ironstones. Whereas most cherty iron-formations are delicately banded, some exhibit granule or oolitic textures similar to those found in ironstones. The most remarkable differences between the two rock types are in chemical compositions and age. With the development of K-Ar and Rb-Sr radiometric dating methods in the 1950s the ages of many Precambrian iron-formations were determined (Goldich, 1973). This work showed that the cherty iron-formations, except for one or two controversial deposits, are older than 1,800 million years, and that on all continents by far the bulk of iron sedimentation occurred in the interval from 1,800 to 2,600 million years ago. In spite of textural and mineralogic differences between various iron-formations they are remarkably similar in chemical composition (Lepp and Goldich, Papers 22 and 28; Trendall, Paper 19). In contrast to the younger ironstones, the iron-formations contain very little alumina, phosphorus, or titanium, and they contain abundant precipitated silica.

In Paper 21, H. L. James summarizes the pertinent differences between the two chief classes of iron sediments. H. Lepp and S. S. Goldich review the chemical characteristics of the two rock types in Paper 22. This excerpt is from their article on the origin of Precambrian iron-formations, part of which is also reproduced as Paper 28.

Although some young ironstones (Lahn-Dill type) are associated with volcanic rocks by far the most extensive deposits are interlayered with and grade into normal marine sediments. These "Minette"-type ironstones are typically oolitic shallow-water marine sediments such as are found in the Jurassic of Alsace-Lorraine. The Silurian "Clinton" beds of the eastern United States, the Wabana iron ores of Newfoundland, the ironstones of the Lower and Middle Jurassic of England, and many others fall into this class.

To illustrate the chemical, mineralogic, and textural characteristics of ironstones, two papers dealing with Mesozoic iron deposits in Britain were selected. The paper by C. D. Curtis and D. A. Spears is a continuation of Paper 7, in which they examined the theoretical conditions for the precipitation of iron minerals. Paper 23, by Vernon Wilson, is a review of the geology, mineralogy, and chemistry of the Jurassic ironstone fields of the East Midlands of England. A comparison of Wilson's analysis for the various ironstones in this district with the average composition of ironstone reported by Lepp and Goldich in Paper 22 (Table 10) shows them to be representative. The average value reported in Paper 22 includes analyses of ironstones from the United States, Canada, France, Germany, Belgium, and other countries in addition to those of England.

Vernon Wilson was educated at Leeds University and at the Imperial College, London. Wilson joined the field staff of the Geological Survey in 1937 and commenced work on the Jurassic rocks of the Yeovil district. During the war years of 1939–1945 he was transferred to the Special Iron Ore Unit and was involved in the mapping of a number of important iron districts. He was coauthor of the Liassic Ironstones Memoir (1952) and of other publications on British ironstones. In 1953 he gave the Abbott Memorial Lecture on the East Midlands Ironstone Fields at the University of Nottingham. Wilson was killed in a car accident in 1971 shortly after his retirement from the Geological Survey.

Samuel S. Goldich is Professor of Geology at Northern Illinois University. He has also held professorships at the University of Minnesota, Pennsylvania State University, and at the University of New York at Stony Brook. Since 1942 he has at various times been on the U.S. Geological Survey, including the period from 1960–1964 as Chief of the Branch of Isotope Geology. Goldich's chief interests are in the origin of laterites and bauxites, petrology, geochemistry, and geochronology. The order of persistence of the common rock-forming minerals during weathering is frequently referred to as the Goldich Stability Series. He is a pioneer in the radiometric dating of Precambrian iron formations and associated rocks (Goldich et al., 1961; Quirke et al., 1960).

Henry Lepp graduated from the University of Saskatchewan and worked for seven years as a mining engineer and exploration geologist in various parts of Canada and in West Africa. He received his Ph.D. from the University of Minnesota and spent ten years on the faculty of the University of Minnesota, Duluth. Since 1964 he has been

Professor and Chairman of Geology at Macalester College. His interest in iron-formations grew out of consulting assignments related to iron ore exploration during the 1950s and early 1960s.

References

Goldich, S. S., 1973, Ages of Precambrian banded iron-formations: Econ. Geol., v. 68, p. 1126–1134.

———, A. D. Nier, H. Baadsgaard, J. H. Hoffman, and H. W. Kreuger, 1961, The Precambrian geology and geochronology of Minnesota: Minnesota Geol. Surv. Bull. 41, 193 p.

Moore, E. S., and J. E. Maynard, 1929, Transportation and precipitation of iron and silica: Econ. Geol., v. 24, p. 272–303, 365–402, 506–527.

Quirke, T. T., S. S. Goldich, and H. W. Kreuger, 1960, Composition and age of the Temiscamie iron-formation, Mistassini Territory, Quebec: Econ. Geol., v. 55, p. 311–326.

Whitehead, T. H., W. Anderson, V. Wilson, D. A. Wray, and K. C. Dunham, 1952, The Liassic ironstones; Great Britain Geol. Surv. Mem., 211 p.

21

Reprinted from *Data of Geochemistry* (U.S. Geol. Survey Prof. Paper 440-W), Chap W, 1966, pp., 46–47

Chemistry of the Iron-Rich Sedimentary Rocks

HAROLD L. JAMES

* * * * * * *

DIFFERENCES BETWEEN IRONSTONE AND IRON-FORMATION

Both ironstone and iron-formation have a wide range in characteristics and associations, but it seems worth while to summarize the differences that exist between the more abundant deposits that may be classed as typical of the two groups, namely ironstone of the minette type, and iron-formation of the Lake Superior type.

1. Age. *Ironstone:* Pliocene to middle Precambrian. Principal beds are of lower Paleozoic and of Jurassic age. Oldest known occurrence is in strata with approximate age of 2,000 million years (Transvaal Series, South Africa); youngest unit of significant size is of Pliocene age (Kerch basin, U.S.S.R.). *Iron-formation:* Cambrian to early Precambrian. Principal formations in the U.S.S.R., South Africa, and North America have an age of about 2,000 million years. "Keewatin-type" iron-formation, generally associated with volcanic rocks, occurs in the oldest known Precambrian strata of several shield areas of the world. Youngest proved age for iron-formation is Cambrian.
2. Thickness. *Ironstone:* major units a few meters to a few tens of meters. *Iron-formation:* major units 50 meters to 600 meters.
3. Original areal extent. *Ironstone:* individual basins of deposition probably rarely more than 100 miles in maximum dimension. *Iron-formation:* difficult to determine, but at least some units had continuity over linear distances of many hundred miles.
4. Physical character. *Ironstone:* massive to poorly banded; silicate and oxide facies oolitic. *Iron-formation:* thinly bedded; has layers of dominantly hematite, magnetite, siderite, or silicate alternating with chert that makes up about half the rock by volume; oolitic structure relatively rare except in hematitic and silicate facies of some areas.
5. Mineralogy. *Ironstone:* dominant oxide is goethite; hematite is fairly common, magnetite relatively rare; chamosite is primary silicate, glauconite (chlorite and stilpnomelane in metamorphosed ironstone) is minor; calcite and dolomite common constituents; pelletal collophane relatively abundant in some rocks. *Iron-formation:* no goethite; magnetite and hematite about equally abundant; primary silicate is greenalite, with minnesotaite, stilpnomelane, and chlorite in rocks of slightly higher metamorphic grade. Quartz (chert) a major constituent; dolomite present in some units but calcite rare or absent. Pelletal phosphate, chamosite, glauconite absent.
6. Chemistry. *Ironstone:* except for high content of iron, no distinctive aspects. *Iron-formation:* remarkably low content of Na, K, Al, and minor elements; phosphorus content generally much lower than in ironstone (Geijer, 1962); Mn/Fe ratio believed by some to be higher (Lepp, 1963).
7. Associated rocks. No distinctive differences. Both ironstone and iron-formation typically are interbedded with shale, sandstone, or graywacke, or their metamorphosed equivalents. Carbonate rocks—limestone and (or) dolomite in the ironstone sequences and dolomite in iron-formation sequences—not rare but subordinate to clastic rocks in immediately associated strata.
8. Relative abundance of facies. No gross differences apparent. Probable order of abundance for ironstone: oxide, silicate (chamosite), siderite, sulfide; for iron-formation, order is similar but siderite facies may be more abundant than silicate facies. Within oxide facies, however, magnetite is far more abundant in iron-formation than in ironstone.

Some of the differences in the above summary can be ascribed to greater degree of metamorphism or simple "aging" of the (generally) older rocks, which result in change of goethite to hematite, chamosite to chlorite, and possibly glauconite to stilpnomelane, but many features remain as distinctive to iron-formation. Chief among them are the notably greater abundance in the Precambrian, the greater dimensions, the interlayered chert, and the extremely low content of the alkalis, alumina, phosphorus, and minor elements.

* * * * * * *

Editor's Note: A row of asterisks indicates that material has been omitted from the original article. References for this article appear at the end of Paper 32.

22

Reprinted from *Econ. Geol.*, **59**(6), 1026, 1030–1041 (1964)

Origin of Precambrian Iron Formations

HENRY LEPP and SAMUEL S. GOLDICH

ABSTRACT

A statistical study of the chemical composition of the Precambrian iron formations of the Canadian Shield affords a new approach to the origin of these unusual formations. The average total iron content of 2,200 samples from the literature and from unpublished mining company analyses is 26.7 percent Fe. The average Fe content for 16 iron formations in the United States and Canada ranges from 24.5 to 34.1 percent. Low contents of Al_2O_3, TiO_2, P_2O_5, and CaO characterize the Precambrian iron formations compared to the relatively large amounts of these constituents in the post-Precambrian iron-bearing sediments. The chemical data emphasize that whereas iron, manganese, and silica were transported and deposited together in the cherty iron formations of the Precambrian, these same elements were chemically differentiated in younger geological time in large but separate deposits of iron and silica.

Isotopic age determinations indicate that cherty iron formations were deposited during a long interval of geologic time from approximately 1,700 to 3,000 million years ago. A model is proposed to explain the origin of the iron formations of the Lake Superior type based on the absence or marked deficiency of free oxygen in the atmosphere prior to the Late Precambrian. Lateritic weathering under these conditions permitted the transport of iron and manganese together with silica. The weathered mantle effectively retained aluminum, titanium, phosphorus, and colloidal clay.

Graphitic material of biogenic origin is closely associated with the Precambrian iron formations. Although it is uncertain whether iron was precipitated directly through biologic processes, the removal of CO_2 and the liberation of oxygen to the sea water through photosynthesis of primitive plants undoubtedly influenced the energy relationships among the iron minerals. As a result of the variable conditions the iron formations commonly are characterized by nonequilibrium mineral assemblages.

In Late Precambrian time a critical level of free oxygen in the atmosphere was attained permitting a marked acceleration in plant growth and in accretion of oxygen. This stage in the development of an oxygenated atmosphere was reached at least 1,200 million years ago and effectively curtailed the development of cherty iron formations of the Lake Superior type.

* * * * * * *

Editor's Note: A row of asterisks indicates that material has been omitted from the original article.

CHEMISTRY OF IRON FORMATIONS

General Statement

Mineralogy, texture, and structure, which generally have been the basis of iron formation studies, are mainly the result of depositional, diagenetic, and metamorphic conditions to which the particular rocks have been exposed. They are products of reactions that occurred during and following the deposition of these environment-sensitive sediments, and hence these properties are not useful as guides to the conditions that caused the accumulation of the iron-rich rocks. The chemical compositions of iron formations, on the other hand, reflect the overall geochemical conditions that produced these concentrations of iron in the lithosphere, and they hold answers to some of the fundamental questions of origin.

The success of applying the chemical approach to the problem of the genesis of iron formations depends largely on obtaining analyses of unaltered rocks. Iron formations are very susceptible to change by the weathering processes as is evidenced by the variety of direct shipping oxide ores formed by the selective leaching of the primary iron sediments. Newly formed ferrous formations are perhaps the most sensitive of all sediments to possible alteration. This fact coupled with the human tendency to sample and report the richer portions of a formation and with the economic factors that localize exploration in areas of known secondary orebodies, makes the problem of determining the exact compositions of unaltered iron formations difficult.

The average iron contents of 16 Precambrian iron formations in Canada and the United States are given in Table 1. Composite or average analyses for some Huronian iron formations are shown in Table 2, and the average compositions of four post-Precambrian iron formations are shown for comparison in Table 3.

Tenor of Iron

The tenor of iron of 16 iron formations from the Canadian Shield (Table 1) ranges from 24.3 to 34.1 percent iron and is remarkably uniform considering that the formations may differ in age by a billion years and that they have been exposed to a variety of diagenetic and metamorphic conditions. The uniformity is even more pronounced when mineralogical differences are considered. Some iron formations are composed chiefly of iron oxides and

TABLE 1

AVERAGE IRON CONTENT OF SOME IRON FORMATIONS OF THE CANADIAN SHIELD

Age	District (See Fig. 1)	Percent Iron	Ref.
Early Precambrian (Keewatin) > 2500 m.y.	Vermilion, Minnesota	34.1	(51)
	Ruth Range, Michipicoten, Ontario	32.7	(67)
	Goulais River, Ontario	31.0	(67)
	Kaministikwia, Ontario	30.1	(76)
	Nakina, Ontario	28.0	(91)
Middle Precambrian (Huronian) 2500-1700 m.y.	Cuyuna, Minnesota	26.1	(a)
	Mesabi, Minnesota	27.0	(32)
	Gunflint, Ontario	27.3	(26)
	Gogebic, Wisconsin-Michigan	28.3	(a)
	Marquette, Michigan	29.2	(32)
	Iron River, Michigan	25.0	(46)
	Mistassini, Quebec	28.8	(82)
	Jeannine Lake, Quebec	31.0	(b)
	Payne and Morgan, Quebec	24.3	(b)
	Quartz Lake, Quebec	31.8	(a)
	Matonipi Lake, Quebec	30.9	(a)

(a) This paper (b) Company news release, Northern Miner Press.

TABLE 2

COMPOSITE ANALYSES OF SOME MIDDLE PRECAMBRIAN (HURONIAN) IRON FORMATIONS

	1	2	3	4
Total Fe	28.81	26.11	28.3	26.1
SiO_2	31.22	51.12	46.0	42.9
Al_2O_3	0.14	1.31	1.3	2.2
Fe_2O_3	12.58	10.81	15.3	13.4
FeO	25.74	23.86	22.8	21.4
MnO	0.68	0.46	0.8	1.8
MgO	3.94	3.26	3.3	3.7
CaO	5.17	0.75	2.2	2.0
TiO_2	0.02	tr.	0.1	0.04
P_2O_5	0.13	0.04	0.1	0.3
CO_2	19.69	4.77	6.3	10.7
H_2O	0.54	3.43	1.6	1.4

1. Mistassini district, Quebec, composite sample of core from five diamond drill holes representing the Temiscamie Iron Formation, except for the lower argillite member (82, Table 1).

2. Main Mesabi district, Minnesota, average composition computed by Gruner (32, Table 11) from 14 chemical analyses of unaltered iron formation.

3. Gogebic district, Wisconsin-Michigan, computed from 32 analyses for major constituents and 10 analyses for minor constituents.

4. Cuyuna district, Minnesota, computed from 70 analyses for total Fe, SiO_2, Al_2O_3, MnO, P; 6 analyses for other constituents.

TABLE 3

COMPOSITE ANALYSES OF SOME POST-PRECAMBRIAN IRON FORMATIONS

	1	2	3	4
Total Fe	27.28	31.2	29.3	31.5
SiO_2	13.5	13.3	36.2	12.0
Al_2O_3	10.2	8.4	5.5	5.1
Fe_2O_3	3.0	9.2	-	45.1
FeO	32.5	32.0	-	-
MnO	0.7	0.2	0.3	0.12
MgO	3.5	1.6	0.8	5.4
CaO	5.0	7.1	2.9	12.2
TiO_2	0.3	-	0.25	0.16
P_2O_5	1.0	1.4	0.76	1.09
CO_2	19.0	20.0	-	17.1
H_2O^+	2.9	-	6.4	1.9
H_2O^-	8.0	-	-	-
Ignition loss	-	6.2	-	-

1. Cleveland district, Great Britain, average of main seam of Liassic ironstone (104).

2. Northamptonshire district, England, average of 12 samples of fresh Jurassic Northampton Sand ironstone (92).

3. Southern Clear Hills, Alberta, average of 5 analyses, Cretaceous (49).

4. Clinton Formation, New York, average of analyses reported by Alling (7, Table 6) with exclusion of Nos. 8, 10, 12, 13 and 14 which contain higher than normal iron for the Clinton and possibly represent weathered material.

TABLE 4

REPRESENTATIVE ANALYSES FOR TOTAL Fe OF FOUR MAJOR IRON FORMATION FACIES FROM THE CANADIAN SHIELD

	Carbonate	Silicate	Magnetite	Hematite
	20.5	26.3	29.5	36.5
	28.1	24.0	34.0	44.2
	27.8	26.2	27.5	34.1
	27.0	20.2	29.4	30.3
	28.0	23.7	27.9.	31.4
	25.2	34.0	26.2	33.1
	25.3	17.1	29.9	34.1
	27.1	26.8	29.5	32.9
	20.5	23.7	30.0	36.3
	31.3	24.9	35.6	25.5
Mean	26.08	24.69	29.95	33.84
Range	20.5-31.3	17.1-34.0	26.2-35.6	25.5-44.2

TABLE 5

ANALYSIS OF VARIANCE FOR DATA OF TABLE 4

Source	Degrees of Freedom	Sum of Squares	Mean Square	F
Between facies	3	509.13	169.71	10.48
Within facies	36	583.13	16.20	$F(0.95)(3,36) = 2.86$
Total	39	1092.26		

gangue, whereas others contain mainly iron carbonate or silicate and chert or carbonate. Such mineralogical differences (facies) account for much of the spread shown in Table 1. For example a siderite iron formation with 25 percent total iron would contain 31.2 percent total iron if the siderite were converted to hematite with no other change.

The averaged values of Table 1, of course, do not indicate the deviations shown by individual analyses. Actually there is a marked consistency in the contents of iron shown by individual 5- to 20-foot core samples of iron formation. The mean iron tenor of 2,200 core samples (Fig. 2) taken in Precambrian iron formations of northeastern North America is 26.7 percent Fe and the standard deviation is 4.7. Only 9 percent of the samples included in the frequency distribution contain over 35 percent total iron, and there

FIG. 1. Map of northeastern North America showing areas of Precambrian iron formations. Adapted from Geological Survey of Canada Map 1045 A-M4 (29).

is no question that many of these represent materials enriched by secondary processes because much of the drilling was near orebodies.

Facies Variations

The iron tenors shown in various tables of this paper and the analyses plotted in figure 2 represent the various iron formation facies. James (46) has described the principal facies of iron formations and indicated that they differ in iron content. Each facies, of course, may show a range of iron tenor but the ranges and means are different for different facies.

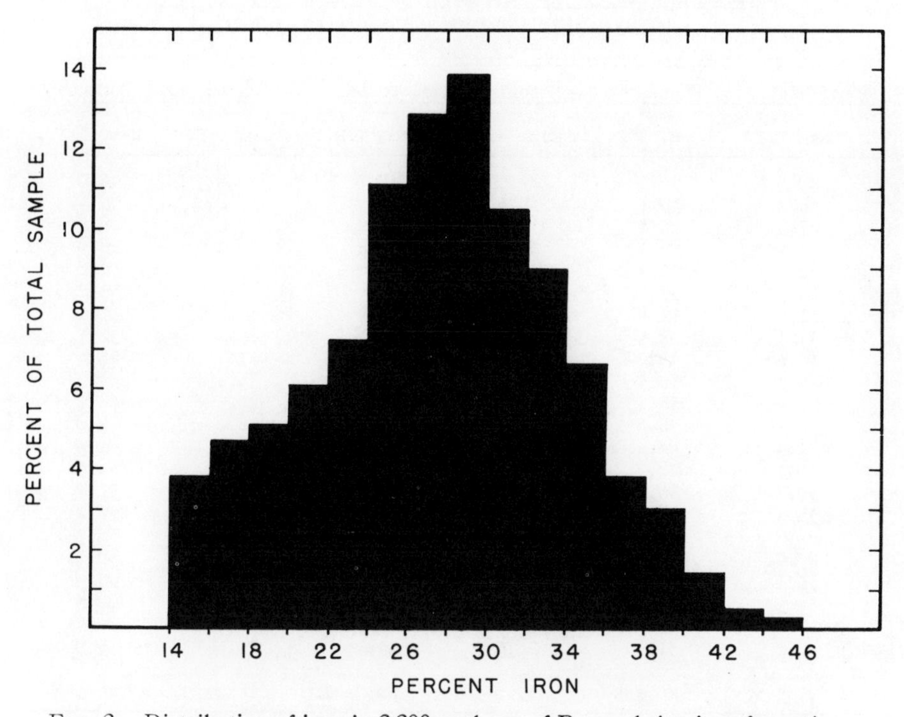

FIG. 2. Distribution of iron in 2,200 analyses of Precambrian iron formations.

Table 4 shows ten values of iron tenor for each of the principal facies of Precambrian iron formation. These values were drawn from published or private reports where the authors reported chemical and at least partial mineralogical analyses. Samples with iron distributed among siderite, magnetite, hematite (martite), and iron silicates in the ratio of 40:25:20:15, for example, were placed in the siderite category. Therefore a certain amount of mineralogic or facies overlap is unavoidably built into these figures.

The ten values for total Fe listed for the four types of iron formation in Table 4 were drawn by chance from collected analyses that ranged from a number of 30 for the carbonate facies to several hundred for the magnetite facies. The sample from which the figures in the table were chosen cannot be considered a true random sample of the conceptual population of all possible ten-foot core samples of Precambrian iron formations in northeastern North America on purely statistical grounds. Nevertheless the extensive drilling and mining of iron formations has shown that they are remarkably uniform in iron tenor, and since the tenor indicated by mining approximates the tenor of the samples employed, it seems not unreasonable to assume that the samples are representative.

TABLE 6

REPRESENTATIVE ANALYSES FOR TOTAL Fe OF MAGNETITE AND HEMATITE IRON FORMATIONS FROM MINNESOTA AND QUEBEC

	Mesabi district, Minnesota		Matonipi Lake, Quebec		Quartz Lake, Quebec	
	Mag. I.F.	Hem. I.F.	Mag. I.F.	Hem. I.F.	Mag. I.F.	Hem. I.F.
	29.4	34.1	24.5	27.8	35.4	40.0
	32.7	33.4	35.3	38.4	37.8	33.4
	27.5	20.5	31.9	31.2	39.2	28.6
	32.4	22.1	28.1	36.2	20.5	28.5
	28.5	30.1	26.9	33.0	20.3	30.8
	24.9	33.3	13.5	39.4	30.2	31.6
	31.2	31.4	30.5	30.4	34.4	35.1
	31.1	32.9	32.4	36.9	26.4	32.7
	32.6	32.7	19.9	26.7	31.1	28.4
	29.5	36.0	24.4	35.5	35.6	34.7
	27.9	34.1	36.2	30.8	29.6	32.2
	27.7	36.5	32.6	41.2	16.8	41.8
	31.4	44.2	25.6	38.4	28.7	41.9
	30.3	28.7	34.9	26.7	24.0	38.5
	30.7	36.7	25.9	21.2	34.7	31.7
	33.1	32.5	26.5	27.7	32.1	36.7
	29.5	34.1	28.3	41.5	31.4	38.7
	29.9	29.2	35.6	38.4	31.3	30.8
	33.1	23.4	27.2	27.7	20.3	35.9
	31.5	25.1	31.7	33.7	35.0	26.5
Mean	30.2	31.6	28.6	33.1	29.6	33.9
Range	27.5-33.1	20.5-44.2	13.5-36.2	21.2-41.5	16.8-39.2	26.5-41.9

The analyses of Table 4 were tested for homogeneity of variance by Cochran's test (14). Table 5 shows the analysis of variance for the facies data. There is a significant difference in the iron tenors of the facies even though many of the samples represent a mixture of minerals. James (46) reported chemical analyses of a number of representative examples of the various facies of Precambrian iron formations. The mean iron tenors calculated from his selected examples check closely with those of Table 4.

Table 6 contains total Fe analyses of 5- to 10-feet core samples of iron formation that were selected at random from a total of about 1,200 individual analyses. The analyzed materials had been logged as either magnetite or hematite iron formation and are considered to be representative of the total population of all possible core samples in each of the districts. It should be noted that where mineralogic studies were made the samples labelled magnetite iron formation also contained one or another of the iron silicates and varying amounts of hematite. Similarly the hematite iron formations invariably in-

TABLE 7

ANALYSIS OF VARIANCE FOR DATA OF TABLE 6

	Degrees of Freedom	Sum of Squares	Mean Square	F
Facies	1	343.07	343.07	12.65[a]
Areas	2	21.50	10.75	0.40[b]
Residual	116	3145.87	27.12	
Total	119	3510.44		

$F_{0.95}(1,116) = 3.91$ $F_{0.95}(2,116) = 3.08$

a/ = significant b/ = not significant

TABLE 8

VARIATIONS IN THE COMPOSITION OF CARBONATE IRON FORMATION

	1	2	3	4
Total Fe	24.66	25.0	25.16	25.34
SiO_2	27.43	32.2	42.37	39.52
Al_2O_3	0.23	1.5	n.d.	0.80
Fe_2O_3	1.64	0.6	1.09	1.05
FeO	30.28	31.6	31.41	31.67
MnO	0.77	1.9	n.d.	1.00
MgO	5.04	2.8	2.48	2.88
CaO	6.64	1.6	0.50	0.59
Na_2O	n.d.	n.d.	n.d.	n.d.
K_2O	n.d.	0.2	n.d.	n.d.
TiO_2	n.d.	0.0	n.d.	0.15
P_2O_5	n.d.	0.8	n.d.	0.02
H_2O	n.d.	0.2	n.d.	1.13
CO_2	28.03	24.8	21.80	21.15
C	0.016	1.8	n.d.	n.d.
S	n.d.	n.d.	n.d.	
Total	100.08	100.0	99.65	99.96

1. Upper sideritic chert member, Temiscamie Formation, Mistassini district, Quebec (81, Table 3, H).

2. Banded chert-carbonate iron formation, Iron River district, Michigan, recalculated by James to total iron content of 25.0 percent which is average for this member for the district (46, p. 253, Table 3, B).

3. Carbonate iron formation, Marquette district, Michigan (46, p. 253, Table 3, C, from Van Hise and Bayley, 1897).

4. Carbonate iron formation, Gogebic district. (Average of analyses II, III, IV and V in Irving and Van Hise (44) given in James (46, p. 253, Table 3, F).

clude some magnetite and, in fact, many of the samples are mixtures of martite and magnetite. The purpose of subdividing the analyses into the two categories magnetite and hematite (Table 6) was to determine if the difference between varieties is greater than the difference between regions.

The data of Table 6 were first tested for homogeneity of variance by means of Cochran's test. No heterogeneity was apparent at the 5 percent significance level. Similarly a test for "interaction" showed none. Table 7 clearly shows that the difference between fields or areas is negligible at the 5 percent significance level, whereas the difference between facies is significant at the same level. The mean of all of the hematite iron formation values is 32.9, whereas that of the magnetite samples is 29.5 percent iron.

The range in iron content shown by the various facies is close to that shown by the total formations as indicated in Table 1. Differences in diagenetic or depositional environments—facies differences—therefore can account for some and possibly all of the spread shown in Table 1.

Table 8 shows the average composition for carbonate members of several iron formations. As expected the iron tenor is remarkably constant within a given facies. The other major constituents, however, vary appreciably and appear unrelated to iron tenor.

The iron formations of the Mesabi district were subdivided into members by Wolff (106) on the basis of lithologic differences, and his terms slaty and cherty members are still widely used. Various investigators, notably Gruner (32), White (103), and Gunderson (34), have elaborated on Wolff's original classification. Textural and structural features are the basis of the expanded terminology including cherty, slaty, mottled, wavy, banded, conglomeratic taconite, and so forth. In general the slaty taconite is thinly laminated and contains a larger amount of iron silicates than the cherty taconite, which commonly is more massive and more likely to exhibit irregular bedding and mottled textures

The average compositions of slaty and cherty types of iron formation in the Biwabik Iron Formation of the Mesabi district are compared in Table 9. There are some differences in the composition, particularly in the minor constituents; however, the chemical differences are much less than might be expected from the marked physical differences of the two types of iron formation. There is a considerable difference in the ratios Fe_2O_3/FeO, which for the slaty members is 0.5 and for the cherty members is 1.0. The average contents of total Fe are similar, although that of the slaty taconite is approximately 10 percent less than that of the cherty variety. This is in keeping with the differences noted in total iron content of silicate-carbonate facies compared to the cherty magnetite and hematite varieties for the Canadian Shield. Silica, the major constituent, is remarkably similar in slaty and cherty members. Of the minor constituents Al_2O_3 and C are notably relatively enriched in the slaty taconite compared to the cherty variety.

Silica

As a group the Precambrian iron formations are characterized by their high content of silica. Chert and quartz are the chief gangue constituents, and the average content of SiO_2 is 43 percent with a range from 7 to 65 percent as opposed to an average of 13 percent and a range from 5 to 56 percent for the younger iron formations (Table 10). The distribution of silica in iron formations is shown in Figure 3. In a general way there is a reciprocal

TABLE 9

AVERAGE COMPOSITION OF SLATY AND CHERTY MEMBERS OF THE BIWABIK FORMATION, MESABI DISTRICT, MINNESOTA

	Slaty Members		Cherty Members	
	Average	No. Samples	Average	No. Samples
Total Fe	27.5	20	30.3	61
SiO_2	47.1	23	47.3	87
Al_2O_3	1.8	23	0.60	86
Fe_2O_3	12.6	17	20.7	41
FeO	24.8	17	19.4	41
CaO	1.1	23	1.3	85
MgO	2.9	24	2.0	87
CO_2	4.5	24	5.6	86
Mn	0.67	9	0.47	49
P	0.04	12	0.03	36
C	0.86	16	0.14	53
H_2O	3.82	17	2.47	74

TABLE 10

COMPARISON OF THE CHEMICAL COMPOSITION OF PRECAMBRIAN AND POST-PRECAMBRIAN IRON FORMATIONS

	Precambrian			Post-Precambrian		
	Average	Range	No. Samples	Average	Range	No. Samples
Total Fe	27.8	17.1 -44.2	158	29.0	15.2 -47.9	118
SiO_2	42.9	7.3 -64.6	158	12.9	4.5 -55.7	100
Al_2O_3	1.6	0.03-13.93	153	6.1	0.24-16.8	100
CaO	1.5	0.01-10.48	148	14.3	0.10-33.0	108
MgO	2.8	0.04-11.22	148	2.9	0.45- 7.84	59
MnO	1.0	0.01- 5.06	108	0.34	0.02- 1.80	57
P_2O_5	0.26	0.03- 4.02	87	0.86	0.14- 2.20	86
TiO_2	0.15	0.02- 0.52	37	0.45	0.17- 2.44	12
C	0.40	0.01- 3.05	57	1.11	0.58- 2.55	5 a/
CO_2	8.1	0.10-31.56	143	17.8	1.50-30.32	31
H_2O^+	2.5	0.05- 9.29	97	4.7	0.26-15.1	23

a/ Peace River, Alberta (49).

TABLE 11

CaO/MgO RATIOS OF IRON FORMATIONS OF DIFFERENT AGES

Age	Average	Range	No. Samples
Precambrian	0.59	0.008- 2.06	26
Paleozoic	8.0	0.03 -19.1	20
Mesozoic	8.8	0.62 -47.0	28

relationship between SiO_2 and CO_2 (Tables 2, 8) with the cherty oxide facies being high in SiO_2 and low in CO_2 and the sideritic carbonate facies showing the reverse. The interdependence of SiO_2 and CO_2 together with the high degree of uniformity in tenor of iron suggests replacement relationships between silica and carbonates in the Precambrian iron formations as will be discussed in a later section.

Lime and Magnesia

The most striking chemical difference between Precambrian and post-Precambrian iron formations is in CaO content, that of the Precambrian formations averaging 1.5 percent in contrast with 14 percent for the post-Precambrian (Table 10). The magnesia contents, however, are similar, 2.8 and 2.9 percent for the Precambrian and for younger iron formations, respectively. A large part of the magnesia is tied up in silicate minerals, and thus it is calcium, largely as carbonate, which sets off the two types of iron formations. This relationship is shown in the ratios CaO/MgO given in Table 11. The average value for CaO/MgO in 26 Precambrian samples is 0.59; whereas for 20 Paleozoic samples the ratio is 8.0, and for 28 Mesozoic iron formations the ratio is 8.8. The great difference in CaO and MgO contents of Precambrian and post-Precambrian iron formations is illustrated in the frequency distribution of the alkaline earths plotted in Figure 3. The

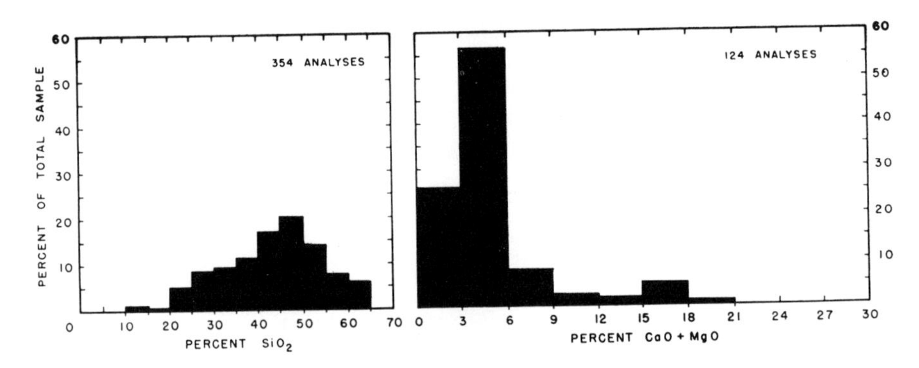

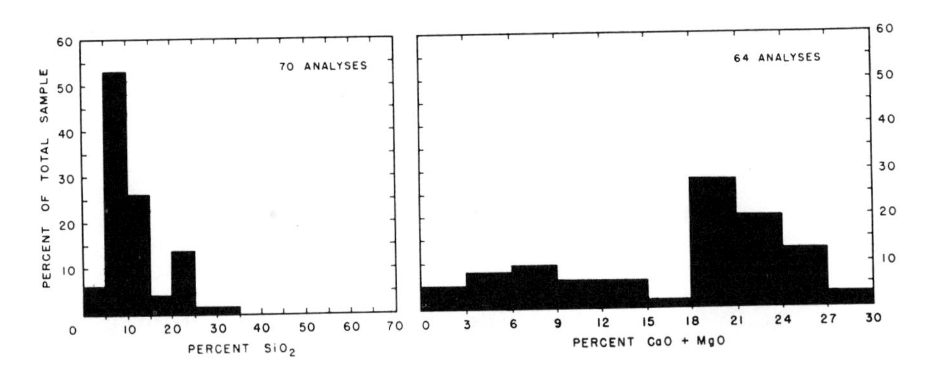

FIG. 3. Distribution of SiO_2 and of CaO+MgO in Precambrian and post-Precambrian iron formations.

larger content of CaO in post-Precambrian iron formations is reflected in their greater average content of CO_2 (Table 10).

Manganese

On the average (Table 10) the content of MnO is three times greater in Precambrian than in the younger iron formations. There are differences in the manganese contents of iron formations between districts and within districts; thus the Mn/Fe ratios, computed from the data of Table 2, are 0.018 for Mistassini, 0.014 for the Main Mesabi, 0.022 for the Gogebic, and 0.054 for the Cuyuna. Differences within a district are related to the facies. The carbonate facies of the Mistassini district (Table 8) has a Mn/Fe ratio of 0.024 as opposed to 0.018 for the Temiscamie Iron Formation as a whole. The slaty members of the Biwabik Iron Formation (Table 9) have a mean ratio Mn/Fe of 0.024 as opposed to 0.016 for the cherty members. The average Mn/Fe computed from Table 10 for Precambrian iron formations is is 0.028 compared to 0.009 for the post-Precambrian iron formations. The ratio for the average igneous rock is 0.025 (57). It is apparent that a marked geochemical separation of manganese from iron has been achieved in the post-Precambrian iron formations compared to the old Precambrian counterparts.

Alumina and Phosphorus

Important differences between the Precambrian and younger iron formations are in the small contents of alumina and phosphorus (Table 10) that characterize the older iron formations. The average Al_2O_3 content of the Precambrian iron formations is 1.6 percent, whereas that of the post-Precambrian is 6.1 percent. A large part of the Al_2O_3 is probably concentrated in the iron silicates, greenalite, stilpnomelane, and minnesotaite (32, Table 1) of the Precambrian formations. This is indicated in the average composition of slaty and cherty members of the Biwabik Iron Formation. The average content of Al_2O_3 for 23 samples of slaty iron formation is 1.8 percent compared with 0.6 percent for 86 samples of cherty iron formation (Table 9). The original source of the small amount of alumina can be attributed to a small quantity of colloidal alumina or very fine-grained clastic material that was either washed or blown into the basins of deposition.

The alumina in the post-Precambrian iron formations may be present in part in silicates such as chamosite; however, clay minerals are more abundant in these deposits which more commonly represent mixed sedimentation. The amount of alumina in iron formations appears to increase with time, but this increase is not a regular one.

The phosphorus content of Precambrian iron formations is low, averaging 0.26 percent P_2O_5 compared to an average value of 0.86 for post-Precambrian formations. The range in P_2O_5 (Table 10) is large, and variations can be expected between districts as well as within a district. The Cuyuna district may be cited to illustrate this point. An earlier average (32, Table 10, No. 4) based on five chemical analyses for the iron formation compares favorably in the major constituents with the figures for the Cuyuna composite of this paper (Table 2, No. 4); however, P_2O_5 is given as 1.28 percent compared to the value of 0.3 percent calculated from 20 determinations.

Carbon and Sulfur

Two constituents that have not been considered quantitatively in this study are carbon and sulfur. These are found in small concentrations throughout most iron formations and locally are in significant amounts. Analyses of graphitic argillites (45; 103) range up to 7 percent in carbon. The average C content of 16 samples from slaty taconite from the Mesabi district is 0.86

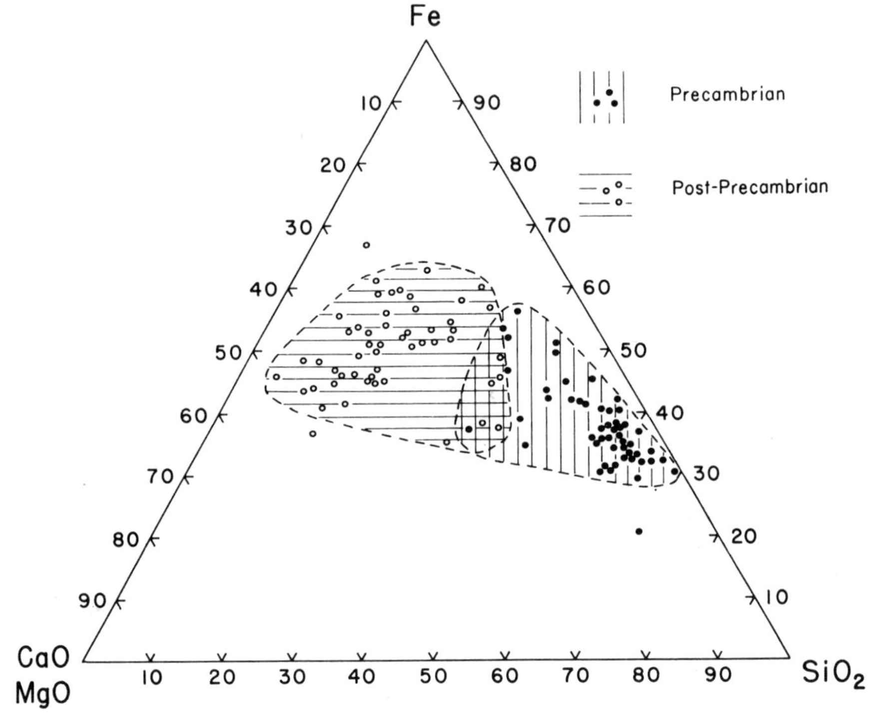

FIG. 4. Variations of $Fe:SiO_2:CaO+MgO$ in Precambrian and post-Precambrian iron formations.

percent, and for 52 samples of cherty taconite is 0.14 percent (Table 9). White (103, p. 13) notes the common association of pyrite with graphite in "black slaty taconite." An analyzed sample of graphitic argillite from the Iron River district of Michigan contains the equivalent of 38.7 percent of FeS_2 (45, p. 255).

* * * * * * *

Editor's Note: References for this article may be found at the end of Paper 27.

23

Reprinted from *Symp. Gisements Fer Monde, Internat. Geol. Congr., Algiers, II,* 1952, pp. 441–449.

CHAPTER IX

THE JURASSIC IRONSTONE FIELDS OF THE EAST MIDLANDS OF ENGLAND

by

Vernon WILSON*

In eastern England rocks of the Jurassic System extend as a broad outcrop from the north-east coast of Yorkshire to that of Dorset in the south. They are made up of *sands*, *clays*, and *limestones* which generally dip to the east or south-east at no more than 2°, and usually 1° or less. The harder beds form well marked hill ranges and other sharp features such as the Cleveland Hills, Lincoln Cliff, Edge Hill and the Cotswolds.

Amongst these Jurassic rocks, ironstones occur as local developments at certain horizons, and when traced laterally they pass into other types of sediment. Ironstones of economic value occur at three horizons (Fig. 7) in descending, order, as follows : —

(1) *The lower part of the Inferior Oolite*, that is, the Northampton Sand Ironstone in the *opalinum Zone* of South Lincolnshire, Rutland and Northamptonshire.

(2) *The upper part of the Middle Lias* or the *Marlstone Rock-bed* in the *spinatum Zone* of South Lincolnshire, Leicestershire and north Oxfordshire with adjacent parts of Warwickshire and Northamptonshire; in Yorkshire only the Main Seam of the *Cleveland sequence* falls within the *spinatum Zone*, the three lower seams belong in the *margaritatus Zone* below.

(3) *The middle part of the Lower Lias* in north-west Lincolnshire, that is, the *Frodingham Ironstone* extending from the base of the *semicostatum Zone* up to the top of the *obtusum Zone*.

As a consequence of the low angle of dip of these ironstones their outcrops are wide and, except in the Cleveland area, they have been exploited largely by opencast mining methods down to the present time (see Fig. 8).

Of all these Jurassic iron ores the Northampton Sand Ironstone provides the greatest variety of lithological types, many of which are similar to those present in the ironstones of other horizons, while others appear to be unique among the ores of this country. The principal iron bearing minerals found in all these ironstones are

(1) an iron carbonate — *siderite;*

(2) an iron aluminosilicate — *chamosite*, and;

(3) a hydrated ferric oxide — *limonite*, together with *pyrite* as a minor constituent and a variety of gangue minerals such as *calcite, quartz, collophane* and *kaolinite*.

(1) *Siderite*, usually impure and having a composition $FeCO_3$ 81 to 86 %, $CaCO_3$ 8 to 10 %, $MgCO_3$ 6 to 8 % and $MnCO_3$ less than 0.5 %, occurs in the fresh ore and as a replacement of chamosite ooliths and shell fragments, as aggregates and as a constituent of the matrix of the rocks.

(2) *Chamosite*, a green or grey-green alumino-silicate of iron occurs as the main constituent of ooliths which are regarded as of primary origin; it also forms areas of very fine paste in the groundmass and crystalline grains are occasionally numerous in the Marlstone ironstone. It has an approximate content of 30 % iron, 25 % silica and 19 % alumina, and conforms in composition to the empirical formula $2SiO_2$, Al_2O_3, $3FeO$, aq. in which some of the Al_2O_3 is replaced by Fe_2O_3 and some of the FeO by MgO.

(3) *Limonite*, the opaque brown or red-brown hydrated ferric oxide, with an iron content of

* Geological Survey of Great Britain.

Editor's Note: A row of asterisks indicates that material has been omitted from the original article.

60-62 %, results from the oxidation, both during sedimentation and later, of chamosite and siderite giving a mixture of hydrated iron oxide and a clay mineral, *kaolinite*. All stages from fresh chamosite to dense limonite may be seen among the ooliths, particularly in the Frodingham Ironstone. Limonite is the principal iron-bearing mineral in the completely oxidised ores of all types in the upper part of the oxidation zone. Crystalline birefringent *goethite* is also present though it is rare.

(4) *Pyrite* is widespread as a minor constituent of the ores and in major amounts only in such unworkable beds as the *Snap* band in the upper part of the Frodingham Ironstone; an occasional nugget of pyrite surrounded by crystalline calcite often occurs in this ironstone.

Among the gangue minerals *calcite* is the most widespread; it is the normal constituent of the abundant fossil fragments; it may also form the nuclei of Chamosite ooliths and in the *lime rich* ores it forms much of the fine-grained ground mass. Detrital quartz is often abundant in some of the ironstones in the form of scattered angular grains but excessive amounts may exert a controlling influence on the value of the ironstone as an ore. *The phosphorus* content of the ironstones is mainly due to the presence of the cryptocrystalline calcium phosphate mineral, *collophane*. *Kaolinite*, in mosaics of fibrous or vermicular form may replace ooliths; it also occurs in irregular pockets and veinlets, and in its fine-grained form is generally associated with chamosite and goethite. It is probably present in many ironstones where it is not obvious under the microscope.

Recent researches on iron-bearing minerals have been directed towards more accurate determinations of their optical characteristics and of their chemical composition.

a) THE NORTHAMPTON IRONSTONE FIELD

This field extends through Northamptonshire, Rutland, east Leicestershire and south Lincolnshire. Though richer in iron than the other bedded ironstones it is considered as a *low grade ore;* its iron content ranges from 28 to 35 %, *silica* 6 to 18 %, *lime* 2 to 10 %. The average content of 0.1 % of *phosphorus* renders it suitable only for basic steel making processes. It extends from Lincoln in the north to the neighbourhood of Stowe, Blisworth and Towcester in the south. The outcrop is narrow between Lincoln and Grantham but farther south it extends as a broad plateau reaching heights of 400-500 ft. in the west, and with deeply dissected valleys in the south. It has a gentle easterly dip with an average fall of from 30 to 40 ft. per mile. *Folding* and *faulting* are locally developed and usually on a small scale. More widespread is the development of *cambering* and associated superficial structures. This results from the movement of the underlying Upper Lias Clay from under the load of the Northampton Sand and higher beds which become cambered towards the valley floors and a vertical lowering of up to 100 ft. is often involved. These phenomena which have been fully described [10] present many local problems in the working of the ore.

Over most of the field the ironstone is between 12 and 20 ft. thick but the workable part is commonly the 7 to 12 ft. at or near the top of the bed; in some cases the whole of the bed may be workable. Generally the ironstone is persistent as a bed throughout the field but it shows variations in character and thickness. Variations in character arise from (*a*) *stratification* within the bed of sediments of differing composition, often unconformable to one another, (*b*) *lateral changes* in the sediments, and (*c*) *the effects of weathering* where the bed is in proximity to the present or preglacial land surface.

The Northampton Sand is divisible into five major lithological groups and workable ore is in the main confined to two of the groups, the other three consist of only poor quality ironstones. These subdivisions are as follows :

(5) Upper Chamosite-Kaolinite group } *unworkable*
(4) Lower Chamonite-Kaolinite group }
(3) Upper Siderite Mudstone Limestone group — *workable over a large part of the field.*
(2) Main Oolitic Ironstone group — *the principal workable beds.*
(1) Lower Siderite Mudstone Limestone group — *usually not worked.*

The Lower Siderite Mudstone Limestone group consists mainly of *sideritic limestones, siltstones* and *mudstones;* the overlying Main Oolitic Limestone group comprises *ooliths,* most commonly of *chamosite* but with subordinate limonite, siderite or kaolinite, set in a groundmass of siderite or of this mineral associated with calcite or chamosite. The Upper Siderite Mudstone Limestone group is represented over much of the field by more or less *sideritic mudstone* or *sideritic sandstone* which pass up, in the south-west, into higher sideritic limestones, mudstones, sandstones and oolitic limestones. The above subdivisions and their relations to one another are illustrated diagrammatically in Fig. 9 and their generalized distribution is shown in Fig. 10, which also shows the limits of the main workable part of the field. The western economic limit is defined either by the outcrop of the formation or by the passage of the ironstone into a sandy unworkable deposit, this is particularly apparent in the south-west beyond Northampton and Towcester. The eastern border of the field, where the Northampton Sand is largely buried beneath a cover of later rocks, is necessarily less clearly defined. It is determined by attenuation and ultimate complete disappearance of the Northampton Sand, by its assuming a siliceous character or by absence of the Main Oolitic Ironstone group leaving only the poor quality material of the other groups.

b) THE MARLSTONE IRONSTONE FIELDS

There are two areas in the East Midlands where the upper part of the Marlstone Rock-bed is developed as an economic ironstone, the northern area covers parts of south-west Lincolnshire, Leicestershire and Rutland, and the southern area covers a large part of north Oxfordshire with adjacent parts of Warwickshire and Northamptonshire.

In the northern field the Marlstone Rock-bed dips gently eastwards; it comprises a *fairly massive sandstone* in its lower part and a *ferruginous oolitic limestone* above which is largely of workable quality. The outcrop of this ironstone is about 30 miles long and extends from Leadenham, 14 miles south of Lincoln, southward to the vicinity of Tilton-on-the-Hill in Leicestershire. Throughout this area it is a low grade ore and is not everywhere of workable quality. In the north it is 5 to 6 ft. thick and averages about 20 % of iron, farther south in Leicestershire it forms a broad surface area and carries 23 to 26 % of iron. There are extensive workings in this area; 7 to 10 ft. are worked in quarries and at Holwell, where it is 14 ft. thick and contains over 30 % of iron, it is mined underground.

Farther south in Rutland the ironstone is not of economic quality by modern blast furnace standards.

The only other areas where the Marlstone Rock-bed contains any workable ironstone are at Burrough-on-the-Hill and Tilton-on-the-Hill farther south in Leicestershire. At the former locality it averages 8 ft. thick and it is about 18 ft. thick at Tilton, though here only the upper half of the bed is workable.

Structurally the field is simple there being only minor folds and faults; cambering and other superficial structures also occur.

No definite subdivisions of this upper ferruginous part of the Marlstone Rock-bed can be recognised though in some exposures there are local lenses of limited dimensions of highly fossiliferous and calcareous stone and occasional thin bands of mudstone. Evidence of interrupted sedimentation is common and usually represented by sharply defined erosion surfaces; wash-outs are also frequent.

The unoxidised rock of the Marlstone ironstone is a *sideritic chamositic limestone;* the dominant constituent being fragmental fossil material preserved in calcite which has generally been recrystallised. Siderite is present in *sharp rhombs* averaging 0.05 to 0.1 mm. across, scattered through the calcite matrix of the rock, or penetrating and replacing the fossil fragments. This mode of occurrence of siderite is a distinctive feature of the Marlstone ironstone. Chamosite forms ooliths of average diameter about 0.2 mm., some have fragments of crystalline chamosite for nuclei, while others are developed round quartz grains. *Pyrite,* in tiny cubes, is a common constituent of the unoxidised rock, occurring particularly within the recrystallised shell fragments. In this are and in the Banbury Field farther south the Marlstone ironstone is remarkably free from detrita material, but occasionally in some localities *clastic angular quartz grains* with subordinate fres *orthoclase* and a little white *mica* are present.

The southern Marlstone Ironstone field, or the Banbury Ironstone Field of north Oxfordshir and the adjacent counties to the north-west and east, is separated from that of Leicestershire b an intervening area in which the Marlstone Rock-bed is much reduced in thickness, or merely present as layers of nodules, or absent altogether. Near the head of the valley of the River Nene about 3 miles south-west of Daventry, it again becomes an ironstone and continues as such as fa south as the Evenlode valley near Charlbury, a distance of about 29 miles. Banbury is situate not far from the centre of this field (Fig. 11). In broad outline the structure of the Marlstone Rock bed in this field is that of a sheet dipping gently to the south-east with a gradient of 1 in 70. Th highest level reached by its base is 700 ft. O. D. on Edge Hill. It is, however, far from formin a uniformly dipping sheet, but the broad gentle folding that prevails is largely masked by *faulting* The major faults run generally either N.W.-S.E. or N.E.-S.W., but turn in places in the centra part of the field into a nearly E.-W. direction. The N.W.-S.E. faults occur mainly in the nort and the N.E.-S.W. faults occur in the south, so that the whole fault system when viewed in rela tion to the ironstone field has the appearance of radiating from a centre some 10 or 11 miles eas of Banbury. The distribution of these faults is such as to divide the ironstone field into relativel narrow belts of disturbed strata between which are broad undisturbed areas where the ironston is exploited and where development will continue in the future. In addition to these major struc tures superficial cambering is widespread in its effect in this field. The ironstone is cambere wherever its outcrop forms plateaux and broad spurs, and on valley sides where the general effec is to produce a nearly universal 'dip' of the ironstone towards the valleys.

The maximum thickness of 25 to 30 ft. of the Marlstone Rock-bed occurs within a broad bel extending southward from Edge Hill to Bloxham; east of this belt it thins to 13 ft. at Banbur and diminishes at about the same rate to the west. Southward from Bloxham the thinning i more gradual down to about 10 ft. near Fawler on the northern side of the Evenlode valley. T the north-east, in the vicinity of Byfield, the thickness is 9 to 10 ft. It is thought that the chie factor in reducing the thickness of the Marlstone Rock-bed towards the margins of the field wa the removal by erosion of its upper part before the deposition of the Upper Lias clays. Thes variations in thickness and the limits of the ironstone field are shown in Fig. 11.

Broad subdivisions of the Marlstone Rock-bed in this field can often be recognised in quarr faces but they never have more than a local application and, indeed, seldom extend for more tha a few yards. Though detailed examination reveals several distinct lithological types in the iron stone, their occurrence is irregular and impersistent. There are, however, two portions of th Rock-bed which are of more than local occurrence. One is a well defined *basement bed* of calcare ferruginous grit or breccia with pebbles of mudstone, chamositic or limonitic, and nodules whic in some cases are phosphatic. This bed has a sharply defined base which indicates a plane c non-sequence and erosion. The second distinctive feature occurs in the eastern part of the fiel where the Rock-bed has a *top layer* of tough, dense, green calcareous and oolitic stone characte rised by numerous *belemnites*. Its thickness is commonly 6 to 8 inches but in places it may l reduced to 2 or 3 inches. It seems probable that this layer is a *residual* or *re-sorted deposit* an indicates an interruption in deposition, accompanied by erosion and re-arrangement by submari currents and wave action, of parts of the ironstone already deposited, but unconsolidated.

Throughout the ironstone field the Marlstone Rock-bed is essentially a *sideritic chamositi chamosite limestone* made up of *shelly, crinoidal* limestone with varying amounts of iron compound in the matrix or as ooliths. Various combinations of the calcareous and ferriferous constituent give rise to a considerable variation in the rock, but there is no constant stratigraphical arrange ment of lithological types. All the available evidence suggests that the ooliths present were *orig.*

nally formed as *chamosite*, and in the unweathered green rock a considerable proportion of them consist, wholly or in part, of this mineral in amorphous or crystalline form. The chamosite of the ooliths may in part be replaced by siderite or by calcite, and even in the green stone many of them have become partly limonitized. The transformation to limonite is mainly due to sub-aerial weathering though in some cases it may in part be due to penecontemporaneous oxidation. The pale green amorphous chamosite also occurs as rounded bodies having no oolitic shape or structure, and as shapeless areas with an interstitial relationship to the other constituents of the rock. Chamosite also forms an important part of the mudstone of pebbles, lenses and interstitial matter of the rock, and of the cryptocrystalline groundmass of cloudy matter. *Siderite* occurs as crystals scattered in the cementing calcite and in the ferriferous mud as cementing interstitial material. *Calcite* is present as fossil debris and as cementing material, where *quartz* is visibly present most of it is of detrital origin. Of minor constituents, *phosphate* is present in some of the organic fragments; *sulphur* occurs in very small amounts and is probably accounted for by the presence of *pyrite* which is often visible in thin sections.

c) THE FRODINGHAM IRONSTONE FIELD

This ironstone field lies in N. W. Lincolnshire with the river Trent to the west and the river Humber to the north. The broad outcrop extends southward from the Humber for a distance of about 10 miles; the ore bed is lenticular in character with a maximum thickness of 32 ft. in the centre and tapering to about 12 ft. at the northern and southern limits of the workings. Beyond these limits the ore deteriorates and becomes interdigitated with shelly limestones and clays. This Lower Lias ironstone ranges from the *semicostatum Zone* up to the *obtusum Zone;* it is a condensed deposit represented in the south of England by some 200 ft. of clays. It has a gentle dip to the east of from 1° to 2°, and its broad outcrop is structurally simple, there being only an occasional small roll and faults of up to 20 ft. throw encountered in the opencast workings. Though the outcrops of the ironstone and later formations run north to south they are locally deflected to a south-easterly direction between Dragonby and Santon, this anomaly being due to the presence of a *monoclinal structure* which has also been affected by a system of *faults* on its north side (Fig. 12). These major faults will affect the future underground development of the concealed ironstone when the opencast workings are stopped by the prohibitive thickness of the overlying strata to the east. There are no superficial structures in this field. Generally up to 70 ft. of overburden is being removed from the ore bed and this overburden consists of the higher clays of the Lower Lias, about 100 ft. thick, covered by varying amounts of blown sand.

Throughout the field the ironstone is evenly bedded in layers averaging from 6 in. to 2 ft., while current bedding and wedge bedding occur locally; some layers are hard and massive while others are soft and friable. In a single working quarry there may be as many as 24 different seams in a single 25-ft. face; in addition each of these seams varies in analysis over a large range in a matter of a few yards. It is obvious then that this ironstone varies considerably in analysis in every direction within the bed. While it may be possible to recognise certain rock types in a series of quarry faces as Davies and Dixie have recently done [in 8], the character of those facies will continually change as the working advances eastward and those changes may be accompanied by some confusion of rock types.

Within the ironstone are also found intraformational bands of *reworked ironstone* which are most common in the northern half of the field, and also the persistent yellowish-grey mudstone band full of finely disseminated pyrites which occurs near the top of the bed in the southern half of the field. The reworked seams are usually only up to 2 to 3 inches thick, they are impersistent and occur at various levels in any quarry face or boring.

The Frodingham Ironstone, like the Marlstone Ironstone, is a *lime-rich ore*, the excessively calcareous nature of the stone being due to the presence of large numbers of thick calcite shells and the high proportion of limestone in its lower part. The dominant rock type is *limonite oolite* in which conversion of the chamosite in the ooliths to limonite has been for the most part completed before their incorporation in the ironstone. All stages from fresh chamosite to dense limonite may be observed among the ooliths, the concentric banding of which is preserved until a late stage in the process of oolith formation in these rocks. In the unweathered Frodingham ore many of the limonite ooliths are mantled with fresh chamosite, indicating an *alternation* of oxidizing and reducing conditions during deposition. Similarly an early generation of partly oxidized siderite may be enclosed in later fresh siderite.

The limits of this field to the north and south are defined by the deterioration of the ironstone and its lateral passage into shelly limestones and clays, these limits take effect within very short distances of the present workings in the north and south of the field. The eastern limit is unknown; the most easterly trial borings in the concealed area of the field in the Ancholme valley have proved the ironstone still to be of workable thickness and quality.

d) THE CHEMICAL COMPOSITION OF THE IRONSTONES

The usual chemical analyses quoted for the full workable thickness of any of the ore beds normally cover a variety of different subdivisions, possibly in varying stages of oxidation. In the following table the averages of a number of analyses of this nature for the different ironstones are set out.

		Fe	SiO_2	Al_2O_3	CaO	P	S	Loss on calcination	Moisture
NORTHAMPTON SAND IRONSTONE	Average of 65 samples of raw stone from different parts of the field	32.3	11.1	5.8	4.5	.72	.22	17.3	
	Average of 90 samples of dried stone from different parts of the field	35.6	12.2	6.9	3.6	—	.23	19.3	
MARLSTONE IRONSTONE OF N. OXFORDSHIRE, ETC.	Average of 21 samples from various parts of the field	23.8	7.7	5.8	21.7	0.31	—	—	
	Average of 43 trial borehole samples from different sites	24.7	10.5	7.4	11.2	0.22	—	—	
	Average of 73 samples from various parts of the field	24.6	9.6	6.7	13.0	0.25	—	—	
MARLSTONE IRONSTONE OF S. LINCS., E. LEIC. ETC.	Average values of siliceous ore	25.5	12.1	8.2	2.9	.3	.1	—	23.2
	Average values of limy ore	24.4	10.5	6.1	15.3	.5	.15	—	15.6
FRODINGHAM IRONSTONE	Average of 19 analyses of raw stone	22.6	8.1	5.07	18.15	.31	.16	—	10.73
	Average of 19 analyses of dried stone	25.4	9.06	5.67	20.3	.35	.18	—	—

They cover widely different points in the various fields and give some indication of the general composition of the ores being worked. The figures for the Northampton Ironstone illustrate the effect of *weathering* in *increasing the iron, silica* and *alumina* content and in *decreasing* the *lime and sulphur.* Variation in the chemical composi tion of the Northampton Ironstone within the ore field is controlled by three main factors :

(1) *The degree of weathering,* giving rise very broadly to high iron, silica and alumina and low lime and sulphur in the oxidized ore at outcrop and under shallow cover.

(2) *Lateral changes in the bed as a whole,* for example, the tendency to become limy locally in the western and south western parts of the field, or to develop a marginal siliceous facies.

(3) *The succession* in the Northampton Sand and the *nature of the subdivisions* which make up the ore bed in different parts of the field.

Of these three factors the third is the most important and it is frequently possible to interpret borehole analyses in the light of the standard lithological succession. Thus a low iron content combined with high silica and alumina is characteristic of rocks of the Chamosite-Kaolinite group. High iron combined with low alumina suggests a siderite mudstone. A rise in the percentage of silica unaccompanied by a rise in alumina is safe evidence of the sandy nature of the ore. High lime combined with low iron is suggestive of a sideritic limestone, usually at the base of the Northampton Sand. High lime combined with relatively high iron is more typical of a member of the Main Oolithic Ironstone group carrying plentiful calcite in the groundmass. The average chemical composition of the various types of ironstone is illustrated diagrammatically in Fig. 13. The ores are divided into three main classes :

(1) The unweathered ferrous ores in which the iron bearing compounds are siderite and chamosite.

(2) The unweathered ferroso-ferric ores in which, in addition to siderite and chamosite, limonite and exceptionally magnetite are present.

(3) The weathered ferric ores in which limonite (goethite) is the predominant iron bearing mineral and ferrous compounds are virtually absent.

Where a number of analyses of a particular rock type existed the diagram represents the average composition. Unweathered ferroso-ferric ores are confined to the oolitic types since ferric minerals are normally present only in the ooliths. Analyses of partially oxidized ore, *i. e.* of a combination of weathered and unweathered material, will, of course, yield diagrams of the ferroso-ferric types.

In the Marlstone ironstone fields the ore is primarily a *ferruginous limestone* in which the principal chemical constituents are iron, silica, lime and alumina. The relative percentages of the first three of these constituents principally determine whether the ore is workable or not. In the Lincolnshire-Leicestershire field the ranges of the average percentages of these constituents in a large number of samples of raw ore, as received, and ore dried at 100°C. are as follows :

Marlstone Ironstone	Iron	Silica	Lime
Raw ore, as received	21 to 33 %	7 to 10.5 %	1 to 18 %
Ore dried at 100° C	25 to 40 %	10 to 15 %	3 to 20 %

The leaching of calcite by *weathering* is the only effective cause of enrichment of the Marlstone ironstone. Samples with unusually high percentages of iron, say over 28 %, are nearly always from well weathered stone with a lime percentage of less than 10, but there are exceptions to this generalization. The ratio of combined silica to alumina approximates on the average to that in kaolinite and chamosite.

In the Northampton Sand Ironstone it has been found that the ratio of combined silica to alumina is *below* the *kaolinite* ratio in fresh ores while in oxidized ores it is commonly *in excess* of that ratio. This suggests that there may be some *removal of alumina* during weathering [4, p. 55]. In the case of the Marlstone ore, however, there is no evidence that the samples which gave silica in excess of the kaolinite ratio are on the average more oxidized than those which did not.

The small percentage of *phosphorus* in the Marlstone ironstone represents a proportion of 0.5 per cent to 50 per cent of iron, on the average. *Magnesia* is present in small and variable amount ranging up to about 3 per cent while *manganese* averages 0.47 per cent and about the same quantity of *titanium oxide* is present.

Reference has already been made to the extremely variable nature of the Frodingham Ironstone. The range of the percentages of the different constituents in the ironstone is as follows :

Iron	32.19	per cent to	17.69	per cent
Silica	17.94	—	3.66	—
Alumina	10.24	—	2.10	—
Lime	28.00	—	7.48	—
Phosphorus	0.45	—	0.20	—
Sulphur	0.42	—	0.05	—
Moisture	16.00	—	5.30	—

In a working quarry there may be as many as 24 different seams of stone in the face, some of which are of inferior quality and each of these seams shows considerable variation in analysis over every few yards; these variations have been studied in detail by ELLIOT [7]. Further, the average analysis of a vertical cut is subject to a wide fluctuation along the quarry face and ELLIOT [7, p. 22] gives the following figures for such variations along a 1,200 - yard face sampled at 25 - yard intervals :

Moisture %	Iron %	SiO_2 %	CaO %	Sulphur %
10.0-14.1	18.3-24.5	3.8-7.1	19.8-26.7	0.04-0.36

It is obvious then from these variations in all directions within the bed how difficult it is to dogmatise on the presence of ore types within the bed.

e) ORIGIN AND CONDITIONS OF DEPOSITION

It is generally agreed that all these bedded iron ores are *chemically precipitated sediments* dominantly of *marine origin* and are, in the main, *shallow water deposits*. Their most striking feature is the *constant recurrence of structures* indicating *erosion* and *redeposition*, particularly in the Marlstone and Frodingham ironstones. *Current bedding*, *intraformational breccias* and "*washouts*" occur in all these ironstones and are all suggestive of *shallow water conditions* with constantly interrupted sedimentation.

It is assumed that the iron was derived from *continental sources* by the normal processes of erosion. *Micro-organisms* are also believed to have played their part in the formation of these sedimentary ironstones for *algal tubules* and what are thought to be *bacterial structures* are occasionally observed in thin sections. The red marls and sandstones of the Trias probably provided most of the iron for the ironstones, while the limestones and clays of the Lias may also have contributed to the formation of the Northampton Sand. Older crystalline rocks no doubt provided some of the clastic material.

There is considerable divergence of opinion as to the chemical state in which iron is most commonly transported. Investigations of the composition of sea water substantiate the view that much of the iron it contains is *not* present in *true solution.* COOPER [6] has shown that the amount of iron in true solution in sea water as ferric or ferrous salts is very small, and may *only* represent some 10 % of the total iron in the water, the remainder occurring in *particulate form.* A considerable proportion of the total iron may be present in the *plankton; foraminifera* contain 0.16-0.65 per cent of ferric oxide in their tests and iron is present in *diatoms* in the ferrous state. HALLIMOND [1] has summarized the principal reactions involved in the precipitation of the minerals present in the bedded iron ores. *Chamosite* is regarded as resulting from the interaction of clay and ferrous iron. Once the solubility product for *chamosite* is reached the clay is progressively transformed into a chamosite mud. *Siderite* is believed to be precipitated from waters in which carbon dioxide is not present in sufficient amounts to maintain all the iron as the soluble bicarbonate. Precipitation would be encouraged in *warm waters* in which the degree of dissociation of the bicarbonate would be relatively high and also by the removal of carbon dioxide in the process of photosynthesis. While siderite mudstones are often associated with estuarine or deltaic formations it is evident that the precipitation of siderite does not occur solely under these conditions. Much of the siderite in the ironstones, however, is not a product of direct precipitation but results from carbonation of chamosite. The replacement of calcite by siderite, another important reaction, is evidently largely of post-accumulation date and was probably a penecontemporaneous reaction. Quartz, felspar and clay are also commonly replaced by siderite. Pyrite in some ironstones may be concentrated at particular horizons, in others it is a widespread constituent. In part it appears to be a primary precipitate, in part a penecontemporaneous replacement of shell fragments and ooliths. Its formation was probably controlled by the temporary development of stagnant patches in the basin where a local concentration of hydrogen sulphide resulted from the decomposition of organic material or reduction of sulphates under anaerobic conditions. Probably the most important part played by micro-organisms was in giving rise to reducing conditions in the deposits by acting on the organic matter in them.

In general, there is little evidence that iron compounds are being precipitated in any quantity in the sea at the present time. In particular, chamosite appears to be completely absent and siderite extremely rare in recent marine sediments. There seems little doubt that sea waters are today exceptionally poor in iron and it is clear that *attempts to explain the origin of the bedded ironstones in terms of present day conditions are unavailing.*

* * * * * * *

g) REFERENCES

The following memoirs of the Geological Survey contain full bibliographies of earlier writings on British Jurassic iron ores and their allied problems : —

1. HALLIMOND, A. F., Iron Ores : Bedded Ores of England and Wales. Petrography and Chemistry. *Spec. Rep. Min. Res. of Gt. Britain*, vol. XXIX, *Mem. Geol. Surv.* 1925,
2. HOLLINGWORTH, S. E., and J. H. TAYLOR, The Mesozoic Ironstones of England. The Northampton Sand Ironstone.— Stratigraphy, Structure and Reserves, *Mem. Geol. Survo.* 1951.
3. LAMPLUGH, G. W., C. B. WEDD and J. PRINGLE, The Bedded Ores of the Lias, Oolites and later formations in England. *Spec. Rep. Min. Res. of Gt. Britain*, vol. XII, *Mem. Geol. Surv.* 1920.
4. TAYLOR, J. H., The Mesozoic Ironstones of England : The Petrology of the Northampton Sand Ironstone Formation. *Mem. Geol. Surv.* 1949.
5. WHITEHEAD, T. H., W. ANDERSON, V. WILSON and D. A. WRAY, The Mesozoic Ironstones of England. The Liassic Ironstones. *Mem. Geol. Surv.* and other works include : 1952.
6. COOPER, L. H. N., Iron in the Sea and in Marine Plankton. *Proc. Royal Soc. London, Ser. B*, vol. CXVIII, pp. 419-438. 1935.
7. ELLIOT, G. D., Ironmaking at the Appleby Frodingham Works of the United Steel Cos., Ltd. *Iron and Steel Inst. Spec. Rep.* No. 30. 1944.
8. HALLIMOND, A. F., and others, The Constitution and Origin of Sedimentary Iron Ores : A Symposium, *Proc. Yorks. Geol. Soc.*, vol. XXVIII, pp. 61-101. 1951.
9. HATCH, F. H., The Jurassic Ironstones of the United Kingdom.— Economically Considered. *Journ. Iron and Steel Inst.*, vol. XCVII, pp. 71-125. 1918.
10. HOLLINGWORTH, S. E., J. H. TAYLOR and G.-A. KELLAWAY, Large scale superficial structures in the Northampton Ironstone Field. *Quart. Jour. Geol. Soc.*, vol. C, pp. 1-44. 1944.

The publications : 6, 7, 8, 9 and 10 are also referred to in the text.

24

Reprinted from *Econ. Geol.*, **63**(3), 262–270 (1968)

The Formation of Sedimentary Iron Minerals

C. D. CURTIS and D. A. SPEARS

Part II. The Application of the Thermochemical Data to the Iron Minerals in Certain British Sedimentary Rocks

D. A. Spears

Introduction

In the first part of this paper reference has been made to the physico-chemical differences that exist in modern sediments between the depositional waters and the water entrapped in the sediments. The importance of variations in the concentrations of reactant species in the formation of the iron minerals has also been stressed. The stability fields have been illustrated not by plotting Eh against pH, but by the more useful plot, so it is believed, of Eh against concentration. The conclusions from the thermochemical calculations are applicable to modern sediments, and in Part II of this paper it is hoped to demonstrate how they can also explain many of the features of iron minerals in sedimentary rocks. The iron minerals in Coal Measure sediments will be dealt with before extending the discussion to include the Jurassic rocks.

Iron Minerals in the Coal Measure Sediments of Yorkshire

The two main iron minerals occurring in the Coal Measure sediments of Yorkshire are pyrite and siderite. Most of the pyrite occurs as framboidal spherules, 4–8 microns in size (Love, 1965), whereas the siderite typically occurs as nodules flattened parallel to the bedding. The nodules are very abundant in parts of the sequence and in the past they have been worked as ore. Within the cyclic Coal Measures certain sedimentary units characteristically contain the pyrite and the siderite, and their occurrence may even be used to define such units. Thus Robertson (1933) described an idealized cycle from the South Wales coalfield and gave a calcareous, pyrite shale or impure limestone as one unit, overlain several units higher by a non-marine mudstone commonly containing ironstone bands and nodules. This is the ideal, for the marine shales may be absent, and if present they are unlikely to contain a band of limestone. One such band will be described below but it is unique in many respects. The important point, however, is that shales with a rich marine fauna contain pyrite, and that these are overlain by mudstones in which non-marine lamellibranchs and siderite are commonly associated. Pyrite is succeeded by siderite upwards through the sedimentary cycle and this is by no means restricted to the Coal Measures, for these are two of the iron facies of James (1954). The oxide and the silicate facies are the other two, and although iron oxides and chamosite have been recorded from the Yorkshire Coal Measures (Carruthers, 1923; Deans, 1934) they are quantitatively unimportant.

A detailed study has been made of a sequence of Coal Measure shales and mudstones from a National Coal Board borehole at Little Smeaton (Grid. Ref. 44/528168). This contains one of the more important marine horizons, the Mansfield (Aegir) Marine Band. In this borehole the marine section is about 4.5 m thick of which only the basal 1.5 m contains a rich fauna. In this sequence the siderite facies overlies the pyrite facies, and because this is typical any conclusions may have widespread application. The explanation most often advanced to account for the change in the iron minerals is one of variations in the Eh controlled by the depth of water. The pioneer work of Krumbein and Garrels (1952) and particularly their diagram (Fig. 8, p. 26) showing the stability fields of haematite, siderite and pyrite, has been quoted in support of this argument, but usually without regard to the anion concentrations and as noted in part I, Garrels and Christ (1965) state that such disregard may invalidate the use of the stability diagrams. In addition to not taking variations in anion concentrations into account this explanation, based on the Eh in the bottom waters, makes no allowances for the fact that if the iron minerals formed in the sediment, then the relevant physico-chemical conditions are those in the sediment and not in the overlying water. These two points are considered in detail in the following discussion.

One question is, therefore: did the iron minerals develop below the water-sediment interface, that is to say, are they diagenetic? The form of both the pyrite and the siderite suggests that this is so. The tiny framboidal spherules of pyrite in these rocks are analogous to those that develop in modern sediments during diagenesis (Love, 1965, p. 189). The flattened nodules of siderite also suggest development within the sediment, where the minimum stresses were horizontal, although of course compaction must have been important. Furthermore, the shale adjacent to the nodules usually appears concordant as though the nodules pushed the sediment aside as they were growing. According to Strakhov (1953, translation p. 37) concretions such as these have only been recorded in the deeper levels of modern sediments, which is good evidence that they are of late diagenetic age. Some aspects of the geochemistry also support the case for a diagenetic origin. For example, the iron minerals extracted part of the iron from the sediment itself (Spears, 1964; Curtis, 1967) and presumably, therefore, they developed surrounded by sediment. Iron also comes from an external source, and as pointed out by Curtis (1967) the ratio of the two types of iron remains constant for the one section irrespective of the iron mineral involved. This he believes is due to iron passing into solution from the lattices of the clay minerals on the one hand, and from a precipitated ferric oxide or hydroxide on the other.

The thermochemical calculations show that very low Eh values are required for the formation of pyrite and siderite, and if it can be shown that these values were not reached in the bottom waters then a diagenetic origin is indicated. As noted earlier, values as low as −0.172 v. have been recorded at depth in the stagnant waters of the Black Sea (Skopintsev et al., 1966). The sea in which the Mansfield sediments accumulated was much shallower however. Terrestrial deposits occur in the borehole only 26 m above the marine strata and therefore, even allowing for compaction the total depth of water was unlikely to have been in excess of 100 m. The sea was also widespread and it is thought that circulation took place, which would inhibit the development of low Eh values in the bottom waters (see Richards, 1965 for a discussion of anoxic basins).

A benthonic fauna is absent and this might be used as evidence in support of reducing conditions in the bottom waters. Although the absence of such a fauna demonstrates that the bottom was inhospitable it need not follow that this was due to the Eh—the physical condition of the fine grained sediment could be responsible. Geochemical evidence of water circulation is provided by the high contents of elements such as U, Pb, Cu, Ni, and Mo in the marine shales. This concentration from the seawater can only have been achieved if there had been renewal of the water body, thus inhibiting the development of very low Eh values in the bottom waters. As pointed out in Part I hematite and other ferric compounds would be stable under these conditions and such iron would be accompanied by manganese. These two elements do correlate with each other in the Mansfield sediments and hence this is also evidence against a very low Eh in the bottom waters.

A case can therefore be made for the sub-surface development of pyrite and siderite on two lines of reasoning, one that there is evidence of these minerals having grown in the sediment, and the other that this is where they must have grown because the Eh in the bottom waters was insufficiently low. If they are diagenetic then it follows that the change from one facies to the other is due to a variation in the physico-chemical conditions within the sediment, which could possibly be unrelated to any variation in physico-chemical conditions at the sediment-water interface.

The first point dealt with, it now remains to be seen if there is any evidence of variations in the concentration of anions affecting the final mineral assemblage. It will be appreciated from Part I of this paper, and Figure 4 especially, how pyrite forms at low Eh values in preference to other iron minerals, unless the concentration of other anions is very high. The change in the iron facies from the pyrite to the siderite could therefore indicate a decrease in the availability of sulfur species. The growth of the siderite stability field at the expense of the pyrite field as the availability of the sulfur species falls has been emphasized by Huber (1958). With this information very much in mind, Dunham (1960, p. 259) suggested that when siderite is forming the reactions involving sulfur are insignificant. This is consistent, so he believes, with the petrographic evidence from most Carboniferous and Jurassic ironstones where the pyrite is local in distribution and clearly of late diagenetic origin. It is therefore clear that the concept of a decrease in the sulfur species being responsible for a change in iron facies from pyrite to siderite is by no means new. Is there any evidence in support of this possibility? Berner (1964) has shown that given a suitable source of utilizable organic matter, the rate of generation of sulfide species by the sulfate reducing bacteria is governed by the rate of sulfate diffusion from the overlying water. The amount of diffusion downwards depends on the concentration of sulfate in the overlying water, and on the rate of sedimentation. During the deposition of the marine sediments in the Mansfield section not only was the sulfate content of the overlying water higher, but the rate of sedimentation was also slower. Thus conditions were ideal for the production of sufide species in these marine sediments, and probably in similar horizons in the Coal Measures. From the pyrite to the siderite facies it is therefore very unlikely that anion concentrations remained constant, almost certainly the concentration of sulfide species fell due to a decrease in the amount of sulfate reduction. A little iron may have reacted to form pyrite, the remainder was then available for reaction with dissolved CO_2 to form siderite. Because changes in salinity and in the rate of sedimentation tend to vary sympathetically in these sediments it is not easy to separate their effect on the sulfate availability. In another section of the Mansfield sediments (Bilby borehole, National Coal Board, Grid Ref. 43/638832) the rate of sedimentation was higher than at Little Smeaton, and in this case abundant siderite nodules are to be found lower in the section and well within the marine strata. This indicates how important the rate of sedimentation must have been on sulfur availability.

The control of the rate of sedimentation is also thought to be responsible for the variation in the composition of the carbonate band within the marine section (Taylor and Spears, 1967). A slow rate leads to sulfate reduction and immobilization of iron as pyrite and the original carbonate alters to ankerite. On the other hand, a high rate enables more iron to compete for lattice sites and siderite is the resulting product. The formation of siderite by these means was outlined in part I; it is also the method of formation advocated by Goldschmidt (1954) for all of the siderite in the sedimentary series, including coal-bearing strata. This was so, he suggested, because it was only under these conditions of oxygen deficiency that siderite would be stable. This has been confirmed by the present stability diagrams. It is doubtful, however, if siderite need always be a replacement of a primary carbonate. In the Yorkshire Coal Measures the band of ankerite-siderite described above is one of the few original deposits of $CaCO_3$, perhaps the only one. There is no evidence of original $CaCO_3$ in the nodules and bands of the siderite facies—it is suggested that these may well have been primary diagenetic precipitates.

It is thought that the pyrite facies is succeeded by the siderite facies because a fall in the concentration of reduced sulfur species left an excess of iron to react with the dissolved CO_2. Although a somewhat passive role has been assigned to the dissolved CO_2 this does not mean its concentration remained constant. Indeed, studies on modern carbonates have shown how complex are the controls on the CO_3^{2-} concentration. The siderite is thought to have formed during diagenesis and it is therefore possible that the CO_3^{2-} was also produced at this time. If of diagenetic origin the bacteria were undoubtedly important (Sisler, 1962) and it may have been that in the siderite facies environmental conditions favored the production of CO_3^{2-}. Alternatively conditions may have been just as suitable, perhaps more so, during the earlier pyrite facies. In this case a gradual build up in the concentration of the CO_3^{2-} in the pore waters could be envisaged, which only reacted with the iron when the reduced sulfur species were no longer dominant and as the pore waters were being expelled upwards during compaction. Bearing in mind the discussion in Part I on the stabilization of siderite, it is also possible that the siderite formed at this time and was then later redistributed. The upwards replacement of the one iron facies by the other can therefore be explained in terms of the sulfate availability. Migrating pore waters also have some bearing on the origin of the iron in the diagenetic minerals. In the earlier discussion it was stated that part of the iron is extracted from the sediment itself, whereas the remainder originates from some external source. The iron extracted from the sediment almost certainly is extracted from within the clay structures. The external source was probably a precipitated ferric oxide or hydroxide which went into solution during diagenesis and reacted to form the diagenetic minerals. This ferric phase may have been precipitated onto the sediment at the site of sedimentation, or alternatively during weathering, and carried in with the detrital sediment, especially as coatings on grains. These surface films are important as a source of iron (Carroll, 1958) and from the evidence of primary red beds in the sequence it is highly likely that these surface films existed on the original Coal Measure sediment. Providing the Eh fell during diagenesis these films would be destroyed and the iron redistributed. This would be achieved by concentration gradients and the actual movement of the pore water itself due to compaction. In view of this redistribution, and the amount of detrital material present in this and other Coal Measure sequences, it is conceivable that all the iron now present was carried to the site of sedimentation as part of the detrital load, and that none actually precipitated onto the sediment.

Thus to summarize, the pyrite and the siderite facies are present in the Yorkshire Coal Measure and based on the evidence from one short sequence it has been argued that these minerals are entirely diagenetic, and that the upwards succession can be attributed to changing anion concentrations.

Iron Minerals in the Jurassic of England, and of Yorkshire in Particular

One shortcoming of the proceeding discussion is that with only two main iron minerals present in the Coal Measures the application of the thermodynamic theory is somewhat limited. This can be overcome by considering the Jurassic where the range of iron minerals is greater. Furthermore, because of their recent exploitation, and in some cases current economic value, these iron minerals have received rather more attention than have those in the Coal Measures. Noteworthy memoirs giving comprehensive accounts of the Jurassic ores have been published by the Geological Survey, including Hallimond (1925) and Taylor (1949). These two authors also contributed to a symposium held by the Yorkshire Geological Society in 1949 on the constitution and origin of sedimentary iron ores. Another paper of this symposium, which will be referred to in the following account, was presented by Hemingway (1951). Finally an excellent relationship to other sedimentary iron ores and current hypotheses on their origin, is to be found in Dunham (1960).

In the Jurassic there are cycles of sedimentation, as in the Coal Measures, in which there is a progressive decrease in the depth of the water as sedimentation proceeds. Three such cycles have been described from the Lias of Yorkshire by Hemingway (1951), and although differing both in scale and tectonic setting, nevertheless siderite again overlies pyrite in the cycle. The pyrite is to be found in the black shales and the siderite in the gray shales. The ideal cycle being a black shale-gray shale-sandy shale or sandstone-ironstone. It was also shown by Hemingway how closely the lithologies of these sediments, with the exception of the ironstones, could be related to the sediments now accumulating in the Black Sea. He therefore concluded that the succession was deposited under conditions comparable with those in the Black Sea, except in depth, during an infilling of the Lias sea over Yorkshire. The changing mineral assemblages he attributed to an increasing degree of oxidation through the cycle—a concept since extended by such authors as James (1954) and Borchert (1952, 1960, 1965). The Lias sea was widespread and over Yorkshire probably did not exceed a few hundred meters in depth. By analogy with modern environments it could be argued, as for the Coal Measures, that it was not stagnant. Even if it had been stagnant it is probable that the low Eh values required for the formation of pyrite and siderite were only attained within the sediment itself. Furthermore, if these minerals are diagenetic, the pH-Eh values in the sediment could be independent of any variation in the overlying water. Clearly, however, the siderite and pyrite facies are related in some way to the depth of water, and if the control was not an Eh variation with depth, what are the possible alternatives? As in the Coal Measures it could be that as the depth of water decreases so the rate of sedimentation increases due to nearness to the shore. The rate of sedimentation, so it was claimed in the proceeding section, can adequately account for the disposition of the two facies because of its control on sulfate reduction. The Lias is a marine sequence and therefore in this case the control of salinity on the variation in sulfate reduction can be eliminated. With the exception of salinity, however, all other controls on the pyrite and siderite facies could be essentially the same for both Coal Measures and Jurassic—the source of iron could also be detrital.

In the Lias of N. Yorkshire (Cleveland) the cycle of sedimentation terminates with an ironstone. The main ironstone types are a sideritic chamosite oolite and a siderite-chamosite mudstone. Thus the ironstones belong to the carbonate-silicate facies of James. The iron minerals were in fact related to the work of James by Dunham (1960, p. 255) who stated that three of the four facies were present, and the oxide facies, although better represented by the Frodingham ore of Lincolnshire, might be said to be presented by the local magnetite oolite at Rosedale. Before discussing the mineralogy of these and other ironstones, the position of the ironstone in the sedimentary sequence calls for some comment. The ironstone in the cycle, according to Hemingway (1951, p. 72), is equivalent to the limestone in the shale-sandstone-limestone cycle of the Middle and Upper Jurassic of the South of England. This is so because the depositional cycle was accompanied by an erosional cycle, and concomitant with the basin silting up peneplanation was achieved. Chemical deposits were thus able to form in the basin because of a lack of clastic material. Why the chemical deposits should be limestones in one case and ironstones in the other might be related, so Hemingway suggested, to the former accumulating in a widespread shallow sea, and the latter in a more restricted arm of the sea, which nevertheless retained full connection with the ocean, as their normal fauna demonstrates.

The environment in which the Northampton Sand ironstone was deposited is thought to be somewhat similar to the Cleveland ores. Thus Taylor (1949, p. 79) envisages a shallow, epi-continental sea, gulf or lagoon freely connected with the open sea and subjected to considerable wave and current action. Evidence of this action is provided by the structures indicative of erosion and redeposition of the sediments, and which, according to Hallimond (1925, p. 9), is one of the most striking features of the British bedded ironstones. The Frodingham ironstone is thought by Hallam to have been deposited on a marine shoal, isolated from the land (1963). The important palaeoecological work by this author shows that the fauna in the ironstone is again normal, for it is typical of that which flourished elsewhere at the same time with few exceptions. The study of the fauna also shows the ironstones are a condensed sequence (Whitehead et al., 1952, p. 70; Hallam, 1963, p. 572). In the oolitic types of ore, a rich bottom fauna occurs, and thus it can be argued that the sea floor was oxygenated. On the other hand, fossils are absent in the siderite-chamosite mudstones, and therefore the bottom conditions are thought by Hallam (1963) to have been reducing. This type of ore is, however, according to Davies and Dixie (1951, p. 93), the least important at Frodingham, and only occurs as discontinuous bands up to an inch or two in thickness. The distribution of fossils in the Cleveland Main Seam is apparently similar for Tate and Blake (1876) record that they are almost entirely confined to the oolitic portion. Shell fragments do occur in some of the siderite mudstones from the Northampton Sand ironstone (Taylor, 1949). Nevertheless the relative unimportance of fossils in the mudstones need not mean that the bottom waters were reducing as the Eh is certainly not the only palaeoecological control. It would thus appear that the ironstones were deposited in a shallow marine environment which was neither stagnant nor reducing, and yet ferrous minerals abound. One way in which this difficulty has been overcome in the past is by postulating temporary stagnant areas in the main basin. Alternatively it has been postulated for some time that bacteria may be important (Hallimond, 1925, p. 14) and since the important work of Zobell (1946) it has been suspected that diagenetic reactions are important in the ironstones and especially those causing a fall in the Eh (Taylor, 1949, p. 84; Hemingway, 1951, p. 70).

Strakhov's work (1953) must be singled out for special mention in this connection for having recognized the importance of diagenesis in modern sediments he argued that diagenesis was just as important in the sedimentary ores. Based on the thermochemical information, it is clearly this approach that finds favor in the present account. In the following pages the petrography of the iron minerals will be reviewed in turn in the light of the thermochemical conclusions.

Pyrite.—Pyrite is a widespread component of the ironstones, and although only traces are generally present, occasionally it becomes the major component as in the "Sulphur Bed" of the Cleveland Main Seam. The "Sulphur Bed" is a pyrite oolite, and Hallimond concluded (1925, p. 54) from the petrography that the pyrite replaced existing chamosite structures, and that this took place in the sea floor material. This diagenetic origin of the pyrite was confirmed by Dunham (p. 47) in a re-examination of the "Sulphur Bed." In addition to replacing ooliths and matrix, pyrite may also replace shell fragments as in the Northampton Sand Ironstone (Taylor, 1949, p. 83) and once again a diagenetic origin can be invoked. Pyrite also occurs as tiny crystals that are thought to have been primary precipitates as there is no evidence of replacement. Taylor suggested (1949, p. 83) that they were precipitated onto the sediment in temporary stagnant patches in the basin. The alternative is that they precipitated within the sediment itself, and as their form is analogous with that of modern diagenetic pyrite this is believed to be the correct explanation. The petrography therefore favors a diagenetic origin for the pyrite, and in the environment in which the ironstones are thought to have accumulated this is consistent with the thermochemical calculations.

Somewhat problematical is the control on the pyrite abundance. Generally it would appear that the shales associated with the ironstones are richer in pyrite. Thus, for example, two average sulfur contents of the ore from the Cleveland Main Seam are 0.05% and 0.20% (Stead, 1910) whereas the sulfur content of the shale which splits the seam is somewhat higher. This was confirmed by Whitehead et al. (1952, p. 44) for an analysis of a bulk sample of this shale showed 1.98% pyrite to be present. According to Hallimond (1925, p. 47) this is reflected in analyses of impure Cleveland stone which often show a correspondence between the content of sulfur, and that of silica, representing detrital or shaly matter. In the Frodingham Ironstone Davies and Dixie (1951, p. 86) have noted that the ore becomes interleaved with pyrite-bearing shales southwards. The abundance of pyrite in the ironstones may therefore be related to the amount of detrital material. One explanation for this is that an increase in the detrital inorganic matter was accompanied by an increase in the detrital organic matter, and it was this that was utilized by the sulfate reducing bacteria. The average organic carbon content of the Cleveland ore is low [0.27% and 0.20% are the two averages quoted by Stead (1910)] whereas the content in the shale split is higher [6.67% for one bulk sample Whitehead et al. (1952, p. 44)]. In the case of the "Sulphur Bed" a high initial concentration of organic matter due to floating vegetation might be postulated as driftwood is common in the Main Seam (Hallimond, 1925, p. 53). Whether or not the organic content did control the pyrite abundance it is clear that during the formation of the major part of the ironstones reduced sulfur species were unimportant. The small amount present was able to react with iron leaving the system relatively unaffected.

Siderite.—Siderite, unlike pyrite, is one of the major minerals in the ironstones where it occurs both as ooliths and in the matrix:—these two modes of occurrence will be discussed in turn. As for pyrite, the calculated Eh of formation is low and a diagenetic origin would again be expected.

The structure of the ooliths in the ironstones is analogous with those in limestones, and this led Sorby (1857, 1906) to suggest that the ironstones were first deposited as oolitic limestones that were subsequently altered. There is little evidence, however, of the replacement of calcite, and most authors have accepted Hallimond's argument (1925, p. 92) that the ooliths are comparable because they developed under similar physical conditions, that is by the action of gentle currents in shallow water. Siderite occurs in the ooliths, but according to Hallimond (1925, p. 92) it is nearly always secondary after chamosite, ooliths of the latter mineral being superficially converted to siderite in granules or rhombs. The possibility of a little of the siderite being a primary mineral in the ooliths was not eliminated however because the evidence of ooliths coated with an outer siderite layer was considered inconclusive. Taylor (1949, p. 82) in dealing with the Northampton Sand Ironstone is more definite however, for he states that "in no case have primary ooliths of siderite been recorded, and it appears that for some reason siderite is not readily precipitated in the form of ooliths." Dunham (1960, p. 256) too concludes that in the region where the ooliths are forming only limonite and chamosite are the stable phases, and not siderite; based on the evidence that ooliths in which siderite and chamosite are interbanded are extremely rare, and also that siderite ooliths are virtually absent. It would thus appear that the region in which the ooliths were forming was the sea floor, and the replacive role of siderite is evidence of its instability in that environment. The petrography supports a diagenetic origin for the siderite in the ooliths, but what of the siderite in the matrix?

When the siderite in the matrix is replacive, a diagenetic origin can be safely ascribed to it. On the other hand much of the siderite in the matrix is apparently not replacive but a primary precipitate. In all probability this precipitation took place in the pore spaces below the water-sediment interface, rather than on top of the sediment, but this is not readily proved. One argument would be that if the latter were true primary ooliths of siderite should occur, as the ooliths predate the matrix. This argument applies to the oolitic ores but what of the siderite mudstones in which ooliths are not so abundant? It is possible that the lack of ooliths denotes quieter water conditions, but it is unlikely that the physicochemical conditions were radically different and therefore by analogy with siderite in the oolites it is concluded that the siderite in the mudstones also formed diagenetically.

Limonite.—The argument developed in the preceding sections is that as the Eh on the sea floor was unlikely to be low, pyrite and siderite should be diagenetic. It also follows from this that ferric iron should be the stable form of iron on the sea floor. This is borne out by the occurrence of limonite as one of the primary minerals in the ooliths. The other primary iron mineral in the ooliths is chamosite and because this is a ferrous mineral it is something of an enigma—however this will be considered in the next section.

The majority of the limonite in the unweathered ores, particularly at Frodingham, occurs as ooliths, and it could be that in this form some protection is afforded against falling Eh values during diagenesis. Limonite in the matrix might be more reactive and this would explain why limonite is not a major mineral in the matrix. Reduction of limonite would enable iron to migrate in the pore solutions, providing a source of iron for the diagenetic pyrite and siderite. Aided by compaction excess iron would migrate upwards to be immobilized again by oxidation in a similar manner to manganese in deep sea sediments (Manheim, 1965).

Compared to other British Ironstones the ores at Frodingham are noteworthy for the high proportion of limonite they contain. This might mean that more limonite was deposited here than elsewhere, or alternatively that more survived diagenesis.

Chamosite.—This complex ferrous silicate is abundant in the ironstones and was regarded by Hallimond (1925, p. 26) as the base of the marine clay ironstones . . . more or less enriched by the presence of siderite, and in some places by limonite ooliths. Chamosite occurs in both the ooliths and the matrix and it is clear that its role in the former is primary (Hallimond, 1925, p. 92)—a view which has been accepted by all subsequent investigators. Chamosite was apparently stable on the sea floor in an environment in which limonite was stable, and yet its Eh requirements are believed to be similar to those of pyrite and siderite. This is borne out by the record of chamosite from modern sediments in which chamosite occurs as mineralized faecal pellets, the product of a specialized micro-environment, and clearly out of equilibrium with the surrounding sediment because of the outer ring of goethite (Porrenga, 1965).

One way in which the occurrence of chamosite as a primary mineral in the ooliths might be explained is by postulating reducing conditions on the sea floor. Even if the depositional environment were reducing, and the geological evidence indicates that it was not, the Eh required for its formation might be no higher than for pyrite or siderite. As these two minerals are thought to be diagenetic it follows that diagenesis may also have been important in the formation of chamosite. In other words, the chamosite now present, as the end product of a diagenetic reaction, differs in some way from the initial precipitate. The initial precipitate may have been a mixed gel, stable at positive values of Eh, and consisting essentially of $Fe(OH)_3$, $Al(OH)_3$ and SiO_2nH_2O. It is conceivable that a gel of this composition could be incorporated into growing ooliths, and that ordering should occur later during diagenesis. The possibility that chamosite developed from a mixed gel was considered by Hallimond (1925, p. 96) but rejected on the ground that it would not give a mineral of constant composition. Caillère and Kraut (1954) also proposed that a gel was involved in the formation of the ooliths from the Lorraine Basin, but that the ooliths formed by concretion within the gel rather than by gentle agitation on the sea floor. Following a similar line of reasoning to that in the present account Strakhov (1953, p. 43) too concluded that chamosite must be diagenetic. In addition however he argued that the oolitic structure was diagenetic. Compound ooliths are his main evidence in favor of this for he considered that they could not have formed in moving bottom waters, whereas they could have been generated during diagenesis. If the compound ooliths are diagenetic, why not all the ooliths? The grading of the ooliths he also suggested was not due to current sorting, but because of crystallization around many centers in the sediment. The diagenetic origin of the oolitic structure would appear to be contrary to most of the petrographic evidence from the British ironstones, and consequently has not found favor (Dunham, 1960, p. 256).

One criticism which might be made of Hallimond's case for rejecting a colloidal origin is that chemical variations in the initial precipitate could be accommodated to a large degree by variations in the mineral assemblage rather than by one mineral alone. An additional point is that chamosite is now known to be more variable than was originally thought (Youell, 1955, 1958). Therefore if it can be shown that there is a variation in the composition of what are apparently primary ooliths then this might be taken as an indication that the initial precipitate was a colloidal gel of variable composition. Naturally ooliths in which there is evidence of secondary alteration must be excluded. The Frodingham ore field is characterized by the abundance of limonite, and as already noted, this might represent a high iron content in the initial precipitate. In the limey ores many of the ooliths consist predominantly of limonite, and in the clayey ores they are commonly composed of interbanded chamosite and limonite (Davies and Dixie, 1951, p. 90). There is thus an overall variation in the composition of the ooliths from one ore to the other, and within the ooliths of one ore. Furthermore the interbanded structure could be due to segregation during crystallization rather than to fluctuating Eh as was originally suggested. In the Cleveland orefield on the other hand, there is widespread opalization of the ooliths (Dunham, 1960, p. 250). Some of this opal may be secondary but the bands within the ooliths mentioned by Hallimond (1925, p. 45) could well be primary, and not secondary after chamosite. Could it be that in this orefield the opal represents an excess of silica in the initial precipitate? Detailed analyses of chamosite from the Northampton Sand ironstone have shown that an appreciable quantity of kaolinite is present, although it cannot be seen under the microscope—presumably because of its fine grain size and intimate association with the chamosite (Taylor, 1949, p. 41). This could also be the composition and mode of occurrence of the clay left when chamosite is dissolved in hot dilute hydrochloric acid. The occurrence of kaolinite might be due to there being more alumina and silica in the initial precipitate than could be accommodated by chamosite.

The ooliths are therefore by no means homogeneous and the apparently primary phases which appear with the chamosite can be explained in terms of the variation in the composition of the original precipitate, and the crystallization of the chamosite at some stage after the ooliths formed, probably during diagenesis. The initial precipitate varied with time and also from place to place. It is also possible that there was a lateral variation within the orefield at any one time, and currents may have swept ooliths together from different areas. This is one possible explanation of the differences that exist between neighboring ooliths and although this may occur, it is suggested that penecontemporaneous erosion was possibly more important. Erosion, for which there is abundant evidence (Hallimond, 1925, p. 9), would uncover different diagenetic levels in the recently deposited sediment, and the derived sediment would therefore contain a mixed assemblage of ooliths.

It could be argued that chamosite developed from an existing crystal structure, which was stable at higher Eh values, rather than from a colloid. An oxidized form of chamosite can be produced from normal chamosite in the laboratory (Brindley and Youell, 1953) and during weathering of normal chamosite (Youell, 1958). It does not follow, however, that because an oxidized chamosite has been recognized as one of the breakdown stages of normal chamosite that a ferric chamosite could precipitate onto the sediment—indeed chemically this is most unlikely.

Summary

Dealing specifically with one sequence of shales and mudstones from the Coal Measures of Yorkshire, it has been deduced that the Eh of the bottom water was, in all probability, higher than that at which either pyrite or siderite could form. If this is so the development of these two minerals was diagenetic, and there is supporting evidence of this. Pyrite and siderite are not distributed randomly within the sedimentary cycle; shales or mudstones containing pyrite are overlain by siderite bearing mudstones—the pyrite and siderite facies of James (1954). Variations in anion concentrations are thought to be responsible for this distribution. A slow rate of sedimentation aided by a higher salinity was responsible for ample sulfate reduction and pyrite formed in preference to other iron minerals. As the rate of sedimentation increased and the salinity decreased however, less sulfate was able to diffuse into the sediment from the overlying water and there was a fall off in the amount reduced. This resulted in a decrease in the size of the pyrite stability field, and it was only then that siderite could form. The same explanation is thought to account for the pyrite and siderite facies in the Lias of Yorkshire, except that in this case the infilling of the basin was not accompanied by a decrease in the salinity of the overlying water and therefore the rate of sedimentation is believed to have been entirely responsible. The Lias in N. Yorkshire differs from the Coal Measures in that the cycle terminates with an ironstone, belonging to the silicate-carbonate facies of James (1954)—the oxide facies is well represented in other British orefields even if not in N. Yorkshire. The ironstones are chemical deposits in an environment in which clastics were absent and Hemingway (1951) has suggested this was because the hinterland had by that time been reduced to a peneplain on which there was intense chemical weathering. The ironstones apparently accumulated in a shallow marine environment that certainly did not appear to have been reducing from the evidence of the structures and the fauna. One could expect limonite to be stable in such an environment, and pyrite and siderite stable below the water-sediment interface. The petrographic evidence supports this contention. Chamosite is more difficult for it occurs apparently as a primary mineral and yet the available information suggests that low Eh values were required for the formation. As diagenetic reactions are thought to be very important in the ironstones, it has been postulated that the chamosite now present differs in some way from the initial precipitate. A mixed gel could have been this initial precipitate, and the chamosite crystallized from it during diagenesis. Certainly there is abundant evidence that the composition of the initial precipitate was not constant, and there are structures which could be due to the crystallization of the chamosite after the oolith had formed.

Acknowledgments

The authors would like to thank their colleagues at Sheffield for the many fruitful discussions, and in particular they are indebted to Dr. L. G. Love.

Department of Geology,
University of Sheffield, England,
Dec. 26, 1967 and Jan. 24, 1968

REFERENCES

1. Baas Becking, L. G. M., Ferguson Wood, E. J., and Kaplan, I. R., 1957, Biological processes in the estuarine environment: XA: The place of the estuarine environment within the aqueous milieu: Koninkl. Nederl. Academie van Wetenschappen. Proc., Ser. B, v. 60, p. 88–95.
2. Berner, R. A., 1963, Electrode studies of hydrogen sulphide in marine sediments: Geochim. Cosmochim. Acta, v. 27, p. 563–575.
3. ——, 1964, Stability fields of iron minerals in anaerobic marine sediments: Jour. Geol., v. 72, p. 826–834.
4. ——, 1964. An idealized model of dissolved sulphate distribution in recent sediments: Geochim. Cosmochim. Acta, v. 28, p. 1497–1503.
5. Borchert, H., 1952. Die Bildungsbedingungen mariner Eisenerzlagerstätten: Chem. d. Erde, v. 16, p. 49–74.

6. ——, 1960, Genesis of marine sedimentary iron ores: Bull. Instn. Min. Metal., v. 69, p. 261–279.
7. ——, 1965, Formation of marine sedimentary iron ores: p. 159–204 in Riley and Skirrow, Chemical Oceanography, v. 2. Academic Press, London and New York.
8. Brindley, G. W., and Youell, R. F., 1953, Ferrous chamosite and ferric chamosite: Miner. Mag., v. 30, p. 57–70.
9. Caillère, S., and Kraut, F., 1954, Les gisements de fer du bassin Lorrain: Mem. Mus. Hist. Nat. Paris, (C), v. 4, p. 1–175.
10. Carroll, D., 1958, Role of clay minerals in the transportation of iron: Geochim. Cosmochim. Acta, v. 14, p. 1–27.
11. Carruthers, J. N., 1923, The Rotherham Red Rock: Trans. Leed. Geol. Assoc., v. XIX, p. 13–16.
12. Castano, J. R., and Garrels, R. M., 1950, Experiments on the deposition of iron with special reference to the Clinton iron ore deposits: ECON. GEOL., v. 45, p. 755–770.
13. Curtis, C. D., 1967, Diagenetic iron minerals in some British Carboniferous sediments: Geochim. Cosmochim. Acta, v. 31, p. 2103–2109.
14. Davies, W., and Dixie, R. J. M., 1951, Recent work on the Frodingham Ironstone: Proc. Yorks. Geol. Soc., v. 28, p. 85–96.
15. Deans, T., 1934, The spherulitic ironstones of west Yorkshire: Geol. Mag., v. 71, p. 49–65.
16. Dunham, K. C., 1951, Recent work on the Cleveland ironstone: Proc. Yorks. Geol. Soc., v. 28, p. 66.
17. ——, 1960, Syngenetic and diagenetic mineralization in Yorkshire: Proc. Yorks. Geol. Soc., v. 32, p. 229–284.
18. Garrels, R. M., and Christ, C. L., 1965, Solutions, Minerals and Equilibria: Harper and Row.
19. Goldschmidt, V. M., 1954, Geochemistry: xi + 730 pp. Oxford. (Edited by A. Muir.)
20. Hallam, A., 1963, Observations on the palaeoecology and ammonite sequence of the Frodingham Ironstone (Lower Jurassic): Palaeontology, v. 6, p. 554–574.
21. Hallimond, A. F., 1925, Iron ores: bedded ores of England and Wales. Petrography and chemistry: Spec. Rep. Min. Resources, G. B., Geol. Surv., 29, v + 139 pp., London.
22. Hemingway, J. E., 1951, Cyclic sedimentation and the deposition of ironstone in the Yorkshire Lias: Proc. Yorks. Geol. Soc., v. 28, p. 67–74.
23. Huber, M. K., 1958, The environmental control of sedimentary iron minerals: ECON. GEOL., v. 53, p. 123–140.
24. James, H. L., 1954, Sedimentary facies of iron-formation: ECON. GEOL., v. 49, p. 235–293.
25. Krumbein, W. C., and Garrels, R. M., 1952, Origin and classification of chemical sediments in terms of pH and oxidation-reduction potentials: Jour. Geol., v. 60, p. 1–33.
26. Love, L. G., 1965, Micro-organic material with diagenetic pyrite from the Lower Proterozoic Mount Isa Shale and a Carboniferous shale: Proc. Yorks. Geol. Soc., v. 35, p. 187–202.
27. Manheim, F. T., 1961, In situ measurements of pH and Eh in natural waters and sediments: Stockholm contributions in Geology, v. 8, p. 27–36.
28. ——, 1965, Manganese-iron accumulations in shallow marine environments: Symposium on marine geochemistry, Occ. Publ. No. 3, Narragansett Marine Laboratory, Univ. Rhode Island, p. 217–276.
29. Porrenga, D. H., 1965, Chamosite in recent sediments of the Niger and Orinoco Deltas: Geologie Mijnb., v. 44, p. 400–403.
30. Richards, F. A., 1965, Anoxic basins and fiords. p. 611–645 in Riley and Skirrow. Chemical Oceanography, vol. 1, Academic Press, London and New York.
31. Robertson, T., 1933, The geology of the South Wales Coalfield, part V. The country around Merthyr Tydfil: Mem. Geol. Surv. xx + 283 pp. London.
32. Sisler, F. D., 1962, Microbiology and biochemistry of sediments and overlying water. P. 64–69 in Cloud, Environment of Calcium Carbonate deposition west of Andros Island, Bahamas: U. S. Geol. Surv. Prof. Paper 350.
33. Skopintsev, B. A., Bomenskaya, N. A., and Smirnov, E. V., 1966, New determinations of the oxidation reduced potential in the Black Sea waters: Okeanologiia Akad. Nauk. S.S.S.R., v. 6, p. 799–806. (English abstract in Oceanographic Abstracts *14* (2), 1967.)
34. Sorby, H. C., 1857, On the origin of the Cleveland Hill ironstone: Proc. Yorks. Geol. Soc., v. 3, p. 457–461.
35. ——, 1906, The origin of the Cleveland ironstone: Naturalist, p. 354–357.
36. Spears, D. A., 1964, The major element geochemistry of the Mansfield Marine Band in the Westphalian of Yorkshire: Geochim. Cosmochim. Acta, v. 28, p. 1679–1696.
37. Stead, J. E., 1910, Cleveland ironstone and iron: Proc. Cleveland Instn. Engrs., (Session 1909–1910), p. 75–117.
38. Strakhov, N. M., 1953, Diagenesis and its importance in sedimentary ore formation. Izv. An. S.S.S.R. ser. geol., v. 5, p. 12–49. (British government Dept. Education and Science Russian Translating Programme, RT.S. 2763, pp. 1–74, 1965.)
39. Tate, R., and Blake, J. F., 1876, The Yorkshire Lias. ix + 475 + xii pp. London.
40. Taylor, J. H., 1949, The Mesozoic Ironstones of England. Petrology of the Northampton Sand ironstone formation: Mem. Geol. Surv., vi + III pp. London.
41. Taylor, R. K., and Spears, D. A., 1967, An unusual carbonate band in the East Pennine Coalfield, England: Sedimentol. v. 9, p. 55–73.
42. Whitehead, T. H., Anderson, W., Wilson, V., and Wray, D. A., 1952, The Liassic ironstones: with contributions on petrography by K. C. Dunham. The Mesozoic Ironstones of England: Mem. Geol. Surv., 211 pp. London.
43. Youell, R. F., 1955, Mineralogy and crystal structure of chamosite: Nature, v. 176, p. 560–561.
44. ——, 1958, Isomorphous replacement in the kaolin group of minerals: Nature, v. 181, p. 557–558.
45. Zobell, C. E., 1946, Studies on redox potential of marine sediments: Bull. Am. Assoc. Petrol. Geol., v. 30, p. 477–513.

V
The Surface Cycle of Iron

Editor's Comments on Papers 25, 26, and 27

25 **Goodwin:** Excerpts from *Facies Relations in the Gunflint Iron Formation*

26 **Borchert:** *Genesis of Marine Sedimentary Iron Ores*

27 **Hallam:** *Depositional Environment of British Liassic Ironstones Considered in the Context of Their Facies Relationships*

The papers in this section are again chiefly concerned with sedimentary iron-formations and ironstones. They differ from the selections in the preceding section in that all consider the problem of the origin of these iron-rich rocks and in that sense they address the question of the surface cycle of iron.

Because of space limitations it was not possible to include the classic early papers on this subject by Van Hise and Leith (1911), Cayeux (1922), Gruner (1922), and many others. Some of their views on the origin of iron sediments are summarized in the papers here reproduced. Furthermore, the most recently published refinements on the question of the origin of iron-formations that appear in the November 1973 issue of *Economic Geology* on Iron-Formations of the World were excluded from this volume to avoid duplication.

Since H. L. James published his paper (Paper 20) on the chemical facies of iron-formations there has been almost complete agreement among geologists that iron-formations and ironstones are chemical sediments. Some earlier investigators had suggested a replacement origin for iron-formations, and others interpreted some of the hematite-quartz rocks as recrystallized clastics. Whereas most geologists are now convinced that these rocks are indeed chemical precipitates, there is no such consensus on the question of the source of the materials in them. As we saw in the introduction, three principal sources have been invoked for the components: volcanic exhalations, weathering solutions from the land areas, and ocean or lake waters. Trendall (Paper 19) refers to these three interpretations as "from below," "from above," and "from within."

A. M. Goodwin is one of the staunchest supporters of a volcanic source. Paper 25 is an excerpt of his article on the Gunflint iron-formation of Ontario, which is an extension of the Biwabik formation of Minnesota. In the unreproduced first part of the paper, Goodwin describes the regional geology and the mineralogy, composition, texture, and structure of the formation. The portion of the paper reproduced contains his views on the origin of the Gunflint. It is interesting to note that one of Goodwin's arguments for a volcanic source is the ". . . improbability of an abnormal reducing atmosphere during Gunflint time, which would have permitted weathering and surface transportation in the ferrous state."

Trendall (Paper 19) similarly favors a "from below" interpretation for the components of iron-formation. Guild (1953) suggested that volcanic emanations may have lowered the pH of the basin in which the iron-formations of Minas Gerais, Brazil, were deposited, thus inhibiting the precipitation of carbonates. He also proposed that such emanations may have contributed at least a part of the iron and silica. R. L. Stanton (1972) argues for a volcanic exhalation or an artesian debouchment source of the components of iron-formations on geochemical grounds. He points to the low alumina and minor element content of the oxide, carbonate, and silicate facies and suggests that alumina, normally a product of surface erosion, may have been swamped by the comparatively rapid deposition of iron and silica from nonweathering sources.

Paper 26, by H. Borchert, represents the oceanic source for the components of iron-rich sediments. Borchert refers to the frequent association of iron-rich sediments and black schists or bituminous rocks. He reasons that iron is dissolved in euxinic areas of the sea bottom and moved by ocean currents through various transitional environments, where it may be deposited as carbonate, silicate, or oxide. Whereas the focus of the paper is on the oolitic ores of the minette type, he proposes that similar conditions prevailed in the Precambrian.

Borchert does not support the idea of an oxygen-poor atmosphere in the Precambrian. More recently. H. D. Holland (1973) argued for an oceanic source for the components of iron-formation. He evaluated the potential role of the oceans as a source of iron under an oxygen-poor atmosphere such as is indicated for the Precambrian. He showed that upwelling of anoxic deep ocean waters was quantitatively a potential source for the iron of large formations such as those of the Hammersley Basin of Australia.

Borchert graduated from the Bergakademie Clausthal (now the Technical University Clausthal) as a mining engineer and he received his doctorate from the Technical University of Berlin. He is Professor Emeritus of the Technical University Clausthal. He has published three books on mineral deposits and geochemistry in addition to many papers in various professional journals. His major text on *Salt Deposits* was translated into English (with R. Muir) in Fairbridge's Van Nostrand series in 1964.

Anthony Hallam, in Paper 27, reconstructs the depositional environments of the British Liassic ironstones from their facies relationships. His studies argue against Borchert's oceanic model at least for the British ironstones. Hallam taught at the University of Edinburgh from 1959 to 1967, the period when this paper was written. Since 1967 he has been on the faculty of the University of Oxford.

References

Cayeux, L., 1922, Études des gîtes minéraux de la France. Les minerais de fer oolithique de la France, Fasc. II: Minerais de fer secondaire, Paris, Imprimerie Nationale, 1051 p.

Gruner, J. W., 1922, Origin of sedimentary iron formations: Econ. Geol., v. 17, p. 408–460.

Guild, P. W., 1953, Iron deposits of the Congonhas district, Minas Gerais, Brazil: Econ. Geol., v. 48, p. 639–676.

Holland, H. D., 1973, The oceans: a possible source of iron in iron-formations: Econ. Geol., v. 68, p. 1169–1172.

Stanton, R. L., 1972, Ore petrology: McGraw-Hill Book Co., New York, p. 399–453.

Van Hise, C. R., and C. K. Lieth, 1911, The geology of the Lake Superior region: U.S. Geol. Surv. Monogr. 52, 641 p.

25

Reprinted from *Econ. Geol.,* **51**(6), 565–566, 588–595 (1956)

FACIES RELATIONS IN THE GUNFLINT IRON FORMATION

A. M. GOODWIN

ABSTRACT

The Gunflint iron formation is part of a Late Precambrian sedimentary-volcanic series that overlies with major unconformity an ancient granite-greenstone pediment surface. Iron- and silica-bearing rocks of the Gunflint were deposited in a marginal basin that bordered open sea water in a region of volcanic activity. Volcanism played a dual role: it provided a steady source of iron- and silica-bearing solutions and induced cyclical fluctuations in the basin of deposition. This resulted in cyclical sedimentation of iron- and silica-bearing rocks.

The fundamental sedimentary cycle consists of the following facies in ascending order: algal chert (thin), tuffaceous shale (thin) and greenalite taconite (thick); taconite facies grade laterally into banded chert-carbonate facies. Where fully developed, the formation contains two cyclical units designated respectively Lower and Upper Gunflint members. The sedimentary facies are described and environments of deposition discussed.

The distribution of hematite in the formation indicates an oxidizing atmosphere during Gunflint time. Magnetite formed largely by thermal metamorphism accompanying diabase intrusions. Some magnetite which has no apparent metamorphic association may have formed by primary precipitation or diagenetic alteration.

Greenalite is the most abundant iron silicate mineral in the Gunflint formation. Greenalite granules appear to have been formed by diagenetic adjustment of a primary hydrous silica-ferrous iron gel. Secondary amphiboles were formed by metamorphic recrystallization of greenalite. Illite is a common constituent of the shale facies and was formed by alteration of tuff fragments. Minnesotaite and stilpnomelane are quantitatively absent in the Gunflint formation in contrast to their abundance in the Biwabik formation of Minnesota. The relations suggest that minnesotaite and stilpnomelane are secondary metamorphic minerals rather than primary or diagenetic. Absence of abundant secondary silicates in the Gunflint may be related to the absence of hematite ore bodies.

* * * * * * *

Source of Iron and Silica

The source of iron and silica contained in Precambrian iron formations has been attributed to either deep-weathering of a basic igneous terrain or

Editor's Note: A row of asterisks indicates that material has been omitted from the original article.

direct volcanic contributions. Proponents of a weathering origin are generally agreed that the iron and silica were leached from a land area of very low relief that was approaching peneplanation. The climate is considered to have been tropical (Gruner, Gill, Moore and Maynard, Sakamota) or possible arid (Woolnough). In either case, mature weathering with attendant chemical weathering is stated or implied. The iron is considered to have been transported either in the ferric state under normal oxidizing environment, or in the ferrous state under an "abnormal" Precambrian reducing environment. On the other hand, a volcanic source for iron and silica was proposed by Winchell (14) and later expanded by Van Hise and Leith (13). The theory proposes that iron and silica were transported to the place of sedimentation either in hot solutions migrating from eruptive material during solidification, as meteoric water working upon subaerially extruded material, or by direct reaction of hot magma with sea water.

The weathering source of iron and silica does not appear to apply to the Gunflint formation. The main objections to such a source are 1) the complete lack of maturely weathered residual material in the Gunflint area or environs; 2) the difficulty of transporting ferric iron in surface waters to the site of deposition followed by reduction to the ferrous state (as prevails in the Gunflint) without the aid of abundant organic matter (which is quantitatively absent in the Gunflint); 3) the improbability of an "abnormal" reducing atmosphere during Gunflint time, which would have permitted weathering and surface transportation of iron in the ferrous state; and finally 4) a principal objection that applies in a broader sense, the absence of Gunflint-type iron formations from all rocks younger than Precambrian in age.

On the contrary, a volcanic source of iron and silica is indicated for the Gunflint formation. A direct and sympathetic relationship between volcanism and the iron formation is indicated by the presence of pyroclastics and lava along certain horizons in the iron-bearing rocks, and, in a larger and more significant sense, the cyclical coordination of volcanism and sedimentation. The cyclical nature of volcanic activity is well known. In this respect, the volcano Santorin (1) in the Aegean Sea is significant. It was first recorded in 1650. The history of the volcano has been one of periodic outbursts—1650, 1707, 1869—during which ash and tuff were deposited in varying quantities, alternating with relatively long periods of rest, which were characterized by sustained discharge of ferrous-carbonate-bearing gases and solutions. Observers of Santorin report that submarine discharges of ferrous carbonate solutions quickly oxidize to red ferric iron precipitate upon approaching surface waters; oxidation is a result of surface oxygen combined with the mildly alkaline influence of sea water. However, in Gunflint time, submarine discharges of ferrous iron would not necessarily oxidize in deep water and in the dominantly acid environment of deposition envisaged for the Gunflint basin. As a result, ferrous iron discharges could remain in the reduced state during transportation, precipitation and lithification.

In conclusion, the main mass of iron and silica contained in the Gunflint formation appears to have been contributed to the basin of deposition as a product of volcanic activity, possibly through hot-spring activity and mineral alteration of extruded volcanic material. Paradoxically, the scarcity of readily recognizable volcanic material such as flow and ash explains, in a sense, the existence of the iron formation itself: explosive volcanic activity was at a minimum during Gunflint time and chemical volcanic activity at a maximum. Had the activities been reversed the Gunflint would be the site not of iron formation but of large masses of pyroclastics and flows. In brief, pyroclastics, flows and iron-silica solutions were all products of volcanic activity during Gunflint time; pyroclastics and flows were the products of brief periods of explosive activity, iron-silica solutions the products of long sustained periods of chemical activity. The ultimate cause of volcanic activity of a type resulting in large scale discharge of iron and silica solutions during Gunflint time, and, indeed, Precambrian time in general remains a petrographic problem.

Environment

Shallow water facies of the Gunflint formation contain a higher proportion of ferric iron in the form of hematite and magnetite compared to deeper water facies. For example, in the Lower algal chert facies, hematite occurs in algal structures and in closely associated granules. In the Lower west taconite, facies, hematite-magnetite-bearing taconite appears in abundance in the upper 100 feet of the facies. The Lower east taconite facies contains hematite-rimmed granules, hematite-bearing algal structures and local concentrations of massive hematite. The Upper algal chert facies contains, from bottom to top: 2 to 10 feet of jaspery taconite with jasper veinlets; 1 to 3 feet of algal chert and 42 to 70 feet of bedded, jaspery taconite. In the Upper taconite facies hematite-bearing granules are abundant in the upper 75 feet of the facies. Thus, ferric oxide minerals occupy several persistent stratigraphic horizons and occur in a large variety of rocks. Studies of the facies have shown that the ferric state of oxidation was largely reached during precipitation and lithification rather than by later weathering or other alteration. It follows that the environment was oxidizing during formation of the hematite-magnetite-bearing rocks. Oxidation may be attributed to organically-produced oxygen in those cases where algal structures are closely associated such as the Lower algal chert facies, Lower east taconite facies and the lower beds of the Upper algal chert facies. However, in the Lower west taconite and Upper taconite facies, algal structures are 100 vertical feet distant from hematite-bearing rocks; similarly, in the Upper algal chert facies, hematite is an abundant constituent 70 vertical feet above the algal-bearing horizon. It is highly improbable that oxidation in these cases resulted from oxygen produced by algal activity. The most reasonable explanation is that the atmosphere of the Gunflint basin was oxidizing during Gunflint time. All surface and near-surface chemical activity would thus be influenced by atmospheric oxygen resulting in the formation of ferric oxide minerals. The mineral composition and facies distribution of the Gunflint formation indicate that such occurred. Hence, an "abnormal" reducing atmosphere during Gunflint time is considered improbable.

The preponderance of ferrous iron minerals together with the quantitative absence of reducing agents in the Gunflint rocks (the banded chert-carbonate rocks excepted) indicate that iron was transported and deposited largely in the ferrous state. This required either a decidedly acid environment or one with a very low oxidation potential on the negative side of zero. Since the evidence points to an atmosphere with a positive oxidation potential during Gunflint time, an acid environment is strongly implied. Such an acid environment appears to have resulted from large-scale discharge of acid volcanic solutions into the basin of deposition.

In conclusion, it is considered that iron- and silica-bearing, acid solutions of volcanic source were contributed to a relatively isolated basin of deposition thus concentrating sufficient iron and silica to permit deposition of the iron formation. The basin of deposition appears to have bordered open sea-water, at least in part, as indicated by abnormally high calcium and magnesium content in northeastern facies of the formation.

Distribution and Origin of Magnetite

Magnetite is present in significant amounts in the following four sedimentary facies of the Gunflint formation—Lower and Upper algal chert, Lower west taconite and Upper taconite. In general, magnetite occupies broad stratigraphic horizons within these facies.

Magnetite-bearing beds have been observed intermittently throughout the length of the Lower algal chert facies. In the Gunflint Lake district, Broderick (2) reports 5 to 10 feet of beds containing from 50 to 60 percent magnetite near the base of the division. In the Bishop Lake area, Gill (4) reports a few thin beds very rich in magnetite; for example, one 4 inch-thick bed contains 75 percent magnetite. In the Little Gull Lake area occurs 4 feet of material with 70 percent magnetite. At Hillside Station near Silver Mountain the facies includes a 5-inch-thick bed of nearly solid magnetite immediately overlying algal chert; four miles north of this point, in the vicinity of Pitch Creek, there is a 6 inch-thick band of nearly solid magnetite overlying algal chert. Finally, where Hodder Avenue crosses the north branch of the Current River north of Port Arthur, a 6- to 12-inch-thick band contains about 75 percent magnetite.

Magnetite is common in the upper beds of the Lower west taconite facies. It occurs as rims around greenalite granules and as disseminated grains in a cherty matrix. It is normally confined to beds ranging up to 4 feet thick that alternate with thicker bands of normal greenalite taconite in which magnetite is absent. Gill (4, p. 87c) reports local concentrations up to 60 percent iron oxides in the North Lake area. In the Bishop Lake area samples of taconite contain 34 percent magnetite. Near Little Gull Lake the facies contains thin beds averaging 30 percent magnetite.

Magnetite is a minor constituent in most rocks of the Upper algal chert facies. It typically occurs towards the centre of mixed greenalite-hematite granules and pisolites. It normally comprises less than 10 percent of the beds. Gill (4, p. 88c) reports that in the North Lake area, where sills appear in close proximity, some beds contain up to 65 percent magnetite and many contain between 30 and 60 percent.

In the Upper taconite facies, magnetite is a common constituent of greenalite granules. The proportion of magnetite varies greatly from one bed to another. In the Little Gull Lake area beds containing 35 percent magnetite by weight are common.

Much of the magnetite in the Gunflint formation was formed by thermal metamorphism accompanying diabase intrusions. Such occurred in much of the Lower and Upper taconite facies in the interval from Little Gull Lake to Gunflint Lake where sills and dykes are abundant. In the northeastern portion of the district, however, diabase intrusives in the Gunflint formation are relatively scarce, and the relationship between intrusive and magnetite obscure. In the Lower algal chert facies, in particular, as well as portions of the Lower taconite facies, magnetite-bearing zones, which are intimately interbanded with unaltered hematite- and carbonate-bearing zones, have no apparent relationship to metamorphic agents. Some of this magnetite may have been formed either by direct primary precipitation or by diagenetic alteration to magnetite of an unstable iron precipitate.

Distribution and Origin of Silicate Minerals

Greenalite is the most common iron silicate mineral present in unaltered phases of the Gunflint formation. It occurs in all facies with the exception of tuffaceous shales and banded chert-carbonates. Greenalite from several localities in the Gunflint was identified initially by X-ray analysis following which optical properties were used for general identification. As previously described greenalite typically forms round to elliptical granules ranging up to 3 mm in diameter. It ranges from light green to olive green in color. The index of refraction averages 1.68. Most granules in fresh taconite show little, if any, sign of alteration. In a few places, magnetite, hematite or siderite are minor constituents of the granules. Greenalite granules are considered to have formed by mineral and textural adjustment during lithification of a primary hydrous silica-ferrous iron gel.

In proximity to diabase sills and dikes, taconite is variably altered to secondary silicates. The secondary minerals generally form small, radiating clusters of bladed and fibrous needles. Generally they are intimately associated with greenalite granules and have clearly formed by recrystallization of greenalite. Magnetite is invariably associated. Increased metamorphism has resulted in complete destruction of the granular form with development of a decussate texture. Most of the secondary silicates have the properties of amphiboles. A variety of minerals appears to be present; however, the properties indicate that actinolite and grunerite are most common.

Illite is a fairly common constituent of tuffaceous shale facies. It occurs both as alteration rims around pyroclastic fragments and in spherical forms similar in shape and size to greenalite granules. A partial analysis of illite [2]

[2] Sample submitted by Professor Tyler to analyst William Pasich, Chief Research Chemist, Jones and Laughlin Steel Corporation Research Laboratory, Negaunee, Mich.

taken from an outcrop of Upper tuffaceous shale on the north shore of Thunder Bay at the common line between MacGregor and McTavish Townships gives the following results: Total Fe—3.45, SiO_2—54.90, Al_2O_3—22.07, TiO_2—0.20, CaO—0.11, MgO—3.63. The material was identified by Professor S. W. Bailey as illite ("low in iron but with some characteristics of glauconite pattern"). H. S. Yoder, Jr., of the Geophysical Laboratory, Washington, D. C., later identified the material sent to him by Professor Tyler as IM-Muscovite. Yoder states, "It is likely that your material was originally IMd-Muscovite [illite] and has been ordered by metamorphism [or time] to IM-Muscovite" (brackets inserted). The relations suggest that IM-Muscovite granules, similar in shape and size to greenalite granules, formed by diagenetic alteration of small pyroclastic fragments, first to illite (IMd-Muscovite), then to IM-Muscovite.

Chloritic material in amygdules of Gunflint lava was identified by Professor Bailey as a mixture of iron-magnesium chlorite with an X-ray pattern similar to that of "type" chamosite from Chamoson, Switzerland (Bannister and Whittard, Min. Mag. 1945, Fig. 3) with traces of illite. Locally, near Blende Lake in the Thunder Bay district, illite grains are altered peripherally to a pale green, fibrous mineral with the optical properties of antigorite or delessite ($N_m = 1.59–1.60$). Alteration of this type is apparently confined to the Thunder Bay area. Rocks in this area are comparatively rich in dolomite and ankerite indicating original concentrations of magnesium salts in this portion of the basin of deposition. The relations suggest that illite was altered authigenetically to antigorite in the presence of magnesium-bearing waters.

Minnesotaite is the most abundant silicate mineral in the Biwabik formation of Minnesota according to Gruner (6). Another common mineral is stilpnomelane. Both minerals characteristically occur aggregated in granular form, as alterations of greenalite granules, as matrix material to greenalite granules, as isolated crystals or radiating needles and sheaves, and as vein minerals with quartz cutting the iron formation. They are considered by Gruner (6) and H. L. James (7) to be primary or diagenetic minerals.

In contrast to the situation in the Biwabik formation, minnesotaite and stilpnomelane are quantitatively absent in the Gunflint formation. This comprises a fundamental difference between the two formations. Their quantitative absence in the Gunflint formation—a relatively unaltered iron formation in which metamorphic effects are negligible—indicates that the two minerals have been formed elsewhere by secondary recrystallization of primary iron minerals rather than by primary precipitation or diagenetic alteration. In this connection, it is noted that the Embarrass granite, intrusive into the Biwabik formation over much of its length, is absent from the Gunflint formation. Absence of younger granite and accompanying metamorphism in the Gunflint formation may explain the absence of minnesotaite and stilpnomelane. It is noted in passing that large scale development of secondary silicates such as minnesotaite and stilpnomelane is considered by Tyler (12) to favor oxidation and leaching of iron formation to form hematite ore bodies. In this connection, absence of minnesotaite and stilpnomelane is possibly related to the absence of hematite ore bodies in the Gunflint in contrast to widespread ore occurrences in the Biwabik. In summary, the relations suggest that in the absence of younger granite, minnesotaite and stilpnomelane did not form in the Gunflint formation, hence, conditions did not favor development of hematite ore bodies.

Historical Resumé

The locus of Gunflint activity was a broad, relatively shallow basin with limited marginal circulation with open sea water. The basin was situated in a region of volcanic activity. Although removed somewhat from the center of activity, it was connected to it by stream flowage and other water circulation. Volcanism played a dual role: it provided a steady source of iron and silica-bearing solutions and it induced cyclical fluctuations in the basin of deposition. The result was cyclic deposition of iron and silica-bearing sediments.

The sedimentary history of the basin began with the strand advancing slowly over a pediment surface. Rubble and rock fragments were worked over and lithified to form a thin basal conglomerate. In the shallow-water environment, algae flourished on wave-swept basement rocks accompanied by precipitation of silica and hematite. Volcanic unrest resulted in sinking of the basin relative to water level. This was accompanied by wide-spread distribution of ash and tuff of the Lower tuffaceous shale facies. Following this, granular rocks of the Lower west taconite facies started to form in deeper portions of the basin. At the same time, shallow, lagoonal marsh conditions prevailed in the Kakabeka Falls-Port Arthur area wherein cherty carbonates of the Lower banded chert-carbonate facies formed. Farther northeastward, beyond the marsh environment and near the margins of the basin, Lower east taconite formed in agitated, oxygenated waters. As water level gradually decreased in the basin, conditions of algal growth returned. This initiated the Upper Gunflint cycle.

Widespread volcanic activity and crustal unrest followed resulting in wholesale distribution of pyroclastics (Upper tuffaceous shale). An occasional tongue of lava moved to rest upon lithifying iron-bearing sediments. The basin sank relative to water level whereupon granular rocks of the Upper taconite facies began to form in deeper portions of the basin to the southwest. Shallow, lagoonal swamps again prevailed northeastward wherein Upper banded chert-carbonate rocks formed. The accumulating sediments of the Upper cycle gradually approached water surface. Before reaching this position, however, violent and long prevailing volcanic activity and crustal unrest induced entry of sea water resulting in formation of the Upper limestone member followed by Rove shale. This marked the close of iron and silica deposition in the Gunflint area.

References

1. Behrend, F., 1936, Eisen und Schwafel Fordernde Gasquellen auf den Kameni Inseln. In Santorin der Werdegang eines Insel vulkans und sein Ausbruch, 1925–1928, by Hans Reck, v. 2, p. 323–327. Berlin.
2. Broderick, T. M., 1920, Economic geology and stratigraphy of the Gunflint iron district, Minnesota: Econ. Geol., v. 15, no. 5, p. 422–452.
3. Davis, E. F., 1918, Radiolarian cherts of the Franciscan group: Calif. Univ. Dept. Geol. Sci., Bull. 11, p. 235–432.
4. Gill, J. E., 1924, Gunflint iron-bearing formation: Geol. Surv., Canada, Sum. Rept., pt. c, p. 28–88.
5. ———, 1927, Origin of the Gunflint iron-bearing formation: ECON. GEOL. v. 27, no. 7, p. 687–728.
6. Gruner, J. W., 1922, The origin of sedimentary iron formations: the Biwabik formation of the Mesabi range: ECON. GEOL., v. 17, no. 6, 407–460.
7. James, H. L., 1954, Sedimentary facies of iron formation: ECON. GEOL., v. 49, no. 3, p. 235–293.
8. Sakamoto, T., 1950, The origin of the Precambrian banded iron ores: Am. Jour. Sci., v. 248, p. 449–474.
9. Stokes, W. L., 1950, Pediment concept applied to Shinarump and similar conglomerates: Bull. Geol. Soc. Amer. v. 61, p. 91–98.
10. Tanton, T. L., 1924, Eastern part of Matawin iron range, Thunder Bay district, Ontario: Geol. Surv., Canada, Sum. Rept., pt. c, p. 1–27.
11. ———, 1931, Fort William and Port Arthur, and Thunder Cape map areas, Thunder Bay district, Ontario: Geol. Surv., Canada, Mem. 167.
12. Tyler, S. A., 1949, Development of Lake Superior soft iron ores from metamorphosed iron formation: Bull. Geol. Soc. Amer., v. 60. p. 1101–1124.
13. Van Hise, C. R., and Leigh, C. K., 1911, The geology of the Lake Superior region: U. S. Geol. Survey, Mon. 52.
14. Winchell, N. H., 1899, The geology of Minnesota: Geol. and Nat. Hist. Surv. Minn., Final Rept., v. 4.
15. Woolnough, W. E., 1941, Origon of banded iron deposits—a suggestion: ECON. GEOL., v. 36, p. 465–489.

26

Reprinted from *Bull. Inst. Min. Met.*, **640**, (*Trans. Inst. Min. Met.*, **69**) 261–279(1960)

Genesis of Marine Sedimentary Iron Ores*

H. BORCHERT,*† Prof. Dr. -Ing.

553.277:551.351.3:553.31

SYNOPSIS

Since trivalent iron is practically insoluble in the presence of oxygen it is contended that the mobilization of iron by weathering solutions in continental regions could not have contributed significantly to the formation of marine iron ore deposits in pre-Devonian times. The mobilization and precipitation of iron must then have been effected within the oceans themselves.

Emphasis is placed on the existence of a CO_2 zone at moderate depths in the ocean wherein abundant iron is dissolved, later to be precipitated mainly in oxygenated shallow waters as limonite ooliths or clay ironstones, and partly in deep waters of the H_2S zone as chamosite.

Distribution of the different facies of limonite, siderite, chamosite and pyrite tends to parallel the coast line and is controlled by the direction of flow of sea currents. Changes in these currents, each with its own characteristic physico-chemical traits, account for the principal vertical and lateral variations in the iron ore facies, small-scale variations being due to climatic changes.

The origin of recent glauconite in marine environments and the physico-chemical controls of iron ore formation are briefly discussed.

THE MODE OF ORIGIN and conditions of formation of sedimentary iron ores are of more than theoretical interest, since a proper understanding of these factors may facilitate the development of mining operations and their extension into adjacent ground. Hitherto it has been generally accepted that, in the course of rock weathering, iron is removed in solution from continental areas and is later precipitated on arrival in an alkaline marine environment so as to form oolitic deposits of 'minette' type.[9,10,22,40,46] According to this hypothesis the main body of such iron deposits should always be located in the immediate vicinity of the contemporary shore line.

Past experience in mining sedimentary ironstones seems to confirm this assumed relationship between ore formation and palaeogeographical conditions, for exploitation has hitherto been preferentially conducted along the margins of the ancient marine basins and troughs. Recent discoveries of several important seams of iron ore below the North German Plain,[77,83] however, appear to show that in this instance wide regions of open sea have repeatedly been the site of precipitation of iron ores.

The question is thus raised as to whether the mobilization of the iron and also its primary precipitation could have been effected *within* a marine basin.

*Paper received by the Institution of Mining and Metallurgy in November, 1959, and published on 3rd March, 1960; for discussion at General Meeting on 21st April, 1960. The paper is based on a lecture delivered by the author at the Imperial College of Science and Technology, London, on 16th March, 1959.

†Director, Institut für Mineralogie, Petrographie und Lagerstättenkunde der Bergakademie Clausthal, Clausthal-Zellerfeld, Germany.

[9]etc. See list of references at the end of the paper.

SOLUBILITY OF IRON UNDER NATURAL CONDITIONS

Iron in the trivalent state is practically insoluble in the presence of oxygen, when its maximum solubility is of the order of 1 mg/cu. m.[9,20,21,72] Any significant solubility of iron in the bivalent state occurs only in acid solutions at a pH value below 7 and then only under reducing conditions and in the absence of free oxygen; in these circumstances its solubility may reach a magnitude of 50 mg/cu. dm, equivalent to 50 000 times greater than that of trivalent iron in the presence of free oxygen.

Recent investigations have shown that the solubility of trivalent iron in normal sea water is of the order of only 3×10^{-5} mg/cu. m.[86] Iron may, therefore, be regarded as being soluble under natural conditions only in a reducing environment such as can usually be obtained only in the presence of organic matter.[16,18,19,26,35,45,70] In the presence of free oxygen iron is chiefly precipitated in the trivalent state.

Consideration of these conditions leads to the conclusion that the mobilization of iron by weathering solutions in continental regions cannot always be accepted as the predominant mechanism whereby the element is mobilized. According to certain Swedish, Finnish and American geologists the earth's atmosphere has contained free oxygen at least since early Pre-Cambrian times,[2,3,39,67] so that even then the well-known 'red bed facies', with its practically insoluble iron, must have predominated in the continental areas.

The earliest land plants were not developed until Devonian times, about 250 million years ago, bringing with them the *first potential cause of reducing conditions in the continental regions.* Prior to that event iron could not have been dissolved and transported to the oceans in large amounts. Yet it is common knowledge that extensive deposits of marine iron ores are not confined to post-Devonian rocks but are also plentiful among Silurian and Cambrian strata, and especially in Pre-Cambrian shield areas.[2,48,57,62,84] *It follows*, therefore, *that the mobilization and subsequent precipitation of iron must have taken place in the oceans themselves.* In what follows an attempt is made to elucidate the genetic conditions under which such marine iron ores were formed.

BEHAVIOUR OF IRON IN CONTINENTAL FACIES

It seems appropriate first to recall the better-known behaviour of iron under continental conditions.[73] Fig. 1 illustrates the conditions characteristic of a Tundra milieu, with its cold and humid climate and high groundwater level. The accumulation of plants and humus in swamps and marshes produces reducing conditions in the surface waters. Such environments are favourable for the solution of iron and to a lesser extent, under extremely acid conditions, of aluminium also. The accumulation of humus is not only important in bringing about a reducing environment, but by causing the partial decomposition of organic matter it also produces abundant CO_2 and $Fe(HCO_3)_2$.[44]

Under the conditions depicted in Fig. 1 it is envisaged that the groundwater contains some free oxygen; the movement of iron-bearing solutions

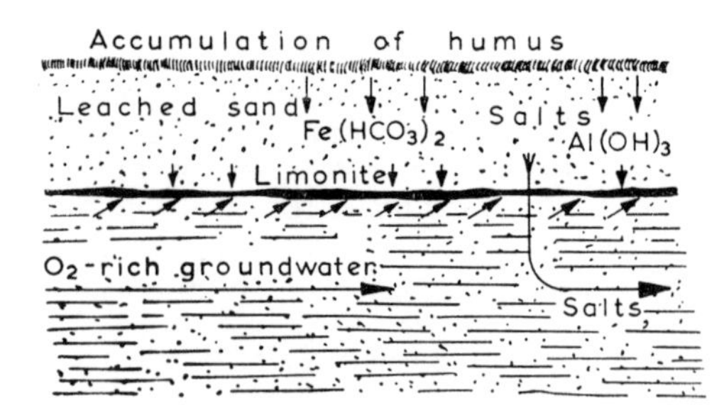

Fig. 1.—Podsol soil and mobilization of iron.

is very confined and the metal is rapidly precipitated at groundwater level to form swamp ore. This type of ore, known in Germany as 'Ortstein', is widely distributed in the soils of cold humid climates. If, however, the swamp and marsh facies have regional dimensions iron may be transported over much

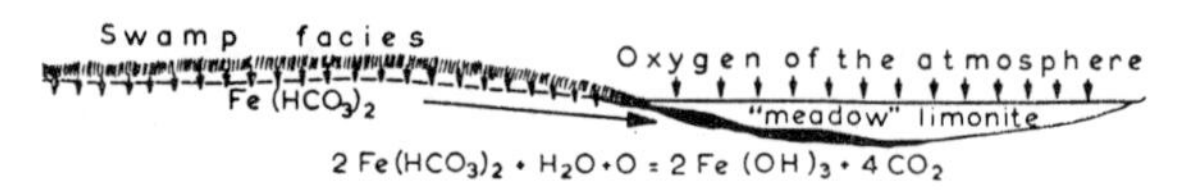

Fig. 2.—Schematic diagram showing the development of continental iron ore deposits (Bog-ore).

greater distances, as shown in Fig. 2. In extensive Tundra the numerous rivers and lakes bring free oxygen from the atmosphere to react with the iron bicarbonate which is transported slowly in the groundwater. These bicarbonate solutions percolate most rapidly through areas of sandy material, as in the bottom sediment, where most of the iron is then fixed as 'meadow' limonite.[16,26,61,70]

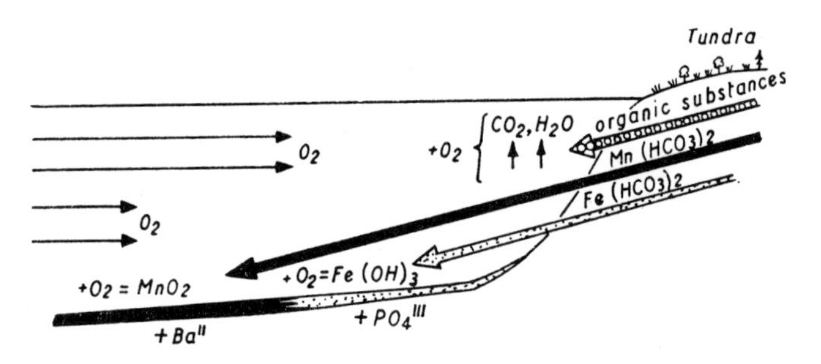

Fig. 3.—Relation of iron and manganese in Tundra milieu solutions.

Fig. 3 illustrates the behaviour of iron and manganese in a bog-ore environment, their distribution being somewhat analogous to those pertaining to marine conditions. The principal processes are as follows.

Groundwaters carry bicarbonates of iron and manganese in solution under the protection of organic substances and these solutions react near the bottom of the lake with oxygenated waters not far distant from the atmosphere. All the organic substances are first oxidized, thereby producing carbonic acid. Then the iron bicarbonate is oxidized in preference to manganese, which is more soluble and has a lesser tendency to oxidize.[19,44,55,59,90] The ionic solutions of manganese bicarbonate therefore attain a colloidal state and coagulate later than the corresponding iron hydroxide. Thus a clear separation of iron and manganese ores normally takes place. However, one factor causes the simultaneous precipitation of iron and manganese—namely, the positive charge of the colloidal iron hydroxide particles, causing adsorption of anions, such as PO_4^{-3}, AsO_4^{-3} and VO_4^{-3}, and the negative charge of the manganese hydroxide particles, which correspondingly cause the adsorption of cations, such as Ba^{+2} and Co^{+2}. These relations are also important in connexion with the origin and structure of ooliths in marine iron ore facies.

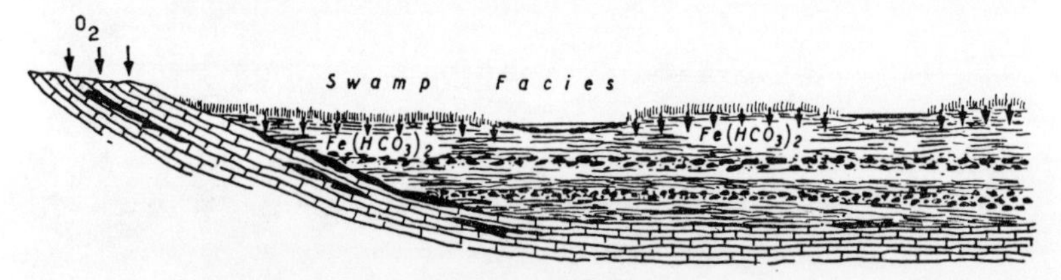

Fig. 4.—Bean-ore ('Bohnerz') and related formations.

Fig. 4 shows Schneiderhöhn's Hunsrück type of iron ore, formerly regarded as being of metasomatic origin. Here, again, the essential control of iron deposition is a reaction between ferrous solutions and oxygen-bearing groundwater.

Limestone is often an important reservoir of oxygen-bearing groundwater, due to the fact that in 'Karst' regions rainwater containing atmospheric oxygen easily reaches great depths owing to the permeability and cavernous nature of most limestones.

In Fig. 4 the oxidizing waters are visualized as reacting with iron bicarbonate solutions derived from a marsh milieu. The principal site of reaction between the two kinds of water is at the junction between the limestone and the overlying deposits, *although the actual level at which the reaction takes place is dependent upon the general hydrological conditions.* If the water in the limestone is under artesian pressure, the groundwater level of the oxygenated water will ascend to a somewhat higher horizon, where the two types of water may coalesce. The iron bicarbonate solutions will then be oxidized, thereby leading to the precipitation of limonite in the form of concretions, 'beans', or spheroidal nodules.[4,28]

If the groundwater level changes due to climatic fluctuations the reaction horizon will correspondingly rise or fall. Thus a series of iron-ore horizons, indicative of fossil water tables, is characteristic of this type of deposit.

Should the water from the marshes and swamps descend to deeper horizons in the limestone, then the locus of the reactions will also be at greater depths, and iron bicarbonate, protected by organic matter, may be precipitated as siderite. This process corresponds to the formation of metasomatic iron ores, represented in England by the deposits of Cumberland which, however, were primarily deposited in the form of hematite.

GENESIS OF MARINE IRON ORES

Fig. 5 depicts the mobilization of iron under special marine conditions now to be considered.[8]

No example is known of the recent formation of oolitic iron ores of the minette type. However, it is clearly recognized that the iron silicate, glauconite, is forming to-day in many places.[34] The mode of origin of this glauconite appears to correspond in general to the processes which in the past have led to the genesis of marine sedimentary iron ores, including the 'fossil' iron silicate, chamosite.[32,43,50,63,74]

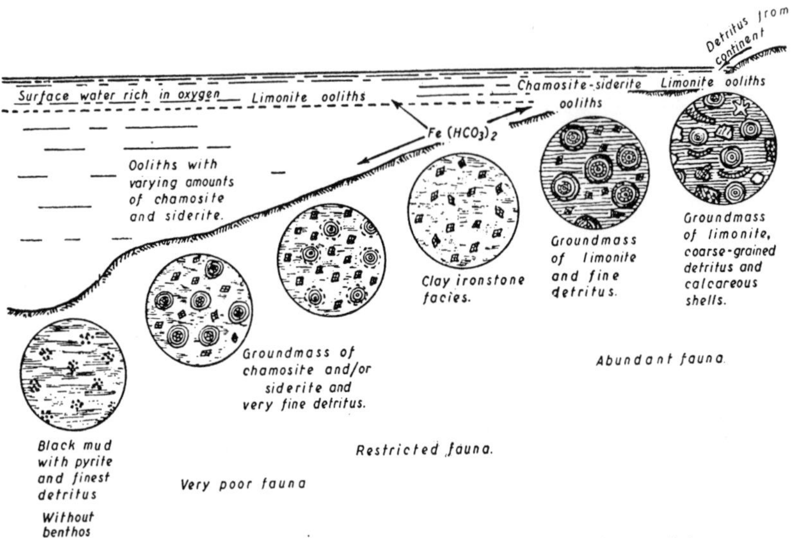

Fig. 5.—Diagrammatic scheme of the iron cycle under marine conditions.

It is significant that the concentration of sedimentary iron ores has largely been effected during those geological periods which are also characterized by the more-or-less abundant development of black schists, bituminous shales and—during Pre-Cambrian times—of graphitic rocks (H. G. Backlund, 1952). This association of iron ores and black schists surely cannot be fortuitous. Indeed, it is highly probable that the fundamental cause of their association during certain geological periods was due to the poles of the earth being then free from ice. This naturally affected the deep circulation of the oceans, since the deep-sea bottoms were then deprived of oxygen-rich polar water. Organic material in the bottom sediments of the ocean was therefore preserved in significant quantities. Instead of red deep-sea clays, which are the characteristic sediments of nearly all abyssal regions of recent oceans, this accumulation of organic matter resulted in the formation of bituminous shales and black schists in the deeper parts of the oceans when the poles were free from ice caps.

In this type of sediment and in the presence of sapropelic water optimum conditions existed for the dissolution of iron from the sediments, as illustrated in Fig. 5. The water in the deeper regions, above the black mud, would be more-or-less saturated with hydrogen sulphide formed by the reduction of seawater sulphates by organic matter, assisted by specialized sulphur bacteria. On the other hand, the more strongly agitated water of the shallow seas would contain free oxygen, as at the present time.

Between the two kinds of water—the oxygenated water of the shallow seas and the H_2S-rich bottom water above the sapropel—there is a *transition zone* which is *of the utmost importance in connexion with the dissolution and mobilization of iron from ordinary sediments.*

Between the bottom zone where the organic matter suffers no oxidation but merely some bacterial decomposition, and the shallow water zone where there is ample oxygen to cause virtually complete oxidation of all organic substances, there must exist a *carbonic acid zone rich in* CO_2 which is conducive to the partial oxidation of organic matter so as to produce abundant CO_2 while maintaining a more-or-less strongly reducing milieu. Within this zone iron may be dissolved in such quantities as to yield concentrations of 50 mg iron bicarbonate per cu. dm.

The loci of precipitation of the dissolved iron bicarbonate, $Fe(HCO_3)_2$, will depend on the velocity of the sea currents and stream cycles, and especially on the rate of water exchange with the oxygen-bearing water of the shallow sea.[11,24]

Under the conditions already described most of the iron dissolved in the CO_2 zone will be deposited in the form of limonite ooliths in shallow water of the shelf zone. Weaker exchange with the oxygen-rich water of the shelf may, however, result in the precipitation of considerable quantities of iron in the CO_2 zone itself so as to form clay ironstone. This corresponds to the formation of blackband ironstones in the Coal Measures which are characterized by concretions of siderite in a groundmass of clay. Such clay ironstones occur in Cambrian and Silurian strata as well as in Jurassic and Cretaceous sediments in many parts of the world, often attaining a thickness of many tens of feet.

Clay ironstones were typically formed during those periods in the earth's history when the poles were devoid of ice caps, contemporaneously with the formation of bituminous shales, black schists and limonite ooliths. All these sediments constitute a genetic unity, each type of deposit being inter-dependent (see Fig. 5).

There may also be some interchange between the water of the CO_2 zone and that of the deeper regions corresponding to the sapropel environment. In this transition zone chamosite is the characteristic precipitate, and its formation is readily explained as follows. Iron for the production of chamosite is supplied from the CO_2 zone, while silica is dissolved in alkaline solutions liberated from the black mud or sapropel owing to the decomposition of nitrogenous organic substances, especially albumin, aided by bacteria, so as to produce ammonia. In fact, concentrations of hydrogen ions as high as 8 or 9 have been measured in recent sapropels, the high alkalinity being due to the development of ammonia.

It is clear, therefore, that exchange between the two kinds of water of the deeper regions of the sea, namely that of the CO_2 zone and that of the

H_2S zone, is capable of mobilizing iron and silica, thus enabling them to combine to form chamosite.[32,43,63,74]

The typical iron-bearing mineral of the sapropel is pyrite, which often displays the structure of bacteria (see Fig. 5). As the currents in the deeper parts of the ocean normally travel slowly, only small quantities of iron will reach the sapropel facies, so that only meagre pyrite impregnations are developed in the clay marls. These bituminous sediments commonly exhibit very fine laminae with rhythms of 0·15–0·2 mm in thickness.

Fig. 5 shows the following sedimentological and biological relations:

In the shelf region of the shallow sea where there are strong currents of oxygen-rich water, the detritus from the continents often consists of sands and even conglomerates. But the shallow waters, rich in oxygen, provide the optimum environment for life, and an abundant fauna therefore contributes calcareous shells for the formation of limestone grit of fairly coarse grain. The normal shallow sea facies contains bedded layers of limonite ooliths mingled with sand and calcareous fossils in a groundmass of limonite.

The clay ironstone facies is characterized by finer detrital material and owing to the diminished oxygen content in its environment only certain specialized animals are able to flourish within it. A fine-grained clayey sediment is thus deposited containing a few, but prolific, fossil species. Siderite develops in the form of very fine-grained rhombohedra or as nodules and concretions which have been re-dissolved and precipitated in the course of diagenetic processes, as is discussed later.

The approach to the sapropelic facies is accompanied by the incoming of chamosite. In general the sedimentary types of this environment differ only slightly from those of the clay ironstone facies; fine-grained clays together with very fine quartz detritus and a few fossil types being characteristic.

The sapropel itself, composed of clays and marls of the finest grain size impregnated with pyrite, displays the thinnest bedding. No highly organized animals are able to exist in this medium, which merely supports bacteria and especially the sulphur varieties. These bacteria decompose the organic matter which sinks from the surface regions to become part of the black mud.[76]

ORIGIN OF RECENT GLAUCONITE

As previously mentioned, no recent examples of the formation of limonite ooliths have yet been discovered. However, glauconite, a mineral related to chamosite, is known from present-day sediments.

The origin of glauconite [34] has been debated in a voluminous literature which can only be very briefly summarized here. There is little doubt that glauconite can be regarded as a mineral of marine origin. In regions where it is now forming the essential iron, silica and potassium are supplied predominantly from the marine environment, and in most cases they have not been transported into the sea by weathering solutions from the continents.

One recent example of the occurrence of glauconite, found off the coast of southwest Africa, in the Atlantic Ocean, can be taken as being representative of numerous other occurrences. Cold and warm currents meet in this part of the Atlantic and the mixing of these waters causes the catastrophic death of animals, so that millions of dead fish and other creatures are thrown up on the shore to decompose and putrefy (M. Brongersma–Sanders, 1948). The almost annual cycle of such events in this region is as follows: cold polar water from the Antarctic area flows northwards along the coast of southwest Africa, as it does also along the margin of South Australia, South America and elsewhere. This polar water carries in solution much phosphorus, nitrogen and other nourishing matter which are vital to living plants and animals.[19] An abundant algal growth provides the basis of life for higher organisms and in consequence a flourishing fauna develops. In due course the available oxygen is unable to support all the prolific marine population and the waters become progressively poisoned by decomposing corpses so that catastrophic extermination of the fauna affects cubic kilometres of the sea.[11,71]

In consequence a carbonic acid zone develops in which the iron of the bottom sediments is dissolved as iron bicarbonate. Even hydrogen sulphide zones may develop in some places, near which ammonia derived from the decomposition of animals dissolves silica out of the sediments on the sea bottom. The precipitation of these dissolved substances occurs where the muddy waters mingle with normal oxygen-rich waters. Here the iron and silica unite to form glauconite, which may adsorb potassium from the sea water; the availability of potassium may be locally augmented by the decomposition of animals and plants.

The sequence of events leading to the formation of glauconite thus resembles in many ways that which conduces to the formation of chamosite. Both minerals are typical products of marine environments and ordinarily have no direct relation to weathering solutions derived from the continents. Nevertheless, the detrital material of the sea bottom, from which the necessary iron and silica are dissolved, was initially derived from the continents.[8,81]

ORIGIN OF MICRO- AND MACRO-VARIATIONS OF IRON ORE FACIES

If there existed H_2S-bearing waters in the deeper parts of the sea together with oxygen-rich surface waters—when the poles were free from ice-caps—the *predominant factor* responsible for the distribution of different facies *was undoubtedly the system of sea currents and not the absolute depth of the sea.*[8,50,57,89]

The development of sedimentary iron ores is greatly influenced by the velocities of sea currents and by their varying oxidation-reduction potentials, which are dependent on the amount of organic matter, CO_2 and free oxygen contained in the waters (H. W. James, 1954).

The areal extent of the different facies in an ocean basin may remain constant so long as a distinct dynamic system of sea currents is constant. In the course of time, however, the distribution of the different facies will vary according to changes in the current cycles due to climatic and morphological factors. Such changes produce lateral and vertical variations in the deposits of limonite, siderite, chamosite and pyrite, which are accompanied by varying quantities of detrital lime, clay and silica.[46,48,51,58]

Macroscopic and microscopic investigations of many samples of sedimentary iron ores from Assuan, Echte, Harzburg, Lorraine, Pakistan and elsewhere, indicate that even in what might be classed as a limonite oolith facies the different layers may contain sideritic clay ironstone, chamositic ore or even pyritic black schist.

The various layers of the different iron ore facies must be predominantly related to variations of sea currents and certainly not to synsedimentary epeirogenic movements, though many geologists still erroneously explain facies variations in time and space by invoking synsedimentary subsidence and uplift of wide sea basins.[50,83] This explanation appears to be false for several reasons. Short-term changes of sedimentary facies must be correlated primarily with variations of sea currents and cycles which are predominantly influenced by climatic factors. Variations of longer range may correspond to changes in the morphology of the sea basins and to slow epeirogenic movements. In most cases, however, even this kind of synsedimentary movement will often not occur throughout whole basins but only in special regions around ridges and narrow channels such as those of the Kattegat, the Dardanelles and the Bosphorus. Similar relations control the formation of salt deposits and especially the degree of saline concentrations in basins separated from each other by barrier ridges.

The intensity of short-range variations of iron ore facies, which must be connected predominantly with changes of current cycles, is also testified by the abundant and virtually synchronous occurrence of limonite and chamosite in oolitic deposits. Investigations of the Northampton Sand Ironstone by E. Cohen (1952) have demonstrated by means of microradiography that the brown colour of the ore is not caused by limonite alone, but is essentially due to oxidized chamosite which is a major constituent of the ore. He has proved the existence of complete transitions ranging from iron-free kaolinite to iron-rich chamosite, due to varying degrees of oxidation which give rise to a colour range from pale green to deep green and brown. The present writer has also determined by microscopic analysis the frequent presence of chamosite in varying states of oxidation in iron ores from Assuan, Echte, Harzburg, Lorraine and other areas. Optical and morphological features often indicate the presence of primary chamosite in these ores, whereas on casual inspection only brown limonite appears to be present.

The common occurrence of partly oxidized chamosite in a predominantly limonitic facies is one of the many features which seem to imply the *frequent exchange of waters of different origin, history and varying oxidation-reduction potential.* The presence of all facies types of iron ores in Mesozoic deposits may be learned from the literature.[5,6,9,12,17,36,46,47,53,58,77,78,82,90] Special investigations on facies types have been made by the author[8] and A. K. Bhattacharya,[6] and for Silurian sedimentary iron ores by D. Hoenes and E. Tröger.[51] The presence of the related types during Pre-Cambrian times has also been shown.[2,3,38,39,48,57,62,67,84,89] Above all, the excellent work of H. L. James[57] has been to demonstrate not only all types of iron ores in connexion with varying amounts of detrital components but also the ordinary tectonic situation of iron ore formation, contrary to geosynclinal types (Lahn–Dill-type) which are connected with differentiation products of initial basaltic magmas.[15,27,66,79]

PHYSICO-CHEMICAL RELATIONS OF IRON ORES

In 1952, W. C. Krumbein and R. M. Garrels[59] investigated the stability fields of some of the most important iron minerals in relation to pH and Eh values. N. K. Huber (1958) extended these studies to a greater range of pH and Eh values and to other iron minerals, notably magnetite and pyrrhotite. For the present purpose it will suffice to deal with only the most prominent iron ore minerals and the middle regions of the pH and Eh fields, and to correlate the different physico-chemical stability fields with the natural facies of iron ore sediments.

Fig. 6 shows the stability fields as determined by Krumbein and Garrels,[59] and three different regions have been selected by taking account of values which have recently been measured in natural environments.[90] In normal oxygen-rich sea water the values of pH vary between about 7·2 and 8·5, whereas the oxidation potentials lie between + 0·05 and + 0·4. The pH values of the carbonic acid zone are approximately 6 to 7·5, while the Eh values range from about + 0·05 to − 0·2. In the zone of the black mud facies alkaline conditions prevail owing to the bacterial production of ammonia, resulting in pH values between 7·2 and 9 together with a strongly reducing milieu with Eh between − 0·2 and − 0·5.

Most geologists[9,10,40] still contend that acid weathering solutions from the continents transport abundant quantities of iron bicarbonate to the sea, where the acid solution of $Fe(HCO_3)_2$ is thought to be oxidized to limonite in the alkaline sea water (horizontal arrow in Fig. 6). The oxygen content of the normal shallow sea and the high electrolyte content of the sea water are supposed to be the main factors causing the precipitation and coagulation of the iron-bearing solutions.

J. W. Gruner (1922) has cited the famous example of the waters of the Amazon, which contain about 3000 mg of iron per cu. m. These waters should, therefore, be capable of supplying an amount of iron equivalent to that in the Lake Superior iron ore deposits, namely 1940 million tons, in the relatively short time of 176 000 years. However, this example of the Amazon waters demonstrates clearly that iron ore deposits are not normally built up in this manner. The Amazon contains an overwhelming mass of clay and other silicate minerals and its relatively small iron content is precipitated together with this detrital material. In fact the sediments in the area of the Atlantic Ocean around the mouth of the River Amazon contain no more iron than other sediments of the Atlantic; for example, the red deep-sea clays are richer in iron (C. W. Correns, 1937).

The prevalent idea that weathering solutions from the continents could have produced ores of the minette type can hardly be correct, even in such cases as the black water types which contain 10–50 mg of iron per cu. dm. *There is no mechanism in the normal oxygen-rich shallow sea capable of separating Si–Al components from the iron.* This is only possible in a CO_2 zone under reducing conditions. Above all, prior to the Devonian period it was absolutely impossible for weathering solutions from the continents to carry any significant amount of iron.

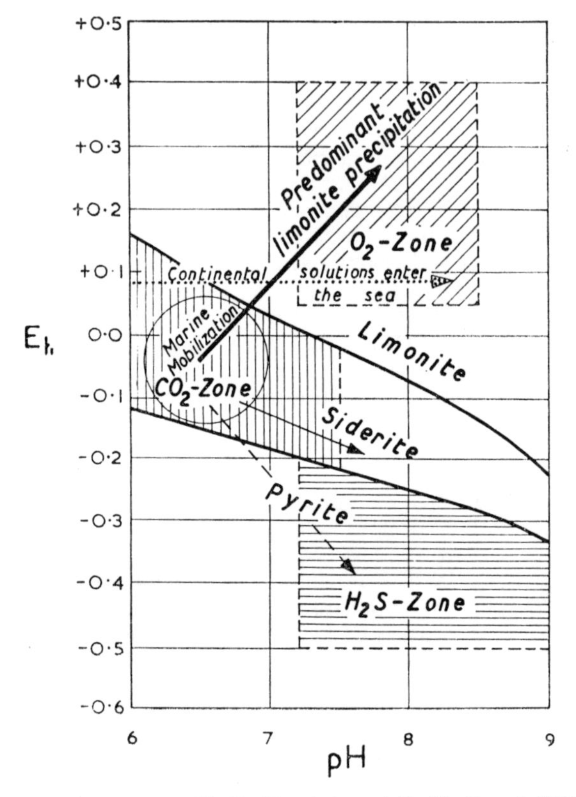

Fig. 6.—Stability fields, after W. C. Krumbein and R. M. Garrels (1952), and the physico-chemical conditions of natural environments.

Fig. 6 illustrates how the iron bicarbonate solutions of the CO_2 zone move to regions of other facies, the thickness of the arrows indicating the relative intensity of transport.

Corresponding to the normal conditions of sea currents the dissolved iron moves predominantly towards the oxygen-rich shallow sea where it is deposited as limonite ooliths. However, a considerable proportion of the dissolved iron is precipitated in the CO_2 zone itself to form sideritic clay ironstone.

Only very little iron reaches the H_2S facies of the deeper zones to be deposited as pyrite, for if the currents were very intense the black mud facies would diminish and finally disappear, and the conditions in the ocean would then resemble those of recent times. Under such conditions only very small quantities of iron could locally be dissolved to form glauconite.

It will be noted that in Fig. 6 no reference to chamosite is made. There can be no doubt, however, that the important milieu of this ferrosilicate must lie between those of siderite and pyrite, for it must be recalled that silica can be dissolved in significant quantities only under rather strongly alkaline conditions.[32,54,55,63] Indeed, it is owing to this fact that the black-mud facies of sapropels is often associated with chert.

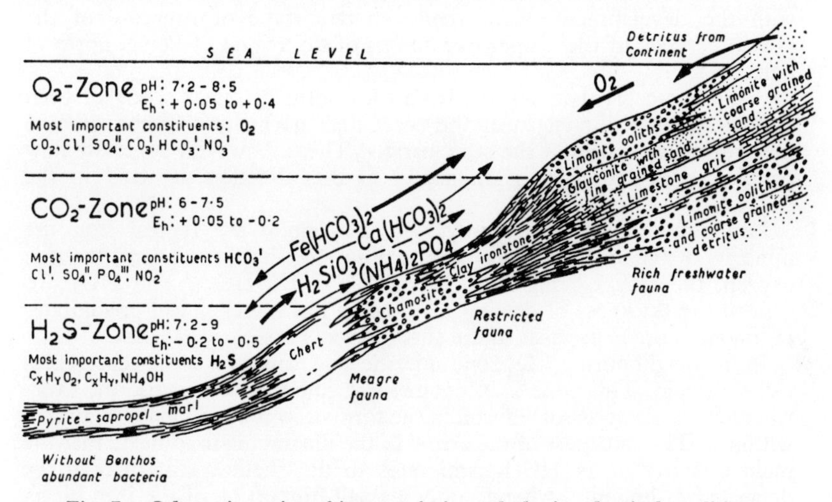

Fig. 7.—Schematic section of iron ore facies and physico-chemical conditions.

Fig. 7 depicts the physico-chemical conditions of iron formation in relation to facies changes. It must be borne in mind that the natural relationships are highly simplified in this pictorial representation. For example, increasing depth of sea is simply correlated with decreasing oxidation potential, whereas in reality the potential depends also on complicated current cycles. In some of the Norwegian fjords black mud water can actually form a layer above heavier sea water rich in oxygen (F. Birzer, 1957).

In Fig. 7, as also in Fig. 5, it has been assumed, for reasons of simplicity, that the velocity of currents and the grain size of detritus decrease systematically with increasing depth of water, even though this is not universally correct.[8,24] Recent measurements have shown that currents exist in deep sea regions with high velocities of 5–10 cm/sec. On the ridge between the northern ice sea and the Atlantic Ocean the maximum velocity of sea currents has been measured as not less than 34 cm/sec, corresponding to a region of submarine erosion on level (G. Dietrich, 1956). Such kinds of erosion must often have been important in past geological times (J. H. Taylor, 1946). The mechanical and chemical effects on marine sediments caused by these sea currents play an important role in the genesis of natural iron ores. In this connexion it is significant that *iron ore deposits are often associated with gaps in the sedimentary sequence and with discordances or even transgressions*, although in most cases major transgressions are not related to the origin of marine iron ores.[6,8,9,31,36,75]

The most important factor in the formation of the oolitic type of iron ore results from processes operating in the CO_2 zone of the sea, and is not due to mechanical treatment and oxidation in the vicinity of the shore line. Processes of the latter kind are of greater importance in connexion with the development of the conglomeratic type of iron ore of the 'Trümmererze' of the Upper Cretaceous of the region of Peine, north of Salzgitter.[31,85]

Fig. 7 indicates that detritus from the continent forms sandy or even conglomeratic sediments near the coast line, normally corresponding to the greatest velocities of the sea currents. These, however, generally flow parallel to the coast, at right angles to the direction depicted in the diagram.

Limonite ooliths and, locally also, glauconite are typical iron ore minerals of the shallow-water zone, whose most important constituent is oxygen, the others being CO_2, Cl', SO_4'', CO_3'', HCO_3' and NO_3'. In general the thickness of detrital material and of the chemical precipitates of limonitic ore is greatest in the shallow-water zone.

In the neighbouring CO_2 zone sideritic clay ironstone is the representative sediment. This zone is of outstanding importance because the overwhelming mass of dissolved iron in the form of iron bicarbonate originates within it. The thickness of the arrow in the diagram is to indicate that the main quantity of $Fe(HCO_3)_2$ migrates to the shallow sea, there to be deposited as limonite, whereas only a small proportion of the iron bicarbonate is transported to the depths.

The $Fe(HCO_3)_2$ which descends from the CO_2 zone unites with silica from the alkaline black-mud zone to form chamosite, or the silica may be precipitated nearer the H_2S zone as pure chert.

DIAGENETIC PROCESSES

Much detailed work by Hallimond, Taylor and others[43] has shown that chamosite is mainly a primary, not a diagenetic, mineral. However, some re-solution of chamosite may take place locally in the sediments (H. Harder, 1951).

The mobilization of carbonates after primary sedimentation within the sediment itself is quite common and here the investigations of A. V. Trofimov (1939) seem to be of considerable importance. Values of pH and Eh in the highest levels of bottom sediments of the 'gyttja' type, according to him, are shown in Fig. 8.

The gyttja facies is characterized by the fact that much organic material is embedded in the sediment, whereas the overlying water contains free

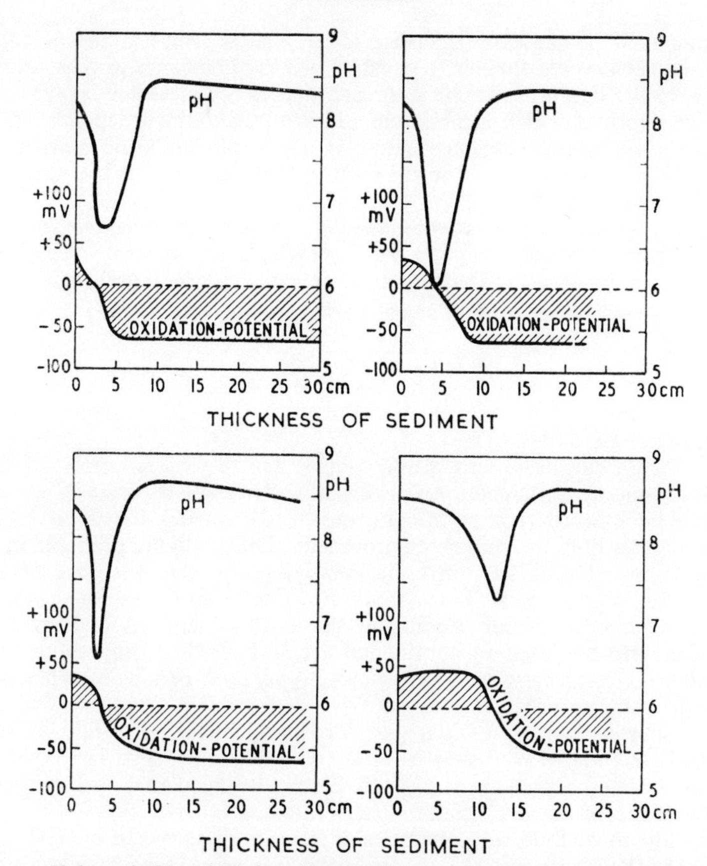

Fig. 8.—Values of pH and Eh in sediments of the gyttja type, after A. V. Trofimov (1939).

oxygen. Hence the upper centimetres of the bottom sediment react with the oxygen-bearing water so that its organic matter is partly decomposed and oxidized. Within the upper parts of the bottom sediment the oxidation potential therefore decreases with increasing depth. Likewise the pH values drop from greater than 8 to acid solutions, owing to the oxidizing decomposition of organic matter and the production of much CO_2. In this region the *conditions are in fact comparable with those of the CO_2 zone,* so that primary carbonates may therefore be re-dissolved in this region of acid solutions. This applies to lime, phosphorite and under reducing conditions also to $Fe(HCO_3)_2$ which can recrystallize as small idiomorphic crystals or as little nodular concretions.

In the deeper zones of the sediment the bulk of the organic matter cannot decompose because the supply of free oxygen is exhausted. Consequently only weak bacterial decomposition takes place, producing ammonia. This causes an increase of pH values, whereas the oxidation potential is lowered further to negative values. The facies of these deeper zones of the bottom sediment approach that of the black muds.

The depth at which a minimum pH value is attained depends on the primary content of organic matter in the sediment. The smaller the content of organic material in the sediment, the deeper lies the minimum of the pH curve.

Thus, the *diagenetic solutions in the different zones of the bottom sediments of the gyttja type are similar to those of the extensive zones of ocean basins* with their limonite, siderite and black mud zones, together with the pyrite zone in the deepest regions.

CONCLUSIONS

The main concepts of marine sedimentary iron ore formation may be summarized as follows:

1. Weathering solutions from continental regions do not normally produce marine sedimentary iron ores of the minette type.

2. The iron content of minette ores and iron ooliths has its origin predominantly in the marine environment. This is highly probable in the case of post-Devonian iron ooliths and is certain in the case of pre-Devonian marine ores. Throughout Pre-Cambrian times the necessary reducing conditions for mobilizing significant quantities of iron could nowhere have existed in continental areas. Indeed, during those times weathering conditions must have yielded a pure red bed facies, where iron is practically insoluble.

3. There are four principal types of iron ore facies: limonite, siderite, chamosite and pyrite, listed in order of decreasing oxidation potential. The characteristic values of pH and Eh can be calculated on the basis of modern measurements in natural environments.

4. The most abundant quantities of iron are dissolved in the CO_2 zone and are later precipitated in the oxygen-bearing shallow-water zone. Smaller amounts of $Fe(HCO_3)_2$ migrate into zones of increasing reduction potential to combine with silica originating in the alkaline H_2S zone so as to form chamosite.

5. The configuration of the different facies of limonite, siderite, chamosite and pyrite tends to follow the coast lines. This arrangement is not due to weathering solutions from the continents transporting iron at right angles to the coast line, but to the fact that the sea currents usually ran virtually parallel to the morphological features of the basins and consequently also to their margins.

6. The most important causes of vertical and lateral variations in the iron ore facies are changes in the sea currents, each with its own characteristic physico-chemical conditions. For small-scale variations in time and space, climatic changes are the most important controlling factors and not epeirogenic synsedimentary vertical movements of the earth's crust.

7. Vertical movements of the crust are the dominant factor in effecting prolonged changes of sedimentary types, but are not responsible for short

rhythms in bedding and sedimentation. Most ores of the minette type were deposited during non-orogenic periods free from major crustal movements.

8. Iron ore ooliths have no direct relation to marine transgressions, though these are important in connexion with the 'Trümmererze' of the Peine type.

9. Iron ore ooliths are not directly related to the saline facies, though both these types of deposits are partly related to the facies of bituminous shales and black schists. Both tend to occur during periods of weak post-paroxysmal movements of the earth's crust.

REFERENCES

1. ALLING, H. L. Diagenesis of the Clinton hematite ores of New York. *Bull. geol. Soc. Amer.*, **58**, 1947, 991–1018.

2. BACKLUND, H. G. The actualistic principle in geological research. *Från* filosofiens och forskningens fält (Skrifter utg. av Föreningen för filosofi och specialvetenskap [Upsala] no. 2), Stockholm, 1950, 86–120.

3. BACKLUND, H. G. Some aspects of ore formation, Pre-Cambrian and later. *Trans. Edinb. geol. Soc.*, **14**, pt. III, 1952, 302–35.

4. BARTZ, J. Die Bohnerzablagerungen in Rheinhessen und ihre Entstehung. *Arch. LagerstForsch.* no. 72, 1940, 57 p.

5. BERG, G. Vergleichende Petrographie oolithischer Eisenerze. *Arch. Lagerst-Forsch.* no. 76, 1944, 128 p.

6. BHATTACHARYA, A. K. Makroskopische und mikroskopische Untersuchung der Brauneisenerzlager im Lias alpha 3 der Grube Friederike bei Bad Harzburg und ihre Deutung für die Genese mariner Eisenerzlagerstätten. *Geol. Jb., Hannover*, **75**, 1958, 251–310.

7. BIRZER, F. Eisenzufuhr und Eisenfällung am Beispiel des Porsangerfjords. *Z. dtsch. geol. Ges.*, **109**, 1957, 63–8.

8. BORCHERT, H. Die Bildungsbedingungen mariner Eisenerzlagerstätten. *Chem. d. Erde*, **16**, 1952, 49–74.

9. BROCKAMP, B., und *Fachgenossen.* Zur Entstehung deutscher Eisenerz-lagerstätten. *Arch. LagerstForsch.* no. 75, 1942, 186 p.

10. BROCKAMP, B. Die Herkunft der Eisenlösungen; Die paläogeographische Stellung der Eisenablagerungen. *Arch. LagerstForsch.* no. 75, 1942, 176–7; 181–6.

11. BRONGERSMA-SANDERS, M. The importance of upwelling water to vertebrate paleontology and oil geology. *Verh. Akad. Wet. Amst., Afd. Natuurkunde*, Sect. 2, **45**, no. 4, 1948, 112 p.

12. CAILLÈRE, S., and KRAUT, F. Les gisements de fer du Bassin Lorrain. *Mém. Mus. Hist. nat., Paris, Ser. C, Science de la Terre*, **4**, no. 1, 1954, 1–192.

13. CASTAÑO, J. R., and GARRELS, R. M. Experiments on the deposition of iron with special reference to the Clinton iron ore deposits. *Econ. Geol.*, **45**, 1950, 755–70.

14. CAYEUX, L. *Études des gites mineraux de la France. Les minerais de fer oolithique de la France. Fasc. II: Minerais de fer secondaires* (Paris: Imprimerie Nationale, 1922), 1051 p.

15. CISSARZ, A. Zur Petrographie und Genesis südwestmazedonischer Eisen-silikatlagerstätten. *Bull. Serv. géol. geophys. Serbie*, **11**, 1954, 261–340.

16. CHARLET, E., and SCHWARTZ, W. Untersuchungen über die Lebensweise von Leptothrix ochracea und einigen begleitenden Eisenmikroben. *Schweiz. Z. Hydrol.*, **16**, no. 2, 1954, 318–42.

17. Cohen, E. The nature of silicates and carbonates of iron in the Northampton sand ironstone of central England. *Sym. Gisements de Fer du Monde (19th Int. geol. Congr., Alger* 1952), **2**, 466–71.

18. Cooper, L. H. N. Iron in the sea and in marine plankton. *Proc. roy. Soc.*, Ser. B, **118**, no. 810, 1935, 419–38.

19. Cooper, L. H. N. Phosphorus, nitrogen, iron and manganese in marine zooplankton. *J. Mar.biol. Ass.*, **23**, 1939, 387–412.

20. Conway, E. J. Mean geochemical data in relation to oceanic evolution. *Proc. R. Irish Acad.*, **48**, Sect. B, no. 8, 1942, 119–59.

21. Correns, C. W. Die Sedimente des äquatorialen atlantischen Ozeans. *Wissenschaftliche Ergebnisse der Deutschen Atlantischen Expedition auf dem Forschungs-und Vermessungsschiff 'Meteor'*, 1925–1927. Bd III, Teil 3. (Berlin und Leipzig: Verlag von Walter de Gruyter and Co., 1935–37.) 298 p.

22. Correns, C. W. Der Eisengehalt der marinen Sedimente und seine Entstehung. *Arch. LagerstForsch.* no. 75, 1942, 47–57.

23. Dengler, H. Das Eisenerzlager im unteren Korallenoolith der Grube Hansa. *Roemeriana*, **1** (Dahlgrün-Festschrift), Clausthal-Zellerfeld, 1954, 273–88.

24. Dietrich, G. Überströmung des Island-Färöer-Rückens in Bodennähe nach Beobachtungen mit dem Forschungsschiff 'Anton Dohrn' 1955–56. *Dtsch. hydrogr. Z.*, **9**, no. 2, 1956, 78–89.

25. Dorff, P. Die Eisenorganismen: Systematik und Morphologie. *Pflanzenforschung* no. 16, 1934, 62 p.

26. Dorff, P. *Biologie des Eisen- und Mangankreislaufs.* (Berlin: Verlagsges. f. Ackerbau, 1935) 106 p.

27. Dunn, J. A. The origin of iron ores in Singhbhum, India. *Econ. Geol.*, **30**, 1935, 643–54.

28. Ehmann, E. A. Chemische Untersuchungen über die Entstehung württembergischer Bohnerze. *Chem. d. Erde*, **6**, 1930, 117–42.

29. Einsele, W. Versuch einer Theorie der Dynamik der Mangan- und Eisenschichtung im eutrophen See. *Naturwissenschaften*, **28**, 1940, 257–64; 280–5.

30. Erd, R. C., and Evans, H. T., Jr. The compound Fe_3S_4 (smythite) found in nature. *J. Amer. chem. Soc.*, **78**, May 5, 1956, 2017.

31. Ferling, P. Mineralogische, petrographische, fazielle und chemische Untersuchung der Brauneisen-Trümmererzlagerstätte von Lengede-Broistedt. *Geol. Jb., Hannover*, **75**, 1958, 555–90.

32. Flaschen, S. S., and Osborn, E. F. Studies of the system iron oxide-silica-water at low oxygen partial pressures. *Econ. Geol.*, **52**, 1957, 923–43.

33. Galliher, E. W. The sulfur cycle in sediments. *J. Sediment Petrol.*, **3**, no. 2, 1933, 51–63.

34. Galliher, E. W. Glauconite genesis. *Bull. geol. Soc. Amer.*, **46**, 1935, 1351–65.

35. Ganter, I.-R., und Schwartz, W. Beiträge zur Biologie der Eisenmikroben. Leptothrix crassa chol. *Schweiz. Z. Hydrol.*, **18**, no. 1, 1956, 171–92.

36. Gaub, F. Die jurassischen Oolithe der Schwäbischen Alb. *Geol. paläont. Abh.*, **9**, 1910, 1–79.

37. Gehlen, K. v., and Harder, H. Zur Genese der kretazischen Eisenerze von Auerbach (Oberpfalz). *Heidelberg. Beitr. Min.*, **5**, 1956, 118–38.

38. Geijer, P. Pre-Cambrian atmosphere: evidence from the Pre-Cambrian of Sweden. *Geochim. et Cosmoch. Acta*, **10**, 1956, 304–10.

39. Geijer, P. Die Herkunft der quarzgebänderten Eisenerze: Eine Übersicht der Problemlage. *N. Jb. Min. Abh.*, **91** (Schneiderhöhn-Festband), June, 1957, 223–38.

40. GRUNER, J. W. The origin of sedimentary iron formations: the Biwabik Formation of the Mesabi Range. *Econ. Geol.*, **17**, 1922, 407–60.

41. HALLIMOND, A. F. Iron ores: Bedded ores of England and Wales. Petrography and chemistry. *Spec. Rep. Miner. Resour. G.B.*, **29**, 1925, 139 p.

42. HALLIMOND, A. F. On the relation of chamosite and daphnite to the chlorite group. *Miner. Mag.*, **25**, Dec. 1939, 441–65.

43. HALLIMOND, A. F., and others. The constitution and origin of sedimentary iron ores; a symposium. *Proc. Yorks. geol. (polyt.) Soc.*, **28**, 1951, 61–101.

44. HALVORSON, H. O. Studies on the transformations of iron in nature: III. The effect of CO_2 on the equilibrium in iron solutions. *Soil. Sci.*, **32**, 1931, 141–65.

45. HARDER, E. C. Iron-depositing bacteria and their geologic relations. *Prof. Pap. U.S. geol. Surv.*, 113, 1919.

46. HARDER, H. Über den Mineralbestand und die Entstehung einiger sedimentärer Eisenerze des Lias-γ. *Heidelberg. Beitr. Min.*, **2**, 1951, 455–76.

47. HARDER, H. Zum Chemismus der Bildung einiger sedimentärer Eisenerze. *Z. dtsch. geol. Ges.*, **109**, 1957, 69–72.

48. HAWLEY, J. E. Origin of some siderite, pyrite, chert deposits, Michipicoten district, Ontario. *Trans. roy. Soc. Can.*, 3rd ser., **36**, Sect. 4, 1942, 79–87.

49. HEGEMANN, F., und ALBRECHT, F. Zur Geochemie oxydischer Eisenerze. *Chem. d. Erde*, **17**, 1954, 81–103.

50. HESSLAND, I. Investigations of the Lower Ordovician of the Siljan District, Sweden. . . . With a special discussion on the formation of chamositic ooids. *Bull. geol. Instn Univ. Upsala*, **33**, 1949, 437–510.

51. HOENES, D., and TRÖGER, E. Lagerstätten oolithischer Eisenerze in Nordwestfrankreich. *Neues Jb. Min. Geol. Paläont.* Beil.-Bd., **79**, Abt. A, 1945, 192–257.

52. HOLLINGWORTH, S. E., and TAYLOR, J. H. An outline of the geology of the Kettering District. *Proc. Geol. Ass., Lond.*, **57**, 1946, 204–33.

53. HOLLINGWORTH, S. E., and TAYLOR, J. H. The Northampton Sand Ironstone: Stratigraphy, structure and reserves. *Mem. geol. Surv. U.K.* (London: H.M.S.O., 1951).

54. HUBER, N. K., and GARRELS, R. M. Relation of pH and oxidation potential to sedimentary iron mineral formation. *Econ. Geol.*, **48**, 1953, 337–57.

55. HUBER, N. K. The environmental control of sedimentary iron minerals. *Econ. Geol.*, **53**, 1958, 123–40.

56. HUMMEL, K. Die Entstehung eisenreicher Gesteine durch Halmyrolyse (= submarine Gesteinszersetzung). *Geol. Rdsch.*, **13**, 1922, 40–81, 97–136.

57. JAMES, H. L. Sedimentary facies of iron-formation. *Econ. Geol.*, **49**, 1954, 235–93.

58. KOLBE, H. Fazies und Geochemie der Kreideerze des nördlichen Harzvorlandes. *Z. dtsch. geol. Ges.*, **109**, 1957, 36–40.

59. KRUMBEIN, W. C., and GARRELS, R. M. Origin and classification of chemical sediments in terms of pH and oxidation-reduction potentials. *J. Geol.*, **60**, 1952, 1–33.

60. LANDERGREN, S. On the geochemistry of Swedish iron ores and associated rocks: a study on iron-ore formation. *Sverig. geol. Unders.*, Ser. C no. 496, Årsbok 42, no. 5, 1948, 182 p.

61. MOLISCH, H. *Die Eisenbakterien.* (Jena: G. Fischer, 1910), 83 p.

62. MOORE, E. S. Origin of iron deposits of the 'Lake Superior' type. *Trans. N.Y. Acad. Sci.*, **9**, Ser. 2, no. 2, 1946, 43–51.

63. MOORE, E. S., and MAYNARD, J. E. Solution, transportation and precipitation of iron and silica. *Econ. Geol.*, **24**, 1929, 272–303, 365–402, 506–27.

64. PAGE, B. M. Chamositic iron ore deposits near Tajmište, Western Macedonia, Yugoslavia. *Econ. Geol.*, **53**, 1958, 1–21.

65. PALMQVIST, S. Geochemical studies on the iron-bearing Liassic Series in Southern Sweden. *Medd. Lunds geol.-miner. Instn*, no. 60, 1935, 204 p.

66. PARK, C. F., JR. The spilite and manganese problems of the Olympic peninsula, Washington. *Amer. J. Sci.*, **244**, 1946, 305–23.

67. PETTIJOHN, F. J. Archean sedimentation. *Bull. geol. Soc. Amer.*, **54**, 1943, 925–72.

68. PRATJE, O. Rezente marine Eisen-Ooide aus der Nordsee. *Zbl. Miner. Geol. Paläont.* Abt. B, 1930, 289–94.

69. PERFILIEV, B. W. Die Rolle der Mikroben in der Erzbildung. *Verh. int. Ver. Limnol. 1925*, Stuttgart, 1927, 330–59.

70. PRINGSHEIM, E. G. Iron bacteria. *Biol. Rev.*, **24**, no. 2, 1949, 200–45.

71. RICHTER, R. Massensterben im Meere, Auftriebwasser und Erdöl-Bildung. *Natur und Volk* (*Ber. senckenb. naturf. Ges.*), **80**, 1950, 21–28.

72. RUBEY, W. W. The geologic history of sea water. *Bull. geol. Soc. Amer.*, **62**, 1951, 1111–47.

73. RUTTNER, F. Eisenlösung und Eisenfällung in Binnengewässern. *Arch. LagerstForsch.* no. 75, 1942, 16–28.

74 ZAPOROZHTSEVA, A. S. The presence of both glauconite and chamoisite in rocks. *Dokl. Ak. Nauk S.S.S.R.*, **97**, no. 5, 1954, 903–5 (Russian text).

75. SCHNEIDERHÖHN, H. Aufbereitungsversuche mit oolithischen Eisenerzen der Makrozephalusschichten bei Gutmadingen (Baden) und ihre sedimentpetrogenetische Bedeutung. *Fortschr. Geol.*, **11**, 1932, 147–81.

76. SCHOUTEN, C. The role of sulphur bacteria in the formation of the so-called sedimentary copper ores and pyritic ore bodies. *Econ. Geol.*, **41**, 1946, 517–38.

77. SEITZ, O. Das Eisenerz im Korallenoolith der Gifhorner Mulde bei Braunschweig und Bemerkungen über den Oberen Dogger und die Hersumer Schichten. *Geol. Jb., Hannover*, **64**, 1950, 1–73.

78. SIEBDRAT, H. G. Parallelisierung von Mineralbestand und chemischer Analyse für verschiedene Eisenerztypen unter besonderer Berücksichtigung der marin-sedimentären Eisenerzlagerstätten. *Archiv Eisenhüttenw.*, **30**, 1959, 61–70.

79. SPENCER, E., and PERCIVAL, F. G. The structure and origin of the banded hematite jaspers of Singhbhum, India. *Econ. Geol.*, **47**, 1952, 365–83.

80. TROFIMOV, A. V. Oxidizing activity and pH of brown sediments of the Barentz sea. *Dokl. Ak. Nauk S.S.S.R.*, **23**, no. 9, 1939, 925–8 (English text).

81. TAYLOR, J. H. Evidence of submarine erosion in the Lincolnshire Limestone of Northamptonshire. *Proc. Geol. Ass., Lond.*, **57**, 1946, 246–62.

82. TAYLOR, J. H. Petrology of the Northampton Sand Ironstone Formation. *Mem. geol. Surv. U.K.* (London: H.M.S.O., 1949).

83. THIENHAUS, R. Zur Paläogeographie der Korallenoolitherze des Wesergebirges. *Z. dtsch. geol. Ges.*, **109**, 1957, 49–62.

84. TYLER, S. A., and TWENHOFEL, W. H. Sedimentation and stratigraphy of the Huronian of Upper Michigan. *Amer. J. Sci.*, **250**, 1952, 1–27, 118–51.

85. WALDECK, H. Der Bildungsraum der Oberkreide-Erze von Peine und seine tektonische Anlage. *Z. dtsch. geol. Ges.*, **109**, 1957, 41–8.

86. WATTENBERG, H. Das Vorkommen des Eisens im Meere. *Arch. LagerstForsch*, no. 75, 1942, 36–47.

87. WERNER, F. Zur Entstehung der Eisenerzlagerstätte im Braunjura beta von Geislingen. *Z. dtsch. geol. Ges.*, **109**, 1957, 10–21.

88. WOOLNOUGH, W. G. Sedimentation in barred basins, and source rocks of oil. *Bull. Amer. Ass. Petrol. Geol.*, **21**, Sept. 1937, 1101–57.

89. WOOLNOUGH, W. G. Origin of banded iron deposits—a suggestion. *Econ. Geol.*, **36**, 1941, 465–89.

90. ZOBELL, C. E. Studies on redox potential of marine sediments. *Bull. Amer. Ass. Petrol. Geol.*, **30**, April 1946, 477–513.

27

Reprinted from *Nature,* **209**(5030), 1306–1309 (1966)

DEPOSITIONAL ENVIRONMENT OF BRITISH LIASSIC IRONSTONES CONSIDERED IN THE CONTEXT OF THEIR FACIES RELATIONSHIPS

By Dr. A. HALLAM
Grant Institute of Geology, University of Edinburgh

Although the petrology of the economically exploitable oolitic ironstones in the British Lias has been intensively investigated and their conditions of formation repeatedly discussed[1–5], a number of outstanding problems still remain. It is believed that some of these can be resolved by studying the ironstones in the context of their facies relationships. It will be shown in addition how this approach facilitates the interpretation of early Jurassic palaeogeography.

The ironstones are typical minette ores and consist characteristically of chamosite ooliths, sometimes altered to limonite, in a sideritic and chamositic matrix, although numerous minor variants occur. For full petrographic details Taylor's monograph[6] on the lithologically similar Northampton Sand ironstone (Middle Jurassic) remains indispensable.

As indicated in Table 1, ironstones are widely distributed in the British Lias, being missing only from the Hettangian and Carixian stages. All are well known except the Ardnish Ironstone near Broadford, Skye, a 2 ft. band which was only recently discovered[7]. The most important ironstones in western Europe are the minette ores of Lorraine, ranging in age from Upper Toarcian to Bajocian (that is, 'Aalenian'); others occur in the Lower Sinemurian and Carixian of north-west Germany and the Carixian of Bornholm. Thin beds containing chamosite or limonite ooliths occur widely and include two in the Hettangian of Baden-Württemberg, the *Psilonotenbank* and *Oolithenbank.* It is evident, therefore, that in north-west Europe as a whole conditions suitable for minette formation occurred locally throughout the Lias.

Table 1

Stage	Scotland	Yorkshire	Midlands
Toarcian	Raasay	Rosedale	
Domerian or Upper Pliensbachian		Cleveland	Marlstone
Carixian or Lower Pliensbachian			
Sinemurian	Ardnish		Frodingham
Hettangian			

Facies Relationships

The extent to which the Liassic ironstones represent condensed deposits has not always been fully appreciated in discussions of their origin. As indicated in Fig. 1 the lateral equivalents of the ironstones in sandstones or shale are substantially thicker. Even this does not give an adequate picture of the extent of condensation, since allowance must be made for post-depositional compaction of the shales. Furthermore, although the Yorkshire coast Liassic succession is one of the thickest in Britain, it still only signifies a moderate rate of sedimentation. Thus the Toarcian shales of the Nordoldenburg Trough in north-west Germany are some 400 m thick[8], about the same as the whole Liassic succession in Yorkshire.

Stratigraphical control for the correlations given in Fig. 1 is good and there is no likelihood of major non-sequences except possibly in the case of the Raasay Ironstone. (This last case has been allowed for so far as possible by correlating the ironstone only with the *commune* sub-zone of the *bifrons* Zone, though it may well span a much longer period of time[9].) On the other hand, it is likely that brief periods of erosion alternated frequently with periods of slow deposition.

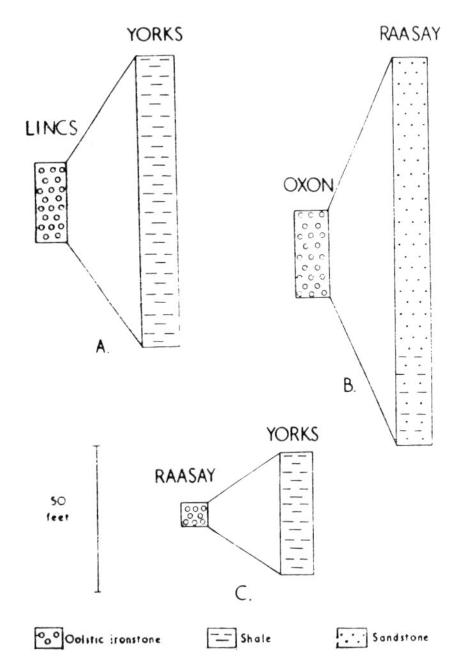

Fig. 1. Diagram to illustrate the condensed nature of oolitic ironstones compared with their lateral equivalents in shale and sandstone: *A*, Frodingham; *B*, Marlstone; *C*, Raasay

Brockamp[10] has observed that the German ironstones often occur at the boundary between sandstones and shales; a comparable association is characteristic of British Liassic ores. Both the Frodingham and Cleveland ironstones pass laterally into silty and sandy shales and the Rosedale and Marlstone ironstones pass laterally into fine sandstones. The lateral equivalents of the more poorly exposed Raasay and Ardnish ironstones are not known, but both beds occur in a sequence of silty and sandy shales.

In considering the general problem of iron enrichment in the sea-water or bottom sediment it is misleading to restrict attention, however, to the chamosite/limonite oolites. This is made evident by examining the facies relationships of the Cleveland Ironstone on the Yorkshire coast. Abundant ammonites allow a detailed correlation from the ironstone in a fairly normal, partly oolitic development near Staithes to its lateral equivalent a few miles to the south-east of a thicker sequence of silty/sandy shales with thin nodule bands of non-oolitic siderite mudstone (Fig. 2). It cannot be seriously supposed that the chemical constitution of the sea-water differed appreciably over such a short distance. Therefore it follows that the concentration of iron in the beds to the north-west, sufficient to make an exploitable ore, is the result of local physical conditions (a higher terrigenous sedimentation rate to the south-east in quieter and probably slightly deeper water). Although, considering the shales in bulk, the iron content is considerably diminished, it has been concentrated in the nodules owing to diagenetic segregation.

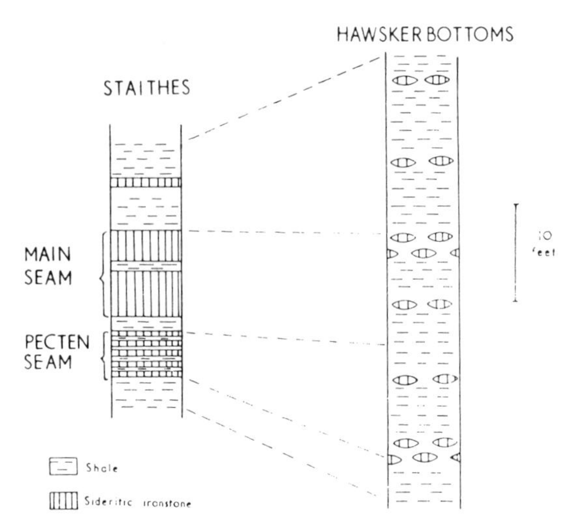

Fig. 2. Correlation of the *spinatum* Zone on the Yorkshire coast, based on Howarth (ref. 21). The Cleveland Ironstone at Staithes comprises the Main and Pecten seams

Obvious as the foregoing deduction may appear, it is nevertheless significant since the facies of silty/sandy shales with sideritic nodules is much more widespread in the Lias than the chamosite oolites. For example, in Yorkshire this facies begins just below the base of the Carixian and continues up to the top of the Domerian. There is a return to normal non-silty calcareous facies in the lower part of the Toarcian but the silty/sandy ferruginous facies returns in the Upper Toarcian.

In the Midlands and South-west England, in contrast, the Lower Lias is largely free of ferruginous beds, the most notable exception being the Lower Sinemurian Frodingham Ironstone in north Lincolnshire. However, the Lower Domerian, that is, the zone preceding that containing the Marlstone and Cleveland ironstones, is marked by a great spread of silty shales with sideritic nodules over most of this region. Apart from the local occurrence of diachronous sandy beds in parts of the south-west, the Toarcian marks a return to normal calcareous clay deposits.

British Liassic rocks can in fact be divided into two distinctive associations which may be termed the 'calcareous' facies and 'ferruginous' facies. The former is the more widespread and consists of argillaceous deposits and limestone. Smooth-textured shales, clays or marls with strongly sub-ordinate detrital quartz of silt grade and subsidiary layers and nodule bands of fine-grained argillaceous limestone were probably deposited in slightly deeper and quieter off-shore waters. Shallower near-shore deposits, as seen in Glamorgan, the Mendips and the Inner Hebrides, contain a higher proportion of limestone, which includes oolitic and bioclastic varieties.

The argillaceous rocks of the ferruginous facies are typically rich in detrital quartz of silt to fine sand grade (on the Wentworth Scale). This gives them a distinctive rough texture, while the abundant muscovite flakes produce a characteristic glint. The associated sideritic nodules correspond to the calcitic nodules in the calcareous clays just as the chamosite oolites may be thought of as the equivalents of the calcareous oolites. Calcareous nodules may also occur, however, though not in intimate association with the sideritic.

Sandstones are subordinate in both facies, although commoner in the ferruginous; they are almost invariably fine grained. Whereas those in the calcareous facies are well sorted, in a calcitic cement (for example, in the Lower Broadford Beds of the Skye area) the sandstones in the ferruginous facies are of several types. One type, well exemplified by the sandstones at the Carixian–Domerian boundary in Yorkshire, is well sorted and clean-washed, with a calcitic cement as in the calcareous facies. Other sandstones, though possessing a calcitic cement, contain limonite associated with the quartz grains (for example, the Upper Broadford Beds sandstones of the Skye area). A third type, strictly confined to the ferruginous facies, consists of intimate mixtures of clay and fine sand. The lithological contrast allows the recognition of mottling exhibiting several varieties of trace fossil including *Chondrites*, *Diplocraterion*, *Rhizocorallium* and *Thalassinoides*. Good examples include the topmost Sinemurian and the topmost Toarcian beds on the Yorkshire coast, and much of the Pliensbachian in the Inner Hebrides.

Bearing of Facies Relationships on Hypotheses of Ironstone Formation

The abundance and diversity of benthonic fossils in dominantly argillaceous sediments signifies a widespread sedimentary environment of quiet but shallow-water marine conditions in the British area during Liassic times, and implies that the associated landmasses were of very subdued relief. In the context of this environmental picture the occurrence of mixed sandy, silty and argillaceous rocks is likely to signify the proximity of rivers. Tidal and longshore currents are of course capable of transporting sand by traction considerable distances from river mouths but the deposits that result from such transportation are normally well sorted—mud and fine silt having been winnowed out. The mixed sand, silt and clay deposits that occur in the ferruginous facies have evidently been buried before any major winnowing action could occur. Such mixed deposits, lacking any trace of lamination because of the activity of burrowing organisms, are characteristic of the distal parts of pro-delta régimes of the present time[11,12]. In support of this interpretation, fossil driftwood appears to be more abundant in the ferruginous than in the calcareous facies of the Lias, due allowance being made for variations in rates of sedimentation. We must now consider the bearing of this interpretation on the various hypotheses of ironstone formation.

The orthodox views of minette ore formation all assume derivation of iron by continental weathering, although opinions differ on the mode of transportation and concentration on the sea bed. A radically different hypothesis has been proposed recently by Borchert[13,14], who believes that the conventional interpretation has several insuperable difficulties and argues that certain deposits on the sea floor, possibly far from land, themselves acted as sources of iron. Though Borchert's ideas were received with some scepticism in the discussion following the reading of his paper in London[15], they were treated sympathetically by Dunham[5] as being possibly valid in the case of certain Liassic ironstones.

It will be convenient to consider Borchert's hypothesis first. He envisages three depth zones in the sea with distinctive chemical characteristics and bottom deposits. The deepest is the hydrogen sulphide zone, characterized by anaerobic bottom waters and sediments consisting of pyritic bituminous mud. The shallowest is the oxygen zone, with a rich bottom fauna, where limonitic ooliths form in agitated water. Between these is the carbonic acid zone, rich in carbon dioxide, where the bottom deposits consist of sideritic muds; iron is supposed to be mobilized from the deposits of this zone. Part of the iron is carried by marine currents into shallower water where it contributes to the formation of limonite. Part is carried towards the hydrogen sulphide zone, where it encounters silica dissolved in alkaline water liberated from the bituminous mud; as a result chamosite forms.

A major difficulty of Borchert's interpretation is that the depth zones and chemical reactions are hypothetical so far as marine conditions are concerned. There is no evidence, for example, of a widespread carbon dioxide zone in seas of the present day where the deeper water is anaerobic. Apart from this, however, these are ample grounds for rejecting his hypothesis for the Liassic ironstones.

The necessary association of ironstones and bituminous shales at the same stratigraphic horizon exists nowhere in western Europe. On the contrary, there is a clear negative correlation, since laminated bituminous shales, such as occur in parts of the Hettangian and Sinemurian of South-west England and the Lower Toarcian of a much more extensive area, invariably belong to the calcareous facies. Borchert actually argues for deep-sea stagnation and bituminous facies on the grounds that, in the absence of polar ice caps during periods of ironstone formation, deep oceanic circulation would be far more sluggish than to-day. Liassic deposits occur in the Mediterranean region (Ammonitico Rosso facies) which were probably laid down in deeper water than anything in north-west Europe; they are, however, strikingly deficient in organic matter and are not especially rich in iron.

The evidence from facies associations lends support in fact to the conventional view of iron derivation, with ferruginous deposits forming close to river deltas. We must now examine briefly certain ideas on the site of ironstone deposition and the transportation and concentration of the iron, in so far as they are pertinent to the Liassic ores.

It has been suggested that ironstones formed close to old shorelines[10,16]. This is not necessarily so. The unequivocal shoreline deposits of Glamorgan and the Mendips are in calcareous facies and include normal oolites and skeletal limestone, as do the near-shore deposits of the Lower Broadford Beds in Skye. In contrast, none of the oolitic ironstones are obviously associated with an old shoreline, though because of inadequate exposure this cannot be decisively ruled out. It has been pointed out, moreover, that certain Asiatic rivers have been observed to carry iron-bearing sediments far into the open sea[17].

Another common belief is that the ironstones did not form in the open sea but in some sort of near-shore lagoon. To be meaningful, the term lagoon should be restricted to partly isolated regions of abnormal salinity, or at least regions protected from strong wave- or tide-induced water disturbance. The Liassic ironstones contain abundant benthonic fossils including many stenohaline types, with no suggestion of abnormal salinity. There is in addition abundant evidence from the rocks themselves of strong water agitation.

Two different solutions have been proposed to account for the rarity of detrital quartz grains in what are evidently shallow-water deposits that have been subjected to agitation sufficient to transport such grains. Hemingway[3], influenced by an approximation in the Yorkshire Lias on three occasions to a cyclic sequence of shale–sandstone–ironstone, has related the sedimentation to erosional cycles on the land. As the latter became peneplaned, mechanical erosion diminished so that finally only chemical derivatives including iron were transported and deposited in shallow restricted arms of the sea. This hypothesis fails to account for the frequent lateral passage of ironstones into clastic rocks and is clearly incompatible with the interpretation adopted in this article. Some sort of 'clastic trap'[18] seems a more plausible explanation. That is, some iron was transported slightly beyond the limit of deposition of the bulk of the terrigenous sediments. We turn now to how this might have been achieved.

The problem of the transportation and concentration of iron to form exploitable ores is singularly acute because of the lack of modern analogies. As is well known, chamosite is apparently forming nowhere in recent marine sediments and siderite is rare, while the concentration of dissolved iron in sea-water is negligible. The most commonly held belief is that the iron was transported in rivers in the ferrous state protected by organic colloids and later deposited on entering the alkaline environment of the sea. Carroll[19] has recently put forward a different suggestion, pointing out that ferric oxide can travel to the sea as particles coating the surface of clay micelles and can be removed by a lowering of the redox potential to negative values, which converts the ferric iron into the more soluble ferrous form. She argues that chamosite may be formed in such a reducing environment by the interaction of iron released in this way with kaolinite.

It seems quite probable that siderite could form as a result of the process Carroll describes, iron released from clay minerals within silty pro-delta muds reacting with carbonate ions in the interstitial water and afterwards segregating to form nodules. In support of this, there is a clear association of siderite with clay in the Lias. Those sandstones in the ferruginous facies which have been winnowed free of clay particles, such as the Marlstone 'sandrock' in Leicestershire and the *davoei-margaritatus* Zone sandstones of Yorkshire, are cemented by calcite not siderite, suggesting that iron has been removed with the clay.

Unfortunately Carroll's interpretation does not solve the problem of chamosite concentrations. All the normal Liassic clays studied by me consist dominantly of illite, kaolinite being markedly subordinate. Yet chamosite is the most abundant clay mineral in the ironstones. The influx of large quantities of illite, just as with detrital quartz, evidently diluted the available iron to such an extent that exploitable ore could not form. Therefore in a sense we are back where we started. It is hard to resist the conclusion that some iron was carried, perhaps as a colloidal solution or suspension, beyond the area where most of the terrigenous sediment was deposited. It could only concentrate on the sea bottom in areas of extremely slow sedimentation, probably off-shore shoals. Chamosite presumably formed authigenically in a reducing environment within fine-grained sediment but was evidently stable in slightly oxidizing conditions, as testified by the rich benthonic fauna. Presumably it was carried to the surface by burrowing organisms and ooliths produced as a result of water agitation. Planktonic organisms such as diatoms could well have contributed to both the iron and silica required for the formation of chamosite, since opaline silica is readily soluble within sediments.

As regards the difficulty concerning the lack of modern analogies, one should bear in mind the following point. Because the world to-day has abnormally high relief terrigenous sedimentation rates on the continental shelf in the vicinity of river deltas are probably a good deal higher than in the shelf sea that covered north-west Europe in the early Jurassic. The concentration of iron coming from rivers need not have been appreciably higher than to-day, so long as sedimentation rates were slight. A comparison with the phosphate deposits that have formed recently off southern California may be apposite; these seem to owe their origin essentially to a conjunction of two factors: (*a*) a slow rate of sedimentation, (*b*) phosphate enrichment in sea-water due to upwelling. The significant point is that even in areas of upwelling phosphate concentration remains low compared with many other ions.

The well-known fact that iron concentrations in rivers are generally much higher than in the sea suggests that much may be deposited not far from the deltas. It would be instructive if studies could be made comparing the interstitial water composition of certain pro-delta and river-distant sediments.

Interpretation of Jurassic Palaeogeography

Distinction of the calcareous and ferruginous facies, and recognition of the probable association of the latter with river deltas, brings out with unexpected clarity important regional similarities and differences in the English Lower and Middle Jurassic. South-west England and Yorkshire show parallel contrasts during this time. The former area remained consistently within the calcareous facies, deeper water clays and calcilutites passing upwards stratigraphically into shallower water calcareous oolites. The Yorkshire Lias exhibits the first hints of a river delta near the base of the Carixian. Following a major marine transgression in the Lower Toarcian[20], when the calcareous facies temporarily returned, the pro-delta facies spread once more. In Middle Jurassic times, owing to shallowing of the sea as in the south-west, the delta itself began to cover the area. The Midlands form an intermediate area. In the Middle Jurassic, several oscillations are seen between calcareous facies (Inferior and Great Oolite limestones) and ferruginous/deltaic facies (Northampton Sand ironstone, Lower and Upper Estuarine Series), bound up possibly with the periodic migration of delta distributaries.

Major rivers evidently did not enter the sea in the area of South-west England, except locally for a short time during the Toarcian. It is tempting to suggest that the Yorkshire delta spread from a river draining the Scandinavian landmass (there is no good evidence supporting a Pennine landmass at the time, as shown in some palaeogeographic reconstructions). The main evidence favouring this is as follows. The only early Mesozoic remnants in Scandinavia are deltaic and ferruginous shallow marine deposits of Rhaetic and Lower Lias age. Also, most of the sandy deposits that spread into the north-west German Basin in Bajocian times came from the north or north-east[8]. Now that boreholes are being drilled below the North Sea off north-east England one may tentatively venture the prediction that they may show the Lias in this area to contain a higher proportion of sandy and ferruginous deposits than in Yorkshire.

1 Hallimond, A. F., *Spec. Rep. Min. Resources, G.B. Geol. Surv.*, 29 (1925).
2 Whitehead, T. H., *et al.*, *The Liassic Ironstones, Mem. Geol. Surv., G.B.* (1952).
3 Hemingway, J. E., *Proc. Yorks. Geol. Soc.*, **28**, 67 (1951).
4 Davies, W., and Dixie, R. J. M., *Proc. Yorks. Geol. Soc.*, **28**, 85 (1951).
5 Dunham, K. C., *Proc. Yorks. Geol. Soc.*, **32**, 229 (1960).
6 Taylor, J. H., *Petrology of the Northampton Sand Ironstone Formation, Mem. Geol. Surv., G.B.* (1949).
7 Hallam, A., *Proc. Yorks. Geol. Soc.*, **32**, 165 (1959).
8 Brand, E., and Hoffman, K., *Proc. Sixth World Petrol. Congr.*, sect. 1, 223 (1963).
9 Hallam, A., *Trans. Edinburgh Geol. Soc.*, **18**, 124 (1961).
10 Brockamp, B., *Archiv. für Lagerstättenforschung*, **75**, 181 (1942).
11 Straaten, L. M. J. U., van, *Geol. en Mijnb.*, **21**, 197 (1959).
12 Straaten, L. M. J. U., van, *Liverpool and Manchester Geol. J.*, **2**, 411 (1959).
13 Borchert, H., *Chem. d. Erde*, **16**, 49 (1952).
14 Borchert, H., *Bull. Instn. Min. Met.*, **69**, 261 (1960).
15 *Bull. Instn. Min. Met.*, **69**, 530 (1960).
16 Correns, C. W., *Archiv. für Lagerstättenforschung*, **75**, 47 (1942).
17 Krejci-Graf, K., *Proc. Yorks. Geol. Soc.*, **34**, 469 (1964).
18 Huber, M. K., and Garrels, R. M., *Econ. Geol.*, **48**, 337 (1953).
19 Carroll, D., *Geochim. Cosmochim. Acta*, **14**, 1 (1958).
20 Hallam, A., *Geol. Mag.*, **100**, 444 (1963).
21 Howarth, M. K., *Proc. Yorks. Geol. Soc.*, **30**, 147 (1955).

Editor's Comments on Papers 28 Through 31

In Paper 28 Lepp and Goldich propose that lateritic weathering in an oxygen-deficient atmosphere produced the chemical differentiation necessary for the accumulation of the low-alumina, low-phosphorus Precambrian iron-formations. They attributed the geochemical separation of iron and silica in the younger ironstones to the evolution of an oxygenated atmosphere which caused iron to be trapped with aluminum during laterization and thus to be separated from silica. The idea that the Precambrian atmosphere may have played a role in accounting for the unique chemistry of iron-formations was not new, but it was a minority view during the 1950s and earlier.

In their model Lepp and Goldich suggest that the iron was initially deposited as carbonate. Cloud (1965, 1968) supported the idea of an oxygen-deficient atmosphere in the Precambrian, but he proposed that primitive photosynthesizers created localized oxidizing conditions which converted ferrous iron to insoluble ferric oxides. Currently the conclusion that the chemical differences between Precambrian and younger iron sediments are related to evolutionary changes in the atmosphere and hydrosphere is widely accepted. Cloud (1973) recently published a revised and expanded version of his thoughts on the origin of iron-formations.

The papers by Gross (Paper 29) and Trendall (Paper 30) are discussions of the Lepp and Goldich article. Paper 31 is from an article by Rhodes W. Fairbridge, the general editor of this series. In the excerpt titled "Revolution II" he examines the period of earth history during which most of the great iron-formations of the world were deposited. Fairbridge recognizes five major biological, geochemical, and environmental revolutions in the history of the earth. Revolution I is marked by the first appearance of life on earth at about 3.8×10^9 years ago. Revolution II began about 2.9×10^9 years ago with the appearance of the first chlorophyllic organisms. Revolution III, at about 6×10^8 years ago, marks the appearance of the first carbonate shells. Revolution IV is the beginning of the great coal age at about 3×10^8 years ago, and Revolution V, at about 1×10^8 years ago, signifies the appearance of small, pelagic carbonate organisms. In this way the earth's populations have successively changed the atmospheric and oceanic chemistry making new environments for their successors.

Rhodes Fairbridge was born in Australia and educated there, in Canada, and in England. After teaching engagements at the University of Western Australia and the University of Illinois, Fairbridge joined the staff of Columbia University in 1955, where he is currently Professor of Geology. His principal research has been in the areas of eustatic sea-level changes, geomorphology, and paleoclimatology. In addition to his many papers in professional journals, he is editor of the Encyclopedia of Earth Sciences Series, general editor of this Benchmark in Geology Series, and editor of other books in geology.

Gordon A. Gross graduated from Queen's University, Ontario, and he received his Ph.D. from the University of Wisconsin. He is a Geologist with the Geological Survey of Canada and was for a number of years assigned to the study of iron ores in Canada. He is the author of *Geology of Iron Deposits in Canada,* a three-volume work published by the Geological Survey of Canada in the period from 1965 to 1968. In his most recent publication on iron-formations he relates their depositional environments to continental drift (Gross, 1973).

References

Cloud, P. E., Jr., 1965, Significance of the Gunflint (Precambrian flora: Science, v. 148, p. 27–35.

———, 1968, Atmospheric and hydrospheric evolution on the primitive earth: Science, v. 160, p. 729–736.

———, 1973, Paleoecological significances of the banded iron-formation: Econ. Geol., v. 68, p. 1135–1143.

Gross, G. A., 1965, Geology of iron deposits in Canada: vol. I, General geology and evaluation of iron deposits: Geol. Survey Canada, Econ. Geol. Rept. 22, 181 p.

———, 1973, Continental drift and the depositional environments of the principal types of Pre-Cambrian iron formation: *in* Genesis of Precambrian iron and manganese deposits, Proc. Kiev. Symp., UNESCO, New York, 1973.

Reprinted from *Econ. Geol.*, **59,** 1047–1060 (1964)

Origin of Precambrian Iron Formations

HENRY LEPP and SAMUEL S. GOLDICH

* * * * * * *

General Statement

The statistical data presented emphasize chemical properties and differences between Precambrian iron formations of the Canadian Shield and post-Precambrian iron formations that must be considered in any hypothesis of origin. Although similar detailed chemical data for other areas are not available, descriptions and analyses given in the literature indicate that the iron formations of the various Precambrian shields closely resemble those of North America. Some notable features of the chemical composition of iron formations may be summarized.

(1) The Precambrian iron formations of the Canadian Shield are characterized by a surprisingly uniform tenor of iron and small contents of Al_2O_3, TiO_2, and P_2O_5.

(2) Within a district the iron contents of the different mineralogic and lithologic varieties or facies are also surprisingly uniform. Apparent differences in the relative weight percentages of iron can be accounted for in large part by the formula differences of the iron minerals. In terms of the major chemical constituents there are no great chemical differences between carbonate, silicate, and oxide facies, or between thin- and thick-bedded slaty or cherty members.

(3) Silica and iron are intimately and genetically related in the Lake Superior type of iron formation. In later geologic time silica and iron were geochemically separated in sediments.

(4) Isotopic age determinations indicate that banded cherty iron formations were deposited in many parts of the world over a long period in Early and Middle Precambrian time.

Precambrian Atmosphere

Early investigators suggested that the origin of the Precambrian iron formations was related to the unusual composition of the Precambrian atmosphere. Some held that carbon dioxide was more abundant than in the present atmosphere and was a factor in accelerating weathering processes; others suggested that oxygen was deficient or lacking. Macgregor (59) stated that the stumbling block in the theories advanced to explain the origin of the Precambrian iron formation was in the assumption that the atmosphere of the time was oxygenated.

It is now generally held that the primitive atmosphere probably was strongly reducing. The probable course of the evolution of this primitive atmosphere to the present oxidizing atmosphere fortunately is one of interest to a number of sciences, and reviews by Kuiper (56), Rubey (84), Urey (97), and Holland (38) contain references to the extensive literature.

Holland (38) considers three stages in the evolution of the present-day atmosphere. In the earliest or pre-core stage metallic iron probably was present in the upper part of the mantle. Volcanic gases evolved during this period contained large amounts of hydrogen, and the atmosphere, as a result,

Editor's Note: A row of asterisks indicates that material has been omitted from the original article.

was in a reduced state with carbon in the form of methane and nitrogen in ammonia. Holland suggests that the first stage was of relatively short duration, probably 500 million years. This period of atmospheric development is well beyond the presently known geologic record.

The second stage of the atmosphere is estimated by Holland to have lasted until approximately 1,800 million years ago, an interval corresponding to the Early and Middle Precambrian eras as used in this paper. Basaltic and granitic rocks with isotopic ages between 3,500 and 2,500 m.y. closely resemble modern igneous rocks chemically. Volcanic gases in equilibrium with Early Precambrian magmas can be assumed to have been similar to the gases evolved from modern lavas. As Holland (38, p. 466) points out, carbonates and hematite in the ancient sedimentary rocks also indicate a relatively low p_{H_2} during this second stage. Methane, ammonia, and hydrogen, important constituents of the primitive atmosphere, were largely eliminated, and the atmosphere was composed principally of N_2 with minor amounts of CO_2 and H_2O. During the second stage the production of oxygen through processes such as photodissociation of H_2O probably was augmented through photosynthesis as will be considered in a later section. We agree with Holland, however, that during Early and Middle Precambrian time oxygen was present in the atmosphere only in trace and nonequilibrium amounts.

The third and present stage of atmospheric development was initiated in Late Precambrian time. The sedimentary mantle formed since then is oxidized. Secondary ferric oxides and sulfates are widely distributed in rocks ranging in age from Recent to Keweenawan. Red beds are common in Late Precambrian sequences in many parts of the world, such as the Keweenawan of the Lake Superior region, the Jotnian of the Baltic region, and the Torridonian of Scotland (9). The red-colored sandstone and shale of the Late Precambrian such as the Fond du Lac Formation (24, p. 93) of the Lake Superior region, indicate an oxygenated atmosphere. More ancient are the red-colored sandstone and shale intercalated with the flows of the North Shore Volcanic Group (24, p. 81). The flows were intruded by the gabbro at Duluth and by diabase at Beaver Bay, Minnesota which have been dated (24) at approximately 1,100 m.y.

Red sericitic argillite (pipestone) occurs as layers in the Sioux Quartzite of southwestern Minnesota and adjacent parts of South Dakota and Iowa. A chemical analysis of the pipestone quoted by Berg (6) gave 3.06 percent Fe_2O_3 and no FeO. Diaspore is common in the quartzite as well as in the argillite of the Sioux Quartzite, and Berg (5) attributed the diaspore to differential leaching. It is unlikely, however, that leaching could produce diaspore after the formation was exposed by erosion. A more reasonable explanation is that the diaspore was formed during folding and was derived from original gibbsite or boehmite. A K-Ar age of 1,200 m.y. (21) probably is the approximate time of folding of the Sioux Quartzite. The time of deposition of the oxidized materials cannot be limited closer than 1,700 to 1,200 m.y., but the blood-red argillite and red-colored quartzite indicate that an oxidizing atmosphere had been established before 1,200 million years ago.

Lateritic Weathering

The lateritic weathering model (Fig. 5) is designed to explain the derivation and accumulation of the Precambrian iron formations under an atmosphere lacking free oxygen. Under these conditions the Eh-sensitive elements iron and manganese accompanied silica.

Chemical Differentiation.—Aluminum and titanium were largely retained in the weathered mantle as oxides and hydrous oxides. Phosphorus was fixed in insoluble compounds with ferric iron and aluminum, and lateritic soils commonly contain relatively large amounts of P_2O_5 (22, p. 70; 23, p. 75; 40, p. 64). Ferric iron and appreciable amounts of silica were also retained, the silica undoubtedly combined in clay minerals which would be expected to form in the less well-drained parts of the profile and below the water table.

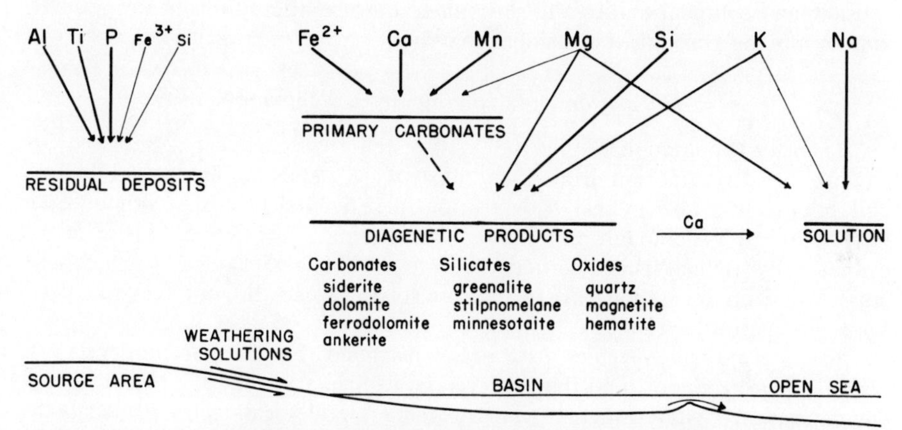

FIG. 5. Lateritic weathering model showing chemical differentiation to produce Precambrian iron formations.

Elements liberated through the lateritic weathering process include Fe^2, Mn^2, Mg, Ca, Na, K, and large amounts of Si. These were transported in true solution; Si as H_4SiO_4, and the others mainly as bicarbonates. Our model thus explains the chemical features of iron formations because under these conditions Fe^2 and Mn^2 behave very much like calcium and magnesium. Although differential adsorption, particularly of potassium, and precipitation of the elements liberated in the source region may have occurred locally, the bulk of the soluble cations probably reached the sea.

Stability of Source Region.—A second important feature of the lateritic weathering model is that it provides for stability in the source region to minimize mechanical erosion. Lateritic soils are characterized by their remarkable porosity and permeability (23, p. 74). Rainfall is quickly absorbed and drained off through the porous laterite, and as a result sheet wash and erosion are limited. We prefer the assumption that the region of weathering was one of moderate rather than of low relief as has been favored by previous writers. Relief is required to provide drainage and to permit rapid removal of silica and soluble elements from the weathered source rocks. Low relief and poor drainage favor kaolinization rather than lateritization. Not only is a large amount of silica thus tied up in silicates, but the resulting clay minerals from an impervious surface, and heavy vegetation would be required to prevent erosion.

Gruner (31) suggested the presence of abundant land vegetation of a low form which aided in the rapid decay of the rocks and provided the organic matter to stabilize the ferric oxide hydrosols and permit transportation of iron. Anaerobic bacteria may have lived in the weathering mantle, but a surface vegetation adequate to prevent erosion under heavy rainfall is most improbable. The problem of the selective transport of the ferric oxide hydrosols has been generally avoided in earlier discussions. Under the conditions of lateritic weathering postulated here, colloidal hydrosols were of minor importance. The permeability of the weathering profile inhibited erosion, and colloidal oxides and clay minerals were filtered out of the groundwaters moving through the residual mantle.

Deposition and Mineralogic Development

Basins.—Woolnough (107, 108) suggested that chemical sediments, including the Precambrian iron formations, were deposited in barred basins, and James (46) also indicated deposition in restricted basins. Although we have followed Woolnough and James in including a barrier in Figure 5, we cannot fully defend this position. White (103) and Cullen (13) whose studies of iron formations are primarily stratigraphic did not feel the need for a circulation barrier.

Facies Approach.—James (46, p. 240) argued that the iron minerals are "equilibrium products" and that differences in primary minerals reflect different depositional environments. He related mineralogical facies primarily to depth of water and to degree of oxygenation on the assumption that the Precambrian atmosphere did not differ appreciably from that of today. James based his explanation in part on the work of Krumbein and Garrels (55) who calculated the stability fields of some of the sedimentary iron minerals in terms of pH and Eh. Huber (42) developed pH-Eh stability diagrams for hematite, siderite, pyrite, and iron sulfide. Garrels (18) has presented a series of new diagrams. These studies are valuable, and the facies concept has greatly advanced our understanding of the iron formations. Our studies, however, suggest that the facies approach to date has fostered an oversimplification of the problem of iron formation origin.

Chemical Approach.—The chemical data afford an opportunity to examine the mode of deposition of iron formations and the development of mineralogical facies that is not bound by assumptions of primary equilibrium mineral assemblages. The statistical study shows that the Precambrian iron formations are remarkably uniform in iron content considering that they are products of natural processes. This we explain as being the result of a fundamental control in the sources of materials.

Iron and calcium are present in the lithosphere in approximately mole proportions of 1:1. These elements in the weathering cycle (Fig. 5), which we postulate was controlled by the absence or marked deficiency of free oxygen in the atmosphere, would be transported in solution to the depositional basins in approximately their proportions in the source rocks. We suggest that the principal minerals deposited were siderite and calcite. Possibly some primary dolomite, ferrodolomite, and ankerite also may have been formed.

At the time of deposition, or following closely, a number of reactions between the primary carbonates and the elements in solution were possible. Dolomite, ferrodolomite, and ankerite were formed by replacement as was also chert. The silicates, greenalite, stilpnomelane, and possibly also minnesotaite, were formed by diagenetic reactions. Small amounts of clay particles or volcanic glass that found their way into the deposition basins probably acted as nuclei for crystallization of the iron silicates. Magnetite and hematite also were formed, for the most part, during diagenesis. As a result of these various interactions carbon dioxide was liberated, and calcium was returned to solution. Calcium and sodium, together with magnesium and potassium, not fixed in a mineral phase, were carried to the open sea by tides and currents (Fig. 5).

Chert.—One of the main arguments employed by James (46) and later by Huber (43) for a primary origin of chert is that the amount of chert varies with the facies. James (46, p. 273) states ". . . for example, the amount of chert in carbonate iron-formation is 30 to 35 percent, whereas that in oxide iron-formation is about 40 percent." We have shown that whereas the tenor of iron is essentially constant, the SiO_2 and CO_2 vary inversely. If we start with an original mixture of 1 $CaCO_3$:1 $FeCO_3$ and replace $CaCO_3$ by SiO_2 on a volume basis, the resulting combination of chert and siderite would contain approximately 45 percent SiO_2. Averages for carbonate iron formation from the Marquette district and the Gogebic district are 42.4 and 39.3 percent SiO_2, respectively (Table 8). If siderite were altered to hematite with no other change except for the replacement of $CaCO_3$ by SiO_2, the resulting rock would contain about 55 percent SiO_2. Only the composite analysis representing the Main Mesabi district (Table 2, No. 2) with 51.1 percent SiO_2 approaches the calculated value of 55 percent. The computed values for SiO_2 are high because in nature the replacement is not so simple; unreplaced carbonate and other mineral phases normally present in the formation were not considered. Of significance, however, is that the difference in SiO_2 contents for carbonate and hematite facies, calculated on the assumption that the chert formed by replacement, is of the order of magnitude exhibited by the rocks.

Ferric-Ferrous Iron Relationships.—In the simplified model the original mud of 1 $CaCO_3$:1 $FeCO_3$ would contain 26 percent Fe. If the $CaCO_3$ were replaced by SiO_2 on a volume basis, the iron content would not be appreciably changed. The mean iron content for carbonate iron formations is 26 percent (Table 4), and the total Fe in composites for four districts ranges from 24.7 to 25.3 percent (Table 8). If the siderite were altered to hematite with no change other than the replacement of $CaCO_3$ by SiO_2, the resulting mixture of hematite and chert would contain approximately 31 percent Fe. The calculation for magnetite in place of hematite gives 32 percent Fe. Our data

(Tables 4, 6) show that the average iron content of magnetite iron formations actually is less than that for hematite iron formations; however, an average of approximately 31 is a good value for the oxide iron formations. The excellent agreement between observed iron contents of carbonate and oxide iron formations with values for these facies predicted from our model is in part fortuitous; nevertheless, the agreement supports our contention that there are no fundamental differences in iron content of the principal iron facies. The oxide iron formations contain no more iron than the carbonate facies when the formulae differences have been considered. If the environment controlled the deposition of the iron-bearing minerals, the broad range of Eh suggested by James (46) should have resulted in great variations in iron content of the facies.

Mineral Relationships.—The ferric-ferrous relationships, and, hence the minerals of iron formations, are obviously related to Eh and pH, and Garrels' (18) diagrams are valuable for an understanding of these relationships. Garrels has pointed out many of the difficulties in applying equilibrium principles to natural occurrences in which reaction rates may be exceedingly low at surface temperatures. Metastable phases commonly are developed, and some may persist for long periods of geologic time.

Huber (42) has made a significant contribution in emphasizing the lack of equilibrium among iron-bearing minerals in natural occurrences. Assemblages indicating disequilibrium have been noted by many writers. Gruner (33, p. 201) has called attention to the commonplace occurrence of mixtures of silicates, oxides, and carbonates in iron formations. Tyler and Barghoorn (94, p. 428) in describing chlorite appendages on magnetite grains in granular ferruginous chert from the Ironwood Iron Formation of Michigan, as incidental information, state that "the rock is composed of chert, siderite, magnetite, hematite, and chlorite." The lack of equilibrium among the minerals of iron formations is commonly so pronounced that it suggests a number of contributing causes. In fact, there is a marked lack of agreement among students of iron formations as to which minerals are primary, diagenetic, or metamorphic. The assemblages, therefore, could represent the sum total of conditions that change appreciably between the time of initial deposition and of final lithification.

Siderite is characteristically deposited in a reducing environment. Under certain conditions an increase in pH would result in magnetite becoming the stable mineral phase. Similarly hematite can be formed in the absence of free oxygen. These reactions can be represented in simple chemical equations for which Garrels (18) has calculated the energy relationships. A number of considerations suggest that in addition to changes in pH changes in Eh effected through biological processes were important in the formation of the oxides, magnetite and hematite. The most logical explanation for the development of the oxides seems to us to demand the presence of free oxygen in the environment. Sources such as the formation of H_2O_2 by ultraviolet irradiation of water can be considered, but a ready source is oxygen formed through photosynthesis.

The red jasper and hematite of the iron formations, however, are not satisfactory evidence for the presence of free oxygen in the atmosphere, because the aqueous environment in which the ferric oxide minerals were formed was not in equilibrium with the atmosphere. The strongly reducing euxinic environment of certain present-day lacustrine and marine basins serves to illustrate this point. Tyler and Barghoorn (94, p. 430) observe that the pyrite and organic matter in the basal Gunflint Iron Formation of Ontario and in the Biwabik Iron Formation of Minnesota indicate "that a reducing or euxinic environment existed on a regional scale at the time these sediments were deposited. The red algal jaspers, which have a restricted occurrence, are presumably the product of local oxidizing environments that existed as microenvironments within the euxinic environment."

Tyler and Barghoorn (94, p. 426) also note the presence of "siderite and ankerite grains and masses as well as siliceous oolites." Some of the oolites have jasper cores. Pettijohn (79, p. 685) states that ferric oolites indicate deposition in turbulent aerated waters and could not have been developed in Precambrian iron formations if the atmosphere was reducing. Pettijohn thus finds it more difficult to conceive of local oxidizing environments under an atmosphere deficient in oxygen than of reducing environments under an oxygenated environment. In fairness to Tyler and Barghoorn it should be said that they do not specifically advocate an oxygen-deficient atmosphere at the time of deposition of the Gunflint and Biwabik Iron Formations.

Biologic Factors.—Graphitic material in argillites and slates, together with structures interpreted as being of biological origin, have long been considered by geologists as evidences of life in the Precambrian. Numerous occurrences of graphitic argillites closely associated with iron formations have been described. Anthracite coal has been reported from the Michigamme Slate of northern Michigan (95). Most remarkable has been the discovery of well-preserved organic forms in chert of the Gunflint Iron Formation near Port Arthur, Ontario, reported by Tyler and Baghoorn (93). Additional fossiliferous material from this area has been described by Moorhouse and Beales (69). Older rocks associated with Early Precambrian iron formations also contain structures and carbon of possible biologic origin, although the interpretations of these occurrences have been questioned from time to time. Dark-colored graphitic slates are abundant in the Knife Lake Group of Minnesota and in the correlative Seine Series of Ontario, and massive graphite was found in the iron mine at Soudan, Minnesota. These rocks were involved in folding 2,500 million or more years ago. Similarly of ancient age, more than 2,500 m.y., are the structures of the Bulawayan Limestone in Southern Rhodesia described as algal by Macgregor (60).

Hoering (36) isolated organic compounds from a number of Precambrian rocks including the coal from the Michigamme Formation and the graphite from the Soudan mine. Preliminary results indicate that the Precambrian carbon was originally kerogen and studies of the isotopic composition of the carbon in coexisting carbonate and carbon show a relative enrichment of C^{13} in carbonates and of C^{12} in reduced carbons. From these results Hoering (37, p. 191) concludes that photosynthesis and biological activity are indicated in the oldest rocks of the Precambrian.

Oparin (74), a long time researcher on the origin of life, postulated that life originated under a strongly reducing atmosphere. This concept in the light of available geologic evidence leads to the conclusion that life must have originated on earth long before the oldest geologic record and well before 3,500 million years ago. A complex history involving an abiogenic origin of organic matter followed by the development of anaerobic heterotrophic bacteria prior to the appearance of photosynthesis is outlined by Oparin (74). It is generally suggested that early photosynthesis utilized H_2 or H_2S rather than H_2O. Hoering's work does not indicate the probable path of the Precambrian photosynthesis.

Harder (35) first emphasized the probable role of bacteria in the development of the Precambrian iron formations. Gruner (31) and also others have suggested that "iron bacteria" played a significant part. A somewhat extreme view of the biologic factor in the origin of the iron formations has been developed by Moorhouse and Beales (69). They regard the "Gunflint rocks as an immense organically controlled accumulation." In their hypothesis iron-secreting organisms reached a major development in the Precambrian, and this unique development is said to have been the controlling factor in the origin of the Precambrian iron formations. Moorhouse and Beales (69, p. 109) rule out "any drastic differences in composition of atmosphere and ocean of Animikie time and of the present." The hypothesis of the accumulation of the Precambrian iron formation being controlled by the activity of organisms, however, fails in a number of respects. The most serious of the shortcomings is the assumed "abundant supply of iron and silica" (69, p. 108). Kaplan, Emery, and Rittenberg (48) have shown that sea water is an inadequate source to explain the development of authigenic pyrite in recent marine sediments of southern California. They conclude that the iron must be derived from detrital sediments.

It seems reasonable to assume that low forms of life such as bacteria and algae may have been important in the precipitation of iron. Whether or not the organisms made direct use of the iron in their life cycle is not demonstrable with the presently available information. The abstraction of CO_2 from sea water and the control of pH and Eh by the primitive organisms certainly would have been effective. One could speculate at considerable length on probable reactions and mechanisms. It may be noted that the distribution of oxygen generated through photosynthesis in sea water might be subject to many of the controls of present-day marine environments in terms of depth and circulation of water. A few of the factors that might be involved are depth of sunlight penetration, rates of sedimentation, and availability of nutrients for plant life. It is useful to consider the biologic factors as part of the total physical environment in which the iron formations were developed. Biologic controls of pH and Eh can be used to explain the mineralogic facies of the iron formations, but the primary mineral equilibrium assemblages are not necessarily indicated. As Harder (35) pointed out many years ago, the formation of iron silicates cannot be explained through the agency of iron-precipitating bacteria, and neither can the silicates be considered a direct precipitation from sea water.

Accepting the time of origin of life as being well back in the Early Precambrian, the rate of evolution of life was exceedingly slow during an interval of two billion or more years. This slow development can be correlated with a slow rate of accumulation of free oxygen in the atmosphere. During this long interval, organisms that developed the faculty of utilizing H_2O as a source of hydrogen, liberating oxygen, had a precarious existence. The production of oxygen through photosynthesis was gradually augmented to a point where a positive balance was established in which the rate of production exceeded the rate of destruction of oxygen in the atmosphere. This condition was well established at least 1,200 m.y. ago as is indicated by the pipestone of the Sioux Quartzite and other clastic sediments of the Late Precambrian. At that time a level of oxygen production had been achieved that permitted a rapid development of plant life. An exceedingly rapid development of invertebrate and vertebrate fauna followed.

CONCLUDING REMARKS

The complexity of the natural laboratory requires no special emphasis, but it is well to call attention to the variable conditions that undoubtedly existed in the different areas and throughout the period of deposition of the Precambrian iron formations. This variability is indicated in the ranges for chemical constituents found in the statistical study. It is important to note that for a period of over a billion years conditions during the Precambrian were favorable for deposition of the chemical iron formations. We may dismiss hypotheses of origin that postulate unusual or freakish geologic conditions that prevailed on the earth once only or for a limited time.

We are of course, advocating a secular change in sedimentation effected by a change in the oxygen content of the atmosphere. Pettijohn (79, p. 689) has given an excellent critique of apparent secular changes in the nature and character of the sedimentary rocks. His analysis emphasizes the need for valid sampling, for a valid chronology, and for the distinction between postdepositional alteration and real differences in the environment of deposition. Many of the Middle Precambrian iron formations have undergone only low-grade metamorphism; hence, their chemical composition probably has not been altered appreciably except for the postdepositional replacements and alterations that are commonly attributed to diagenesis. The higher grade of metamorphism and replacement of the iron formation by crystalline specularite exhibited by Early Precambrian iron formations, however, suggests possible oxidation of iron by reaction with H_2O at high temperature.

Many Precambrian iron formations are inadequately dated and sampled. Geologic relationships indicate an Early Precambrian age for the iron formation in the Atlantic district of Wyoming. Four analyses (89, p. 18) give 43, 42, 39, and 27 percent of Fe. The disparity between these values points up the difficult problem of sampling. A recent analysis given by Bayley (4, p. C-10) quotes 56 percent of SiO_2 and 29 percent of Fe, values that fit well within the range for iron formations of the Canadian Shield. We feel that the data presented in our statistical study are representative of Precambrian iron formations. If there are important differences between the

Precambrian iron formations of the different continents, their nature and extent must await further studies.

We do not argue the point that some Late Precambrian and post-Precambrian iron formations resemble the Lake Superior type. Possibly the cherty iron formations such as the Morro do Urucum of Brazil represent a transitional type. The reverse relationship for post-Precambrian minette-type of iron formation should also be mentioned. Precambrian iron formations that obviously contain detrital materials and resemble chemically the post-Precambrian iron formations should be expected. Such deposits occur in South Africa and have been described by Wagner (102). These deposits have been excluded from the present discussion.

The origin of the iron formations is a very old problem, and the informed reader is aware that the ideas incorporated in this paper have been anticipated in some form or other by previous writers. It is probably inevitable that our emphasis and references have slighted some valuable contributions to the geology of the iron formations. Our treatment of the evolution of the atmosphere and of the origin of life is of necessity brief. Rutten (85) gives a more elaborate presentation of "the geological aspects of the origin of life on earth." His division of exogenic geologic processes into actualistic and pre-actualistic suggests a rather abrupt transition from an anoxygenic to the present oxygenic atmosphere. The data considered as a whole are quite against an abrupt change from a primitive reducing atmosphere to the present-day oxidizing atmosphere. Biologic factors in the deposition and development of iron formations have received little attention since Harder's contribution some 40 years ago. It is encouraging to note increasing interest in the field that may be called geomicrobiology.

It may be noted that our model for the origin of the Precambrian cherty iron formations is not opposed to the concept of uniformitarianism. The products of lateritic weathering are found the world over in rocks ranging from Recent to Late Precambrian, if we include the Sioux Quartzite. Conditions of source rocks, climate, topography, and related factors, however, must be favorable. Similarly iron formations of the Lake Superior type were developed the world over under locally favorable conditions. These deposits range from Late Precambrian ($\sim$ 1.7 b.y.) to the oldest known sedimentary sequences ($\sim$ 3 b.y.) in age.

Some aspects of the origin of the Precambrian iron formations present unusually difficult problems because of the antiquity of the deposits and the complicated geologic history subsequent to deposition. The major problem of origin, however, can be seen logically only in proper perspective against a background of knowledge of the Precambrian. The problems of the evolution of the continents and of the ocean basins, of the origin of the atmosphere and the hydrosphere, and of life on the earth, are now attracting wider attention. Considerable progress toward a better understanding of the Precambrian is a reasonable expectation.

ACKNOWLEDGMENTS

This paper has been in preparation for a number of years at the University of Minnesota, and during that time we have had the benefit of discussions with many iron company geologists. We are indebted to these gentlemen and to the companies who have made available to us their files of chemical and mineralogic data. J. V. N. Dorr II, R. M. Grogan, and R. W. Marsden read and criticized the manuscript at several stages in its preparation. Their friendly criticism and encouragement are appreciated. The writers, however, are solely responsible for shortcomings of the data and of the presentation. W. J. Croke, J. R. Haigh, and L. E. Warren assisted in the compilation under a National Science Foundation program for undergraduate research participation at the University of Minnesota, Duluth. The financial support of the Graduate School of the University of Minnesota and of the National Science Foundation is gratefully acknowledged.

UNIVERSITY OF MINNESOTA, DULUTH,
DULUTH, MINNESOTA,
PRESENT ADDRESS: MACALESTER COLLEGE,
SAINT PAUL, MINNESOTA.
AND
U. S. GEOLOGICAL SURVEY,
WASHINGTON, D. C.
March 27, 1964

REFERENCES

1. Aldrich, H. R., 1929, The geology of the Gogebic iron range of Wisconsin: Wisconsin Geol. Nat. Hist. Survey, Econ. Ser., Bull. 71, 279 p.
2. Alevandrov, E. A., 1955, Contributions to studies of origin of Precambrian banded iron ores: ECON. GEOL., v. 50, p. 459–468.
3. Alling, H. L., 1947, Diagenesis of the Clinton hematite ores of New York: Geol. Soc. America Bull., v. 58, p. 991–1017.
4. Bayley, R. W., 1963, A preliminary report on the Precambrian iron deposits near Atlantic City, Wyoming: U. S. Geol. Survey Bull. 1142-C, 23 p.
5. Berg, E. L., 1937, An occurrence of diaspore in quartzite: Am. Mineralogist, v. 22, p. 997–999.
6. Berg, E. L., 1938, Notes on catlinite and the Sioux quartzite: Am. Mineralogist, v. 23, p. 258–268.
7. Bien, G. S., Contois, D. E., and Thomas, W. H., 1958, The removal of soluble silica from fresh water entering the sea: Geochim et Cosmochim. Acta, v. 14, p. 35–54.
8. Blondel, F., 1955, Iron deposits of Europe, Africa, and the Union of Soviet Socialistic Republics, *in* Survey of World Iron Ore Resources: United Nations, Dept. Economic and Social Affairs, New York, p. 224–264.
9. Brinkmann, R., 1960, Geologic evolution of Europe: Hafner Publ. Co., New York, 161 p.
10. Burwash, R. A., Baadsgaard, H., and Peterman, Z. E., 1962, Precambrian K-Ar dates from the Western Canada sedimentary basin: Jour. Geophys. Research, v. 67, p. 1617–1625.
11. Cahen, L., 1961, Review of geochronological knowledge in middle and northern Africa: New York Acad. Science Annals, v. 91, p. 535–566.
12. Craig, J. J., 1961, The use of iron ore pellets: Skillings' Mining Review, v. 50, p. 1, 4, 5.
13. Cullen, D. J., 1963, Tectonic implications of banded ironstone formations: Jour. Sed. Petrology, v. 33, p. 387–392.
14. Dixon, W. J., and Massey, F. J., Jr., 1951, Introduction to Statistical Analysis: McGraw-Hill Co., New York, 370 p.
15. Dorr, J. V. N., 2d., 1945, Manganese and iron deposits of Morro do Urucum, Mato Grasso, Brazil: U. S. Geol. Survey Bull. 946-A, 47 p.
16. Durum, W. H., and Haffty, J., 1963, Implications of the minor element content of some major streams of the world: Geochim. et Cosmochim. Acta, v. 27, p. 1–11.
17. Dutton, C. E., 1955, Iron ore deposits of North America and the West Indies, *in* Survey of World Iron Ore Resources: United Nations, Dept. Economic and Social Affairs, New York, p. 179–208.
18. Garrels, R. M., 1960, Mineral equilibria: Harper and Brothers, New York, 254 p.
19. Geijer, P., and Magnusson, N. H., 1952, The iron ores of Sweden, *in* Symposium sur les gisements de fer du Monde: 19th International Geol. Congr., Algiers, v. 2, p. 477–499.

20. Gill, J. E., 1927, Origin of the Gunflint iron-bearing formation: ECON. GEOL., v. 22, p. 687–728.
21. Goldich, S. S., Baadsgaard, H., Edwards, G., and Weaver, C. E., 1959, Investigations in radioactivity-dating of sediments: Am. Assoc. Petroleum Geologists Bull., v. 43, p. 654–662.
22. Goldich, S. S., and Bergquist, H. R., 1947, Aluminous lateritic soil of the Sierra de Bahoruco area, Dominican Republic, W. I.: U. S. Geol. Survey Bull. 953-C, p. 53–84.
23. Goldich, S. S., and Bergquist, H. R., 1948, Aluminous lateritic soil of the Republic of Haiti, W. I.: U. S. Geol. Survey Bull., 954-C, p. 63–109.
24. Goldich, S. S., Nier, A. O., Baadsgaard, H., Hoffman, J. H., and Krueger, H. W., 1961, The Precambrian geology and geochronology of Minnesota: Minnesota Geol. Survey Bull. 41, 193 p.
25. Goodwin, A. M., 1956, Facies relations in the Gunflint iron formation: ECON. GEOL., v. 51, p. 565–595.
26. Goodwin, A. M., 1960, Gunflint iron formation of the Whitefish Lake area: Ontario Dept. Mines, v. 59, p. 41–63.
27. Graves, R. W., Jr., 1954, Geology of Hood Spring quadrangle, Brewster County, Texas: Texas Univ. Bur. Econ. Geology Rept. Inv., no. 21, 51 p.
28. Graves, R. W., Jr., Letter, March 1963.
29. Gross, G. A., 1959, Metallogenic map for iron in Canada: Geol. Survey Canada Map 1045 A-M4.
30. Grout, F. F., Gruner, J. W., Schwartz, G. M., and Thiel, G. A., 1951, Precambrian stratigraphy of Minnesota: Geol. Soc. America Bull. 62, p. 1017–1078.
31. Gruner, J. W., 1922, The origin of sedimentary iron formations: the Biwabik formation of the Mesabi Range: ECON. GEOL., v. 17, p. 407–460.
32. Gruner, J. W., 1946, The mineralogy and geology of the taconites and iron ores of the Mesabi Range Minnesota: Office of the Commissioner of the Iron Range Resources and Rehabilitation, St. Paul, Minn., 127 p.
33. Gruner, J. W., 1956, The Mesabi Range, *in* Precambrian of northeastern Minnesota: Geol. Soc. America Guidebook ser., Minneapolis Meeting, p. 182–215.
34. Gunderson, J. N., 1960, Lithologic classification of taconite from the type locality: ECON. GEOL., v. 55, p. 563–573.
35. Harder, E. C., 1919, Iron-depositing bacteria and their geologic relations: U. S. Geol. Survey Prof. Paper 113, 89 p.
36. Hoering, T. C., 1962, The isolation of organic compounds from Precambrian rocks: Carnegie Inst. Washington Year Book 61, p. 184–187.
37. Hoering, T. C., 1962, The stable isotopes of carbon in the carbonate and reduced carbon of Precambrian sediments: Carnegie Inst. Washington Year Book 61, p. 190–192.
38. Holland, H. D., 1962, Model for the evolution of the earth's atmosphere, *in* Petrologic Studies: Geol. Soc. America Buddington Volume, p. 447–477.
39. Holliday, R. W., and Lewis, H. E., 1962, Iron ore, *in* 1961 Minerals Yearbook, U. S. Bur. Mines, v. 1, p. 649–680.
40. Hose, H. R., 1963, Jamaica type bauxites developed on limestone: ECON. GEOL., v. 58, p. 62–69.
41. Hough, J. L., 1958, Fresh-water environment of deposition of Precambrian banded iron formations: Jour. Sed. Petrology, v. 28, p. 414–430.
42. Huber, N. K., 1958, The environmental control of sedimentary iron minerals: ECON. GEOL., v. 58, p. 123–140.
43. Huber, N. K., 1959, Some aspects of the origin of the Ironwood iron foramtion of Michigan and Wisconsin: ECON. GEOL., v. 54, p. 82–118.
44. Irving, R. D., and Van Hise, C. R., 1892, The Penokee iron-bearing series of Michigan and Wisconsin: U. S. Geol. Survey Mon. 19, 534 p.
45. James, H. L., 1951, Iron formation and associated rocks in the Iron River district, Michigan: Geol. Soc. America Bull., v. 62, p. 251–266.
46. James, H. L., 1954, Sedimentary facies of iron formations: ECON. GEOL., v. 49, p. 235–293.
47. James, H. L., 1958, Stratigraphy of pre-Keweenawan rocks in parts of northern Michigan: U. S. Geol. Survey Prof. Paper 314-C, p. 27–44.
48. Kaplan, I. R., Emery, K. O., and Rittenberg, S. C., 1963, The distribution and isotopic abundance of sulphur in recent marine sediments off southern California: Geochem. et Cosmochim. Acta, v. 27, p. 297–331.
49. Kidd, D. J., 1949, Iron occurrence in the Peace River region, Alberta: Research Council Alberta, Prelim. Rept. 59-3, 38 p.
50. King, P. B., 1937, Geology of the Marathon region, Texas: U. S. Geol. Survey Prof. Paper 187, 148 p.

51. Klinger, F. L., 1956, Geology of the Soudan Mine and vicinity, *in* Precambrian of northeastern Minnesota: Geol. Soc. America Guidebook ser., Minneapolis Meeting, p. 120–134.
52. Krauskopf, K. B., 1956, Dissolution and precipitation of silica at low temperatures: Geochim. et Cosmochim. Acta, v. 10, p. 1–26.
53. Krishnan, M. S., 1955, Iron ore deposits of the Middle East and of Asia and the Far East, *in* Survey of World Iron Ore Resources: United Nations, Dept. Economic and Social Affairs, New York, p. 265–334.
54. Krishnan, M. S., 1960, Pre-Cambrian stratigraphy of India, *in* Pre-Cambrian stratigraphy and correlations: 21st Internat. Geol. Congr. (Norden), Copenhagen, pt. IX, p. 95–107.
55. Krumbein, W. C., and Garrels, R. M., 1952, Origin and classification of chemical sediments in terms of pH and oxidation-reduction potentials: Jour. Geology, v. 60, p. 1–33.
56. Kuiper, G. P., 1952, Planetary atmospheres and their origin, *in* The Atmospheres of the Earth and Planets: Univ. Chicago Press, 434 p.
57. Lepp, H., 1963, The relation of iron and manganese in sedimentary iron formations: Econ. Geol., v. 58, p. 515–526.
58. Lepp, H., Goldich, S. S., and Kistler, R. W., 1963, A Grenville cross section from Port Cartier to Mount Reed, Quebec, Canada: Am. Jour. Sci., v. 261, p. 693–712.
59. Macgregor, A. M., 1927, The problem of the pre-Cambrian atmosphere: South African Jour. Sci., v. 24, p. 155–172.
60. Macgregor, A. M., 1940, A pre-Cambrian algal limestone in Southern Rhodesia: Geol. Soc. South Africa, Trans., v. 43, p. 9–16.
61. Macgregor, A. M., 1951, Some milestones in the Precambrian of Southern Rhodesia: Geol. Soc. South Africa, Trans., v. 54, p. 27–71.
62. Mann, V. I., 1961, Iron formations in the southeastern United States: Econ. Geol., v. 56, p. 997–1000.
63. Marmo, V., 1956, Banded ironstones of the Kangari Hills, Sierra Leone: Econ. Geol., v. 51, p. 798–810.
64. Miles, K. R., 1942, The blue asbestos-bearing banded iron formations of the Hamersley Ranges, Western Australia, Part 1: Geol. Survey Western Australia Bull. 100, p. 5–37.
65. Miles, K. R., 1946, Metamorphism of the jasper bars of Western Australia: Geol. Soc. London Quart. Jour., v. 102, p. 115–154.
66. Moore, E. S., 1918, The iron-formation on Belcher Islands, Hudson Bay, with special references to its origin and its associated algal limestones: Jour. Geology, v. 26, p. 412–438.
67. Moore, E. S., and Armstrong, H. S., 1946, Iron deposits in the district of Algoma: Ontario Dept. Mines 55th Ann. Rpt., v. 55, 118 p.
68. Moore, E. S., and Maynard, J. E., 1929, Solution, transportation, and precipitation of iron and silica: Econ. Geol., v. 24, p. 272–303; 365–402; 506–527.
69. Moorhouse, W. W., and Beales, F. W., 1962, Fossils from the Animikie, Port Arthur, Ontario: Royal Soc. Canada, Trans., v. 56, p. 97–110.
70. Nalivkin, D. V., 1960, The Geology of the U. S. S. R., *in* Internat. Ser. Monographs on Earth Science (translation): Pergamon Press, New York, 170 p.
71. Nicolaysen, L. O., 1962, Stratigraphic interpretation of age measurements in southern Africa, *in* Petrologic Studies: Geol. Soc. America Buddington Volume, p. 569–598.
72. Nicolaysen, L. O., de Villiers, J. W. L., Burger, A. J., and Strelow, F. W. E., 1958, New measurements relating to the absolute age of the Transvaal System and of the Bushveld igneous complex: Geol. Soc. South Africa Trans., v. 61, p. 137–163.
73. Oftedahl, C., 1958, A theory of exhalative-sedimentary ores: Geol. Fören. Stockholm Förh., v. 80, p. 1–19.
74. Oparin, A. I., 1961, Life, Its Nature, Origin, and Development (translated): Academic Press, Inc., New York, 207 p.
75. O'Rourke, J. E., 1961, Paleozoic banded iron-formation: Econ. Geol., v. 56, p. 331–361.
76. Parsons, A. L., 1921, Economic deposits in the Thunder Bay district: Ontario Dept. Mines Rept., v. 30, p. 27–38.
77. Patterson, C. C., 1956, Age of meteorites and the earth: Geochim. et Cosmochim. Acta, v. 10, p. 230–237.
78. Percival, F. G., 1955, Nature and occurrence of iron ore deposits, *in* Survey of World Iron Ore Resources: United Nations, Dept. Economic and Social Affairs, New York, p. 45–76.
79. Pettijohn, F. J., 1957, Sedimentary Rocks, 2nd ed., Harper and Brothers, New York, 718 p.
80. Polkanov, A. A., and Gerling, E. K., 1960, The Pre-Cambrian geochronology of the Baltic Shield, *in* Pre-Cambrian stratigraphy and correlations: 21st Internat. Geol. Congr. (Norden), Copenhagen, Pt. IX, p. 183–191.

81. Quirke, T. T., Jr., 1961, Geology of the Temiscamie iron-formation, Lake Albanel iron range, Mistassini Territory, Quebec, Canada: Econ. Geol., v. 56, p. 299–320.
82. Quirke, T. T., Jr., Goldich, S. S., and Krueger, H. W., 1960, Composition and age of the Temiscamie iron-formation, Mistassini Territory, Quebec, Canada: Econ. Geol., v. 55, p. 311–326.
83. Rhoden, H. N., 1961, Paleozoic banded iron-formations: Econ. Geol., v. 56, p. 1473.
84. Rubey, W. W., 1955, Development of the hydrosphere and atmosphere, with special reference to probable composition of the early atmosphere, *in* Crust of the earth, Geol. Soc. America Special Paper 62, p. 631–650.
85. Rutten, M. G., 1962, The Geological Aspects of the Origin of Life on Earth: Elsevier Publishing Co., Amsterdam, 146 p.
86. Sakamoto, T., 1950, The origin of the pre-Cambrian banded iron ores: Am. Jour. Sci., v. 248, p. 449–474.
87. Sarkar, S. N., and Saha, A. K., 1963, On the occurrence of two intersecting pre-Cambrian orogenic belts in Singhbhum and adjacent areas: India: Geol. Mag., v. 100, p. 69–92.
88. Semenenko, N. P., Rodionov, S. P., Usenko, I. S., Lichak, I. L., and Tsarovsky, I. D., 1960, Stratigraphy of the Pre-Cambrian of the Ukrainian Shield, *in* Pre-Cambrian stratigraphy and correlations: 21st Internat. Geol. Congr. (Norden), Copenhagen, Pt. IX, p. 108–115.
89. Spencer, A. C., 1916, The Atlantic gold district and the north Laramie Mountains, Fremont, Converse, and Albany Counties, Wyoming: U. S. Geol. Survey Bull. 626, 85 p.
90. Stockwell, C. H., 1963, Second report on structural provinces, orogenies, and time-classification of rocks of the Canadian Precambrian Shield: Geol. Survey Canada, Paper 62-17, p. 123–133.
91. Swenson, W. T., 1960, Geology of the Nakina iron property, Ontario: Am. Inst. Min. Eng. Trans., v. 217, p. 451–457.
92. Taylor, J. H., Davies, W., and Dixie, R. J. M., 1952, The petrology of the British Mesozoic ironstones and its bearing on problems of beneficiation, *in* Symposium sur les gisements de fer du Monde, 19th Internat. Geol. Congr., Algiers, v. 2, p. 453–471.
93. Tyler, S. A., and Barghoorn, E. S., 1954, Occurrence of structurally preserved plants in pre-Cambrian rocks of the Canadian Shield: Science, v. 119, p. 606–608.
94. Tyler, S. A., and Barghoorn, E. S., 1963, Ambient pyrite grains in Precambrian cherts: Am. Jour. Sci., v. 261, p. 424–432.
95. Tyler, S. A., Barghoorn, E. E., and Barrett, L. P., 1957, Anthracite coal from Precambrian Upper Huronian black shale of the Iron River district, northern Michigan: Geol. Soc. America Bull., v. 68, p. 1293–1304.
96. Tyler, S. A., and Twenhofel, 1952, Sedimentation and stratigraphy of the Huronian of Upper Michigan: Am. Jour. Sci., v. 250, p. 1–27; 118–151.
97. Urey, H. C., 1959, The atmospheres of the planets, *in* Handbuch der Physik, Springer-Verlag, Berlin, p. 363–418.
98. Van Hise, C. R., and Bayley, W. S., 1897, The Marquette iron-bearing district of Michigan: U. S. Geol. Survey Mon. 28, 608 p.
99. Van Hise, C. R., and Leith, C. K., 1911, The geology of the Lake Superior region: U. S. Geol. Survey Mon. 52, 641 p.
100 Vinogradov, A. P., Komlev, L. V., Danilevich, S. I., Savonenko, V. G., Tugarinov, A. I., and Filippov, M. S., 1960, Absolute geochronology of the Ukrainian Pre-Cambrian, *in* Pre-Cambrian stratigraphy and correlations: 21st Internat. Geol. Congr. (Norden), Copenhagen, Pt. IX, p. 116–132.
101. Vinogradov, A. P., and Tugarinov, A. I., 1961, Geochronology of the Precambrian: Geochemistry, no. 9, p. 787–800 (translation of Geokhimia).
102. Wagner, P. A., 1928, The iron deposits of the Union of South Africa: Union of South Africa, Dept. Mines and Industries, Geol. Survey Mem. 26, 264 p.
103. White, D. A., 1954, The stratigraphy and structure of the Mesabi Range, Minnesota: Minnesota Geol. Survey Bull. 38, 92 p.
104. Whitehead, T. H., Anderson, W., Wilson, V., and Wray, D. A., 1952, The Liassic ironstones: Geol. Survey Great Britain Mem., 211 p.
105. Wilson, A. F., Compston, W., and Jeffery, P. M., 1961, Radioactive ages from the pre-Cambrian rocks of Australia: New York Acad. Sci., Annals, v. 91, p. 514–520.
106. Wolff, J. F., 1917, Recent geological developments on the Mesabi iron range: Am. Inst. Min. Eng. Trans., v. 56, p. 142–169.
107. Woolnough, W. G., 1937, Sedimentation in barred basins, and source rocks of oil: Am. Assoc. Petroleum Geologists Bull., v. 21, p. 1101–1157.
108. Woolnough, W. G., 1941, Origin of banded iron deposits—a suggestion: Econ. Geol., v. 36, p. 465–489.

29

Reprinted from *Econ. Geol.*, **60**(5), 1063–1065 (1965)

Discussion of Origin of Precambrian Iron Formations

G. A. GROSS

Sir: The paper in ECONOMIC GEOLOGY, vol. 59, no. 6, 1964, by Henry Lepp and Samuel S. Goldich, on the origin of Precambrian iron-formations is based on the assumption that the Precambrian atmosphere had a relatively low oxygen content and that this was a primary factor in controlling the composition of these formations. Information and data concerning this factor have been considered but their argument is found to be inconclusive and misleading on a number of essential points. The statistical study of data for the chemical compositions of iron-formations is, however, a very useful and commendable contribution.

Following their definition, iron-formation is "a chemical sediment typically bedded and commonly laminated, containing 15 percent or more iron of sedimentary origin, commonly but not necessarily containing layers of chert." This definition includes a great variety of ferruginous sediments of all ages but the authors want their argument restricted to the cherty Precambrian iron-formations of Lake Superior type. They overlook the fact that cherty iron-formations also occur in some Paleozoic and younger rocks that are lithologically similar to many of the Precambrian beds. If a low oxygen content in the atmosphere was an essential factor in the deposition of the Precambrian cherty iron-formations, was it not also essential for deposition of the younger formations? One is led to believe that the composition of the atmosphere was not a significant factor in the formation of these sediments.

A great variety of ferruginous sediments formed in the Precambrian under a wide range of geological conditions. The Precambrian formations indicated in Figure 1 of this paper were classified as two major types on the source map referred to, but the authors have grouped all of the Precambrian cherty formations together in their genetic study. Why then did they exclude the cherty iron-formations that occur in Lower Paleozoic rocks in the Bathurst area, New Brunswick, which are similar in every respect to many of the Early Precambrian formations? The authors also state that they have excluded Precambrian "minette type" iron-formations in their theory of origin. If it is to be demonstrated that the iron-formations formed because of certain conditions that prevailed during Precambrian time only, then evidence from all of the different types of Precambrian iron-formation must be considered, and evidence must also be recognized from all the iron-formations of a chosen type regardless of their age. The origin of some of the formations that appear to be exceptions to the type required by the model must be explained, or else the model should be modified. It is not satisfactory to simply ignore the exceptions.

Chemical composition is not the only line of evidence to be considered in studying the origin of iron-formations. However, deductions based on this should be compatible with the wealth of evidence revealed by studies of the tectonic and depositional environments, by associated sediments or volcanic rocks, by textures, mineralogy, and primary depositional features. Cherty iron-formations were deposited under physical-chemical conditions that varied greatly from place to place. Some formed near shorelines or in shallow water on continental shelves and others formed in eugeosynclinal basins. The sedimentary rocks associated with them vary accordingly but it is significant that evidence of volcanic activity contemporaneous with the deposition of these iron-formations is consistently present. Silica and iron could have been contributed by processes that were related to this volcanic activity and there is abundant evidence in many areas that they were. Compositional features of iron-formations described by Lepp and Goldich do not reflect a unique source or mode of origin for the iron and silica.

The authors' argument, however, rests on the assumption that cherty iron-formations generally contain a uniform amount of iron in the appropriate quantities to be expected if iron and calcium were precipitated as carbonate followed by replacement of the calcium carbonate by silica. Satisfactory evidence has not been presented to show that this in fact took place. If the authors believe that there is an absence of evidence indicating direct precipitation of silica, then why do they suggest that the less abundant and more soluble calcium and iron constituents precipitated separately and in advance of the silica?

Statistical studies have indicated typical average iron content for various formations but averages do not demonstrate a uniform iron content. The tables show a range in iron content of 30 percent and, moreover, beds with less than 15 percent iron were excluded by definition. Other constituents also have a wide range in composition. Because iron and calcium are present in the lithosphere in approximately mole proportions of 1:1 the authors assume that these proportions were typical of source areas for all the iron-formations and that these elements were dissolved, transported and precipitated in these proportions. These assumptions require a uniformity and stability in the physical-chemical environment that should also be reflected by the rocks intimately associated with the iron-formations. But considerable variation in the depositional environment is recorded in associated dolomite, chert, coarse and fine clastic rocks, in the variable amounts of carbon, periodic influxes of acid or basic tuffs, or by wide variations in physical and chemical conditions shown by the concentric rings in oolites and by thin laminated beds.

It is not necessary to postulate a low oxygen content of the atmosphere in order to bring about large concentrations of sedimentary iron or silica. The Mesozoic "minette type" iron-formations and thin bedded chert formations of recent age are evidence of this. Chert and iron are not geochemically separated in all sediments younger than Precambrian and are not always intimately related in Precambrian sediments. To consider only one factor related to the origin of iron-formations and only features compatible with that factor seems to beg the question.

30

Reprinted from *Econ. Geol.*, **60**(5), 1065–1070 (1965)

Discussion of Origin of Precambrian Iron Formations

A. F. TRENDALL

Sir: May I offer rather belatedly some critical comments on the interesting paper by Lepp and Goldich on the origin of Precambrian iron formation published in this journal some months ago (1). I believe that they have wrongly used their chemical data, that by restricting their attention too narrowly to iron formations they have overlooked an important objection to their genetic model, and that they have not referred to important characteristics of Precambrian iron formation which must not be omitted from any complete hypothesis of origin; these three points are expanded in order below.

Although geologists' use of both chemistry and statistics is traditionally informal some basic rules are: (1) before two sets of chemical data are compared there must be some geological grounds for the comparison, (2) where the chemistry of a group of rocks fits a particular genetic model this is valueless as evidence in favor of that model if it fits many other models equally well, (3) those characteristics of the data that are the result of the manner of their selection must be distinguished from those that are geologically meaningful, and (4) there should be some attempt at proper statistical treatment. Lepp and Goldich have transgressed each of these rules; examples follow, numbered as above.

1. No reason is given for the geological equivalence, in all respects other than time, or Precambrian iron formations of Lake Superior type and post-Precambrian bedded ores of minette type. In the Northampton Sand of Britain, quoted (1; Table 3) as a chemical example of the latter, "periodic incursions of sandy detritus have resulted in the local abundance of quartz grains" (2; p. 8). The silica of Precambrian iron formations is almost certainly not detrital. Of what use is it then to compare "SiO_2" percentages in the two groups of rocks, however numerous and accurate, when the two quantities represent different geological things? The two rock types are linked economically in that they are the two main commercial sources of iron, but this is not relevant to their geological equivalence.

2. The inverse correlation of SiO_2 and CO_2 compared with the constancy of Fe (1; pp. 1037-8) cannot itself suggest replacement relationships between silica and carbonates. It is true that it fits the particular genetic model suggested later (1; p. 1051); but it fits replacement of quartz by carbonate equally well, and a variety of other models not involving replacement relations between these two constituents (for example, coprecipitation of carbonates and silica, with later selective removal of one or other of these constituents).

3. This is best illustrated by the same point as 2—the correlation of SiO_2 and CO_2. Where a rock has a small number of major components (1; Table 8–2 minerals give three analyzed constituents averaging 90.6% of the rocks) an inverse correlation between any two of them is required by the condition that $A + B + C + \text{etc.} = 100\%$. In other words, if a given volume of a sample of iron formation is occupied by quartz it cannot also be occupied by carbonate, and statistical analysis alone cannot extract any more significant information from the situation. Chayes (3) has discussed this matter at some length. Another point coming under the same heading is that the distribution of Fe-content shown by Lepp and Goldich for 2,200 analyses of Precambrian iron formation (1; Fig. 2) is exactly what would be expected from definition of the rock (1; p. 1027). A similar histogram of Fe-content could easily be constructed for a large number of analyses of, say, gabbro; it would provide information mainly about the definition of the rock.

4. One of the main features of Lepp and Goldich's depositional model is the replacement of $CaCO_3$ by SiO_2, for which the main evidence cited is a supposed inverse correlation of SiO_2 and CO_2 (1; p. 1051). This relationship between Precambrian and later iron formations (1; Table 10, 11, Fig. 3) is not relevant here; attention must be confined to the Precambrian. The SiO_2 and CO_2 values of the 8 composite analyses used to demonstrate the relationship within Precambrian iron formations show poor correlation when plotted graphically against each other, and in view of the fact that some inverse correlation must exist more convincing evidence is needed here. It would be instructive to see a plot of all individual analyses of Precambrian iron formations available to Lepp and Goldich which include SiO_2 and CO_2; from the scatter of points for the Precambrian in Figure 4 (2; p. 1041) it does not seem likely that a particularly strong correlation would be found. It is misleading to mix the appearance of rigorous statistical treatment (1; pp. 1034–1037) with an assertion of the existence of a correlation for which no proper evidence is presented.

However, the lack of chemical evidence in direct support of the proposed model does not invalidate its claim to consideration as a hypothesis. Turning to my second major point concerning Lepp and Goldich's paper, there is a strong objection to their genetic model when iron formations are considered in their stratigraphic environment rather than in isolation. This can best be illustrated by reference to the Brockman Iron Formation (age between 2,900 and 2,100 m.y.) of Western Australia (4).

This formation had a thickness of about 2,000 feet over some 25,000 square miles of the northern part of Western Australia, and consists of regularly interbedded shale and banded iron formation (5). Its mean iron content is probably close to 25%, with a bulk density about 3.12, and it thus contains about 50 lbs of iron per cubic foot. The older Precambrian rocks from which this iron could have been derived by differential weathering of the type suggested by Lepp and Goldich consist of granites, metasediments and metavolcanics, for which a bulk estimate of about 6 lbs of iron per cubic foot is reasonable, unless it be supposed that there were abundant older iron formations; but this would hardly be an attempt to solve their origin. This bulk estimate for the older shield is derived from a mixture of 4 parts of granite and 1 part of mafic rocks (both by volume). The iron and alumina contents, and the Fe/Al ratio, of such a model are not far from Grout's (6) estimate for the average Precambrian of Canada and Sederholm's (7) estimate for the Finnish Precambrian. The relevant figures, and those for the Brockman Iron Formation, are given in Table 1. Thus the extraction of all the iron from about 8 vertical feet of surrounding country, assuming the eroded area was equal to the area of deposition, would have been necessary for each vertical foot of this iron formation. If, on the other hand, the area of supply was eight times the area

TABLE 1

IRON AND ALUMINIUM CONTENT, BY WEIGHT AND VOLUME, OF IRON FORMATIONS AND ASSOCIATED ROCKS, AND OF VARIOUS POSSIBLE PARENT ROCKS

Number in key below	Fe		Al		Fe/Al
	Wt. %	lbs/ft³	Wt. %	lbs/ft³	
1	30	64	0.2	0.4	150
2	13	21	6	9.7	2.2
3	25	50	1.8	3.5	14
4	8.3	15	8.4	15	1.0
5	2.52	4.1	7.73	12.5	0.33
6	—	6.3	—	13	0.48
7	4.01	7.0	9.00	15.7	0.45
8	3.40	5.9	7.84	13.7	0.43
9	26.2	54	1.02	2.1	26
10	5.6	9.1	11.2	18.2	0.5
11	10	18	8.5	14.9	1.2
12	8.8	16.5	8.5	15.9	1.04

Key:
1. Brockman Iron Formation, iron formation proper.
2. Brockman Iron Formation, interbedded shale.
3. Estimated bulk composition, Brockman Iron Formation.
4. Mean of 30 Western Australian mafic rocks (13; Table N).
5. Daly's average of 546 granites, from (8).
6. Hypothetical older Precambrian source material for Brockman Iron Formation: one part of 4 and four parts of 5 by volume.
7. Average Canadian Precambrian (from 6).
8. Average Finnish Precambrian (from 7).
9. Trommald formation, Cuyuna area: (12) recalculated by (11).
10. Rabbit Lake formation, Cuyuna area: ref. as above.
11. Four parts Rabbit Lake formation to one part Trommald formation, by volume.
12. Daly's average of 198 basalts, from (8).

N.B. For the calculation of some of these figures it has been necessary to assume densities.

of deposition (this seems a reasonable maximum) all the iron from 2,000 vertical feet over 200,000 square miles would have been needed for the whole formation, leaving behind, after extraction also of the required silica, alumina, and other materials, about 600 feet of aluminous laterite, if most of the silica is assumed to be removed in solution (1; p. 1049).

If Lepp and Goldich's model were followed more closely, and the originally ferric iron remained behind, then an even greater thickness of parent material would have been necessary. Quite apart from the fact that preferential extraction of some constituents by weathering to these orders of depth is difficult to reconcile with a relief sufficiently slight to prevent significant transport of clastic debris the resultant sedentary aluminous sheet becomes an embarrassment when the iron formation is considered in its stratigraphic context; neither above nor below the Brockman Iron Formation are there rocks any richer in alumina than the postulated older shield, and the shales interbedded within the formation are relatively richer in iron than mafic igneous rocks (Table 1). W. N. MacLeod, of this Survey, has drawn my attention to possible examples, but at the moment these appear to be local and atypical.

Although I have used an Australian example to show the inadequacy of Lepp and Goldich's model the same argument, with appropriately modified figures, could be applied to the Animikie group iron formations of the Lake Superior area. Stated in its general form the problem is as follows. The bulk chemical composition of a typical Precambrian basin with iron formations shows an excess of iron and a deficiency in aluminium compared with any reasonable average composition of an older Precambrian shield. (For clarity, these two elements may usefully be considered in isolation, since, compared with the average composition of the lithosphere (8; p. 133), they are the major constituents in which iron formations are richest and poorest, respectively.) Aluminium must therefore be removed or iron added during the conversion of parent material to iron formation. Extraction of aluminium by differential weathering hypotheses involves its accumulation of the neighboring land, and this is geologically inadmissible if a sufficiently thick stratigraphic sample is taken.

One possible method of disposing of excess alumina, by solution and permanent retention in the oceans, may be disposed of on quantitative grounds. The oceans now contain about $13{,}500 \times 10^6$ long tons of aluminium (from data in 9 and 10—the error may be very large); this represents the amount present in one vertical foot of Daly's average granite over less than 100,000 square miles. This is a ridiculously small amount.

Govett (11), while supporting Lepp and Goldich in their preference for a selective weathering hypothesis for the origin of Precambrian iron formations, has realized that the disposal of alumina represents a real difficulty, and has used Schmidt's (12) work on the Cuyuna area to equate, in bulk, the 2,000 feet of the Rabbit Lake (argillite) formation and the 500 feet of the underlying Trommald (iron) formation with a basaltic rock. It is true that, purely chemically, the equation has a reasonable balance for Fe and Al. (For comparison these two constituents are set out in Table 1 both by weight and by volume, for each formation separately, for the two together, and for average basalt.) But the geological objections already noted for the Brockman Iron Formation still apply. It is difficult to see how particular constituents could have been extracted from such a great bulk of parent rock by weathering. A basalt sheet 2,500 feet thick with the same area as the basin in which the Cuyuna rocks were laid down would have been needed, or a thinner sheet of proportionately greater area. And in this area the clastic Mahnomen formation, which lies conformably below the Trommald formation, appears to approximate chemically to an average Precambrian shield (12; pp. 14–15. cf. Table 1 of this letter). Where, then, was the parent basalt, and when was it extruded? If it was poured out over the supply areas of the basin at about the time equivalent of the Mahnomen-Trommald junction then there may be less difference between the volcanic and weathering hypotheses of iron formation origin than had previously been thought!

However that may be, the problem of alumina disposal is a real one. If there is a big lack of alumina in bulk composition of Precambrian basins with iron formation (and more data are needed badly here) then addition of iron must have taken place. It is useless in any present considerations of the origin of iron formation to confine attention to the iron formation itself.

Turning to the final point, I believe that Lepp and Goldich have, by ignoring the banding that is characteristic of most Precambrian iron formations, failed to show how this could affect their presentation of the chemistry, and how it is related to their hypothesis of precipitation. These points are both important, since Precambrian banded iron formations are characteristically among the least homogeneous of all rocks.

In the Brockman Iron Formation, already referred to, there is a prominent alternation of chert, magnetite, carbonate and mixed bands. The range of Fe-content between different types of band is approximately 7 to 70 percent. The distribution of Fe-content described by Lepp and Goldich (1: pp. 1033–1037) is vitally affected by sample size used for analysis, in that the 5- to 10-feet samples analyzed represent composite samples of many petrographically distinct components. Variations between samples of this size indicate mainly variation in proportions of these different components, rather than in their nature. The relevance of this for their depositional model is that a hypothesis is not needed for precipitation of material remarkably uniform in iron content (1; p. 1050), but for material varying in Fe-content by several hundred percent. Banding is a complex and puzzling feature of Precambrian iron formations, and some explanation of it must be included in any serious attempt to explain their origin.

It is disappointing that, as Lepp and Goldich (1; p. 1056) themselves point out, their paper contributes little new thought to the iron formation problem. The old ground of vulcanicity versus differential weathering has now been thoroughly worked and reworked in many papers, and if further progress is to be made speculation must be replaced by search for new evidence.

A. F. Trendall

Geological Survey of Western Australia,
Perth, Western Australia,
March 27, 1965

REFERENCES

1. Lepp, H., and Goldich, S. S., 1964, The origin of Precambrian iron formations: Econ. Geol., v. 59, p. 1025–1060.
2. Taylor, J. H., 1949, Petrology of the Northampton Sand Ironstone Formation: Mem. Geol. Surv. Great Britain, 111 p.
3. Chayes, F., 1962, Numerical correlation and petrographic variation: Jour. Geol., v. 70, p. 440–452.
4. MacLeod, W. N., de la Hunty, L. E., Jones, W. R., and Halligan, R., 1963, A preliminary report on the Hamersley Iron Province, North-West Division: West. Australia Geol. Survey Ann. Rept. 1962, p. 44–54.

5. Trendall, A. F., in press, Progress report on the Brockman Iron Formation in the Wittenoom-Yampire area: West. Australia Geol. Survey Ann. Rept. 1964.
6. Grout, F. F., 1938, Petrographic and chemical data on the Canadian shield: Journ. Geol., v. 46, p. 486–504.
7. Sederholm, J. J., 1925, The average composition of the earth's crust in Finland: Comm. geol. Finlande Bull., v. 12, no. 70, 20 p.
8. Poldervaart, A., 1955, Chemistry of the Earth's Crust: Geol. Soc. America Spec. Pap. 62, p. 119–144.
9. Defant, A., 1961, Physical Oceanography, Volume 1: Pergamon Press, Oxford, London, New York, Paris.
10. Harvey, H. W., 1955, The chemistry and fertility of sea water: Cambridge University Press, Cambridge.
11. Govett, G. J. S., in press, Origin of banded iron formations: Geol. Soc. America Bull.
12. Schmidt, R. G., 1963, Geology and Ore Deposits of the Cuyuna North Range, Minnesota: U.S.G.S. Prof. Pap. 407, 96 p.
13. Joplin, G. A., 1963, Chemical Analyses of Australian Rocks. Part 1: Igneous and Metamorphic: Bur. Min. Res. Geol. and Geophysics Bull. 65, 446 p.

31

Reprinted from *Carbonate Rocks*, G. V. Chilingar, H. J. Bissell, and R. W. Fairbridge, eds., Elsevier Publ. Co., Amsterdam, 1967, pp. 416–418

Cabonate Rocks and Paleoclimatology in the Biochemical History of the Planet

RHODES W. FAIRBRIDGE

* * * * * * *

Revolution II

At a certain stage, it is evident that primitive chlorophyllic organisms (probably bacterial autotrophs) began to use CO_2 and liberate oxygen as a by-product of sugar synthesis. The beginning of this *Revolution II* ("Eparchean") probably took place shortly before the time of the oldest radio–isotope–dated stromatolitic limestones, say about $2.9 \pm 0.2 \cdot 10^9$ years ago. This removal of CO_2 from solution in sea water would raise the pH, especially if it took place in shallow coastal lagoons, and $CaCO_3$ would be precipitated. The structures in the early carbonates, however, do not suggest evaporites or primary precipitates; they are probably organogenic rocks. The first carbonate fossil traces are stromatolitic algal structures, and are found all over the world in Precambrian formations, the oldest of which are the Bulawayan dolomites that are over $2.7 \cdot 10^9$ years old by absolute dating methods. Measurements of the $^{12}C/^{13}C$ ratios in these rocks may be helpful (WICKMAN, 1956); organic carbonates tend to be enriched in the ^{13}C isotope. The stromatolites (*Collenia*, *Cryptozoon*, etc.) are not skeletal material secreted by multicellular plants, but are wrinkled mats of $CaCO_3$ precipitated against the outer surface of unicellular green Algae colonies, just as observed today in Florida (GINSBURG, 1960) and in Shark Bay, W. Australia (LOGAN, 1961). The growth of this mat in shallow lagoons may well have sheltered the early cyanophytes from excess UV radiation. This revolution gradually led to the build-up of an oxygen-rich atmosphere, though initially all the O_2 would have been reabsorbed by mineral oxidation. RUTTEN (1965) suggested that about $1.6 \cdot 10^9$ years ago the O_2 level reached 0.01 P.A.L. (present atmospheric level). The so-called "Pasteur Level" (p_{O_2} at 1% of the present atmospheric level) was probably achieved only at the end of the Precambrian (HOLLAND, 1962; BERKNER and MARSHALL, 1964). Nevertheless, it permitted the evolution of the ancestors of all modern animals. Rutten suggested that the first primitive fauna began to evolve about $1.0 \cdot 10^9$ years ago.

The end of the Precambrian era is sometimes called the "Lipalian interval" (WALCOTT, 1910) to cover an imaginary epoch, when modern shell-bearing invertebrates were supposed to have evolved. This evolution must have been fantastically rapid and complex, for the Lower Cambrian discloses already the trilobites, representatives of the highest phylum of the invertebrates together with many other

Editor's Note: A row of asterisks indicates that material has been omitted from the original article.

forms. Trilobites are, crudely speaking, ancestral to the modern horse-shoe crab, and such organisms are provided with a highly developed nervous system, brain, eyes, prehensile organs, digestive system, articulated skeletal system, complex musculature and a sophisticated bisexual reproductive system. It has been postulated that such organisms burst out from single-celled primitives in a brief evolutionary explosion at the very close of the Precambrian time to fill a newly created ecologic niche (CLOUD and ABELSON, 1961). Modern genetics offer no support for such a revolutionary event. In any case, the very existence of a world-wide stratigraphic gap corresponding to the Lipalian was disproven with the discovery of many fine, unmetamorphosed sedimentary sequences that spanned the whole interval, e.g., the Adelaide System of South Australia (DAVID and BROWNE, 1950; GLAESSNER, 1966).

One is forced, therefore, to conclude that the oxygen-breathing invertebrates evolved during an extended time-span of the middle and late Precambrian, although traces of these organisms are extremely sparse and restricted to some impressions, tracks and worm casts. The geochemical environmental conditions appear to have been reasonably acceptable for organisms similar to those living today with but one exception: the sea-water composition was such that they could not secrete carbonate skeletons (SCHINDEWOLF, 1956; CHILINGAR and BISSELL, 1963b; FAIRBRIDGE, 1964a). Examples of the fauna are known, and worm tracks are relatively common. The Ediacara fauna of South Australia, with its hydrozoa, etc., appreciably antedates the late Precambrian Sturtian Tillite (GLAESSNER, 1962; GLAESSNER and DAILY, 1959). The primitive segmented fauna, presumably arthropods, of the Belt Series of Montana, formerly considered of very late Precambrian or even Lower Cambrian age, is now considered to be a "Middle" Precambrian stage (GILLULY, 1963; PFLUG, 1965a). Also about one billion years old are the probable Foraminifera reported by PFLUG (1965b).

It would appear, therefore, that the middle and late Precambrian sea must have been acceptable for modern invertebrate life in every way, but for this peculiar feature about the carbonate shell secretion. Only the intertidal or lagoonal Algae seemed to have been able to lead to such precipitation. In an acid environment this process would be applicable. In lakes and rivers, modern fresh-water arthropods secrete chitinous shells (with only small clots of calcite) by raising the pH of their own body fluids, regardless of the low pH (5–7) of the environment. It seems possible, therefore, that up till the end of the Precambrian, the oceanic pH did not exceed 7 or a little over. As a matter of interest, all lakes in acid igneous rock areas today have a pH below 7 (HUTCHINSON, 1957); and HOUGH (1958) has demonstrated that the great silica-iron deposits that are known all over the world in the Middle and Late Precambrian, *but at no other time*, could be readily explained by the geochemistry of a lacustrine regime. A predictable low p_{O_2} would also favor this deposition (LEPP and GOLDICH, 1964) (Fig.13).

There seems to be good justification for the idea of BERKNER and MARSHALL

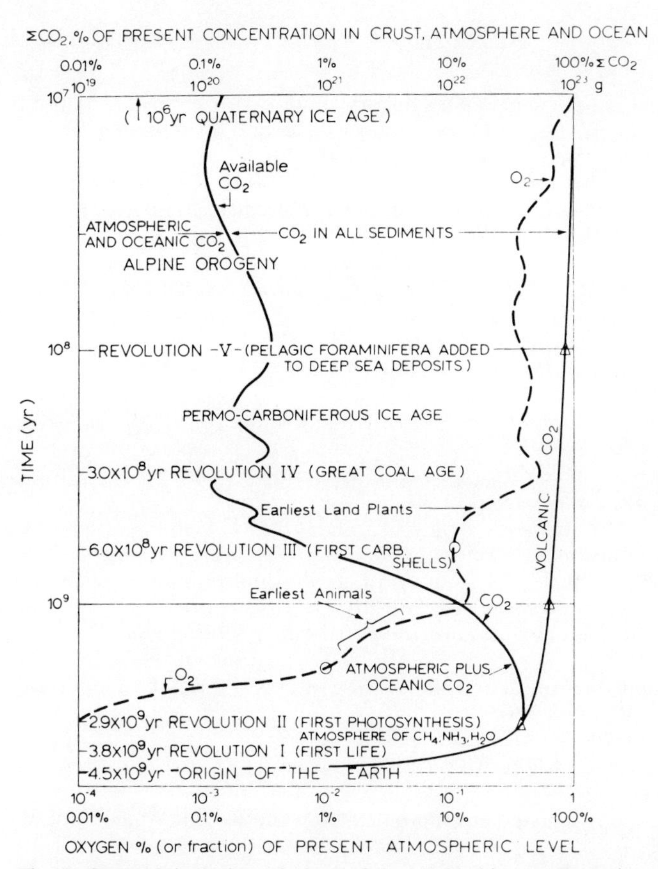

Fig.13. Great biological revolutions of the earth's history. Tentative suggestions of the variation in partial pressures of atmospheric oxygen (largely by photosynthesis; partly by photodissociation of H_2O) and CO_2 (from volcanic emanation).

(1964) that with the extremely thin O_2 and H_2O vapor atmospheric blanket in the early Precambrian, UV-synthesized ozone would be formed directly on the land surface. Inasmuch as ozone, rather like hydrogen peroxide, is a very strong oxidizing agent, the rate of chemical erosion would be very high and continue until such time as the atmospheric blanket is thickened. The production of the enormous silica-iron deposits would be greatly facilitated by such erosion. It must not be forgotten, however, that very important mechanical, unweathered deposits also occur during this period. Inasmuch as the iron deposits are not continuous, a series of oscillatory ozone build-ups may have alternated with less reactive epochs. Their world-wide distribution merely suggests a rather brackish, acid ocean. Alkalinity, however, may have been moderately high owing to the presence of borates and sulphates, as well as limited amounts of the principal sea salt (NaCl) which slowly increased through time. Late Precambrian gypsum and magnesite are known but there is no trace of halite evaporites.

* * * * * * *

References

Berkner, L. V. and Marshall, L. C., 1964. The history of growth of oxygen in the earth's atmosphere. In: B. J. Brancazio and A. G. W. Cameron (Editors), *The Origin and Evolution of Atmosphere and Oceans.* Wiley, New York, N.Y., pp. 102–126.

Chilingar, G. V. and Bissell, H. J., 1963b. Note on possible reason for scarcity of calcerous skeltons of invertebrates in Precambrian formations. *J. Paleontol.,* 37: 942–943.

Cloud, Jr., P. E. and Abelson, P. H., 1961. Woodring conference on major biologic innovations and the geologic record. *Proc. Natl. Acad. Sci. U.S.,* 47: 1705–1712.

David, T. W. E. and Browne, W. R., 1950. *The Geology of the Commonwealth of Australia.* Arnold, London, 1: 747 pp. 2: 618 pp., 3: maps.

Fairbridge, R. W., 1964a. The importance of limestone and its Ca/Mg content to paleoclimatology. In: A. E. M. Nairn (Editor), *Problems in Palaeoclimatology.* Wiley, New York, N.Y., pp. 431–530.

Gilluly, J., 1963. The tectonic evolution of the western United States. *Quart. J. Geol. Soc. London,* 119: 133–174.

Ginsburg, R. N., 1960. Ancient analogues of Recent stromatolites. *Intern. Geol. Congr., 21st, Copenhagen, 1960, Rept. Session, Norden,* 22: 26.

Glaessner, M. F., 1962. Precambrian fossils. *Biol. Rev.,* 37: 467–494.

Glaessner, M. F., 1966. Precambrian palaeontology. *Earth-Sci. Rev.,* 1(1): 29–50.

Glaessner, M. F. and Daily, B., 1959. The geology and Late Precambrian fauna of the Ediacara fossil reserve. *Rec. S. Australian Museum,* 13: 363–401.

Holland, H., 1962. A model for the evolution of the earth's atmosphere. *Geol. Soc. Am.* (Buddington Vol.), pp. 447–477.

Hough, J. L. 1958. Fresh-water environment of deposition of Precambrian banded iron formations. *J. Sediment. Petrol.,* 28: 414–430.

Hutchinson, G. E., 1957. *A Treatise on Limnology.* Wiley, New York, N.Y., 1: 1015 pp.

Lepp, H. and Goldich, S. S., 1964. Origin of Precambrian iron ore formations. *Econ. Geol.,* 59: 1025–1060.

Logan, B., 1961. *Cryptozoon* and associated stromatolites from the Recent, Shark Bay, Western Australia. *J. Geol.,* 69: 517–533.

Pflug, H.D., 1965a. Organische Reste aus der Belt-Serie (Algonkium) von Nordamerika. *Palantol. Z.,* 39: 10–25.

Pflug, H. D., 1965b. Foraminiferen und âhnliche Fossilreste aus dem Kambrium und Algonkium. *Palaeontographica,* 125(A): 46–60.

Rutten, M. G., 1965. Geologic data on atmospheric history. *Palaeogeography, Palaeoclimatol., Palaeoecol.,* 2(1): 47–57.

Schindewolf, O. H., 1956. Über präkambrische Fossilien. In: F. LOTZE (Editor), *Geotektonisches Symposium zu Ehren von Hans Stille.* Eerd. Enke, Stuttgart, pp. 455–480.

Walcott, C. D., 1910. Abrupt appearance of the Cambrian fauna on the North American continent. *Smithsonian Misc. Coll.,* 57: 1–16.

Wickman, F. E., 1956. The cycle of carbon and stable carbon isotopes. *Geochim. Cosmochim. Acta,* 9: 136–153.

Editor's Comments on Papers 32 and 33

32 James: Excerpt from *Chemistry of the Iron-Rich Sedimentary Rocks*

33 Govett: Excerpts from *Origin of Banded Iron Formations*

Paper 32 is another excerpt of H. L. James's monograph on the chemistry of iron-rich sedimentary rocks. It is an excellent summary of the views that have been proposed for the genesis of the iron-rich sediments. Furthermore, the paper carefully reviews the pertinent observed facts that must be accounted for in any depositional model. James presents a brief summary of his views on the origin of these rocks, but he concludes that ". . . most surely they are not the final answers." He presents a more quantitative analysis of the effect of increased CO_2 in the Precambrian atmosphere in the monograph on the geology and ore deposits of the Iron River–Crystal Falls district (Paper 17).

G. J. S. Govett presents a different interpretation of the origin of banded iron-formations in Paper 33. He favors formation in a lacustrine or closed basin environment for several reasons. The seasonal stratification and annual turnover of many lakes provides a possible explanation for the compositional banding in iron-formations as proposed by Hough (1958). Furthermore, the waters of lakes have much greater variability in chemical parameters (pH, Eh) than do marine waters.

While recognizing that the Precambrian atmosphere may have been somewhat different than the present, he proposes that the separation of iron and alumina, which is such a striking characteristic of iron-formations, was dictated by the development of biotic systems rather than through atmospheric evolution. He points to evidence indicating that kaolinite can form only in the presence of organic material and proposes that there may have been little or no clay in the Precambrian in the absence of terrestrial life. He suggests that hematite is the only primary iron mineral.

Govett notes the change from purely banded iron-formations in the early Precambrian to the pronounced development of granules in some middle Precambrian formations. In his view there is insufficient evidence to determine whether the granules are fossil protoorganisms or purely inorganic features. La Berge (1973) recently suggested an organic origin for the spherical structures of the Lake Superior iron-formations.

Govett graduated from the University of Wales (Cardiff) in 1955 and obtained a Ph.D. in applied geochemistry from Imperial College, London, in 1958. He was Industrial Mineralogist and Geochemist for the Research Council of Alberta (Canada) until 1966 and is now Professor with the Department of Geology at the University of New Brunswick.

Govett has worked on various United Nations mineral projects in the Philippines, Cyprus, Jordan, and Ethiopia; as a consultant to the Organization for Economic Cooperation and Development in Greece; and for governmental and private agencies in Europe, Africa, and South America. He has published widely in the fields of mineral resources, mineral exploration, origin of mineral deposits, and analytical techniques. His main research interests are now directed toward the related problems of geochemical exploration for deeply buried sulfide deposits, their genesis, and the mechanisms of geochemical dispersion of elements in rocks and overburden.

References

Hough, J. L., 1958, Fresh-water environment of deposition of Precambrian banded iron formations: Jour. Sed. Petrology, v. 28, p. 414–430.

James, H. L., C. E. Dutton, F. J. Pettijohn, and K. L. Wier, 1968, Geology and ore deposits of the Iron River–Crystal Falls district, Iron County, Michigan: U.S. Geol. Surv. Prof. Paper 570, 131 p.

La Berge, G. L., 1973, Possible biological origin of Precambrian iron-formations: Econ. Geol., v. 68, p. 1098–1109.

32

Reprinted from *Data of Geochemistry* (U.S. Geol. Survey Prof. Paper 440-W), Chap. W, 1966, pp. 47–60

Chemistry of the Iron-Rich Sedimentary Rocks

HAROLD L. JAMES

* * * * * * *

ORIGIN

The lack of modern-day examples of ironstone and iron-formation deposition makes the subject of origin a fertile one for speculation. Furthermore, the question is not a simple one: it has many facets, some interrelated and some for the most part independent. Fairly definite conclusions can be drawn as to the distribution patterns and basic chemistry of iron deposition: both ironstone and iron-formation were formed as chemical sediments in marine or brackish-water basins of restricted circulation, or in marginal seas of modest extent, the mineralogy of the iron precipitates being governed principally by relative availability of oxygen, carbon dioxide, and sulfur. Beyond this, many major and minor problems remain unsettled. Chief among them are the source and mode of transport of iron (and, for the iron-formation, also silica) and the relation between ironstone and iron-formation.

The various mechanisms that have been proposed for derivation of the iron are as follows:

1. Iron is derived from weathering of land masses under humid tropical or subtropical conditions (Gruner, 1922; Gill, 1927; Moore and Maynard, 1929; Taylor, 1949; Sakamoto, 1950; Alexandrov, 1955; Hough, 1958); under arid conditions (Woolnough, 1941); or by weathering under an atmosphere of lower oxygen and higher CO_2 content than at present (MacGregor, 1927; Tyler and Twenhofel, 1952).
2. The iron is derived from sea-bottom reactions on chiefly clastic materials (Strakhov, 1959; Borchert, 1960a; Braun, 1964), and concentrated by solution and selective sea-bottom precipitation (Borchert), or mainly by diagenetic reactions (Strakhov).
3. The iron (and also silica in the iron-formations) is derived from processes related to contemporaneous volcanic and igneous activity (Van Hise and Leith, 1911; Moore, *in* Moore and Maynard, 1929; Goodwin, 1956; Oftedahl, 1958; Gruner, 1959, written communication, a reversal of views published in 1922; Harder, 1963).

Each of these mechanisms—other than that calling for atmospheric modification—can be either observed or reasonably inferred on a small-scale basis at the present. For example, the bog iron deposits represent leaching of iron from surface and subsurface materials and lateral movement to sites of deposition—essentially a weathering process; sideritic concretions and some glauconite concentrations surely represent mobilization of iron from surrounding sediments by sea-bottom or diagenetic reaction; present-day deposition of iron related to volcanism is known from at least a few localities. None of the processes are mutually exclusive; the question is one of scale and of which process is dominant. Of the three possibilities, it would seem to the present writer that the second—sea-bottom or diagnetic reactions—is quantitatively inadequate, particularly with respect to the iron-formations, unless the chemistry of seawater differed profoundly from that of today. If this judgment is accepted, then only two major possibilities need to be considered: derivation of iron by weathering processes, and derivation of iron by processes related to volcanism and igneous activity.

Assessment of the role of volcanism and related processes to iron deposition is not easily made, as it depends largely upon inferences drawn from associated rocks. Nevertheless, a close and probable genetic relation seems reasonably proved for a few ironstones and iron-formations—for example, the Devonian ironstone of the Lahn-Dill district of Germany, and the "Keewatin-type" Precambrian iron-formations, ex-

Editor's Note: A row of asterisks indicates that material has been omitted from the original article.

emplified in the Michipicoten district of Canada. Another well-documented example is that of Meggen, Germany (Ehrenberg, Pilger, and Schroder, 1954), where pyritic beds of Devonian age grade laterally into barite. In others, such as the deposits of Kazah, U.S.S.R. (Maksimov, 1958), the iron-rich strata interfinger with and grade into manganese-rich beds. These various deposits, which have been classed as exhalative-sedimentary, typically exhibit rapid changes in thickness and lithic facies, and all have close spatial relations to volcanic rocks or other evidence of volcanic and igneous activity.

For most of the major ironstone units of younger age, however, for which time-equivalent relations can be established with other rocks—so that contemporaneous volcanic or igneous activity in surrounding regions can be excluded—derivation of iron by weathering processes, or at least nonvolcanic processes, seems certain. Typical of the deposits of nonvolcanic association are the many ironstone beds of Jurassic age of northern Europe, which were deposited in isolated or semi-isolated marine basins on the order of several tens of miles in maximum dimension, marginal to or within an epicontinental sea. The iron seemingly can only have been derived from weathering of adjoining land areas, as concluded by Taylor (1949) for the Northampton Sand ironstone of England.

Most of the major iron-formations of the world similarly are devoid of apparent volcanic associations, although the possibility of a relationship cannot be as readily dismissed, at least for units of Precambrian age, in view of the great difficulty or perhaps (at present) impossibility of establishing true time-equivalence between dissimilar rocks of separated areas. Nevertheless, sufficient information on the enclosing geology of these areas is at hand to show that the relationship, if it existed, was not an immediate one; the iron and silica were not derived from thermal waters of volcanic or igneous source within the basins of deposition.

Deposition of both ironstone and iron-formation of nonvolcanic affiliation requires a more efficient means of transporting iron to the site of deposition and of separation from other materials than that now evident in dominant surface processes, in which the bulk of the iron is transported in the form of colloidal iron oxide and is inextricably tied up with the clastic fraction.

For the ironstones of nonvolcanic origin, with ages as young as Pliocene, significant atmospheric or biospheric modification seems an unlikely possibility: the range of environmental conditions in the Pliocene could not have differed greatly from those of the present except in relative importance. The only process now yielding iron concentrations, other than by volcanic contributions, is that of bog-ore formation, which involves shallow subsurface leaching of iron from permeable sands, and transportation in bicarbonate ground waters of low Eh and pH. It does not seem unreasonable to invoke this process on a much larger scale. The process and general setting may be visualized as follows: during a period of widespread and dominantly clastic sedimentation in a shallow epicontinental sea, local warping resulted in emergence of low broad island areas separated by shallow and generally interconnected basins. Climatic conditions—probably warm and humid—permitted development of a thick cover of deeply rooted vegetation on the emergent blocks of permeable and weakly lithified sediments. Deep penetration of ground waters rich in CO_2 and organic acids—the CO_2 content augmented by subsurface production from root processes—resulted in leaching of fine-grained iron oxides and iron sulfides in near-surface zones, with the products of leaching being transported by acid ground waters to bordering seas via subsurface routes. If the sites of debouchement of the ground waters were fully open to oceanic circulation, then most of the dissolved material was dispersed, but if the site was a relatively small basin with restricted circulation, then the iron could be trapped and ultimately precipitated according to the Eh–pH conditions prevailing. Clastic components—sand and clay—and associated clastic rocks would represent contribution and periodic influx of surface-transported materials, which would be interlayered and in part intermixed with the products of chemical precipitation.

For several reasons the process suggested for deposition of ironstone appears inadequate to explain deposition of iron-formation. Chief among these are the far greater dimensions of the depositional units, the more complete separation of iron from constituents other than silica, and the presence of interbedded chert. Most layers within iron-formation are finely laminated, with thicknesses of laminae being on the order of 0.1 mm. If these represent yearly precipitations, an iron-formation 200 m thick would take about a million years to accumulate, even assuming no breaks in sedimentation. It is more likely that the laminae represent longer time intervals, and that sedimentation was not continuous, so that a thick iron-formation may well have taken some tens of millions of years to accumulate. Maintenance for such a long period of time of topographic conditions appropriate for continued groundwater flow of the type outlined seems improbable. Furthermore, in pre-Devonian time the landscape would not be covered with deeply rooted vegetation, if indeed it was covered at all.

Finally, the ground water hypothesis would offer no obvious explanation for the interbedded chert.

Neither the dual occurrence of ironstone and iron-formation in strata at least as young as Cambrian, nor the fact that ironstone could be deposited both in Pliocene time and in a period far back in the Precambrian, eliminates the possibility of a significant relation between evolution of the earth's atmosphere and origin of iron-formation. An atmosphere appreciably different from that of the present could have persisted at least into early Paleozoic time. Strong limits on this speculation are imposed, however, by evidence from within the iron-formation units and their associated rocks. Any proposed system must permit or account for the following facts:

1. Depositional environments for iron had comparable ranges in Eh to those inferred for younger ironstone. This fact is derived from the observed range in facies (oxide to sulfide), from the relative abundance of facies types, and from the relation of the facies to physical features of the rocks that give independent evidence on environment of origin. Oolitic structure, for example, which surely in part reflects deposition in shallow and turbulent—and therefore well-aerated—water, is confined to oxide and silicate facies, as it is in younger ironstone; never is it present in sideritic facies.
2. The precipitation of calcium, magnesium, and minor elements was strongly repressed during the iron-formation cycles.
3. Chert rarely occurs as separate units in strata associated with iron-formation. Furthermore, within iron-formation the amount of chert varies systematically with the facies defined by iron minerals. The implication, therefore, is that precipitation of silica was not independent of that of iron.
4. Thick units of dolomite are present in strata associated with some units of iron-formation. The dolomite actually interbedded with or adjacent to iron-formation commonly contains magnetite, but the principal units—as much as 2,000 feet thick—contain no more iron than dolomites of younger age.
5. Associated clastic rocks, such as quartzite, graywacke, and argillite, are quite similar in mineralogy and chemistry to equivalent rocks of younger age. Clastic feldspar is common in the quartzites and graywackes, which indicates that chemical breakdown of rocks during erosion was not entirely dominant over physical processes.

A number of workers have suggested that the earth's atmosphere during the time of iron-formation deposition was higher in CO_2 than during later eras. The existence of thick and widespread oxidic facies seemingly eliminates the possibility that an actual reducing atmosphere prevailed, but it does not eliminate the possibility that the partial pressure of CO_2 was significantly greater. If, for example, in a dominantly oxidizing atmosphere, though perhaps much lower in oxygen than today, the partial pressure of CO_2 were 0.03 atmosphere, instead of the present 0.0003 atmosphere, the equilibrium pH of surface waters would be reduced from 8.17 to about 6.1 (Rubey, 1951, p. 1129). If the total volume of surface waters were less than at present, the pH would be still lower. Surface waters would then to some degree have similar chemical attributes, particularly the capacity to leach and transport iron, that is now characteristic of acid ground waters. Furthermore, if the pH of marine water in fact was much lower than at present, either because of the direct equilibration with CO_2 of the atmosphere or because of higher concentration of some other constituent—chlorine, for example—then an additional important factor is introduced: namely, that the sea itself could have been a major reservoir for iron in solution.

The validity of this model is open to some question. Revelle and Fairbridge (1957, p. 246) conclude that the present CO_2 content of the atmosphere is an approximate equilibrium value, controlled in large part by carbonate precipitation and silicate weathering. The specific situation analyzed, however, is that of a sudden increase in partial pressure of CO_2 and its effects on seawater equilibrium, with the implicit assumption of element concentrations similar to those of present oceans. This assumption is not necessarily an acceptable one; conceivably, for example, seawater at the time of iron-formation deposition might have been much undersaturated with respect to elements such as calcium. Cloud (1965) questions the existence of an oxygen-bearing atmosphere in early and middle Precambrian time, as do Lepp and Goldich (1964). Cloud develops the concept of photosynthetically generated oxygen to provide local oxidizing environments. The concept is a valuable one, but whether local generation of oxygen is quantitatively adequate for precipitation of thick oxidic sediments remains to be demonstrated.

It is clear, however, that an increase in the partial pressure of CO_2 to relatively modest levels would have profound effect on the cycle of iron, and vastly increase the efficiency of iron extraction and transport. Accepting this as a probable condition, and considering the limiting factors previously outlined, the proposition is here presented that—

1. The earth's atmosphere has been dominantly oxidizing since at least mid-Precambrian time—that is, for the past 2 billion years—and that oxygen,

perhaps locally generated by photosynthesis, was available even at the time of formation of the oldest known stratified rocks (3 billion years or more in age).

2. During mid-Precambrian time, the atmosphere contained a considerably greater amount of CO_2 than at present, and that this relatively high CO_2 content persisted but in diminishing amounts until at least early Cambrian time.
3. The iron-formations typically were deposited adjacent to long-exposed low-lying land masses during intervals in which clastic contributions to the sea were almost nil. Reduction of the land surface during the iron-formation cycle was almost entirely by deep chemical weathering, with complete chemical breakdown of silicates so as to yield abundant iron and silica in solution.
4. An important event leading to the deposition of major iron-formations was the formation of shallow restricted troughs or basins, marginal to the old landmass, in which the products of chemical weathering could be accumulated, and in which abnormal bottom conditions, particularly of Eh, could exist. Some units of iron-formation consisting only of oxide facies, however, could have been deposited in the relatively unrestricted shallows of low-sloping continental shelves.
5. The precipitation of such elements as Ca, Mg, K, and Na was inhibited by the low pH of the sea water, possibly also by low concentrations; whereas iron, transported as bicarbonate, and silica, derived from breakdown of silicates and transported as monomeric H_2SiO_4 (Siever, 1962), reached saturation levels. The intimate association of iron minerals and chert, therefore, is due to the manner in which the elements were extracted from the landmass and trapped: the breakdown of silicates to yield the necessary amounts of iron in solution would at the same time place large amounts of silica in solution. The fractionation of iron and silica from other elements was not accomplished at the source, but rather during the precipitation process.
6. The rhythmic layering so characteristic of iron-formation is due to some periodic, perhaps seasonal change in environment. Sakamoto (1950) suggests that this change is one of alternating wet and dry seasons, with consequent effect on the pH of waters tributary to the basin of deposition; Hough (1958), by analogy to present-day lakes, concludes that the layering is due to seasonal overturn. It is here proposed that the layering is due to explosive growth of silica-secreting organisms in response to periodic (seasonal?) increase in either the nutrient content or the temperature of surface waters in the basin of deposition. According to this concept, iron would be precipitated at a slow and nearly constant rate, whereas the silica-rich layers would represent relatively brief interludes during which organically precipitated silica was showered down from near-surface levels in the water.
7. Periodic influx of clastic material, now represented by rocks such as graywacke and quartzite, represent intervals of structural disturbance during which chemical weathering became subordinate to physical disintegration of the land surface. During these periods the supply of iron and silica in solution was greatly reduced, so that iron-formation and clastic sedimentary rocks, in general, now are mutually exclusive.
8. Thick units of iron-free dolomite, which, if present in the iron-formation sequences generally are separated by some distance stratigraphically from the main iron-formation units, were formed either before the restriction on open-sea circulation was established or during periods when it was destroyed. During these intervals the iron and silica being contributed were lost to the open sea, whereas the carbonate rock could have been precipitated from water not significantly different in composition from that of the oceanic reservoir, in response to some special conditions such as those now prevailing on the Bahama Banks.
9. The time of maximum development of iron-formation, about 2,000 million years ago, was near or at the close of a very long and perhaps world-wide period of stable structural conditions. In the Canadian Shield, at least, to judge from the geochronologic data now available, this structural stability had lasted for about 500 million years. In this, the region of greatest iron-formation occurrence, the formation of the necessary marginal basins was the earliest stage of what was to develop into a eugeosynclinal and orogenic cycle of major proportions.

Both ironstone and iron-formation, therefore, may have been formed by essentially similar processes—extraction of iron by weathering from adjacent land areas and precipitation in (generally) restricted basins. The great differences between the rocks could be ascribed to primarily two factors: (1) the greater efficiency of the weathering process in Precambrian time, which would permit the close association of abundant iron and abundant silica in solution; and (2) the far lengthier periods of structural stability, two of which had durations as long as from the Cambrian to the present—approximately from 2,500 to 2,000 million years and from 1,000 to 500 million years ago. The lesser, though by no means insignificant, amount of iron-formation of Cambrian age could be due to a diminished CO_2 content of the atmosphere.

These suggestions for origin of ironstone and iron-formation should be taken for what they are—that is, plausible speculations. They are offered to provide targets for further research, by means of which specific aspects can be either verified or rejected; most surely they are not final answers.

REFERENCES

Aarnio, V., 1920, Über die Seebildung in einigen Südfinnishen Biuneseen: Fennia, v. 1, no. 4, 38 p.

Adkins, W. S., 1933, The Mesozoic systems in Texas, Part 2 *of* Geology of Texas: Texas Univ. Bull. 3232, p. 239–518.

Agard, J., Destombes, J., Naudet, R., and Van Leckwijck, W., 1952, Les gisements de fer du Maroc: Internat. Geol. Cong., 19th, Algiers 1952, Symposium . . . fer, v. 1, p. 145–161.

Aleksandrov, I. V., and Zmeenkova, A. V., 1958, Evolution of rocks during progressive metamorphism, as exemplified by the middle suite of the Krivoi Rog Series: Geokhimiya, no. 1, p. 47–59; English translation, Geochemistry (Geochem. Soc.), no. 1, p. 62–82 [1959].

Alexandrov, E. A., 1955, Contribution to studies of origin of Precambrian banded iron ores: Econ. Geology, v. 50, p. 459–468.

——— 1962, Review of Dobrokhofov, M. N., and others, Geologiya rudnykh mestorozhdenii: Econ. Geology, v. 57, p. 837.

Alling, H. L., 1947, Diagenesis of the Clinton hematite ores of New York: Geol. Soc. America Bull., v. 58, p. 991–1018.

Ancion, Ch., 1952, Les minerais de fer de la Belgique: Internat. Geol. Cong., 19th, Algiers 1952, Symposium . . . fer, v. 2, p. 75–91.

Anderson, C. A., and Creasey, S. C., 1958, Geology and ore deposits of the Jerome area, Yavapai County, Arizona: U.S. Geol. Survey Prof. Paper 308, 185 p.

Argentina, Direccion General de Fabricaciones Militares, 1952, Yacimiento de hierro de la Republica Argentina: Internat. Geol. Cong., 19th, Algiers 1952, Symposium . . . fer, v. 1, p. 267–284.

Arkell, W. J., 1956, Jurassic geology of the world: New York, Hafner Pub. Co., 806 p.

Arkhangelskii, A. D., 1933, Sulphurous iron in Black Sea deposits: Soc. Naturalistes Moscou Bull., v. 42, Sec. Géol. v. 12, p. 431–440. (In Russian, English summary, p. 440).

Arkhangelskii, A. D., and Kopchenova, E. V., 1934, In reference to dependence of chemical composition of sedimentary iron ores on conditions of their formation: Soc. Naturalistes Moscou Bull., v. 42, Sec. Géol. v. 12, p. 262–278. [In Russian, translated by V. P. Sokoloff.]

——— 1935, On the chemical composition of the iron ores of U.S.S.R.: [U.S.S.R.] Sci. Inst. Geology Mineralogy Trans., no. 11, p. 1–67. [In Russian, English summary, p. 63–66).]

Asano, Goro, 1953, The banded iron ore deposits of An-Shan and the other districts: U.S. Geol. Survey, Pacific Geol. Surveys. Rept. 159, 25 p. [In Japanese, English translation by U.S. Geol. Survey.]

Attia, M. I., 1954, Topography, geology, and iron ore deposits of the district east of Aswan: Cairo, Egypt Geol. Survey, 262 p.

Auger, P. E., 1954, The stratigraphy and structure of the northern Labrador trough, Ungava, New Quebec: Canadian Mining Metall. Bull., v. 47, p. 529–532.

Ayres, V. L., 1940, Mineral notes from the Michigan iron country: Am. Mineralogist, v. 25, p. 432–434.

Baker, C. L., 1935, Metallic and non-metallic minerals and ores, *in* Geology of Texas, v. 2, pt. 3, Economic geology of Texas (exclusive of petroleum): Texas Univ. Bull. 3401, p. 402–640.

Baker, George, 1960, Some Australian occurrences of microspherular pyrite: Neues Jahrb. Mineralogie, Abh., v. 94, p. 564–583.

Barghoorn, E. S., 1957, Origin of life, Chap. 4. *of* Ladd, H. S., ed., Paleoecology: Geol. Soc. America Mem. 67, v. 2, p. 75–85.

Bates, T. F., and Strahl, E. O., 1957, Mineralogy, petrography, and radioactivity of representative samples of Chattanooga Shale: Geol. Soc. America Bull., v. 68, p. 1305–1314.

Bayley, R. W., 1959, Geology of the Lake Mary quadrangle, Iron County, Michigan: U.S. Geol. Survey Bull. 1077, 112 p.

——— 1963, A preliminary report on the Precambrian iron deposits near Atlantic City, Wyoming: U.S. Geol. Survey Bull. 1142–C, 23 p.

Belevtsen, Ya. N., ed., 1957, Geologicheskoe stroenie i zheleznye rudy Krivorozhskogo basseina [Geologic structure and iron ores of the Krivoi Rog basin]: Moskva, Gosudar. Nauch.-Tekh. Izd. Lit. Geol. i Okhrane Nedr, 280 p. [Partial translation by M. C. Blake.]

Belousov, A. K., 1933, Geologicheskoe stroenie i zheleznye rudy Muromskogo i Vyksinskogo raionov Gorkovskogo kraia [Geologic structures and iron ores of Murom and Vyksa districts, Gorkii region]: Moskov. Obshch. Ispytatel Prirod, Byull., Otdel geol., v. 11 (3), p. 245–271. [Translated by V. P. Sokoloff.]

Bergeat, A., 1914, Die Meggener Kies-Schwerspatlager als Ausscheidung auf dem Grunde des mittledevonischen Meeres: Zeitschr. prakt. Geologie, v. 22, p. 237–249.

Bernal, J. D., Dasgupta, D. R., and Mackay, A. L., 1959, The oxides and hydroxides of iron and their structural interrelationships: Clay Minerals Bull., v. 4, no. 21, p. 15–30.

Berner, R. A., 1962, Tetragonal iron sulfide: Science, v. 137, p. 669.

——— 1963, Electrode studies of hydrogen sulfide in marine sediments: Geochim. et Cosmochim. Acta, v. 27, p. 563–574.

——— 1964, Iron sulfides formed from aqueous solution at low temperatures and atmospheric pressure: Jour. Geology, v. 72, p. 293–306.

Bertholf, W. E., 1960, Magnetite taconite rock in Precambrian formations in Rio Arriba County, New Mexico: New Mexico Bur. Mines and Mineral Resources Circ. 54, 24 p.

Berz, K. C., 1922, Über Magneteisen in marinen Ablagerungen: Zentralblatt für Mineralogie, Geologie und Paläontologie, 1922, p. 569–577.

Bétier, G., and others, 1952, Études sur les gisements de fer de l'Algérie: Internat. Geol. Cong., 19th, Algiers 1952, Symposium . . . fer, v. 1, p. 35–77.

Beyschlag, F., Krusch, P., and Vogt, J. H. L., 1909, Die Lagerstätten der nutzbaren Mineralien und Gesteine: Stuttgart. [English translation, New York, 1915.]

Bichelonne, J., and Angot, P., 1939, Le bassin ferrifére de Lorraine: Nancy-Strasbourg, Imprimerie Berger-Levrault, 483 p.

Bjerrum, J., Schwarzenbach, G., and Sillen, L. G., compilers, 1957, Organic ligands, Part 1 *of* Stability constants of metal ion complexes: London, Chem. Soc., Spec. Pub. 6, 105 p.

Blondel, F., 1952, Les gisements de fer de l'Afrique occidentale française: Internat. Geol. Cong., 19th, Algiers 1952, Symposium . . . fer, v. 1, p. 5–34.

——— 1955, Iron ore deposits of Europe, Africa, and the Union of Soviet Socialist Republics, *in* United Nations Dept. Econ. and Social Affairs, 1955, p. 224–264.

Blondel, F., and Marvier, L., eds., 1952, Symposium sur les gisements de fer du monde: Internat. Geol. Cong., 19th, Algiers 1952, v. 1, 638 p., v. 2, 594 p.

Borchert, Hermann, 1952, Die Bildungsbedingungen mariner Eisenerzlagerstätten: Chemie Erde, v. 16, p. 49–74.

——— 1960a, Genesis of marine sedimentary iron ore: Inst. Mining and Metallurgy, Bull. 640 (Trans., v. 69) p. 261–279.

——— 1960b, Geosynklinale Lagerstätten, was dazu gehört und was nicht dazu gehört, sowie deren Beziehungen zu Geotektonik und Magmatismus: Freiberger Forschungshefte, H. C79, p. 8–61.

Branson, C. C., 1939, Pennsylvanian formations of central Wyoming: Geol. Soc. America Bull., v. 50, p. 1199–1226.

Branson, E. B., and Branson, C. C., 1941, Geology of the Wind River Mountains, Wyoming: Am. Assoc. Petroleum Geologists Bull., v. 25, p. 120–151.

Braun, Horst, 1964, Zur Enstehung der marin-sedimentären Eisenerze: Berlin, Gebrüder Borntraeger, Clausthaler Hefte Lagerstättenkunde und Geochemie mineralischen Rohstoffe, v. 2, 133 p.

Brindley, G. W., 1951, The crystal structure of some chamosite minerals: Mineralog. Mag., v. 29, p. 502–529.

Brindley, G. W., and Youell, R. F., 1953, Ferrous chamosite and ferric chamosite: Mineralog. Mag., v. 30, p. 57–70.

Brodskaya, N. G., and Martova, T. G., 1957, Forms of iron in Recent sediments of the Okhotsk Sea: Akad. Nauk SSSR Doklady, Geol. Sci. Sec., v. 114, p. 165–168. [English translation published by Consultants Bureau, Inc., N. Y., 1958.]

Bruevich, S. W., 1938a, Oxidation-reduction potentials and pH of sea bottom deposits: Internat. Vereiningung für theoretische und ungewandte Limnologie, Verh. v. 8, p. 35–49.

——— 1938b, Oxidation-reduction potential and pH of sediments of the Barentz and Kara seas: Akad. Nauk SSSR Doklady, v. 19, no. 8, p. 637–640.

Bugge, J. A. W., 1948, Rana Gruber; geologisk beskrivelse av jernmalmfeltene i Dunderslandsdalen: Norges Geol. Unders økelse [Pub.] no. 171, 149 p. (English summ.)

——— 1953, Sydvaranger geology: Mining World, v. 15, no. 11, p. 52–53.

Burchard, E. F., 1913, The red iron ores of east Tennessee: Tennessee Geol. Survey Bull. 16, 173 p.

——— 1931, Iron ore on Canyon Creek, Fort Apache Indian Reservation, Arizona: U.S. Geol. Survey Bull. 821–C, p. 51–78.

Burchard, E. F., and Butts, Charles, 1910, The iron ores, fuels, and fluxes of the Birmingham district, Alabama, with chapters by E. C. Eckel on the origin of the ores: U.S. Geol. Survey Bull. 400, 204 p.

Burst, J. F., 1958a, "Glauconite" pellets; their mineral nature and application to stratigraphic interpretation: Am. Assoc. Petroleum Geologists Bull., v. 42, p. 310–327.

——— 1958b, Mineral heterogeneity in "glauconite" pellets: Am. Mineralogist, v. 43, p. 481–497.

Caillère, Simonne, and Hénin, Stéphane, 1951, Observations on the chlorites of iron ores: Clay Minerals Bull., v. 1, no. 5, p. 134–37.

Caillère, Simonne, and Kraut, François, 1946, Étude minéralogique des accidents magnétiques de la couche grise du bassin de Briey: Houille, Minerais, Pétrole, v. 1, no. 3–4, p. 109–115.

——— 1953, Considerations sur la genèse des minerais de fer oolithiques lorrains: Internat. Geol. Cong., 19th, Algiers 1952, Comptes rendus sec. 10, p. 101–117.

——— 1957, Sédimentation et métamorphisme dans de gisement de fer de Diélette (Manche): Acad. Sci [Paris] Comptes rendus, v. 245, no. 25, p. 2349–2351.

Canavan, F., 1953, The iron ore deposits of Yampi Sound, W[estern] A[ustralia]: Empire Mining and Metall. Cong., 5th, Pub., v. 1, p. 276–283.

Carroll, Dorothy, 1958, The role of clay minerals in the transportation of iron: Geochim. et Cosmochim. Acta, v. 14, p. 1–28.

Carstens, Harold, 1955, Jernmalmeme i det vestlige Trondhjemsfelt og forholdet til kisforekomstene: Norsk Geol. Tidsskr., v. 35, p. 211–220.

Castaño, J. R., and Garrels, R. M., 1950, Experiments on the deposition of iron with special reference to the Clinton iron ore deposits: Econ. Geology, v. 45, p. 755–770.

Cayeux, Lucien, 1909, Les minerais de fer oolithique de France. I. Minerais de fer primaires: Paris, Imprimerie nationale, 344 p.

Chebotarev, M. V., 1958, Geologicheskoye stroyeniye yuzhnokhinganskogo margantsevego mestorozhdeniya i veschestvenny sostovvgo rud: Sovetskaya Geologiya, no. 8, p. 114–136. [English translation by E. A. Alexandrov and Assoc., 1960, Geological structure of the South Khingan manganese deposit and essential composition of its ores: Internat. Geology Rev., v. 2, p. 851–866.]

Chilingar, G. V., 1956, Joint occurrence of glauconite and chlorite in sedimentary rocks—a review: Am. Assoc. Petroleum Geologists Bull., v. 40, p. 493–498.

Cilliers, J. J. Le R., Freeman, A. G., Hodgson, A., and Taylor, H. F. W., 1961, Crocidolite from the Koegas-Westerberg area, South Africa: Econ. Geology, v. 56, p. 1421–1437.

Clarke, F. W., 1924, The data of geochemistry, 5th ed.: U.S. Geol. Survey Bull. 770, 841 p.

Cloud, P. E., Jr., 1955, Physical limits of glauconite formation: Am. Assoc. Petroleum Geologists Bull., v. 39, p. 484–492.

——— 1965, Significance of the Gunflint (Precambrian) flora: Science, v. 148, p. 27–35.

Coche, L., Dastillon, D., Deudon, M., and Emery, P., 1954, Complements à l'étude du bassin ferrifère de Lorraine. Le Bassin de Landres—Amermont: Centre documentation sidérurgique, Paris, 33 p.

——— 1955, Complements àl 'étude du bassin ferrifère de Lorraine. Le Bassin de Landres: Tucqueqnieux et Anderny: Centre documentation sidérurgique, Paris, 77 p.

Cochrane, G. W., and Edwards, A. B., 1960, The Roper River oolitic ironstone formations: Australia, Commonwealth Sci. and Indus. Resources Organization, Mineragraph. Inv. Tech. Paper 1, 28 p.

Cohen, E., 1952, The nature of silicates and carbonates of iron in the Northampton Sand ironstones of central England *in* Robertson, Thomas, and others: The iron ore deposits of Great Britain: Internat. Geol. Cong., 19th, Algiers 1952 Symposium . . . fer, v. 2, p. 466–471.

Collins, W. H., Quirke, T. T., and Thomson, E., 1926, Michipicoten iron ranges: Canada Geol. Survey Mem. 147, 175 p.

Colombia Servicio Geológico Nacional, 1952, Yacimientos de hierro en Colombia: Internat. Geol. Cong., 19th, Algiers 1952, Symposium . . . fer, v. 1, p. 361–368.

Correns, C. W., 1937, Die Sedimente des äquatorialen Atlantischen Ozeans: Deutsche Atlantische Exped. "Meteor" (1925–27), Wissenschaftliche Ergebnisse, v. 3, pt. 3, p. 135–298.

——— 1952a, Mineralogische Untersuchungen an sedimentären Eisenerzen: Internat. Geol. Cong., 19th, Algiers 1952, Comptes rendus, v. 2, p. 28–30.

——— 1952b, Zur Geochemie des Eisens: Internat. Geol. Cong., 19th, Algiers 1952, Symposium . . fer, v. 2, p. 23–27.

Correns, C. W., and Engelhardt, W. von, 1941, Roentgenographische Untersuchungen über den Mineralbestand sedimentärer Eisenerze: Akad. Wiss. Göttingen, Nachr., Math. Phys. Kl., Jahrg. 1941, no. 3, p. 131–137.

Cotelo Neiva, J. M., 1953, Genèse des principaux gisements Portugais de minerais de fer: Internat. Geol. Cong., 19th, Algiers 1952, Comptes rendus, sec. 10, p 121–132.

Cullen, D. J., 1963, Tectonic implications of banded ironstone formations: Jour. Sed. Petrology, v. 33, p. 387–392.

Cusset, F., Torcy, F. de, and Maubeuge, P., 1952, Études sur les gisements de fer français: Internat. Geol. Cong, 19th, Algiers 1952, Symposium . . . fer, v. 2, p. 129–222.

Davidson, C. F., 1961, Oolitic ironstones of fresh-water origin: Mining Mag., v. 104, no. 3, p. 158–159. (Review of Yanitsky, A. L., 1960, [Oligocene oolitic iron ores of northern Turgai and their genesis]: Akad. Nauk. SSSR, Inst. Geologii Rudnykh Mestorozhdenii, Petrografii, Mineralogii, i Geokhimii, Trudy, v. 37, 219 p. (in Russian)).

Deer, W. A., Howie, R. A., and Zussman, J., 1962, Rock-forming minerals, v. 3, Sheet silicates: London, Longmans, Green, 270 p.

DeJesus, A. M., and Cotelo Neiva, J. M., 1952, Informations sur les minerais de fer Portugais: Internat. Geol. Cong., 19th, Algiers 1952, Symposium . . . fer, v 2, p. 401–404.

DeMunck, V. C., 1956, Iron deposits in Montana: Montana Bur. Mines and Geology, Inf. Circ. 13, 55 p.

Deudon, Madeleine, 1955, La chamosite orthorhombique du minerai de Sainte-Barbe, couche grise: Soc. française minéralogie et crystallographie Bull., v. 78, p. 475–480.

——— 1957, Présence de maghemite ($Fe_2O_3-\gamma$) dans le minerai de fer de Lorraine: Soc. française minéralogie et cristallographie Bull., v. 80, p. 239–241.

Déverin, Louis, 1945, Étude pétrographique des minerais de fer oolithiques du Dogger des Alpes suisses: Beitr. Geologie der Schweiz, Geotech. ser., Lf. 13, v. 2, 115 p.

Dobrzhanskaia, M. A., and Pshenina, T. I., 1958, Some data on the content and distribution of iron in the Black Sea: Akad. Nauk. SSSR, Doklady, Geochem. Sec., v. 122–123, nos. 1–6, p. 895–897. [In Russian; translation published by Consultants Bureau, N. Y., 1959, p. 91–93.]

Dorr, J. V. N., 2d, 1945, Manganese and iron deposits of Morro do Urucum, Mato Grosso, Brazil: U.S. Geol. Survey Bull. 946–A, 47 p.

——— 1958, The Cauê itabirite: Soc. Brasileira Geologia Bol., v. 7, no. 2, p. 61–62.

Dorr, J. V. N., 2d, and Barbosa, A. L. M., 1963, Geology and ore deposits of the Itabira district, Minas Gerais, Brazil: U.S. Geol. Survey Prof. Paper 341–C, 110 p.

Dorr, J. V. N. 2d, Guild, P. W., and Barbosa, A. L. M., 1952, Origin of the Brazilian iron ores: Internat. Geol. Cong., 19th, Algiers 1952, Symposium . . . fer, v. 1, p. 286–310.

Doss, B., 1912, Melnikovit, ein neues Eisenbisulfid, und seine Bedeutung für die Genesis der Kieslagerstätten: Zeitschr. prakt. Geologie, v. 20, p. 453–483.

Du Preez, J. W., 1945, The structural geology of the area east of Thabazimbi and the genesis of the associated iron ores: Stellenbosch Univ., Annals, v. 22, sec. A, nos. 1–14, p. 263–360.

Eckel, E. B., 1938, The brown ores of eastern Texas: U.S. Geol. Survey Bull. 902, 151 p.

Edwards, A. B., 1936, The iron ores of the Middleback ranges, South Australia: Australasian Inst. Mining Metallurgy Proc., v. 102, p. 155–207.

——— 1953, Mineralogy of the Middleback iron ores: Empire Mining and Metall. Cong., 5th, Pub., v. 1, p. 464–472.

——— 1958, Oolitic iron formations in northern Australia: Geol. Rundschau, v. 47, p. 668–682.

Edwards, A. B., and Baker, G., 1951, Some occurrences of supergene iron sulphides in relation to their environments of deposition: Jour. Sed. Petrology, v. 21, p. 34–46.

Ehrenberg, H., Pilger, A., and Schroder, F., 1954, Das Schwefelkies-Zinkblende-Schwerspatlager von Meggen (Westfalen): Geol. Jahrb. Beihefte, v. 12, 353 p.

Einecke, G., 1950, Die Eisenerzvorrate der Welt: Dusseldorf, Verlag Stahleisen M. B. H., 2 v.

El Wakeel, S. E., and Riley, J. P., 1961, Chemical and mineralogical studies of deep-sea sediments: Geochim. et Cosmochim. Acta, v. 25, p. 110–146.

Engelhardt, W. von, 1942, Die Strukturen von Thuringit, Bavalit und Chamosit und ihre Stellung in der Chloritgruppe: Zeitschr. Kristallographie, v. 104, p. 142–159.

Erd, R. C., Evans, H. T. Jr., and Richter, D. H., 1957, Smythite, a new iron sulfide, and associated pyrrhotite from Indiana: Am. Mineralogist, v. 42, p. 309–333.

Evans, H. T., Jr., Milton, Charles, Chao, E. C. T., Adler, Isidore, Mead, Cynthia, Ingram, Blanche, and Berner, R. A., 1964, Valleriite and the new iron sulfide, mackinawite: U.S. Geol. Survey Prof. Paper 475–D, p. 64–69.

Flaschen, S. S., and Osborn, E. F., 1957, Studies of the system iron oxide–silica–water at low oxygen partial pressures: Econ. Geology, v. 52, p. 923–943.

Florensky, V. P., and Balshina, B. V., 1948, Siderite in the Devonian deposits of the western part of the Bashkirskoi ASSR: Akad. Nauk SSSR Doklady, v. 62, no. 5, p. 689–692. [In Russian.]

Foslie, Steinar, 1949, Hafjellsmulden i Ofoten og dens sedimentaere jern-mangan-malmer [The Hafjell syncline in Ofoten and its sedimentary iron manganese ores]: Norges Geol. Undersøkelse [Pub.] no. 174, 129 p. [In Norwegian, English summ.]

Friedman, G. M., 1959, The Samreid Lake sulfide deposit, Ontario, an example of a pyrrhotite-pyrite iron formation: Econ. Geology, v. 54, p. 268–284.

Gaertner, H. R. von, 1952, Die Eisenerze de Paläozoikums von Thuringen: Internat. Geol. Cong. 19th, Algiers 1952, Symposium . . . fer, v. 2, p. 15–16.

Gair, J. E., 1962, Geology and ore deposits of the Nova Lima and Rio Acima quadrangle, Minas Gerais, Brazil: U.S. Geol. Survey Prof. Paper 341–A, 65 p.

Gair, J. E., and Wier, K. L., 1956, Geology of the Kiernan quadrangle, Michigan: U.S. Geol. Survey Bull. 1044, 88 p.

Garrels, R. M., 1953, Mineral species as functions of pH and oxidation-reduction potentials: Geochim. et Cosmochim Acta, v. 5, p. 153–158.

——— 1959, Reactions at low temperatures and pressures, p. 25–37 *in* Abelson, P. H., ed., Researches in geochemistry: New York, John Wiley and Sons, 511 p.

——— 1960, Mineral equilibria at low temperature and pressure: New York, Harper and Bros., 254 p.

Gastil, Gordon, and Knowles, D. M., 1960, Geology of the Wabush Lake area, southwestern Labrador and eastern

Quebec, Canada: Geol. Soc. America Bull., v. 71, p. 1243-1254.

Geijer, P. A., 1938, Stripa odalfälts geologi—Geology of the Stripa mining field: Sveriges Geol. Undersökning, ser. Ca, no. 28, 42 p. [In Swedish, English summ.]

——— 1962, Some aspects of phosphorus in Precambrian sedimentation: Arkiv Mineralogi och Geologi, v. 3, no. 9, p. 165-186.

Geijer, P. A., and Magnusson, N. H., 1948, Geological history of the iron ores of central Sweden: Internat. Geol. Cong., 18th, London 1948, pt. 13, p. 84-89.

——— 1952, The iron ores of Sweden: Internat. Geol. Cong., 19th, Algiers 1952, Symposium . . . fer, v. 2, p. 477-499.

Gill, J. E., 1927, Origin of the Gunflint iron-bearing formation: Econ. Geology, v. 27, p. 687-728.

Goldich, S. S., Nier, A. O., Baadsgaard, H., Hoffman, J. H., and Krueger, H. W., 1961, The Precambrian geology and geochronology of Minnesota: Minnesota Geol. Survey Bull. 41, 193 p.

Goldschmidt, V. M., 1954, Geochemistry: Oxford, Clarendon Press, 730 p.

Goodwin, A. M., 1956, Facies relations in the Gunflint iron formation: Econ. Geology, v. 51, p. 565-595.

——— 1962, Structure, stratigraphy, and origin of iron-formations, Michipicoten area, Algoma district, Ontario: Geol. Soc. America Bull., v. 73, p. 561-586.

Gottis, Charles, 1952, Les gisements de fer en Tunisie: Internat. Geol. Cong., 19th, Algiers 1952, Symposium . . . fer, v. 1, p. 211-222.

Grout, F. F., and Broderick, T. M., 1919, The magnetite deposits of the eastern Mesabi Range, Minnesota: Minnesota Geol. Survey Bull. 17, 58 p.

Grout, F. F., Gruner, J. W., Schwartz, G. M., and Thiel, G. A., 1951, Precambrian stratigraphy of Minnesota: Geol. Soc. America Bull., v. 62, p. 1017-1078.

Grout, F. F., and Thiel, G. A., 1924, Notes on stilpnomelane: Am. Mineralogist, v. 9, p. 228-229.

Grout, F. F., and Wolff, J. F., 1955, The geology of the Cuyuna district, Minnesota: Minnesota Geol. Survey Bull. 36, 144 p.

Gruner, J. W., 1922, Organic matter and the origin of the Biwabik iron-bearing formation of the Mesabi range: Econ. Geology, v. 17, p. 407-460.

——— 1935, The structural relationship of glauconite and mica: Am. Mineralogist, v. 20, p. 699-713.

——— 1936, The structure and chemical composition of greenalite: Am. Mineralogist, v. 21, p. 405-425.

——— 1937, Composition and structure of stilpnomelane: Am. Mineralogist, v. 22, p. 912-925.

——— 1944a, The composition and structure of minnesotaite, a common iron silicate in iron formations: Am. Mineralogist, v. 29, p. 363-372.

——— 1944b, The structure of stilpnomelane reexamined: Am. Mineralogist, v. 29, p. 291-298.

——— 1946, Mineralogy and geology of the Mesabi Range: St. Paul, Minn., Iron Range Resources and Rehabilitation Comm., 127 p.

Gudden, H., Schmidt-Thome, P., Tillman, H., and Karrenberg, H., 1952, Die Eisenerze Bayerns: Internat. Geol. Cong., 19th, Algiers 1952, Symposium . . . fer, v. 2, p. 20-23.

Guild, P. W., 1957, Geology and mineral resources of the Congonhas district, Minas Gerais, Brazil: U.S. Geol. Survey Prof. Paper 290, 90 p.

Hadding, Assar, 1929, The Paleozoic and Mesozoic sandstones of Sweden, Part 3 *of* The pre-Quaternary rocks of Sweden: Lunds Univ. Årsskr., N.F. avd. 2, v. 25, no. 3, 287 p.

——— 1932, Glauconite and glauconitic rocks, Part 4 *of* The Pre-Quaternary sedimentary rocks of Sweden: Lunds Univ. Årsskr., N.F. avd. 2, v. 28, no. 2, 175 p.

——— 1933, Den järnmalmsförande lagerserien i sydöstra Skåne: Sveriges Geol. Undersökning, ser. C, no. 376, 31 p.

Hallimond, A. F., 1925, Iron ores—Bedded ores of England and Wales—Petrography and Chemistry: Great Britain Geol. Survey Mem., Spec. Repts. Mineral Resources v. 29, 139 p.

——— 1939, On the relation of chamosite and daphnite to the chlorite group: Mineralog. Mag., v. 25, p. 441-465.

Hallimond, A. F., and Enos, F. R., 1924, On stilpnomelane from North Wales: Mineralog. Mag., v. 20, p. 193-197.

Harder, E. C., 1908, The iron ores of the Appalachian region in Virginia: U.S. Geol. Survey Bull. 380-E, p. 215-254.

——— 1919, Iron depositing bacteria and their geologic relations: U.S. Geol. Survey Prof. Paper 113, 89 p.

Harder, E. C., and Johnston, A. W., 1918, Preliminary reports on the geology of east-central Minnesota, including the Cuyuna iron-ore district: Minnesota Geol. Survey Bull. 15, 178 p.

Harder, Hermann, 1951, Über den Mineralbestand und die Enstehung einiger sedimentärer Eisenerze des Lias-gamma: Heidelberger Beitr. Mineralogie Petrographie, v. 2, no. 5, p. 455-476.

——— 1954, Beitrag zur Petrographie und Genese der Hämatiterze des Lahn-Dill Gebietes: Heidelberger Beitr. Mineralogie Petrographie, v. 4, nos. 1-2, p. 54-66.

——— 1955, Konvergenzerscheinungen der Mineralbildung einiger sedimentärer deutscher Eisenerze: Geol. Rundschau, v. 43, p. 515-518.

——— 1960, Rezente submarine vulkanische Eisenausscheidungen von Santorin, Griechenland: Fortschr. Mineralogie, v. 38, p. 187-189.

——— 1963, Zur Diskussion über die Entstehung der Quarzbandererze (Itabirite): Neues Jahrb. für Mineralogie, Monatsh., no. 12, p. 303-314.

Harrison, J. M., 1952, The Quebec-Labrador iron belt, Quebec and Newfoundland: Canada Geol. Survey Paper 52-20, 21 p.

——— 1953, Iron formations of Ungava Peninsula, Canada: Internat. Geol. Cong., 19th, Algiers 1952, Comptes rendus, sec. 10, p. 19-33.

Harvey, H. W., 1932-33, Note on colloidal ferric hydroxide in sea water: Marine Biol. Assoc. United Kingdom Jour., v. 18, p. 221-225.

Hawley, J. E., and Beavan, A. P., 1934, Mineralogy and genesis of the Mayville iron ore of Wisconsin: Am. Mineralogist, v. 19, p. 493-514.

Hayes, A. O., 1915, The Wabana ores of Newfoundland: Canada Geol. Survey Mem. 66, 163 p.

——— 1919, Nova Scotian oolitic iron deposits of sedimentary origin: Canadian Inst. Mining Trans., v. 22, p. 112-122.

——— 1929, Further studies of the origin of the Wabana iron ore of Newfoundland: Econ. Geology, v. 24, p. 1-4.

Hazell, J. R. T., 1958, The Enugu ironstone, Udi division, Onitsha province [Nigeria]: Nigeria Geol. Survey Records, 1955, p. 44-58.

Hegemann, F., and Albrecht, F., 1954, Zur Geochemie oxydischer Eisenerze: Chemie Erde, v. 17, no. 2, p. 81-103.

Hem, J. D., 1960a, Restraints on dissolved iron composed by bicarbonate redox potential, and pH: U.S. Geol. Survey Water-Supply Paper 1459-B, p. 33-55.

Hem, J. D., 1960b, Some chemical relationships among sulfur species and dissolved ferrous iron: U.S. Geol. Survey Water-Supply Paper 1459–C, p. 57–73.

——— 1960c, Complexes of ferrous iron with tannic acid: U.S. Geol. Survey Water-Supply Paper 1459–D, p. 75–94.

Hem, J. D., and Cropper, W. H., 1959, Survey of ferrous-ferric equilibria and redox potentials: U.S. Geol. Survey Water-Supply Paper 1459–A, 31 p.

Hendricks, S. B., and Ross, C. S., 1941, Chemical composition and genesis of glauconite and celadonite: Am. Mineralogist, v. 26, p. 683–708.

Herz, Norman, Hurley, P. M., Pinson, W. H., and Fairbairn, H. W., 1961, Age measurements from a part of the Brazilian shield: Geol. Soc. America Bull., v. 72, p. 1111–1120.

Hesemann, Julius, 1952, Die Eisenerze Nordrhein-Westfalens: Internat. Geol. Cong., 19th, Algiers 1952, Symposium . . . fer, v. 2, p. 8–10.

Hessland, Ivan, 1949, Lithogenesis and changes in level in the Siljan district during a period of the Lower Ordovician, Pt. 4 *of* Investigations of the Lower Ordovician of the Siljan district, Sweden: Upsala Univ. Geol. Inst. Bull., v. 33 p. 437–506.

Hoehne, Karl, 1955, Zum Vorkommen von Magnetit in oolithischem Eisenerz: Neues Jahrb. Mineralogie, Monatsh., no. 4, p. 80–86.

Hoenes, D., and Tröger, E., 1945, Lagerstätten oolithischer Eisenerze in Nordwestfrankreich: Neues Jahrb. Mineralogie, Geologie u. Paläontologie, Abh. A, v. 79, no. 2, p. 192–255.

Holzner, Julius, 1933, Beitrage zur Kenntnis der varistischen Gesteins-und Mineralprovinz im Lahn-Dillgebiet; 2. Über den Stilpnomelan von Grube Theodor (Lahngebiet) und einen beim Trennen mit Clericilösung auftretenden Basenaustausch: Neues Jahrb. Mineralogie, Geologie, u. Paläontologie, Beil.-Bd. 66, Abt. A, no. 3, p. 213–225.

Hough, J. L., 1958, Fresh-water environment of deposition of Precambrian banded iron-formations: Jour. Sed. Petrology, v. 28, p. 414–430.

Hower, John, 1961, Some factors concerning the nature and origin of glauconite: Am. Mineralogist, v. 46, p. 313–334.

Hubach, Enrique, 1953, Yacimientos de mineral de hierro, de carbón y de caliza en Colombia, como base de la industria siderúrgica: Colombia, Ministerio Minas y Petroleos, Bol. Geol., v. 1, no. 1, p. 1–30.

Huber, N. K., 1958, The environmental control of sedimentary iron minerals: Econ. Geology, v. 53, p. 123–140.

——— 1959, Some aspects of the origin of the Ironwood iron-formation of Michigan and Wisconsin: Econ. Geology, v. 54, p. 82–118.

Huber, N. K., and Garrels, R. M., 1953, Relation of pH and oxidation potential to sedimentary iron mineral formation: Econ. Geology, v. 48, p. 337–357.

Hummel, K., 1922, Die Entstehung eisenreicher Gesteine durch Halmyrolse: Geol. Rundschau, v. 13, p. 40–81.

Hutchinson, G. E., 1957, A treatise on limnology *in* Volume 1, Geography, physics, and chemistry: New York, John Wiley and Sons, 1015 p.

Hutton, C. O., 1938, The stilpnomelane group of minerals: Mineralog. Mag., v. 25, p. 172–206.

——— 1945, Additional optical and chemical data on the stilpnomelane group of minerals: Am. Mineralogist, v. 30, p. 714–718.

——— 1956, Further data on the stilpnomelane mineral group: Am. Mineralogist, v. 41, p. 608–615.

Hutton, C. O., and Seelye, F. T., 1941, Composition and properties of some New Zealand glauconites: Am. Mineralogist, v. 26, p. 595–604.

Irving, R. D., and Van Hise, C. R., 1892, The Penokee iron-bearing series of Michigan and Wisconsin: U.S. Geol. Survey Mon. 19, 534 p.

Jakob, Johann, 1927, Der Stilpnomelan vom Mont Chemin (Wallis): Schweizer. mineralog. petrog. Mitt., v. 7, p. 311–313.

James, H. L., 1951, Iron formation and associated rocks in the Iron River district, Michigan: Geol. Soc. America Bull., v. 62, p. 251–266.

——— 1954, Sedimentary facies of iron formation: Econ. Geology, v. 49, p. 235–291.

——— 1955, Zones of regional metamorphism in the Precambrian of northern Michigan: Geol. Soc. America Bull., v. 66, p. 1455–1488.

——— 1958, Stratigraphy of Pre-Keweenawan rocks in parts of northern Michigan: U.S. Geol Survey Prof. Paper 314–C, p. 27–44.

——— 1960, Problems of stratigraphy and correlation of Precambrian rocks with particular reference to the Lake Superior region: Am. Jour. Sci. (Bradley volume), v. 258–A, p. 104–114.

James, H. L., Clark, L. D., Lamey, C. A., and Pettijohn, F. J., 1961, Geology of central Dickinson County, Michigan: U.S. Geol. Survey Prof. Paper 310, 176 p.

James, H. L., Dutton, C. E., Pettijohn, F. J., and Wier, K. L., 1959, Geologic map of the Iron River-Crystal Falls district, Iron County, Michigan: U. S. Geol. Survey Mineral Inv. Map MF–225.

James, H. L., and Wier, K. L., 1961, Geologic and magnetic maps of the Carter Creek and Kelly iron deposits, Madison and Beaverhead Counties, Montana: U.S. Geol. Survey open-file report.

James, H. L., and Wier, K. L., 1962, Geologic and magnetic maps of iron deposits near Copper Mountain, Madison County, Montana: U.S. Geol. Survey open-file report.

Johnson, R. F., 1962, Geology and ore deposits of the Cachoeira do Campo, Dom Bosco, and Ouro Branco quadrangles, Minas Gerais, Brazil: U.S. Geol. Survey Prof. Paper 341–B, 39 p.

Jolliffe, F. J., 1935, A study of greenalite: Am. Mineralogist, v. 20, p. 405–425.

Jones, H. A., 1958, The oolitic ironstones of the Agbaja Plateau, Kabba province [Nigeria]: Nigeria Geol. Survey Records, 1955, p. 20–43.

Juan, V. C., 1946, Mineral resources of China: Econ. Geology, v. 46, p. 399–474.

Jung, H., and Köhler, E., 1930, Untersuchungen über den Thuringit von Schmiedefeld in Thüringen: Chemie Erde, v. 5, p. 182–200.

Kaplan, I. R., Emery, K. O., and Rittenberg, S. C., 1963, The distribution and isotopic abundance of sulphur in recent marine sediments off southern California: Geochim et Cosmochim. Acta, v. 27, p. 297–331.

Kazakov, G. A., and Polevaya, N. I., 1958, Some preliminary data on elaboration of the post-Precambrian scale of absolute geochronology based on glauconites: Geokhimiya [in English translation], 1958, no. 4, p. 374–387.

Kelley, V. C., 1951, Oolitic iron deposits of New Mexico: Am. Assoc. Petroleum Geologists Bull., v. 35, p. 2199–2228.

Kennedy, W. Q., 1936, An occurrence of greenalite-chert in the Ordovician rocks of the southern uplands of Scotland: Mineralog. Mag., v. 24, p. 433–436.

Kern, Anton, 1952, Die Eisenerzlagerstätten der Österreichisch-Alpinen Montangesellschaft: Internat. Geol. Cong., 19th, Algiers 1952, Symposium . . . fer, v. 2, p. 41–73.

Kesler, T. L., 1950, Geology and mineral deposits of the Cartersville district, Georgia: U.S. Geol. Survey Prof. Paper 224, 97 p.

Kolbe, H., 1952, Erzbergbau G.m.b.H. Salzgitter: Internat. Geol. Cong., 19th, Algiers 1952, Symposium . . . fer, v. 2, p. 3–8.

——— 1953, Aperçu stratigraphique des gisements de fer sédimentaire en Allemagne et en Lorraine: Internat. Geol. Cong., 19th, Algiers 1952, Comptes rendus, sec. 10, p. 119.

Konstantov, S. V., Kechek, G. A., Belorusov, V. V., and Krasilnikov, L. K. 1933 [The Kerch iron ore deposits]: [U.S.S.R.] Vses. geol.-razved. obyedeneniya Trudy, no. 325, p. 1–128. (In Russian) English summ., p. 120–128).

Korolev, D. F., 1958, The role of iron sulfides in the accumulation of molybdenum in sedimentary rocks of the reduced zone: Geokhimiya [in English translation 1958] no. 4, p. 452–463.

Kouvo, Olavi, and Vuorelainen, Yrjö, 1063, A tetragonal iron sulfide: Am. Mineralogist, v. 48, p. 511–524.

Krauskopf, K. B., 1955, Sedimentary deposits of rare metals: Econ. Geology, Fiftieth anniversary volume, p. 411–463.

——— 1957, Separation of manganese from iron in sedimentary processes: Geochim. et Cosmochim. Acta, v. 12, p. 61–84.

Krishnan, M. S., 1952, The iron ores of India: Internat. Geol. Cong., 19th, Algiers 1952, Symposium . . . fer, v. 1, p. 503–532.

——— 1955, Iron ore deposits of the Middle East and of Asia and the Far East, *in* United Nations Dept. Econ. and Social Affairs, Survey of world iron ore resources . . . : New York, p. 265–334.

Krotov, B. P., 1950, Vydelenie gidrookislov zheleza i mangantsa v ozerakh [Precipitation of iron and manganese hydroxides in lakes]: Akad. Nauk SSSR Doklady, v. 71, no. 3, p. 533–536. [Translation by V. P. Sokoloff.]

Krumbein, W. C., and Garrels, R. M., 1952, Origin and classification of chemical sediments in terms of pH and oxidation-reduction potentials: Jour. Geology, v. 60, p. 1–33.

Lamplugh, G. W., Wedd, C. B., and Pringle, J., 1920, Iron ores—Bedded ores of the Lias, Oolites and later formations in England: Great Britain Geol. Survey Mem., Spec. Repts. Mineral Resources, v. 12, 240 p.

Landergren, Sture, 1948, On the geochemistry of Swedish iron ores and associated rocks: Sveriges Geol. Undersökning Årsbok 42, No. 5, ser. C, no. 496, 182 p.

Latal, E., 1952, Die Siderit- und Hematitlagerstätten von Vares in Mittlebosnien, *in* Die Eisenlagerstätten Jugoslaviens: Internat. Geol. Cong., 19th, Algiers 1952, Symposium . . . fer, v. 2, p. 544–549.

Latimer, W. M., 1952, Oxidation potentials, 2d ed.: New York, Prentice-Hall, 392 p.

Leith, C. K., 1903, The Mesabi iron-bearing district of Minnesota: U.S. Geol. Survey Mon. 43, 316 p.

Leith, C. K., Lund, R. J., and Leith, A., 1935, Precambrian rocks of the Lake Superior region: U.S. Geol. Survey Prof. Paper 184, 34 p.

Lepp, Henry, 1957, The synthesis and probable geologic significance of melnikovite: Econ. Geology, v. 52, p. 528–534.

——— 1963, The relation of iron and manganese in sedimentary iron formations: Econ. Geology, v. 58, p. 515–526.

Lepp, Henry, and Goldich, S. S., 1964, Origin of the Precambrian iron formations: Econ. Geology, v. 59, p. 1025–1060.

Lesure, F. G., 1957, Geology of the Clifton Forge iron district, Virginia: Virginia Polytech. Inst. Bull., Eng. Expt. Sta. Ser. 118, 130 p.

Lewis, G. J., Jr., and Goldberg, E. D., 1954, Iron in marine waters: Jour. Marine Research, v. 13, p. 183–197.

Lindgren, W., 1933, Mineral deposits, 4th ed.: New York, McGraw-Hill Book Co., 930 p.

Little, O. H., and Attia, M. I., 1943, The development of the Aswan district, with notes on the minerals of south-eastern Egypt: Egypt Geol. Survey, 107 p.

Ljunggren, Pontus, 1953, Some data concerning the formation of manganiferous and ferriferous bog ores: Geol. fören. Stockholm, Förh., v. 75, no. 473, p. 277–297.

——— 1955a, Geochemistry and radioactivity of some manganese and iron bog ores: Geol. fören. Stockholm, Förh. v. 77, no. 470, p. 33–44.

——— 1955b, Differential thermal analysis and X-ray examination of iron and manganese bog ores: Geol. fören. Stockholm, Förh., v. 77, no. 470, p. 135–147.

Love, L. G., 1957, Micro-organisms and the presence of syngenetic pyrite: Geol. Soc. London Quart. Jour., v. 113, p. 429–440.

——— 1962a, Biogenic primary sulfide of the Permian Kupferschiefer and Marl Slate: Econ. Geology, v. 57, p. 350–366.

——— 1962b, Pyrite spheres in sediments, *in* Jensen, M. L., ed., Biogeochemistry of sulfur isotopes; proceedings of a National Science Foundation symposium held at Yale University, April 12–14, 1962: [New Haven], p. 121–143.

Love, L. G., and Zimmerman, D. O., 1961, Bedded pyrite and micro-organisms from the Mount Isa Shale: Econ. Geology, v. 56, p. 875–896.

Lovering, T. S., 1929, The Rawlings, Shirley, and Seminoe iron-ore deposits, Carbon County, Wyoming: U.S. Geol. Survey Bull. 811–D, p. 203–235.

Lowdon, J. A., Stockwell, C. H., Tipper, H. W., and Wanless, R. K., 1963, Age determinations and geological studies: Canada Geol. Survey Paper 62–17, 140 p.

Lowe, E. N., 1914, Preliminary report on iron ores of Mississippi: Mississippi Geol. Survey Bull. 10, 70 p.

Lucius, Michel, 1945, Beitrage zur Geologie von Luxemburg. Band IV. Die Luxemburger Minnetteformation und die jungeren Eisenerz bildungen: Luxembourg Service carte geol. 347 p.

Luttrell, G. W., 1955, Bibliography of iron ore resources of the world (to January 1955): U.S. Geol. Survey Bull. 1019–D, p. 187–371.

MacGregor, A. M., 1927, The problems of the Precambrian atmosphere: South Africa Jour. Sci., v. 24, p. 155–172.

MacGregor, M., Lee, G. W., and Wilson, G. V., 1920, Iron ore. The iron ores of Scotland: Great Britain Geol. Survey Mem., Spec. Repts. Mineral Resources, v. 11, 240 p.

Mackay, A. L., 1962, β ferric-oxhydrate-akaganeite: Mineralog. Mag., v. 33, p. 270–280.

Mahmoudi, M., 1952, Note sur les gisements de fer de l'Iran: Internat. Geol. Cong., 19th, Algiers 1952, Symposium . . . fer, v. 1, p. 533–535.

Maksimov, A. A., 1960, Types of manganese and iron-manganese deposits in central Kazakhstan: Internat. Geology Rev., v. 2, p. 508–520.

Malakhovsky, V. F., 1956, [Geochemistry and the principal problems of the origin of the supergene ores of Kerch]: Voprosy mineralogii osadochnykh obrazovanii, v. 3-4, p. 190-202.

——— 1959, Organichesky ugerod i sera v Kerchenskikh rudakh [Organic carbon and sulfur in the Kerch iron ores]: Akad. Nauk SSSR Doklady, v. 128, no. 6, p. 1262-1265. [In Russian. English translation published by Am. Geol. Inst., 1960, p. 1027-1029.]

Mansfield, G. R., 1920, The physical and chemical character of New Jersey greensand: Econ. Geology, v. 15, p. 547-566.

——— 1922, Potash in the greensands of New Jersey: U.S. Geol. Survey Bull. 727, 146 p.

Markevich, V. P., 1960, The concept of facies, Part 1: Internat. Geology Rev., v. 2, p. 367-379, 1960.

Marmo, Vladi, 1952, The iron ores of Finland: Internat. Geol. Cong., 19th, Algiers 1952, Symposium . . . fer, v. 2, p. 117-127.

Mason, Brian, 1958, Principles of geochemistry, 2d ed.: New York, John Wiley and Sons, 310 p.

Matheron, Georges, 1955, Le gisement de fer de Gara Djebilet: Algeria Bur. Recherches Minieres Bull. Sci. and Écon., no. 2, p. 51-63.

Matsuzawa, Isao, 1953, The Sinian system in the district of Pangchiapu, southern Chahar, north China, and consideration of its contained Hsuanlung type iron ore deposits: Mining Geology (Soc. Mining Geology Japan), v. 3, no. 10, p. 220-235. [In Japanese, English summ.]

Mellon, G. B., 1962, Petrology of Upper Cretaceous oolitic iron-rich rocks from northern Alberta: Econ. Geology, v. 57, p. 921-940.

Meyer, F. H., Riggs, O. L., McGlasson, R. L., and Sudbury, J. D., 1958, Corrosion of mild steel in H_2O environments: Corrosion, v. 14, no. 2, 109 p. [Reference not seen; given as in Berner, 1964.]

Miles, K. R., 1941, Magnetite-hematite relations in the banded iron-formations of Western Australia: Australasian Inst. Mining Metallurgy Proc., v. 124, p. 193-201.

——— 1953, Banded ironstones in Western Australia: Empire Mining and Metall. Cong., 5th, Pub., v. 1, p. 159-171.

——— 1954, The geology and iron ore resources of the Middleback Range area: South Australia Geol. Survey Bull. 33, 247 p. [1955].

Miropolskaya, G. L., 1949, O litologii rudonosnoi tolshchi v Omutninskikh zhelezorudnyky mestorozhdeniyakh: Akad. Nauk SSSR Doklady, v. 67, no. 1, p. 129-132.

Miropolsky, L. M., 1949, O devonskikh oolitovykh zheleznykh rudakh v zapadnoi Bashkirii i vostochnoi Tatarii [Devonian oolitic ores of western Bashkiria and the east Tatar Republic]: Akad. Nauk SSSR Doklady, v. 66, no. 1, p. 105-107.

Moore, E. S., 1919, Iron deposits on the Belcher Islands, Hudson Bay: Canadian Mining and Metall. Inst. Trans., v. 22, p. 100-111.

Moore, E. S., and Maynard, J. E., 1929, Solution, transportation, and precipitation of iron and silica: Econ. Geology, v. 24, p. 272-303, 365-402, 506-527.

Murakami, Hanzô, 1922, Geology of the An-shan iron mine district, South Manchuria: [Dairen?] South Manchuria Railway Co. Pub., 53 p.

Nalivkin, D. V., 1960, The geology of the U.S.S.R., a short outline: London, Pergamon Press, 170 p. [Translated by S. I. Tomkeieff.]

Nassim, G. L., 1950, The oolitic hematite deposits of Egypt: Econ. Geology, v. 45, p. 578-581.

Nef, Eduardo, 1952, Los yacimientos de hierro en el Chile: Internat. Geol. Cong., 19th, Algiers 1952, Symposium . . . fer, v. 1, p. 353-359.

Nelson, B. W., and Roy, R., 1954, New data on the composition and identification of chlorites, *in* Swineford, Ada, and Plummer, N. V., eds., Clays and clay minerals—proceedings of the 2d National Conference on Clays and Clay Minerals, Columbia, Mo., 1953: Natl. Research Council Pub. 327, p. 335-348.

Neumann, Henrich, 1950, Pseudomorphs of pyrrhotine after pyrite in the Ballachulish slates: Mineralog. Mag., v. 29, no. 210, p. 234-238.

Newhouse, W. H., 1927, Some forms of iron sulphide occurring in coal and other sedimentary rocks: Jour. Geology, v. 35, p. 73-83.

Newland, D. H., and Hartnagel, C. A., 1908, Iron ores of the Clinton formation in New York State: New York State Mus. Bull. 123, 76 p.

Nicolaysen, L. O., 1962, Stratigraphic interpretation of age measurements in southern Africa, *in* Engel, A. E. J., and others, eds., Petrologic studies—a volume in honor of A. F. Buddington: New York, Geol. Soc. America, p. 569-598.

Nöth, Ludwig, 1952, Die Eisenlagerstätten Jugoslaviens: Internat. Geol. Cong., 19th, Algiers 1952, Symposium . . . fer, v. 2, p. 529-563.

Oftedahl, Christoffer, 1958, A theory of exhalative-sedimentary ores: Geol. fören. Stockholm Förh., v. 8, no. 1, p. 1-19.

Orcel, Jean, 1923, Sur la bavalite de Bas-Vallon: Acad. Sci. [Paris] Comptes rendus, v. 177, p. 271-273.

Orcel, Jean, Hénin, Stéphane, and Caillère, Simonne, 1949, Sur les silicates phylliteux des minerais de fer oolithiques: Acad. Sci. [Paris] Comptes rendus, v. 229, p. 134-135.

O'Rourke, J. E., 1961, Paleozoic banded iron-formation: Econ. Geology, v. 56, p. 331-361.

——— 1962, The stratigraphy of Himalayan iron ores: Am. Jour. Sci., v. 260, p. 294-302.

Ostroumov, E. A., 1955, Iron in bottom sediments of the Okhotsk Sea: Akad. Nauk SSSR Doklady, v. 102, p. 129-132. [In Russian. Reported in Chem. Abs., v. 50, p. 3812, 1956.]

Ostroumov, E. A., and Shilov, V. M., 1956, Iron sulfide and hydrogen sulfide in the bottom deposits of the northwestern part of the Pacific Ocean: Akad. Nauk SSSR Doklady, v. 106, p. 501-504. [In Russian; English translation by Consultants Bureau, 1956.]

Page, B. M., 1958, Chamositic iron ore deposits near Tajmiste, western Macedonia, Yugoslavia: Econ. Geology, v. 53, p. 1-21.

Palache, Charles, Berman, Harry, and Frondel, Clifford, 1944, The system of mineralogy, 7th ed., New York, John Wiley and Sons, v. 1, 834 p.

Pallister, H. D., 1953, Development of a previously unmined deposit of hematite-magnetite iron ore in southwestern Talladega County, Alabama: Alabama Acad. Sci. Jour., v. 24, p. 159-160.

Palmqvist, Sven, 1935, Geochemical studies on the iron-bearing Liassic series in southern Sweden: Lunds Geol.-Mineral. Inst. Medd., no. 60, 204 p.

Pantó, Gábor, ed., 1952, Le fer en Hongrie: Internat. Geol. Cong., 19th, Algiers, 1952, Symposium . . . fer, v. 2, p. 227-246.

Pavlides, Louis, 1960, Structurally localized metamorphism of manganese deposits, Aroostook County, Maine: U.S. Geol. Survey Prof. Paper 400-B, p. B463-B465.

Pavlides, Louis, 1962, Geology and manganese deposits of the Maple and Hovey Mountains area, Aroostook County, Maine: U.S. Geol. Survey Prof. Paper 362, 116 p.

Pavlosky, E. V., and Belichenko, V. G., 1958, Osadochnyye formatsii verkhnego Proterozoya Sayano-Baykalskogo nagorya i svyazannyye s nim polyeznyye iskopayemyye: Zakonomernosti razmeshcheniya poleznykh iskopaemykh, Upper Proterozoic formations of the Sayan-Baykal upland and ore minerals associated with them: Internat. Geology Rev., v. 2, p. 461–465, 1960. [English translation.]

Pennington, J., and Davis, V. C., 1953, Investigation of iron sulfide deposits in south-central Aitkin County and Carlton County, Minn.: U.S. Bur. Mines Rept. Inv. 4937, 33 p.

Penta, Francesco, 1952, Memoria sul ferro in Italia: Internat. Geol. Cong., 19th, Algiers 1952, Symposium . . . fer, v. 2, p. 247–347.

Percival, F. G., 1955a, Nature and occurrence of iron ore deposits, *in* United Nations Dept. Econ. and Social Affairs, Survey of world iron ore resources . . . New York, p. 45–76.

——— 1955b, Iron ore deposits of Australia, New Zealand, and New Caledonia, *in* United Nations Dept. Econ. and Social Affairs, Survey of world iron ore resources . . . New York, p. 335–345.

Pettijohn, F. J., 1963, Chemical composition of sandstones: U.S. Geol. Survey Prof. Paper 440–S, 21 p.

Pichamuthu, C. S., 1962, Some observations on the structure, metamorphism, and geological evolution of peninsular India: Geol. Soc. India Jour., v. 3, p. 106–118.

Plaksenko, N. A., 1959, Certain structural features of Precambrian metamorphics of the Kursk magnetic anomaly (K.M.A.), their causes and stratigraphic significance: Akad. Nauk SSSR Izv., Ser. Geol., 1959, no. 3, p. 46–64. [In Russian; English translation pub. by Am. Geol. Inst., 1960.]

Polovinkina, Yu. Ir., and Rozina, B. B., 1956, Zhelezistye kvartsity Karsakpaya [Iron-bearing quartzites of Karschkpai district, central Kazakhstan, USSR]: Vsesoyuznyi Nauchno-Issledovotelskii Geol. Inst. Materialy, novoya ser., no. 8 (Geol. i Polez Iskopaemye), p. 87–104.

Posnjak, E., and Merwin, H. E., 1919, The hydrated ferric oxides: Am. Jour. Sci., v. 47, p. 311–348.

Poulsen, A. O., 1952, The iron ore resources of Norway: Internat. Geol. Cong., 19th, Algiers 1952, Symposium . . . fer, v. 2, p. 389–397.

Pourbaix, M. J. N., 1949, Thermodynamics of dilute aqueous solutions: London, Edward Arnold and Co., 136 p.

Pratje, O., 1930, Rezente marine Eisen-Ooide aus der Nordsee: Zentralblatt Mineralogie, Geologie, Paleontologie, Abt. B., p. 289–294.

Protich, Mirko, 1955, Étude minéralogique des phyllites de quelques minerais de fer de Serbie (Yougoslavie): Soc. Française Mineralogie et Cristallographie Bull., v. 78, p. 528–534.

Pulfrey, William, 1933, The iron ore oolites and pisolites of North Wales: Geol. Soc. London Quart. Jour., no. 356, v. 89, pt. 2, p. 401–430.

Putzer, Hannfrit, 1943, Die oolithischen Brauneisenerz-Lagerstätten der Kertsch Halbinsel: Zeitschr. angew. Mineralogie, v. 4, p. 363–378.

Quiring, Heinrich, 1955, Eisenerzlager vom Lahn-Dill-Typus in Nordspanien: Neues Jahrb. Geologie Paläontologie, Monatsh 2, p. 49–52.

Quirke, T. T., Jr., 1961, Geology of the Temiscamie iron-formation, Lake Albanel iron range, Mistassini territory, Quebec, Canada: Econ. Geology, v. 56, p. 299–320.

Quirke, T. T., Jr., Goldich, S. S., and Krueger, H. W,. 1960' Composition and age of the Temiscamie iron-formation' Mistassini territory, Quebec, Canada: Econ. Geology, v. 55' p. 311–326.

Radhakrishna, B. P., 1951, The iron ore resources of Mysore: Mysore Geologists Assoc. Bull. 2, 38 p.

Ramdohr, Paul, 1955a, Der Würfel als herrschende Form beim Magnetit: Neues Jahrb. Mineralogie Monatsh, no. 4, p. 76–79.

——— 1955b, Die Erzmineralien und ihre Verwachsungen: Berlin, Akad.-Verlag, 875 p.

Rastall, R. H., and Hemingway, J. E., 1949, The Yorkshire Dogger: Geol. Mag., v. 86, p. 201–225, 265–278.

Rechenberg, H. P., 1956, Die Eisenerzlagerstätte "Vivaldi" bei Ponferada, Leon, Spanien: Neues Jahrb. Mineralogie Abh., v. 89, no. 1, p. 111–136.

Reed, D. F., 1949, Investigation of Talladega gray iron ores, Talladega County, Alabama: U.S. Bur. Mines Rept. Inv. 4426, 29 p.

Revelle, R. R., 1944, Marine bottom samples collected on the Pacific Ocean by the Carnegie on its Seventh Cruise: Carnegie Inst. Washington Pub. 556, pt. 1, 180 p.

Revelle, R. R. and Fairbridge, Rhodes, 1957, Carbonates and carbon dioxide, Chapter 10 *of* Hedgpeth, J. W., ed., Ecology: Geol. Soc. America Mem. 67, p. 239–295.

Richarz, Stephen, 1927, Grunerite rocks of the Lake Superior region and their origin: Jour. Geology, v. 35, p. 690–708.

Roth, Zdeněk, and Matějka, Alois, 1953, Pelosiderity moravskoslezských Beskyd . . . [The pelosiderites of the Moravosilesian Beskydy]: Geotechnica (Česk. Akad. Věd), sv. 16, 110 p. (In Czech, English summ.).

Rubey, W. W., 1930, Lithologic studies of fine-grained Upper Cretaceous sedimentary rocks of the Black Hills region: U.S. Geol. Survey Prof. Paper 165–A, 54 p.

——— 1951, The geologic history of sea water: Geol. Soc. America Bull., v. 62, p. 1111–1147.

Ruckmick, J. C., 1963, The iron ores of Cerro Bolivar, Venezuela: Econ. Geology, v. 58, p. 218–236.

Rudd, E. A., and Miles, K. R., 1953, Iron ores of the Middleback Range: Empire Mining Metall. Cong., 5th, Pub., v. 1, p. 449–436.

Sakamoto, Takao, 1950, The origin of the pre-Cambrian banded iron ores: Am. Jour. Sci., v. 248, p. 449–474.

Schaefer, M. B., and Bishop, Y. M. M., 1958, Particulate iron in offshore waters of the Panama Bight and in the Gulf of Panama: Limnology and Oceanography, v. 3, p. 137–149.

Schmidt, R. G., 1963, Geology and ore deposits of the Cuyuna North Range, Minnesota: U.S. Geol. Survey Prof. Paper 407, 96 p.

Schock, E. P., 1918, Chemical analyses of Texas rocks and minerals: Texas Univ. Bull. 1814, 256 p.

Schouten, Cornelius, 1946, The role of sulfur bacteria in the formation of the so-called sedimentary copper ores and pyritic ore bodies: Econ. Geology, v. 41, p. 517–538.

Seitz, O., Hoffman, K., and Preul, F., 1952, Die mesozoischen Eisenerze in Niedersachsen, Schleswig-Holstein, und im nordlichen Westfalen: Internat. Geol. Cong., 19th, Algiers 1952, Symposium . . . fer, v. 2, p. 3–8.

Semenenko, N. P., 1959, Geokhronologiya dokembriya absolyutnom letoischislenii [Precambrian geochronology on the absolute-time scale]: Akad. Nauk SSSR Izv., Ser. Geol. 1959, no. 5, p. 1–11. [English translation pub. by Am. Geol. Inst., 1960.]

Semenenko, N. P., Polovko, N. I., Zhukov, G. V., Ladieva, V. D., and Makukhina, A. A., 1956, Petrografiya zhelezistokremnistykh formatsii Ukrainskoi SSR [Petrography of siliceous iron-formations of the Ukrainian SSR]: Kiev, Akad. Nauk Ukrainskoi SSR, Inst. Geol. Nauk, 536 p. [Partial English translation by M. Blake, U.S. Geol. Survey.]

Shapiro, Joseph, 1964, Effect of yellow organic acids on iron and other metals in water: Am. Water Works Assoc. Jour., v. 56, p. 1062–1082.

Shepard, F. P., and Moore, D. G., 1955, Central Texas Coast sedimentation—characteristics of sedimentary environment, recent history, and diagenesis: Am. Assoc. Petroleum Geologists Bull., v. 39, p. 1463–1593.

Siever, Raymond, 1962, Silica solubility, 0°–200°C., and the diagenesis of siliceous sediments: Jour. Geology, v. 70, p. 127–150.

Singewald, J. T., Jr., 1909, The iron ores of Maryland: Econ. Geology, v. 4, p. 530–544.

——— 1911, Report on the iron ores of Maryland: Maryland Geol. Survey, v. 9, pt. 3, p. 121–324.

Skinner, B. J., 1958, The geology and metamorphism of the Nairne Pyritic Formation, a sedimentary sulfide deposit of South Australia: Econ. Geology, v. 53, p. 546–562.

Skinner, B. J., Erd, R. C., and Grimaldi, F. S., 1964, Greigite, the thiospinel of iron; a new mineral: Am. Mineralogist, v. 49, p. 543–555.

Smith, F. G., and Kidd, D. J., 1949, Hematite-goethite relations in neutral and alkaline solutions under pressure: Am. Mineralogist, v. 34, p. 403–412.

Smulikowski, Kazimierz, 1954, The problem of glauconite: Archiwum Mineralogiezne (Polska Akad. Nauk, Komitet Geologiczny) v. 18, p. 21–120. [In English.]

Spencer, E., and Percival, F. G., 1952, The structure and origin of the banded hematite jaspers of Singhbhum, India: Econ. Geology, v. 47, p. 365–383.

Stam, J. C., 1963, Geology, petrology, and iron deposits of the Guiana Shield, Venezuela: Econ. Geology, v. 58, p. 70–83.

Starostina, Z. M., 1959, Conditions of distribution of siderite ores throughout the host rocks of the Bakal group of ore deposits, southern Urals: Akad. Nauk SSSR Izv., Ser. Geol., 1959, no. 7, p. 33–50. [In Russian; English translation pub. by Am. Geol. Inst., 1961.]

Steadman, R., and Youell, R. F., 1958, Mineralogy and crystal structure of greenalite: Nature, v. 181, no. 4601, p. 45.

Stout, Wilbur, 1944, The iron-bearing formations of Ohio: Geol. Survey Ohio, ser. 4, Bull. 45, 230 p.

Strahan, Aubrey, Gibson, W., Cantrill, T. C., Sherlock, R. L., and Dewey, H., 1920, Iron ores—Pre-Carboniferous and Carboniferous bedded ores of England and Wales: Great Britain Geol. Survey Mem., Spec. Repts. Mineral Resources, v. 13, 123 p.

Strakhov, N. M., 1948, Raspredelenie zheleza v osadkakh ozernykh i morskikh vodoemov i faktory, ego kontroliruyushchie [Distribution of iron in sediments of lake and marine basins and the controlling factors]: Akad. Nauk SSSR Izv., Ser. Geol. 1948, no. 4, p. 3–50. [English translation by V. P. Sokoloff.]

——— 1959, Schema de la diagenese des depots marins: Eclogae Geol. Helvetiae, v. 51, p. 761–767.

Strakhov, N. M., Radionova, K. F., and Zalmanzon, E. D., 1959, A contribution to the geochemistry of reservoir formations: The Lower Frasnian of the Volga-Urals: Internat. Geology Rev., v. 1, no. 5, p. 1–24.

Strong, M. W., 1956, Marine iron bacteria as rock forming organisms: Adv. Sci., v. 12, no. 49, p. 583–585.

Sverdrup, H. U., Johnson, M. W., and Fleming, R. H., 1942, The oceans, their physics, chemistry, and general biology: New York, Prentice-Hall, 1087 p.

Svitalsky, N. I., 1937, Krivoy Rog and the iron ores of this district: Internat. Geol. Cong., 17th, Moscow, 1937, Guidebook of the Southern Excursion, The Ukrainian SSR, p. 51–77.

Sweeting, G. S., 1944, Wealden iron ore and the history of its industry: Geol. Assoc. London Proc., v. 55, pt. 1, p. 1–20.

Tageeva, N. V., and Tikhomirova, M. M., 1957 [Some features of the early diagenesis of sediments in the northwestern part of the Black Sea]: Akad. Nauk SSSR, Doklady, Geol. Sci. Sec., v. 112, p. 513–515. [In Russian.]

Taylor, J. H., 1949, Petrology of the Northampton sand ironstone formation: Great Britain Geol. Survey Mem., 111 p.

Tegregen, F. R., 1921, Iron ores and iron industry of China: China Geol. Survey Mem., Ser. A., no. 2, pt. 1, 180 p.

Teodorovich, G. I., 1947, Sedimentary geochemical facies: Soc. Naturalistes Moscou Bull., v. 52, Sec. Géol., v. 22 (1), p. 3–24. [In Russian, English summ.]

Thiel, G. A., 1924, Iron sulfides in magnetic belts near the Cuyuna range: Econ. Geology, v. 19, p. 466–472.

Tochilin, M. S., 1952, Primary formation of hydrogoethite oolites in siderite-chamosite ores: Akad. Nauk SSSR, Doklady, v. 87, p. 269–271. [In Russian. Reported in Chem. Abs., v. 49: 15655.]

Tröger, E., 1950, Lagerstätten oolithischer Eisenerze in der Normandie: Fortschr. Mineralogie, v. 26, p. 125.

Tsuru, Kazuo, 1931, [Geology and ore deposits of the Miao Erh Kou iron mine district]: Ryojun College of Eng. Repts., v. 1, no. 3. [In Japanese, English summ.]

Tyler, S. A., 1949, Development of Lake Superior soft iron ores from metamorphosed iron formation: Geol. Soc. America Bull., v. 60, p. 1101–1124.

——— 1950, Sedimentary iron deposits, *in* Trask, P. D., ed., Applied sedimentation: New York, John Wiley and Sons, p. 506–523.

Tyler, S. A., and Barghoorn, E. S., 1963, Ambient pyrite grains in Precambrian cherts: Am. Jour. Sci., v. 261, p. 424–432.

Tyler, S. A., and Twenhofel, W. H., 1952, Sedimentation and stratigraphy of the Huronian of Upper Michigan: Am. Jour. Sci., v. 250, p. 1–27 and 118–151. [in two parts.]

Tyndale-Biscoe, R., 1952, Iron ores in Southern Rhodesia: Internat. Geol. Cong., 19th, Algiers 1952, Symposium . . . fer, v. 1, p. 171–174.

United Nations Dept. of Economic and Social Affairs, 1955, Survey of world iron ore resources—occurrence, appraisal and use: New York, 345 p.

Valdes, B. L., 1955, Iron ore deposits of South America, *in* United Nations Dept. of Economic and Social Affairs Survey of world iron ore resources: New York, p. 209–223.

Vallentyne, J. R., 1962, A chemical study of pyrite spherules isolated from sediments of Little Round Lake, Ontario, *in* Jensen, M. L., ed., Biogeochemistry of sulfur isotopes; proceedings of a National Science Foundation symposium held at Yale University, April 12–14, 1962: [New Haven] p. 144–152.

Van Hise, C. R., and Bayley, W. S., 1897, The Marquette iron-bearing district of Michigan: U.S. Geol. Survey Mon. 28, 608 p.

Van Hise, C. R., and Leith, C. K., 1911, The geology of the Lake Superior region: U.S. Geol. Survey Mon. 52, 641 p.

Vartanova, N. S., Artemenko, I. N., and Galkina, R. G., 1950, O sideritakh v kamennougolnykh otlozheniyakh Lvovskoi muldy [Siderite in the coal deposits of the Lvov basin]: Mineralog. Sbornik (Lvov. Geol. Obshch.), no. 4, p. 299–302. [In Russian; translated by V. P. Sokoloff.]

Vasyutinsky, N. A., and Nevoysa, G. G., 1961, Nekotorye osobennosti raspredeleniya myshyaka v Kerchenskikh zheleznykh rudakh: [Some characteristics of arsenic distribution in Kerch iron ores]: Akad. Nauk SSSR, Doklady, v. 141, p. 197–200. [English translation pub. by Geochem. Soc. 1963, p. 1121–1124.]

Vestal, F. E., 1954(?), Iron ores of Mississippi: Mississippi Acad. Sci. Jour., v. 5 (1951–53), p. 206–208.

Volkov, I. I., 1959, [Free hydrogen sulfide and iron sulfide in mud sediments of the Black Sea]: Akad. Nauk SSSR, Doklady, v. 126, p. 163–166. [In Russian; English translation pub. by Consultants Bureau, 1960, p. 396–398.]

——— 1961, Iron sulfides, their interdependence and transformation in the Black Sea bottom sediments: Akad. Nauk SSSR, Inst. Okeanol. Trudy, v. 50, p. 68–92. [In Russian; reference given in Berner, 1964.]

Volkov, I. I., and Ostroumov, E. A., 1957, Iron sulfide concretions in Black Sea deposits: Akad. Nauk USSR, Doklady, Geochem. Sec., v. 116, p. 645–648. [In Russian; English translation pub. by Consultants Bureau, Inc., 1958, p. 83–86.]

Von Gaertner, H. R. *See* Gaertner, H. R. von.

Wagner, P. A., 1928, The iron deposits of the Union of South Africa: South Africa Geol. Survey Mem. 26, 268 p.

Wakeel, S. E. El. *See* El Wakeel, S. E.

Wanless, H. R., Belknap, R. L., and Foster, Helen, 1955, Paleozoic and Mesozoic rocks of the Gros Ventre, Teton, Hoback, and Snake River ranges, Wyoming: Geol. Soc. America Mem. 63, 90 p.

Westervelt, R. D., 1957, The Knob Lake iron ore deposits: Canadian Mining Metall. Bull., v. 50, no. 547, p. 678–688.

White, D. A., 1954, The stratigraphy and structure of the Mesabi range, Minnesota: Minnesota Geol. Survey Bull. 38, 92 p.

White, D. E., Hem, J. D., and Waring, G. A., 1963, Chemical composition of subsurface waters: U.S. Geol. Survey Prof. Paper 440–F, 67 p.

Whitehead, T. H., Anderson, W., Wilson, V., and Wray, D. A., 1952, The Mesozoic ironstones of England. The Liassic ironstones: Great Britain Geol. Survey Mem., 211 p.

Willden, Ronald, 1960, Sedimentary iron-formation in the Devonian Martin formation, Christmas quadrangle, Arizona: U.S. Geol. Survey Prof. Paper 400–B, p. B21–B23.

——— 1961, Composition of the iron-formation of Devonian age in the Christmas quadrangle, Arizona: U.S. Geol. Survey Prof. Paper 424–D, p. D304–D306.

Woodtli, R. A., 1961, Iron ore resources of the north-eastern Congo: Econ. Geology, v. 56, p. 1385–1391.

Woolnough, W. G., 1941, Origin of banded iron deposits—a suggestion: Econ. Geology, v. 36, p. 465–489.

Youell, R. F., 1958, A clay mineralogical study of the ironstone at Easton Neston, Northamptonshire: Clay Minerals Bull., v. 3, p. 264–269.

Zelenov, K. K., 1958, On the discharge of iron in solution into the Okhotsk Sea by thermal springs of the Ebeko volcano (Paramushir Island): Akad. Nauk SSSR, Doklady, v. 120, p. 1089–1092. (In Russian; English translation pub. by Consultants Bur., Inc., 1959, p. 497–500.)

——— 1960, Migration and accumulation of iron and aluminum in volcanic regions of the Pacific Ocean: Akad. Nauk SSSR Izv., Ser. Geol. 1960, no. 8, p. 58–74. (In Russian; English translation pub. by Am. Geol. Inst. 1961 p. 47–59)

Zobell, C. E., 1946, Studies on redox potential of marine sediments: Am. Assoc. Petroleum Geologists Bull., v. 30, p. 477–513.

Reprinted from *Geol. Soc. America Bull.,* **77,** 1191–1197, 1199–1211 (Nov. 1966)

G. J. S. GOVETT *Research Council of Alberta*

Origin of Banded Iron Formations

Abstract: It is concluded from the present-day geochemistry of iron, and its probable paleogeochemistry that a primary accumulation of this element cannot arise in a marine environment. The Precambrian banded iron formations are, therefore, suggested to have been formed in a lacustrine or closed-basin environment. Known limnological processes are invoked to provide a mechanism for the common rhythmic banding of iron and silica. The difference between the dominantly nondetrital, low-alumina, banded Early-Middle Precambrian and the dominantly detrital, high-alumina, oölitic Late Precambrian and post-Precambrian iron formations is linked to the effects upon weathering processes of a change in the character of the earth's crust and of the development of biotic systems. Hematite is considered to be the only primary iron mineral in sedimentary rocks; other iron minerals, particularly the ferrous silicates, are regarded as essentially diagenetic (although probably preconsolidation) in origin. Organic matter has an important influence on both weathering and diagenetic processes.

CONTENTS

INTRODUCTION

If the wide divergence of opinion in even the recent literature accurately reflects current geological thought, the sedimentary iron-bearing formations are still little understood. The most the present writer can claim is a different combination of mechanisms for the origin of the Precambrian iron formations such that the post-Precambrian iron formations may be explained as a logical evolution of a general process.

The turmoil surrounding the classification of the Precambrian, and the great advances made in recent years that invalidate much of the earlier terminology, make it necessary to define the terms used in this paper. The Precambrian has been divided into Early, Middle, and Late units corresponding to >2.5 billion years (b.y.), 2.5–1.7 b.y., and 1.7–0.6 b.y. (*after* Goldich and others, 1961). This has been adopted simply as the most convenient classification to deal with the iron formations. In cases where data are considered inadequate to place formations in the three-fold classification, the terms in the works quoted, *e.g.*, Archaean and Proterozoic, have been used to avoid possible misinterpretation.

ACKNOWLEDGMENTS

The writer is indebted to J. G. Urie (Swaziland Geol. Survey) for data concerning Precambrian iron formations in Swaziland, and J.

Editor's Note: A row of asterisks indicates that material has been omitted from the original article.

H. Lord (Director, Geol. Survey Western Australia) for data on Precambrian iron formations in Western Australia. Gratitude is expressed to the writer's colleagues at the Research Council of Alberta for discussions and suggesting sources of information. Special thanks are due to Mrs. E. Smithies of the Research Council library for her patient efforts in obtaining copies of the large number of papers not available in Edmonton.

GENERAL DESCRIPTION

Precambrian iron formations are found on all continents and, superficially at least, are remarkably constant in their lithology and composition. The term "iron formation" has been defined by James (1954, p. 239–240) as "a chemical sediment, typically thin-bedded or laminated, containing 15 per cent or more iron of sedimentary origin, commonly but not necessarily containing layers of chert." The essential constituents of the sedimentary rocks are quartz, and silica and iron in various mineralogical forms.

James (1954) recognizes four main lithological types, or facies, in the Lake Superior area: sulphide, silicate, carbonate, and oxide. The sulphide type is represented by relatively restricted deposits of pyritic slate. Iron silicates are characteristic of the iron formation rocks and occur widely as a major constituent, and as a minor constituent in the oxide and carbonate facies. According to James, there are two main types of silicate iron formation: (1) ellipsoidal granules about 0.5 mm in diameter composed of greenalite, minnesotaite, or stilpnomelane in a matrix of chert or another silicate where the bedding is marked by chert, carbonate, or iron oxide layers; (2) a thinly bedded or laminated nongranular variety, associated with magnetite or carbonate. Siderite is ubiquitous: James (1954) states that almost all the varieties of iron formation in the Lake Superior region contain some carbonate. Iron oxides are found as both hematite and magnetite. The hematite rocks are composed essentially of interbedded chert and hematite. The rock is comprised of layers typically 0.1–0.5 inches thick, the layers themselves being composed of laminae about 0.01 inches thick (James, 1954). Hematitic oöliths with an average diameter of 0.5 mm are common; some oöliths are entirely of hematite, others are mainly silica with the structure defined by hematite. Magnetite-banded rocks are a major lithological type, and are almost invariably found in association with the silicate facies and grade imperceptibly into the latter.

Occurrences elsewhere differ mainly in that the oxide facies is predominant, in many cases to the complete exclusion of the silicate and carbonate types (although this is attributed by some authors to secondary oxidation).

A lack of detrital minerals is very marked and has been noted all over the world: in North America "In general clastic quartz is scarce throughout . . . the iron formation" (Huber, 1959, p. 86); in India ". . . no evidence was seen of detrital minerals . . ." (Spencer and Percival, 1952, p. 373); in Kenya "No author who has described the Kenya ironstones mentions any quantity of detrital material in them" (Saggerson, 1956, p. 54); in South Australia "A considerable search has failed to reveal any trace of detrital minerals . . ." (Edwards, 1953, p. 471).

CHEMICAL COMPOSITION

A statistical review of the chemical composition of Precambrian and later iron formations has been made by Lepp and Goldich (1964), and the main differences between them noted. A somewhat different approach to the differences is taken in this paper; the composition of iron formations in terms of $SiO_2 + Al_2O_3 + Fe_2O_3$ is plotted on Figure 1. Figure 1 does not represent a weighted distribution; an average of 136 analyses of North American banded iron formations is represented by a single point, while a relatively small Tertiary limonite deposit in Australia is also represented by a single point. Nevertheless, the compositional differences are quite definitive; no post-Precambrian iron formation of any type falls within the compositional field of the Precambrian banded iron formations; the Precambrian oölitic iron formations are clearly similar to the post-Precambrian oölitic iron formations, and the oölitic iron formations are, in general, more closely related to laterites than the banded iron formations.

PREVIOUS THEORIES OF ORIGIN

General Statement

The discussion that has proceeded unabated throughout this century has centered around three main related topics: the environment of deposition, the mechanism of banding, and why the banding is restricted to Precambrian deposits. In this brief review no attempt will be made to discuss the tremendous volume of writings on these topics; the main schools of thought will be delineated and the reader is referred to References Cited for a full account.

Environment of Deposition

The North American formations were clearly recognized as sedimentary deposits by Newberry in 1880, and universally accepted as such because of the work of Van Hise and Leith in 1911. Huber (1959) and White (1954) favor a marine environment. James (1954) suggests that deposition took place in restricted marine basins where the lack of free circulation permitted the development of abnormal conditions.

Gruner (1922) believed that precipitation of iron and silica was caused chiefly by algae and bacteria, although probably inorganic reactions caused much colloidal silica and iron to be precipitated. While not committing himself to a lacustrine origin, Gruner (1922, p. 459) stated "There is little to indicate that the iron-bearing cherts could not have been precipitated in fresh water." Many have proposed a lacustrine environment but, as far as the writer is aware, Hough (1958) is alone in specifically invoking limnological processes to explain the iron formations. Consideration of Hough's mechanism will be deferred until the presentation of the writer's views since they are fundamentally similar.

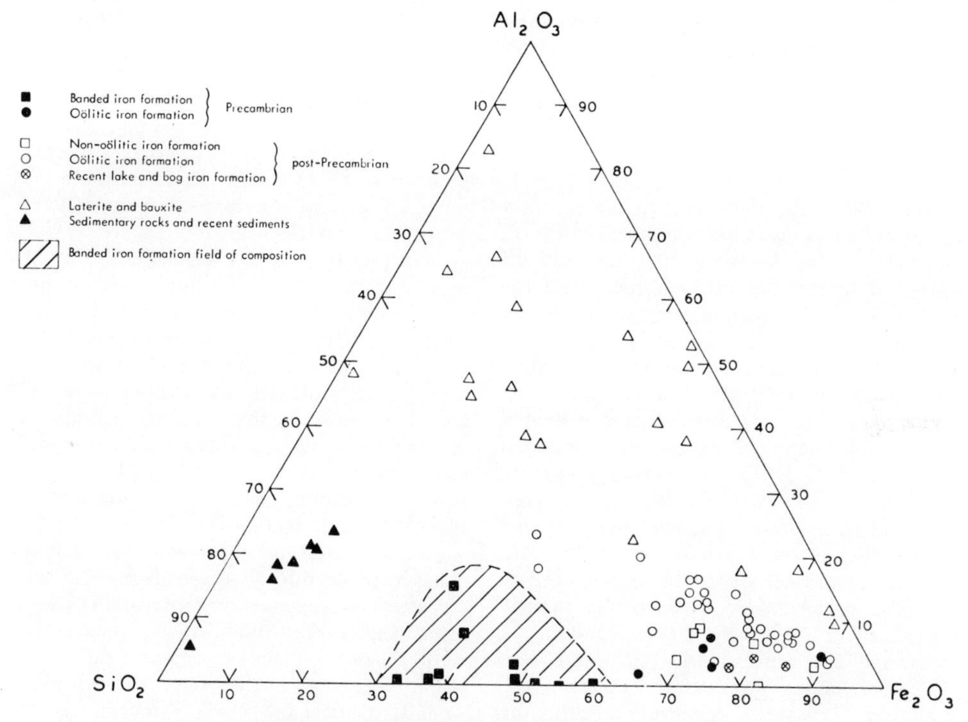

Figure 1. Variation in Al_2O_3:SiO_2:Fe_2O_3 in iron formations, rocks, and soils. Analyses and descriptive data are given in appendices (*see* footnote 1).

Banding

Huber (1959, p. 113) "... has no ready explanation for the alternate layering of iron and silica ..." but he suggests that, in analogy with the known seasonal activities of present-day plankton, a cyclical variation in the activity of organisms may be responsible.

Tyler and Twenhofel (1952) point out that sediments collecting in present-day lakes in Wisconsin (U.S.A.) generally lack stratification, which they attribute to the activities of mud-dwelling and mud-eating organisms. The preservation of laminations in the Huronian is therefore suggested to be due to the absence of such organisms at this time.

Moore and Maynard (1929) attribute the banding to differential settling in sea water of freshly precipitated ferric hydroxide and silica, or to differential rates of precipitation of stabilized colloidal ferric hydroxide and silica. Sakamoto (1950) attributes banding to a combination of Moore and Maynard's postulate woven into a complex cycle dependent upon seasonal rainfall: ferrous iron is supplied in the wet season when the lake water is acid, and silica in the dry season when the lake water becomes alkaline. Seasonal variation in the quantities of silica and iron brought into solution is also suggested by Woolnough (1941).

Reasons for Restriction to the Precambrian

Notwithstanding the claims to the contrary by O'Rourke (1961), the typically banded, nondetrital, iron formations do seem to be restricted to the Precambrian rocks and the great difficulty in formulating a satisfactory mechanism to explain their morphology is to account for their nonoccurrence in later times. Hough (1958), suggested that the particular circumstances simply have not been repeated and this echoes the general consensus as stated by White (1954, p. 51): "If the essential nature of conditions has not changed since pre-Cambrian times, it seems unlikely that a given combination of these conditions could leave such an abundant record in the later pre-Cambrian and yet leave little record in subsequent times." White (p. 50) concludes ". . . that some environmental factor in the pre-Cambrian was unlike that in later periods." White (p. 51) states ". . . a difference in the pre-Cambrian atmosphere seems to be a reasonable postulate." This view is subscribed to by Tyler and Twenhofel (1952), and the difference referred to is summed up by Sakamoto (1950, p. 463) "... it is generally accepted that the Pre-Cambrian atmosphere was very rich in CO_2 gas."

CHEMISTRY OF IRON, SILICA, AND ALUMINUM IN NATURAL AQUEOUS SYSTEMS

Marine Environment

Sea water normally has a pH of between 7.5 and 8.4, although higher values (pH 8.6) may be found in areas of active photosynthesis such as bays and estuaries, while in restricted areas where H_2S is generated, the pH may approach neutrality or even become acid (Sverdrup, Johnson, and Fleming, 1942). Iron in sea water has received considerable attention from Cooper (1935, 1937–1938, 1938, 1947–1948). Most of the iron is present in particulate form in very variable quantities probably as both ferric and ferrous. The total iron is generally in the range of 0.01–0.025 mg/l (Cooper, 1935). The greater part of the iron in true solution in sea water is present as Fe^{2+} and $FeOH^{2+}$ ions, and the total soluble iron in equilibrium does not exceed the following (Cooper, 1938):

3×10^{-11} mg/l at pH 8.5
4×10^{-10} mg/l at pH 8.0
4×10^{-8} mg/l at pH 7.0
5×10^{-6} mg/l at pH 6.0.

An appeal is frequently made to greater quantities of CO_2 in the Precambrian atmosphere to account for the greater quantities of ferrous iron in the iron formations. While a partial pressure of one atmosphere of CO_2 represents more than 3000 times the amount in the present-day atmosphere, Rubey (1951) has calculated that even if this were possible, an equilibrium pH of 7.3 would be attained. It must be remembered that although dissolved CO_2 is the major hydrogen ion control and that one atmosphere would theoretically give a pH of less than 5.0, under such acid conditions bases are dissolved and an equilibrium is attained. In fact, Rubey (1951) concludes that the CO_2 content of the atmosphere has not changed much during recorded geologic time.

Variation in the redox potential will significantly affect the solubility of iron and the stability of iron minerals. For example, at pH 8.0 a decrease in the potential from +0.6V to 0.0V causes a 3×10^{10} increase in the activity of the ferrous ion (Cooper, 1938). Cooper (1937–1938) has stated that it will lie between +0.43V and +0.75V, and that in sea water it is dependent only upon the partial pressure of oxygen and the pH of the water. In fact, of these two factors, pH is much the more important. Thus, decreasing the oxygen saturation 10 times will lower the potential 0.02V, while an increase of 0.3 pH units will have the same effect (Cooper, 1937–1938). In the absence of oxygen and where there are significant quantities of organic matter, however, the redox potential will likely be determined ultimately by an organic oxidation-reduction system. At this point it is well to emphasize that CO_2 has no reducing *capacity* since it is the most fully oxidized form of carbon.

The possibility for direct precipitation of iron minerals in significant quantities from sea water seems remote; moreover, even the concentration of total iron is singularly unpromising as a potential source of iron formations under present conditions. The possibility of mobilization and reaction of iron in marine sediments is distinctly better. Here, in general, oxygen contents will be least and organic matter highest, therefore, the mobility of iron greatest. According to Zobell (1955) oxygen is depleted in the uppermost layers of sediment due to oxidation of the more readily decomposable organic compounds and, in most fine-grained sediments, there is an oxygen deficit a few centimeters below the surface and the sediments are quite highly reducing.

The aqueous chemistry of silica has been placed on a firm foundation in recent years, and an excellent summary has been given by Krauskopf (1959) of both his own contributions and the work of others. Briefly, the solubility of amorphous silica is 100–150 ppm at ordinary temperatures, and is independent of pH below 9.0, thereafter abruptly increasing. When sea water is substituted for fresh water the solubility is not appreciably affected but the rate at which equilibrium solubility is attained is increased. Electrolytes in general have no effect on the solubility, but cations capable of forming very insoluble silicates such as Fe or Al (Iler, 1955) will reduce the solubility. Almost the entire silica content of natural waters is present in true solution as H_4SiO_4 and not as colloidal silica. This is not surprising in view of the fact that all natural waters are greatly undersaturated with respect to SiO_2, particularly sea water which has a concentration of 0.1–4 ppm in surface waters and 5–10 ppm in deep water (Krauskopf, 1959). The surprising fact is that the SiO_2 content is so low; a further problem is presented in the drastic reduction from about 14 ppm in river water (Davis, 1964). The earlier theories proposing removal by coagulation of colloidal SiO_2 by electrolytes in sea water have now been shown to be untrue on the basis of the fact that SiO_2 brought into the sea is not colloidal, and that electrolytes do not cause a reduction in solubility. Biologic removal, especially through the activities of diatoms (Iler, 1955; Krauskopf, 1959), has been shown to be a factor, but Bien and others (1959) have suggested that these organisms cannot entirely account for the loss of silica. The latter authors have shown that electrolytes in the presence of colloidal or suspended material will cause a reduction in SiO_2 of the magnitude recorded in nature; neither is effective alone.

Alumina is present in sea water to the extent of 0.16–1.8 mg/l (Sverdrup and others, 1942). These values almost certainly include colloidal and complexed forms and the amount in true solution is probable very much less.

Notwithstanding Gruner's (1922, p. 455) now-famous calculation that "... the Amazon River in 176,000 years could carry . . . the amount [of iron] assumed for the Biwabik formation," the fact remains that there is not an accumulation of iron in the Amazon offshore area, nor any other area of marine sedimentation. The sediments of the Black Sea have received considerable attention. Glagoleva (1961) has shown that iron in rivers draining into the Black Sea is carried principally in suspension in the fine fraction of the sediment load, and that the distribution of iron in Black Sea sediments is controlled by this fact. Thus, sands contain 1.2–2.7 per cent Fe, while the clay muds contain 3.7 per cent Fe. Studies in the Gulf of Paria (Hirst, 1962) show that apart from the formation of glauconite, iron does not appear to participate in any chemical reactions, and the great bulk of it is deposited in particulate form derived from the land areas.

Modern marine environments, then, show no signs of iron concentrations remotely resembling those of the iron formations of the Precambrian or any other age. The most that has been reported is mobilization of iron (and manganese) in organic-rich sediment and concentration and reprecipitation as Mn-Fe nodules, as for example in the Baltic Sea (Manheim, 1961).

Lacustrine Environment

The most important feature of lakes is their characteristic development (commonly seasonal) of density stratification of the water. This is due in part to the fact that the physical environment of a lake is fairly uniform compared with marine waters that strive, by horizontal current flows, to reach equilibrium with a connected ocean system responding to widely different conditions. Some of the characteristics of lacustrine density stratification are due to the fact that fresh water achieves its maximum density at about 4° C, and decreases in density as the temperature falls toward the freezing point and as it rises above 4° C. As a result of this, and the fact that heat exchanges occur only at the surface of a lake, all except the shallowest lakes that are kept mixed by the wind develop a density stratification (known as *thermal stratification*) for at least part of the year. Thus, the surface water—the *epilimnion* —will become warmed in spring and early summer and will overlie cooler, deeper water—the *hypolimnion.* This condition of stable stratification persists during the summer but in autumn heat is lost from the lake surface and the temperature of the epilimnion falls until it is similar to the temperature of the hypolimnion. When this condition exists complete circulation is possible and the stratification disappears consequent upon mixing of the waters of the hypolimnion and epilimnion. This is the autumn, or fall, *overturn.* If the temperature of the water does not cool below 4° C circulation will continue during winter until stratification is developed during the following spring. Such a lake is termed *warm monomictic* and is typical of, but not restricted to, the warm temperate or subtropical climates. Full descriptions of the variations in thermal properties of lakes are given by Hutchinson (1957).

The thermal stratification of lakes has considerable chemical significance, for while the epilimnion of a stratified lake is more or less in equilibrium with the atmosphere, the hypolimnion certainly is not. An important result of this is that if there are oxygen-consuming reactions occurring in the hypolimnion an oxygen deficit, sometimes amounting to a complete removal of this gas from the water, will occur toward the bottom of the lake.

Lake waters tend to be more acid and have a greater pH range than marine waters, the usual range being 6.0–9.0. In the normal range the pH is reasonably assumed to be controlled by the CO_2—bicarbonate—carbonate system; pH values below 6.0 are probably due to other acid systems, especially H_2SO_4 (Hutchinson, 1957), and possibly organic acids (Shapiro, 1957).

Lakes are normally oxidizing during periods of circulation, having an Eh of about +0.5V. During periods of stagnation there is normally a marked decrease in Eh in the hypolimnion; as already discussed with respect to marine environments, oxygen concentration has little effect upon Eh, and in most lakes the ferrous-ferric system is the most important factor although in some instances an organic oxidation-reduction system may be important (Hutchinson, 1957).

Iron is practically insoluble in ionic form at the pH and Eh values prevailing in the epilimnion of most lakes. Hutchinson (1957) quotes 0.05–0.2 mg/l as the normal order of magnitude, occurring partly as $Fe(OH)_3$ in suspension or adsorbed, and partly in solution or as a colloid of an Fe-organic complex that is very stable. The precise nature of the iron-organic complex is not known, although mention should be made of the hydroxycarboxylic aliphatic organic acids isolated by Shapiro (1957; 1958). This acid, present to the extent of about 5 mg/l, has been found capable of maintaining iron in a nonprecipitable state up to a pH of 13.2. In the hypolimnion of small lakes and in the vicinity of deep-water sediments of many large lakes Eh values of less than +0.3V are common. Under these conditions the iron may be expected to occur exclusively in the ferrous state, probably as bicarbonate and some ferrous complex (Hutchinson, 1957). The type of dramatic increase of iron in the hypolimnion is illustrated by the data in Table 1 for Lake Aburagafuchi, Japan, where the ferrous iron increases from <0.02 mg/l to over 30 mg/l (Tanaka, 1953). Exceptionally high values are found when density stratification is due to, or aided by, chemical stratification (as is the case of Lake Aburagafuchi where stability of the stratification is aided by invasion of sea water).

The iron content of the hypolimnion has two sources: firstly, suspended $Fe(OH)_3$ will be reduced and go into solution as it sinks from the oxygenated epilimnion into the hypolimnion and also, according to Tanaka (1953), from the reduction and solution of iron from alumino-silicates that sink into the hypolimnion; and secondly, from the lake sediments. The latter is considered to be the most important (Hutchinson, 1957). During periods of oxygenated circulation iron cannot migrate from the sediments because it becomes oxidized at the sediment-water interface and is immobilized. This oxidized microzone also forms a barrier preventing the migration of other cations and anions due to adsorption (Mortimer, 1941–1942). The great difference between the stagnation and circulation periods in the iron content of the deep water of Lake Aburagafuchi is shown by the data in Table 1.

Iron may be removed from the hypolimnion under conditions of extreme stagnation accompanied by the production of H_2S. This is because of the insolubility of ferrous sulphide, minute black balls of which are common in lake sediments. Inasmuch as ferrous iron occurs in quantity when the Eh reaches +0.2V–+0.3V (at pH 7.0) and H_2S does not appear until Eh +0.06V–+0.1V, considerable ferrous iron can enter the hypolimnion from the mud before H_2S becomes important (Hutchinson, 1957).

Silica in lake waters is present as undissociated silicic acid. The concentration is considerably below equilibrium solubility, although not to the same extent as in the oceans. Most river and ground water, according to figures quoted by Krauskopf (1959) contains less than 35 ppm SiO_2. Davis (1964) gives a mean value for silica in ground water of the United States of 17 ppm, and 14 ppm for streams; the world average for rivers is 13.1 ppm (Livingstone, 1963). Hutchinson (1957) gives data for the surface water of lakes showing a mean of 1.0–2.0 mg/l SiO_2 (range 0.0–25 mg/l) in temperate regions, while suggesting higher values are found in tropical regions, for example a mean of 48.1 mg/l in Guatemala and El Salvador. The variation in silica content in lake waters, apart from its fluctuation due to diatom activity, seems to be closely connected with the oxidation state of iron at the mud-water interface (Hutchinson, 1957). The silica content increases in the hypolimnion during stagnation, as shown by the data in Table 1, largely by movement from the sediment. It has been suggested (Mortimer, 1941–1942) that this is due to reduction of ferric silicate previously formed in the superficial mud when in contact with oxygenated water.

Hutchinson (1957) states that the surface water of lakes contain 0.1–1.0 mg/l total alumina while Davis (1964) states that river water probably contains less than 0.1 mg/l. The vertical distribution of alumina in lakes is similar to that of iron and silica, and the data given in Table 1 show the typical variation in its concentration during periods of stagnation and circulation.

TABLE 1. VERTICAL DISTRIBUTION OF ELEMENTS IN WATER OF LAKE ABURAGAFUCHI, JAPAN
After Tanaka, 1953, period of stagnation table 1, period of circulation table 3

Time	Depth meters	O_2 cc/l	Si mg/l	Fe^{2+} mg/l	Fe total mg/l	Al mg/l
Period of stagnation	0	5.27	10.0	<0.02	0.67	1.20
	1	5.40	8.0	<0.02	0.66	1.25
	2	3.98	6.7	<0.02	0.53	0.98
	3	1.33	4.8	<0.02	0.33	0.94
	4	2.91	3.6	<0.02	0.43	0.60
	4.54	..	11.0	3.7	24.08	0.80
	4.69	0.00	11.3	23.8	24.8	0.80
	4.89	..	12.1	28.6	37.3	2.90
	4.94	..	18.7	29.0	38.0	4.45
	4.99	0.07	36.4	27.4	35.5	7.30
	5.00	..	42.4	34.6	39.5	8.10
Period of circulation	0	8.15	11.8	<0.02	0.29	0.44
	1	8.68	8.2	<0.02	0.39	0.42
	2	9.25	4.3	<0.02	0.25	0.50
	3	9.75	2.2	<0.02	0.48	0.51
	4	7.72	3.0	<0.02	0.25	0.49
	4.70	6.78	1.6	<0.02	0.42	0.68
	4.90	7.14	1.7	<0.02	0.58	0.62
	5.00	7.07	1.7	<0.02	1.43	0.70

* * * * * * *

ORIGIN AND ENVIRONMENT OF PRECAMBRIAN IRON FORMATIONS

The most reasonable interpretation of all foregoing discussion is that, once the hydrosphere had developed, the only significant geochemical differences in the Precambrian environment compared with later times lie in the effects of the presence of life. The concentration of oxygen and carbon dioxide in the atmosphere at present is the result of a broad equilibrium between biologic activity, the oxidation level of the earth's crust, and the base-carbonate buffering in aqueous environments. Inasmuch as it is reasonable to suppose that this general principle has been true since the formation of the hydrosphere (except that in prephotosynthetic times, inorganic reactions producing oxygen and carbon dioxide take the place of biologic activity) it is also reasonable to interpret the chemistry of the Precambrian deposits by careful analogy with present-day processes.

It has been demonstrated that iron cannot become concentrated to any great degree in a marine environment. The loci of iron accumulation are the land masses and associated bodies of water. The great iron-rich laterites may be cited from the land, while iron is known to accumulate today in bogs, swamps, and lakes. The writer is in essential agreement with Hough (1958, p. 423) who stated "The annual cycle in monomictic lakes . . . makes this type of lake very appealing as a possible environment for the deposition of the banded iron formations." The banded iron formations, in the writer's opinion, can best be interpreted if it is assumed they were deposited in a lacustrine environment. For the purposes of this paper, a lacustrine environment, as distinct from a marine environment, will be taken to mean a restricted basin that lies essentially within a single climatic regime wherein a seasonal stratification could develop in the water, and not necessarily to imply fresh water. Whereas the hypothesis to be proposed is developed upon the basis of a fresh-water, warm, monomictic lake cycle, the same conclusions could be derived equally well from consideration of a saline body of water. In the latter case the seasonal variation in surface density could arise from accession of fresh water during a rainy season that would overlie denser, saline water. Evaporation during a dry season would increase the salinity, hence the density of the surface waters until they become similar in density to the deeper water, and circulation would become possible. Whatever the precise mechanism, the essential prerequisite is only that there shall be at least one period during the year when the waters are stratified and an oxygen deficiency can occur in the deep water and at least one period during the year when circulation is possible and oxidizing conditions can develop in the deeper water.

Hough explains the rhythmic precipitation of silica and iron on the basis of the cyclical oxidation and reduction of iron in the hypolimnion of lakes. His explanation for the apparent rhythmic precipitation of silica consists of two possibilities. His first suggestion is that SiO_2 is precipitated regularly during the year, and that in conjunction with the cyclic precipitation of iron this results in bands of silica alternating with iron-rich silica bands. This is indeed possible, since many apparent iron oxide bands or oölites in deposits of all ages have been found on detailed examination to be siliceous (*e.g.*, James, 1954; Hayes, 1915); discussing the banded iron formations in South Africa, Wagner (1928, p. 61) states that "... the chert layers are rarely quite free from oxide . . ." Further credence is lent to this hypothesis by some analyses by Edwards (1953) of the coarser bands of the banded iron formation of the Middleback Range, Australia. The average of five analyses showed 27.6 per cent Fe_2O_3 in the quartz bands and 32.8 per cent SiO_2 in the iron bands. The second alternative of Hough is that silica is delivered to the depositional site in greater quantities in the warm season. In substantiation of this possibility, it should be noted that Mortimer (1941–1942) found an increase in the supply of SiO_2 to lakes in the English Lake District in summer.

The characteristic low level of aluminum in the typical Precambrian iron formations has been recently remarked on by Lepp and Goldich (1964). Regardless of the reasons for its absence (a matter that will be more fully discussed later) the existence of this peculiarity is, in the writer's opinion, of fundamental importance in the depositional history of the Precambrian iron deposits. The notable undersaturation of SiO_2 in natural waters has already been noted. The general pattern of behavior of Fe and Si has been described and, as may be seen in Table 1, Al has a similar cycle. However, in the absence of fluctuations in the relative quantity of silica delivered to the depositional site, the dependence of the silica cycle upon the oxidation state of iron (*see* preceding paragraph) will lead not to alternate layers of silica and iron, but to relatively homogeneous ferrous or ferric silicates (depending upon the reducing capacity of the sediment) possibly alternating with bands of hematite. The writer, while not denying that SiO_2 is removed from the hypolimnion during periods of circulation as proposed by Mortimer (1941–1942), suggests that aluminum is at least as important in the inorganic seasonal cycle of SiO_2 in lakes, and probably of major importance in maintaining the undersaturation of SiO_2 in river and lake waters.

So far, the only recorded low-temperature synthesis of kaolin has required an organic acid as an intermediary (Siffert and Wey, 1961). Purely inorganic solutions of alumnina and silica give gels with the Al ion having a four-fold coordination. Kaolinite requires six-fold coordination for Al, and this was achieved by mixing $[Al\ (C_2O_4)_3]^{3-}$ with silicic acid, eliminating part of the oxalic acid, and then reducing the pH. Al^{3+} ions having six-fold coordination were liberated and reacted with the silicic acid and formed kaolinite. This is one manner in which silica may be removed from solution by aluminum, provided that there are suitable organic compounds in solution. It is known that Al^{3+} ions reduce the solubility of silicic acid (Okamoto and others, 1957) by the formation of an insoluble alumino-silicate or by coprecipitation with Al_2O_3; the latter will cause the precipitation of SiO_2 and hence reduce its solubility (Bien and others, 1959). A recent investigation by Jones and Handreck (1963) has shown that the solubility of SiO_2 is decreased by both Fe_2O_3 and Al_2O_3. In the pH range of 5–9 the solubility of SiO_2 was reduced from 120 ppm to 70–80 ppm by Fe_2O_3, and 25–30 ppm by Al_2O_3. In soil solutions the solubility was reduced from 48 ppm to 7–12 ppm by Al_2O_3. In the case of both oxides the maximum reduction in solubility occurs at about pH 9.0, the effect decreasing with both increasing and decreasing pH.

In hypolimnitic lake waters where there is an abundant supply of alumino-silicates and organic matter, iron as ferric hydroxide, or ferric hydroxide-complex, or ferric silicate, will be reduced and go into solution, and similarly iron in alumino-silicates will be leached. Any silica that is associated with iron will go into solution. Aluminum also goes into solution, possibly in ionic form but much more likely as an organic complex as proposed by Tanaka (1953). Under these circumstances both iron and aluminum lose their properties of reducing the solubility of silica. At the time of circulation when oxygenated waters are brought to lower levels again, several reactions can occur. SiO_2 can be taken out of solution by the formation of ferric silicate, and the solubility can be reduced by adsorption on Fe_2O_3. The Al-organic complex is likely to be destroyed, either by direct oxidation or by interaction with ferric iron. As a result of this kaolinite may form by interaction of the released aluminum ions with silica, or again a simple adsorption mechanism of precipitated Al_2O_3 may remove the silica. Whatever the precise mechanism, it is clear that aluminum may very well be more important than iron in maintaining the low level of concentration of silica in oxygenated waters.

Turning now to the banded hematite iron formations and assuming, as a hypothesis, that deposition occurred in a lacustrine, warm monomictic environment, with insufficient reducing capacity in the sediments to maintain iron in the ferrous state, *in the essential absence of aluminum* the following sequence of events would occur:

SUMMER: The ferric iron in the uppermost sediment layer is reduced as the oxygen in the water is consumed and goes into solution in ionic and perhaps a complex form. Any silica held as ferric silicate will be released and go into solution until the limiting solubility of 100–150 ppm is reached. This process may leave a layer of silica in the topmost sediment. Iron hydroxide brought into the lake during summer will settle into the hypolimnion, be reduced and go into solution, while silica will be precipitated once equilibrium is established.

AUTUMN: When circulation commences, the iron in the hypolimnion is oxidized and sedimented. The solubility of silica is now reduced to 70–80 ppm; therefore, the precipitation of iron must necessarily take some silica with it either as a coprecipitate or as ferric silicate. It is possible that a gradation will occur; ferric iron precipitates first followed by ferric iron-silica.

WINTER: Ferric iron and silica entering the lake will be deposited.

Therefore, since it is postulated that there is insufficient organic matter to maintain reducing conditions in the sediments, the layering will persist as follows:

Winter	Fe_2O_3–SiO_2	goes into solution the following summer
Autumn	Fe_2O_3	banded hematite
Summer	SiO_2	

The second case to consider is that in which there is sufficient organic material to maintain the sediments in a reduced state, again *in the essential absence of aluminum.* The same basic sequence will occur: deposition of silica in the summer; ferric iron in the autumn; and ferric iron and silica in winter, the winter sediment largely being removed during the following summer. As a consequence of there being sufficient organic matter buried with sediments to reduce ferric iron there is much greater chemical mobility. Thus, with moderate reduction and mobility iron silicate and chert layers develop, while complete reduction and mobility will give iron silicate and carbonate layers. Circumstances may be such that a modification of the sequence may occur whereby iron carbonate is precipitated during summer and iron silicate in autumn, thus giving the carbonate-silicate layering. However, the writer believes it much more likely that iron carbonate forms only in the sediment. The granules, which are characteristic of many Precambrian iron silicate and chert layers are, in the writer's view, an indication of rearrangement of materials in a supersaturated or, more likely, colloidal state in the unconsolidated sediment. Obviously, variation in the amount of organic material, cyclic climatic changes, accidents in supply, and so on will cause considerable variation in the rigid pattern outlined above. In the absence of aluminum, however, the essential sequence will remain: layers of iron-rich silica alternating with layers of iron-poor silica. By this hypothesis, only hematite can be a primary mineral in the sense that it is precipitated directly from solution or sedimentated as a clastic material. Iron silicates and carbonate arise as a result of diagenetic modifications.

An extension of the hypothesis regarding the origin of the Precambrian iron-chert banding leads to a tentative hypothesis for the origin of some bedded cherts. In the essential absence of ferric iron, fine clastic material, and especially alumina, the concentration of silica might reasonably be expected to reach its limiting solubility of 100–150 ppm. Such conditions may be expected in a pure limestone or dolomite environment. An influx of fine clastic materials in the presence of electrolytes, or the effect of ferric iron and alumina leached from the clastic materials, would reduce the solubility of silica from 100–150 ppm to the more normal 4 ppm, and silica would be precipitated.

DISCUSSION

A marine environment is shown on chemical grounds under present-day conditions to be the most unlikely environment for a primary accumulation of iron. There seems to be no good reason for assuming that the fundamental chemical conditions as they affect the solubility of iron were any different in Precambrian times. The atmosphere in prephotosynthetic times was low in oxygen; it is quite likely that it was also low in carbon dioxide. In any case, even if the partial pressure of CO_2 was indeed much higher this would not be likely to cause a significant change in pH conditions since equilibrium would be established by dissolution of bases. More important, CO_2 has no reducing capacity, and iron could not be transported in surface waters as a bicarbonate in the presence of even trace amounts of oxygen. The absolute quantity of oxygen in the atmosphere is unimportant provided that there is a chemically rapid reaction to maintain a definite amount. It has, in fact, been computed that the upper limit of oxygen concentration that could have been produced by photodissociation of water in the primitive atmosphere is about 0.001 of the present concentration (for an account of the inorganic production of oxygen in the atmosphere, *see* Berkner and Marshall, 1964). Fixation of any free oxygen as an oxide would upset the dynamic inorganic equilibrium and cause the production of more oxygen to maintain the equilibrium concentration in the atmosphere. It is probable that the prephotosynthetic oxygen budget was controlled to a considerable extent by the oxidation of iron on the surface of the earth and in surface waters.

The proposal of a nonmarine milieu for the banded iron formations and a limnological mechanism to account for their morphology does not account for their limitation to the Precambrian, nor the compositional difference between the banded iron formations and the oölitic iron formations. The data in Figure 1 indicate that the composition of the banded iron formations (in terms of Al_2O_3 + SiO_2 + Fe_2O_3) is quite distinct from that of other sedimentary and residual rocks and soils, while the composition of the oölitic iron formations could be viewed as an end member of bauxites and laterites. If the differences between the Precambrian and younger iron formations are symptomatic of fundamental changes in the earth's environment and processes, it is reasonable to expect that the gėologic record would show other manifestations of such changes. In common with most other writers on the subject, this author presumes that the iron formations are chemical precipitates more or less *in situ*, and are an expression of extreme chemical weathering under climatic conditions similar to those prevailing in present-day laterite zones. Their widespread distribution in time and space and their remarkable freedom from clastic materials require extensive and rigorous peneplanation. These conditions imply long periods free from orogenic activity and the compilations by Gastil (1960a; 1960b) are significant in this respect. His evidence indicates a remarkably long quiescent period in North America between about 1.9 b.y. and 2.5 b.y. (*i.e.*, as long as the time from the beginning of the Cambrian to the present), a period that includes the deposition of the Huronian iron formations on that continent. On a world-wide basis, Gastil's data indicate exceptional quiescence before 2.7 b.y., 2.5 b.y.–2.2. b.y., and 0.9 b.y.–0.6 b.y. Reference to the ages of the iron formations listed in Table 2 show that essentially their age corresponds with the two oldest periods of quiescence.

Such exceptionally long periods of orogenic quietude would probably permit peneplanation on a continental scale. However, as Hough (1958) points out, large lakes in a maturely weathered terrain are unlikely occurrences and, geologically, lakes tend to be transient features. Another line of evidence tends to suggest that the validity of such uniformitarian interpretation is doubtful. There is now assembled an impressive mass of data to substantiate the hypothesis of continental drift (for recent data, *see* Creer, 1964). It seems highly probable that in Precambrian times there was a single continent, Pangaea. Such a land mass would provide ample scope for widespread stable conditions and maintenance of large inland bodies of water. An even more interesting possibility that is gaining credence (Carey, 1958; Creer, 1965a; 1965b) is that the earth was little over half its present size in Precambrian times and that Pangaea covered the entire surface. Under such conditions, where gravity, rate of rotation of the earth, and possibly the climatic belts, were quite different from the present the application uniformitarian principles becomes difficult. More important in the present context is the distribution of land and water under such conditions. It is unlikely that there would be a connected ocean system, but rather a number of isolated "inland" seas; indeed, the concept of "marine" and "nonmarine" environments under these conditions may have little meaning. This condition, together with the prolonged periods of tectonic stability, provide ideal physical conditions for the deposition of the banded iron formations, and for their preservation in the geologic record. Accumulations of iron in nonmarine environments under conditions more closely approaching those extant today would rarely survive *in situ*, and would more likely be preserved as derived deposits in a near-shore facies. It is noteworthy that the oölitic iron formations are characteristically derived clastic deposits, and are essentially post-Precambrian in age; moreover, Carey (1958) has suggested that Pangaea fragmented into Gondwanaland and Laurasia in the Late Precambrian.

The gross morphological differences between the banded iron formations and later occurrences may be accounted for by the hypothetical environmental differences. However, other explanations must be sought for the detailed morphological and compositional differences. The characteristic development of granules in iron formations of Middle Precambrian age is essentially coeval with the probable development of biotic processes; moreover, the similarity between the morphology of the granules and the structures obtained in coacervate drops is highly suggestive. In writing about the chert layers in the iron formations of South Africa, Wagner (1928, p. 61) describes them as "... being made up of minute dusty-looking oval or rounded bodies separated by thin clear zones." These granules have been recorded in both the Transvaal and Swaziland Systems. Attention must be drawn to the property of coacervate drops to absorb foreign particles as shown in Plate 2 (Bungenburg de Jong, 1949). Spencer and Percival (1952, p. 375) describe concretionary bodies in the jasper bands of the iron formations of Singhbhum, India, which "... consist of a central core or spherule of dense iron oxide with a surrounding clear 'halo' of crystalline silica...." These granules exhibit another property of coacervates (p. 375): "... in many cases joining up in pairs or multiples." Granules occur in the silicate facies of the Mesabi and Gunflint Ranges, and according to James (1954, p. 267) they "... lack concentric structure but commonly show an obscure mottling that in some sections is seen to consist of tiny 'spherites' of nearly circular cross section." These latter structures should be compared with the vacuoles that develop in coacervate drops as illustrated in Plates 1 and 2 (Bungenberg de Jong, 1949).

Whether the granules are an expression of purely inorganic coacervation or other process, or whether they may be viewed as mineralized fossil proto-organisms, cannot be determined on the evidence given. However, without being able to determine unequivocally if a causal relationship exists, the following empirical corre-

TABLE 2. AGE AND DESCRIPTION OF PRECAMBRIAN IRON FORMATIONS

Age	Formation, location, and description
Late Proterozoic	*Late Proterozoic, Northern Territory, Australia.* Oölitic and pisolitic; hematite siderite, greenalite (Edwards, 1959)
1.7–2.5 b.y.	*Huronian, North America.* Banded silicate-carbonate, silicate-chert, granule bearing. Banded hematite, oölitic hematite (James, 1954; Goldich and others, 1961*)
1.8–1.9 b.y.	*Karelides-Svecofennides, Eastern Baltic Shield* (Polkanov and Gerling, 1960*)
≃2.0 b.y.	*Transvaal, South Africa.* Banded hematite-chert; oölitic and pisolitic chamosite-hematite-magnetite-siderite (Wagner, 1928; Nicolaysen, 1962*)
2.0–2.5 b.y.	*Proterozoic, Western Australia.* Banded chert-carbonate, ferruginous chert (McKinstry, 1945; Lord, personal communication*)
>2.1 b.y.	*Krivoi Rog, Russia.* Banded iron formation (Vinogradov, 1960*)
≃2.5 b.y.	*Dharwar, Iron ore series, India.* Banded hematite chert (Krishnan, 1960*)
2.5 b.y.	*Saamides, Baltic Shield* (Polkanov and Gerling, 1960*)
2.0–2.5 b.y.	ORIGIN OF LIFE?
Archaean (>2.5 b.y.?)	*Middleback, South Australia.* Banded hematite-chert (Edwards, 1953)
>2.5 b.y.	*Archaean, Western Australia.* Banded hematite-quartzites, jaspilites (McKinstry, 1945; Lord, personal communication*)
>2.5 b.y.	*Soudan Iron formation, North America.* Banded hematite-chert (Goldich, 1961*)
>2.5 b.y.	*Shamvian, Southern Rhodesia.* Banded hematite-chert (MacGregor, 1951; Nicolaysen, 1962*)
>2.6 b.y.	*Bulawayan, Southern Rhodesia.* Banded hematite-chert (MacGregor, 1951; Nicolaysen, 1962*)
Underlies Bulawayan	*Sebakwian, Southern Rhodesia.* Banded hematite-chert (MacGregor, 1951; Nicolaysen, 1962*)
>2.8 b.y.	*Nyanzian, Kenya.* Banded hematite-chert (Saggerson, 1956*)
>3.0 b.y.	*Swaziland, Swaziland.* Banded hematite-chert (Way, 1952; Nicolaysen, 1962*)
>3.0 b.y.	*Swaziland, South Africa.* Banded hematite-chert; magnetite-siderite-slate (Wagner, 1928; Nicolaysen, 1962*)

* References giving age-dating data

lations between development of biotic processes and changes in the character of iron formations are noted (*see also* Table 2):

(1) Deposits older than 2.5 b.y. are all banded and at most exhibit granular chert. The alumina content is very low. These predate the probable time of the origin of life
(2) Deposits in the time range 2.5 b.y.–1.7 b.y. are banded, but a number show a pronounced development of granules, some have oöliths, and there is one example of an oölitic deposit that is typical of post-Precambrian occurrences. Except in the latter, the alumina content is very low. This time period coincides with biogenesis.
(3) Iron formations younger than 1.7 b.y. are nearly all oölitic, and the alumina content is relatively high. These postdate the establishment of life.

Ferrous iron becomes an important primary constituent of iron formations only during and subsequent to the probable period of biogenesis. It appears to be generally absent from iron formations older than 2.5 b.y. Notwithstanding the oxygen-poor conditions, early aqueous environments are unlikely to have had great reducing capacity due to the low concentration of organic materials. Paradoxically, it is probable that the greatest potential for reduction capacity only occurred after the development of photosynthetic organisms.

The possible influence of developing organic processes upon the character of iron formations has been proposed, and it is at least worth speculating that the reverse might be true. The inferred conditions necessary for the deposition of iron formations are still, clastic-free water, warm climate, and stable conditions for very long periods of time. These conditions are also inferred for the development of biotic processes (Bernal, 1959). Furthermore, the silica gels to provide a rigid framework for coacervate reactions and the presence of abundant iron for a catalyst were surely ideal circumstances for organic reaction and polymerization leading to biogenesis.

A characteristic feature of the banded iron formations already remarked upon is their low alumina content compared with oölitic deposits of any age, and post-Precambrian non-oölitic deposits; a better distinction may be made by the low Al_2O_3:SiO_2 ratio. It is necessary, however, to combine this parameter with the high SiO_2:Fe_2O_3 ratio of the Precambrian banded iron formations to uniquely define their composition. The two high-alumina banded iron formations plotted on Figure 1 (Appendix 1, nos. 16–19 and 27[2]) are compositionally distinct from other iron formations by reason of their high SiO_2:Fe_2O_3 ratio. On the other hand, the Morro Do Urucum hematite-quartz formation of Silurian age (Dorr and others, 1952) is quite clearly outside the compositional field of the Precambrian banded iron formations by virtue of its low SiO_2:Fe_2O_3 ratio (Appendix 2, no. 38[2]) despite its negligible alumina content. It is suggested that the compositional differences (in terms of $Al_2O_3 + SiO_2 + Fe_2O_3$) between Precambrian banded iron formations and all other types would be even more marked if corrections were made for their detrital quartz content in all cases. The reason for the high SiO_2:Fe_2O_3 ratio in the Precambrian banded iron formations is attributed to two factors: the deduced physical conditions and extremity of chemical weathering implies, by analogy with present-day lateritization, that only silica (in solution) and iron or alumina (in colloidal, complexed, or precipitated state) could be transported by the drainage system; alumina demonstrates its scarcity in a transportable form by its low concentration in or even absence from the banded iron formations and, due to its effect upon the solubility of silica (discussed in the previous section) this would permit a higher concentration of silica in solution. The two high-alumina banded formations already noted are distinguished by the presence of derived clastic materials that account for the alumina, and it is presumed that the clastic materials were introduced into an existing high SiO_2:Fe_2O_3 ratio environment. There is no absolute shortage of alumina in Precambrian rocks. On the contrary, Nanz (1953) claims a significant decrease in Al_2O_3 and an increase in SiO_2 from the Precambrian to the Cenozoic in argillaceous rocks. The significant point, about which there are little data, is the manner in which alumina occurs in Precambrian sedimentary rocks. The writer is not aware of a definitive study on any Early or Middle Precambrian sequence that establishes the presence of clay minerals of undoubted clastic origin, as distinct from those of diagenetic or metamorphic origin.

There is reason to believe that most clay

[2] The appendices have been deposited with the ADI Auxiliary Publications Project, Photoduplication Service, Library of Congress, Washington 25, D. C., as Document number 9075. A photocopy or microfilm may be obtained by citing this Document number and by remitting $1.25 or check or money order payable to: Chief, Photoduplication Service, Library of Congress.

minerals have their origin in a terrestrial environment and at most are modified after incorporation into sediment (Keith and Degens, 1959; Hirst, 1962; Vikulova, 1964; Seidov, 1964). Russian work (*as summarized by* Jacks, 1953) suggests that the finer particles of mineral soils cannot be produced by inorganic chemical and mechanical weathering alone; biologic activity is considered to be essential, the decomposition of the organism leaving a clay-humus residue. Theories on the origin of low-temperature kaolin deposits always invoke acid-organic conditions, and the low-temperature synthesis of kaolin has been achieved only through an organic intermediary (Siffert and Wey, 1961). Grim (1953) has remarked that kaolin is much less abundant in the pre-Devonian rocks than in those of later ages, and he attributes this to metamorphism; it is tempting to ascribe this to the great evolutionary surge of vascular plants in Devonian times which must have provided an abundance of organic debris on land and thereby facilitated the formation of kaolin. There are probably few environments under present-day conditions where the aqueous component does not contain organic compounds in solution. Although pertinent data on the role of organic compounds in normal temperature and pressure mineral reactions are scarce, there is circumstantial evidence to support a tentative hypothesis that they are important in the formation of clay minerals.

The presumed conditions for the deposition of iron formations required a very mature landscape and only the very finest particles—clay minerals, colloids, and solutions—would be carried to the site of deposition. The implied negligible mechanical erosion obviates significant contributions of clay-sized material through physical comminution because such conditions are essentially antipathetic to dominant chemical weathering producing iron concentrations. Under these conditions alumina could probably reach the site of deposition only in the form of clay minerals. If indeed low-temperature clay minerals form in a terrestrial environment only through biotic or abiotic organic intermediaries, it is unlikely that there would be any true clay minerals derived from the land until Late Precambrian times (*i.e.*, until land areas were colonized by biota that upon degradation provided soluble organic compounds) and this may explain the lack of alumina in banded iron formations.

If, for one reason or another, clastic materials including alumino-silicates are introduced into the depositional area, it is to be expected that by virtue of the postulated lacustrine environment, reactions will proceed to give iron alumino-silicates provided that there is an adequate supply of organic matter. Stilphomelane, although not certainly an original mineral, shows the highest Al:Si ratio of the typical Precambrian iron silicate minerals, and it is significant that it is associated with fine-grained clastic rocks (James, 1954). Moreover, iron-rich chloritic rocks of the Huronian appear to be limited to those containing fine-grained clastic material (James, 1954). James concludes that the high-alumina iron silicates arise by interaction between iron-rich sea water and fine clastic materials; apart from James' specification of sea water, the writer agrees with this interpretation.

Chamosite contains the highest alumina of the sedimentary iron alumino-silicates and is typically associated with clastic-bearing oölitic iron formations. As far as the writer is aware, there is only one recorded instance of its occurrence in pre-Late Precambrian rocks: this is in the oölitic iron formation of the Transvaal System in South Africa (Wagner, 1928). It is significant that even those English Jurassic chamositic iron formations that are apparently free of detrital matter show on detailed analysis a clay residue corresponding to kaolin (Hallimond, 1925); moreover, individual shells in apparent chamosite oöliths range in composition from pure chamosite to pure kaolin (Cohen, 1952). Chamosite is structurally closely related to kaolinite and is considered to be one of the kaolin clay minerals (Warshaw and Roy, 1961; Nelson and Roy, 1954; Brindley, 1951; 1961) and chemically may be represented as kaolinite + 3 FeO. It is therefore suggested that chamosite is either a diagenetic modification of kaolin under iron-rich reducing conditions, the oölitic morphology being inherited from pre-existing kaolin oöliths (oölitic structures are common in sedimentary aluminous deposits), or it is the diagenetic mineral that forms in unconsolidated sediment by interaction of ferrous iron, silica, and alumina, and is the alumina-rich equivalent of the alumina-poor greenalite. The presence of alumina has been attributed to the development of biotic processes and the consequent concentration of soluble organic compounds; oölitic structures may be due to an inherent property of kaolin clay minerals under certain conditions, or this too may be attributable directly to organic reactions.

Notwithstanding the fact that a hypothesis has been erected to account for its absence in the banded iron formations, there should be some indication in the geologic record of the fate of the alumina. Davies and Urie (1957, p. 10) recognize this problem in their discussion of the iron formations of Swaziland and they conclude that the sequence of events requires "... the larger portion of the residual aluminous minerals of this deeply weathered terrain being subsequently transported to the site of deposition ... and being now represented by the upper shales which overlie the banded ironstone." In this respect it is noteworthy that in the Cuyuna Range of North America the slates of the Rabbit Lake Formation (which overlie the iron formation) are richer in alumina and poorer in iron and silica than the Precambrian average compiled by Nanz (1953); argillites of the underlying Mahnomen Formation are richer in silica and poorer in alumina and iron than the Precambrian average. A weighted average of the Rabbit Lake Formation (assuming a minimum thickness of 2000 feet, Schmidt, 1963) and the iron formation (assuming a maximum thickness of 500 feet, Schmidt, 1963) yields a composition, in terms of $Al_2O_3 + SiO_2 + Fe_2O_3$, similar to a basaltic rock which is the most likely source for the iron. Another item of interest is that the lower few hundred feet of the Rabbit Lake Formation are exceptionally rich in TiO_2. Titanium minerals are normally residual, and will become concentrated in aluminous deposits (Sherman, 1952). An even greater contrast in the distribution of alumina and silica is shown between the shales underlying and overlying the iron formation of Singhbhum district, India: the underlying Mohundi shale contains 74.8 per cent SiO_2 and 16.04 per cent Al_2O_3, while the overlying shale contains 56.35 per cent SiO_2 and 22.5 per cent Al_2O_3 (Spencer, 1931).

The scope of the proposed hypotheses has been circumscribed by the fundamental premise that basic laws of chemistry and physics as they affect processes at the surface of the earth have not changed with time, *i.e.*, provided precisely the same conditions obtained at one time or place as another time or place the results should be the same. However, conditions have not been the same throughout geologic history; the development of biotic processes is a major factor, as is the immensely long periods free from orogenic activity and, while perhaps not yet proved, the concept of a single continent covering a much smaller earth would obviously profoundly affect the degree and intensity of surface processes. The morphological characteristics of the banded iron formations and their restriction to the first two thirds of the earth's history have been accounted for within the framework of hypotheses devised by others to give a rational interpretation to the earth's biotic and tectonic history. The writer's interpretation of the banded iron formations is only credible insofar as it is consonant with these other more general hypotheses; the determinative criterion for the probable validity of the latter is that other geologic features besides iron formations shall be accountable within their context.

REFERENCES CITED

Ancion, C., 1952, Les minerais de fer de la Belgique, p. 75–91 *in* Blondel, F., and Marvier, L., *Editors*, Symposium sur les gisements de fer du monde: Algeria, 19th Internat. Geol. Cong., tome II, 594 p.

Ancion, C., and Cahen, L., 1952, Les minerals de fer du Congo Belge, p. 83–100 *in* Blondel, F., and Marvier, L., *Editors*, Symposium sur les gisements de fer du monde: Algeria, 19th Internat. Geol. Cong., tome I, 638 p.

Aric, C., 1953, Iron ore containing oölites and fossils found in the Paleozoic formations around Istanbul: Chem. Abstracts, v. 51 (1957), 9431b

Barghoorn, E. S., and Tyler, S. A., 1965, Microorganisms from the Gunflint Chert: Science, v. 147, p. 563–577

Berkner, L. V., and Marshall, L. C., 1964, The history of growth of oxygen in the earth's atmosphere, p. 102–124 *in* Brancazio, P. J., and Cameron, A. G. W., *Editors*, The origin and evolution of atmospheres and oceans: New York, John Wiley and Sons, Inc., 312 p.

Bernal, J. D., 1959, The problem of stages in biopoesis, p. 38–53 *in* Clark, F. C., and Synge, R. L. M., *Editors*, 1st Internat. symposium on the origin of life: London, Pergamon Press, 436 p.

Beyschlag, F., Vogt, J. H. L., and Krusch, P., 1916, The deposits of useful minerals and rocks, Volume II: London, Macmillan and Co., Ltd., 1262 p. (English translation *by* S. J. Truscott)

Bien, G. S., Contois, D. E., and Thomas, W. H., 1959, The removal of soluble silica from fresh water entering the sea, p. 20–35 *in* Ireland, H. A., *Editor,* Silica in sediments: Soc. Econ. Paleontologists and Mineralogists, Special Pub. no. 7, 185 p.

Blondel, F., 1955, Iron deposits of Europe, Africa, and the Union of Soviet Socialist Republics, p. 224–264 *in* Survey of world iron ore resources: New York, United Nations Dept. Econ. and Social Affairs, II, D5, 345 p.

Brindley, G. W., 1951, The crystal structure of some chamosite minerals: Mineralog. Mag., v. 29, p. 502–525

—— 1961, Kaolin, serpentine, and kindred minerals, p. 51–131 *in* Brown, G., *Editor,* The X-ray identification and crystal structures of clay minerals: London, The Mineralog. Soc., 544 p.

Bungenberg de Jong, H. G., 1949, Morphology of coacervates, p. 434–482 *in* Kruyt, H. R., *Editor,* Colloid science, Volume II: New York, Elsevier Publishing Co., Inc., 753 p.

Carey, S. W., 1958, A tectonic approach to continental drift, p. 177–355 *in* Continental drift, a symposium: Univ. Tasmania, 363 p.

Cochrane, G. W., and Edwards, A. B., 1960, The Roper River oölitic ironstone formations: Australia, Commonwealth Sci. and Indus. Res. Organization, Mineragraphic Inv. Tech. Paper no. 1, 28 p.

Cohen, E., 1952, The nature of silicates and carbonates of iron in the Northampton Sand ironstones of central England, p. 466–471 *in* Blondel, F., and Marvier, L., *Editors,* Symposium sur les gisements de fer du monde: Algeria, 19th Internat. Geol. Cong., tome II, 594 p.

Cooper, L. H. N., 1935, Iron in the sea and in marine plankton: Royal Soc. London Proc., ser. B., v. 118, p. 414–439

—— 1937–1938, Oxidation-reduction potential in sea water: United Kingdom Marine Biol. Assoc. Jour., v. 20, p. 167–176

—— 1938, Some conditions governing the solubility of iron: Royal Soc. London Proc., ser. B, v. 124, p. 299–307

—— 1947–1948, Some chemical considerations on the distribution of iron in the sea: United Kingdom, Marine Biol. Assoc. Jour., v. 27, p. 314–321

Creer, K. M., 1964, A reconstruction of the continents for the Upper Palaeozoic from palaeomagnetic data: Nature, v. 203, p. 1115–1120

—— 1965a, An expanding Earth?: Nature, v. 205, p. 539–544

—— 1965b, Tracking the earth's continents: Discovery, v. 26, p. 34–39

Davies, D. M., and Urie, J. G., 1947, The Bomvu Ridge hematite deposits: Swaziland Geol. Survey Special Rept. no. 3, 24 p.

Davis, S. N., 1964, Silica in streams and groundwater: Am. Jour. Sci., v. 262, p. 870–891

de la Hunty, L. E., 1962, Report on some limonite iron ore deposits in the vicinity of Port Hedland, Pilbara goldfield, W. A.: W. Australia Dept. Mines, Geol. Survey Branch Rept., p. 15–21

Dorr, J. V. M., 1947, Manganese and iron deposits of Morro Do Urucum, Mato Grosso, Brazil: U. S. Geol. Survey Bull. 946-A, 47 p.

Dorr, J. V. M., Guild, P. W., and Barbosa, A. L. M., 1952, Origin of the Brazilian iron ores, p. 286–298 *in* Blondel, F., and Marvier, L., *Editors,* Symposium sur les gisements de fer du monde: Algeria, 19th Internat. Geol. Cong., tome I, 638 p.

Dos Santos, J. L. G., 1953, Gisement de fer de Guadramil (N.E. du Portugal): Algeria, 19th Internat. Geol. Cong., sec. X, La genèse des gites de fer, p. 133–147

Eckel, E. B., 1938, The brown iron ores of eastern Texas: U. S. Geol. Survey Bull. 902, 157 p.

Edwards, A. B., 1953, Mineralogy of the Middleback iron ores, p. 464–472, *in* Edwards, A. B., *Editor,* Geology of Australian ore deposits: Australasian Inst. Mining and Metallurgy, 1290 p.

—— 1959, Oölitic iron formations in Northern Australia: Australia, Commonwealth Sci. and Indus. Res. Organization, v. 47, p. 668–682

Ehrensvärd, G., 1962, Life, origin and development: Chicago, Univ. Chicago Press, 164 p.

El Wakeel, S. K., and Riley, J. P., 1961, Chemical and mineralogical studies of deep-sea sediments: Geochim. et Cosmochim. Acta, v. 25, p. 110–146

Eyles, V. A., 1952, The composition and origin of the Antrim laterites and bauxites: Northern Ireland Geol. Survey, 90 p.

Fehlmann, H., and de Quervain, F., 1952, Les gisements de fer de la Suisse, p. 501–527 *in* Blondel, F., and Marvier, L., *Editors,* Symposium sur les gisements de fer du monde: Algeria, 19th Internat. Geol. Cong., tome II, 594 p.

Gastil, G., 1960a, The distribution of mineral dates in time and space: Am. Jour. Sci., v. 258, p. 1–35

—— 1960b, Continents and mobile belts in the light of mineral dating: Copenhagen, 21st Internat. Geol. Cong., pt. IX, p. 162–169

Glagoleva, M. A., 1961, Regularities in the distribution of chemical elements in modern sediments of the Black Sea: Am. Geol. Inst., Doklady Acad. Sci. U.S.S.R., Earth Sci. Secs., v. 136 (1962), p. 1–4

Goldich, S. S., Nier, A. O., Baadsgaard, H., Hoffnan, J. H., and Krueger, H. W., 1961, The Precambrian geology and geochronology of Minnesota: Minn. Geol. Survey Bull. 41, 193 p.

Goldschmidt, V. M., 1954, Geochemistry: Oxford, Clarendon Press, 730 p.

Goodwin, A. M., 1962, Structure, stratigraphy, and origin of iron formations, Michipicoten area, Algoma district, Ontario, Canada: Geol. Soc. America Bull., v. 73, p. 561–586

Gottis, C., 1952, Les gisements de fer en Tunise, p. 212–220 *in* Blondel, F., and Marvier, L., *Editors,* Symposium sur les gisements de fer du monde: Algeria, 19th Internat. Geol. Cong., tome I, 638 p.

Griffin, P. H., 1892–1893, The manufacture of charcoal-iron from the bog- and lake-ores of Three Rivers District, Province of Quebec, Canada: Am. Inst. Min. Eng., Trans., v. 21, p. 974–992

Grim, R. E., 1953, Clay mineralogy: New York, McGraw-Hill Book Co., Inc., 384 p.

Gruner, J. W., 1922, The origin of sedimentary iron formation, the Biwabik formation of the Mesabi Range: Econ. Geology, v. 17, p. 407–460

—— 1946, The mineralogy and geology of the taconites and iron ores of the Mesabi Range, Minnesota: St. Paul, Minn., Office of the Commissioner of the Iron Range Resources and Rehabilitation, 127 p

Hall, A. L., 1938, Analyses of rocks, minerals, ores, coal, soils, and waters from South Africa: S. Africa Geol. Survey, Memoir 32, 876 p.

Hallimond, A. F., 1925, Iron ores–bedded ores of England and Wales; Special reports on the mineral resources of Great Britain, XXIV: Great Britain Geol. Survey Memoir, 139 p.

Hayes, A. O., 1915, Wabana iron ore of Newfoundland: Canada Geol. Survey, Memoir 78, 163 p.

Hegemann, F., and Froehlich, F., 1962, Geochemical examination of iron ore ooliths of the Dogger sandstone in Northeastern Bavaria: Chem. Abstracts, v. 58 (1963), 9973g

Hirst, D. M., 1962, The geochemistry of modern sediments from the Gulf of Paria; I, The relationship between the mineralogy and distribution of major elements: Geochim. et Cosmochim. Acta, v. 26, p. 309–334

Hough, J. L., 1958, Fresh-water environment of deposition of Precambrian banded iron formations: Jour. Sed. Petrology, v. 28, p. 414–430

Huber, N. K., 1959, Some aspects of the origin of the Ironwood iron-formation of Michigan and Wisconsin: Econ. Geology, v. 54, p. 82–118

Hutchinson, G. E., 1957, A treatise on limnology: New York, John Wiley and Sons, Inc., 1015 p.

Iler, R. K., 1955, The colloid chemistry of silica and silicates: New York, Cornell Univ. Press, 324 p.

Imperial Mineral Resources Bureau, 1922, Iron ore, Part I, United Kingdom: London, 237 p.

Jacks, G. V., 1953, Organic weathering: Sci. Progress, v. 41, p. 301–305

James, H. L., 1954, Sedimentary facies of iron formation: Econ. Geology, v. 49, p. 235–285

Jirgensons, B., and Straumanis, M. E., 1962, A short textbook of colloid chemistry: New York, The Macmillan Book Co., 500 p.

Joffe, J. S., 1949, Pedology: New Brunswick, N. J., Pedology Pub., 662 p.

Jones, L. H. P., and Handreck, K. A., 1963, Effect of iron and aluminum oxides on silica in solution in soils: Nature, v. 198, p. 852–853

Junner, N. R., and James, W. T., 1947, Chemical analyses of Gold Coast rocks, ores, and minerals: Gold Coast Geol. Survey, Bull. 15, 66 p.

Keith, M. L., and Degens, E. T., 1959, Geochemical indicators of marine and fresh-water sediments, p. 38–61 *in* Abelson, P. H., *Editor,* Researches in geochemistry: New York, John Wiley and Sons, Inc. 511 p.

Krauskopf, K. B., 1959, The geochemistry of silica in sedimentary environments, p. 4–19 *in* Ireland, H. A., *Editor,* Silica in sediments: Soc. Econ. Paleontologists and Mineralogists, Special Pub. no. 7, 185 p.

Krishnan, M. S., 1952, The iron ores of India: Indian Minerals, v. 6, p. 113–130

—— 1960, Pre-Cambrian stratigraphy of India: Copenhagen, 21st Internat. Geol. Cong., pt. IX, p. 95–107

Lepp, H., and Goldich, S. S., 1964, Origin of Precambrian iron formations: Econ. Geology, v. 59, p. 1025–1060

Libby, F. W., Lowry, W. D., and Mason, R. S., 1944, Preliminary report on high alumina ores in Washington County, Oregon: Oreg. Dept. Geology and Mineral Industries, G.M.I. Short Paper no. 12, 23 p.

Livingstone, D. A., 1963, Data of geochemistry: U. S. Geol. Survey Prof. Paper 440-G, 64 p.

MacGregor, A. M., 1951, Some milestones in the Precambrian of Southern Rhodesia: Geol. Soc. S. Africa Trans., v. 54, p. xxvii–lxxi

Manheim, F. T., 1961, A geochemical profile in the Baltic Sea: Geochim. et Cosmochim. Acta, v. 25, p. 52–70

Marshall, C. G. A., May, J. W., and Perret, C. J., 1964, Fossil micro-organisms—possible presence in Precambrian Shield of Western Australia: Science, v. 144, p. 290–292

McKinstry, H. E., 1945, Pre-Cambrian problems in Western Australia: Am. Jour. Sci., v. 243-A (Daly Volume), p. 448–466

Mellon, G. B., 1962, Petrology of Upper Cretaceous oölitic iron-rich rocks from Northern Alberta: Econ. Geology, v. 57, p. 921–940

Mohr, E. C. J., and van Baren, F. A., 1954, Tropical soils: London, Interscience Pub., 498 p.

Moore, E. S., and Maynard, J. E., 1929, Solution, transportation, and precipitation of iron and silica: Econ. Geology, v. 24, p. 272–303, 365–402, 506–527

Mortimer, C. H., 1941–1942, The exchange of dissolved substances between mud and water in lakes: Jour. Ecology, v. 29, p. 280–329; v. 30, p. 147–201

Nanz, R. H., 1953, Chemical composition of pre-Cambrian slates with notes on the geochemical evolution of lutites: Jour. Geology, v. 61, p. 51–64

Nelson, B. W., and Roy, R., 1954, New data on the composition and identification of chlorite, p. 335–348 *in* Swineford, A., and Plummer, N., *Editors*, Clays and clay minerals: Natl. Acad. Sci.–Nat. Res. Council Pub. 327, 498 p.

Newberry, J. S., 1880, The genesis of our iron ores: Columbia Univ., The School of Mines Quart., p. 1–17

Newland, D. H., and Hartnagel, C. A., 1908, Iron ores of the Clinton Formation in New York State: N. Y. State Mus. Bull. 123, 76 p.

Nicolaysen, L. O., 1962, Stratigraphic interpretation of age measurements in Southern Africa, p. 569–598 *in* Engel, A. E. J., James, H. L., and Leonard, B. F., *Editors*, Petrologic studies: Geol. Soc. America, Buddington Volume, 660 p.

Nicou, M. P., 1910, The iron ore resources of the world: Stockholm, 11th Internat. Geol. Cong., v. 1, p. 3–39

Noth, L., 1952, Die eisenerzlagerstatten Jugoslaviens, p. 529–563 *in* Blondel, F., and Marvier, L., *Editors*, Symposium sur les gisements de fer du monde: Algeria, 19th Internat. Geol. Cong., tome II, 594 p.

Okamoto, G., Okura, T., and Goto, K., 1957, Properties of silica in water: Geochim. et Cosmochim. Acta, v. 12, p. 123–132

Oparin, A. I., 1953, The origin of Life: New York, Dover Pub. Inc., 270 p. (English translation *by* J. Morgulis)

—— 1957, The origin of life on the earth: Edinburgh, Oliver and Boyd, 495 p. (English translation *by* A. Synge)

—— 1961, Life, its nature, origin and development: Edinburgh, Oliver and Boyd, 207 p. (English translation *by* A. Synge)

O'Rourke, J. E., 1961, Paleozoic banded iron-formations: Econ. Geology, v. 56, p. 331–361

Palmqvist, S., 1935, Geochemical studies on the iron-bearing Liassic Series in Southern Sweden: Lunds Geol.-Miner. Inst., Medd. no. 60, 204 p.

Penta, F., 1952, Memoria sul ferro in Italia, p. 247–347 *in* Blondel, F., and Marvier, L., *Editors*, Symposium sur les gisements de fer du monde: Algeria, 19th Internat. Geol. Cong., tome II, 594 p.

Percival, F. G., 1931, The iron-ores of Noamundi: Min. and Geol. Inst. India Trans., v. 26, p. 169–271

Pettijohn, F. J., 1949, Sedimentary rocks: New York, Harper and Bros., 526 p.

Polkanov, A. A., and Gerling, E. K., 1960, The Pre-Cambrian geochronology of the Baltic Shield: Copenhagen, 21st Internat. Geol. Cong., pt. IX, p. 183–191

Pulfrey, W., 1933, The iron-ore oolites and pisolites of North Wales: Geol. Soc. London Quart. Jour., v. 89, p. 401–430

Quirke, T. T., Goldich, S. S., and Krueger, H. W., 1960, Composition and age of the Temiscamie iron formation, Mistassini Territory, Quebec, Canada: Econ. Geology, v. 55, p. 311–326

Rubey, W. W., 1951, Geologic history of sea water: Geol. Soc. America Bull., v. 62, p. 1111–1148

Saggerson, E. P., 1956, The banded ironstones of the Nyanzian System, Kenya: Comm. for Tech. Co-operation in Africa South of the Sahara, 1st mtg. East-Central Regional Comm., Dar-es-Salaam, p. 49–56

Sakamoto, T., 1950, The origin of the Pre-Cambrian banded iron ores: Am. Jour. Sci., v. 248, p. 449–474

—— 1953, Alternate deposition of iron oxide and silicates in a bed of Permian aluminous shale in Manchuria: Algeria, 19th Internat. Geol. Cong., Sec. X, in La genèse des gites de fer, p. 153–171

Santos-Ynigo, L., 1953, The geology of the iron ore deposits of the Philippines: Philippine Geologist, v. 7, p. 122–164

Schmidt, R. G., 1963, Geology and ore deposits of the Cuyuna North Range, Minnesota: U. S. Geol. Survey Prof. Paper 407, 96 p.

Seidov, A. G., 1964, Some problems relating to the mineralogy of sediments: Clay Minerals Bull., v. 5, p. 329–337

Shapiro, J., 1957, Chemical and biological studies on the yellow organic acids in lake water: Limnology and Oceanography, v. 2, p. 161–179

—— 1958, Yellow acid-cation complexes in lake water: Science, v. 127, p. 702–704

Sherman, G. D., 1952, The genesis and morphology of the alumina-rich laterite clays, p. 154–161 *in* Frederickson, A. F., *Editor*, Problems of clay and laterite genesis—symposium: New York, Am. Inst. Min. Met. Eng., 244 p.

Siffert, B., and Wey, R., 1961, Sur la synthese de la kaolinite à temperature ordinaire: Comptes Rendus Acad. Sci., v. 253, p. 142–144

Singewald, J. T., 1909, The iron ores of Maryland: Econ. Geology, v. 4, p. 530–543

Sokolov, V. A., 1959, The evolution of the atmosphere of the earth, p. 54–66 *in* Clark, F. C., and Synge, R. L. M., *Editors*, 1st International symposium on the origin of life: London, Pergamon Press, 436 p.

Spencer, E., 1931, Discussion on the iron-ores of Noamundi: Mining and Geol. Inst. India Trans., v. 26, p. 322–330

Spencer, E., and Percival, F. G., 1952, The structure and origin of the banded hematite jaspers of Singhbhum, India: Econ. Geology, v. 47, p. 365–383

Stockwell, C. H., 1961, Structural provinces, orogenies, and time-classification of rocks of the Canadian Precambrian Shield: Canada Geol. Survey paper 61–17, p. 108–127

Stout, W., 1944, The iron-ore bearing formations of Ohio: Ohio Geol. Survey 4th ser., Bull. 45, 230 p.

Sverdrup, H. U., Johnson, M. W., and Fleming, R. H., 1942, The oceans, their physics, chemistry, and general biology: New York, Prentice-Hall, 1087 p.

Tanaka, M., 1953, Etude chimique sur le metabolisme mineral dans les lacs: Jour. Earth Sci., Nagoya Univ., v. 1, p. 119–134

Taylor, J. H., 1949, Petrology of the Northampton Sand iron formation: Great Britain Geol. Survey Memoir, 111 p.

Tessier, F., 1954, Oolithes ferrugineuses et fausses laterites dans l'est de l'Afrique Occidentale Francaise: Inst. des Haute Études de Dakar; Ann. de l'École Superieuse des Sciences, tome I, p. 113–128

Tyler, S. A., and Twenhofel, W. H., 1952, Sedimentation and stratigraphy of the Huronian of Upper Michigan: Am. Jour. Sci., v. 250, p. 1–27, 118–151

Uhlig, V., 1910, Iron ore resources of the world: Stockholm, 11th Internat., Geol. Cong., v. 1, p. 143–174

Urey, H. C., 1959, Primitive planetary atmospheres and the origin of life, p. 16–22 *in* Clark, F., and Synge, R. L. M., *Editors*, 1st International symposium on the origin of life: London, Pergamon Press, 436 p.

Van Hise, C. R., and Leith, C. K., 1911, The geology of the Lake Superior region: U. S. Geol. Survey Mon. 52, 641 p.

Vikulova, M. F., 1964, Effect of the origin of the Lower Carboniferous clays in the western part of the Moscow basin on the alterations of their clay minerals, p. 417–428 *in* Von Straaten, L. M. J. U., *Editor*, Deltaic and shallow marine deposits, Developments in sedimentology, v. 1: Amsterdam, Elsevier Publishing Co., 464 p.

Vinogradov, A. P., Komlev, L. V., Danilevich, S. I., Savonenko, V. G., Tugarinov, A. I., and Filippov, M. S., 1960, Absolute geochronology of the Ukrainian Pre-Cambrian: Copenhagen, 21st Internat. Geol. Cong., pt. IX, p. 116–132

Wagner, P. A., 1928, The iron deposits of the Union of South Africa: S. Africa Geol. Survey Memoir 26, 264 p.

Warshaw, C. M., and Roy, R., 1961, Classification and a scheme for the identification of layer silicates: Geol. Soc. America Bull., v. 72, p. 1455–1492

Way, H. J. R., 1952, Iron ore in Swaziland, p. 191–192 *in* Blondel, F., and Marvier, L., *Editors*, Symposium sur les gisements de fer du monde: Algeria, 19th Internat. Geol. Cong., tome I, 638 p.

White, D. A., 1954, The stratigraphy and structure of the Mesabi Range, Minnesota: Minn. Geol. Survey Bull. 38, 92 p.

Whitehead, T. H., Anderson, W., Wilson, W., Wray, D. A., and Dunham, K. C., 1952, The Liassic ironstones: Great Britain Geol. Survey Memoir, 211 p.

Wilson, G. V., 1922, The Ayrshire bauxitic clay: Scotland Geol. Survey Memoir, 28 p.

Woolnough, W. G., 1941, Origin of banded iron deposits—a suggestion: Econ. Geology, 36, p. 465–489

ZoBell, C. E., 1955, Occurrence and activity of bacteria in marine sediments, p. 416–427 *in* Trask, P. D., *Editor*, Recent marine sediments: Soc. Econ. Paleontologists and Mineralogists Special Pub. no. 4. 736 p.

Editor's Comments on Papers 34 and 35

34 Becker and Clayton: Excerpts from *Carbon Isotopic Evidence for the Origin of a Banded Iron-Formation in Western Australia*

35 Perry and Tan: *Significance of Carbon Isotope Variations in Carbonates from the Biwabik Iron Formation, Minnesota*

The preceding papers in this section reviewed the many theories that have been suggested for the genesis of the iron-rich sediments. The various theories or models of iron-formation deposition were formulated on the observed physical, chemical, and mineralogical characteristics of iron-formations and ironstones. It is interesting to note that each of the various models tends to concentrate on some aspect of the iron-sediments. For example, the frequent association of Precambrian iron-formations with volcanics is suggestive of a volcanic source for the materials. Lepp and Goldich (Papers 22 and 28) developed their model to account for the chemical characteristics of iron-formations. Hough's (1958) limnologic model seems to be built primarily as an explanation for the banding. The evaporite model of Trendall and Blockley (1970) similarly leans heavily on the parallelism in banding between the two rock types. Borchert's (Paper 26) oceanic model is an attempt to explain the varying mineralogy (facies) of iron-formations and ironstones.

The following two papers deal with the application of isotopic measurements on the components of iron-formations as a means of testing the various theories of origin.

Paper 34, by R. H. Becker and R. N. Clayton, examines the carbon isotopic evidence for the origin of the banded iron-formation in the Hammersley Range area of Western Australia. The paper is based upon Becker's (1971) Ph.D. thesis at the University of Chicago. Becker is on the faculty of Gannon College. Robert H. Clayton is well known for his work on natural variations of stable isotope abundances. He has degrees from Queen's University, Ontario, and from the California Institute of Technology. Clayton has been at the University of Chicago since 1958. He is Professor of Chemistry and holds a joint appointment in the Enrico Fermi Institute for Nuclear Studies and the Departments of Chemistry and the Geophysical Sciences. He is Master of Physical Sciences Collegiate Division and Associate Dean of the Physical Sciences.

E. C. Perry, Jr., and F. C. Tan apply isotope evidence to the problem of the origin of the Biwabik iron formation of Minnesota. The work was conducted while both were at the University of Minnesota. Perry received his degrees from the Georgia Institute of Technology and the Massachusetts Institute of Technology. Since 1972 he has been on the staff of Northern Illinois University. His principal research interest is the stable isotope chemistry of metamorphic rocks and ancient sediments.

F. C. Tan received his degrees from the University of Taiwan, McGill University, and Pennsylvania State University. He is currently with the Bedford Institute of Oceanography, Dartmouth, Nova Scotia.

References

Becker, R. H., 1971, Carbon and oxygen isotope ratios in iron-formation and associated rocks from the Hammersley range of Western Australia and their implications: Ph.D. thesis, Univ. Chicago.

Borchert, H., 1960, Genesis of marine sedimentary iron ores: Inst. Min. Met. Bull. 640 (Trans., v. 69), p. 261–279.

Hough, J. L., 1958, Fresh-water environment of deposition of Precambrian banded iron formations: Jour. Sed. Petrology, v. 28, p. 414–430.

Lepp, H., and S. S. Goldich, 1964, Origin of Precambrian iron formations: Econ. Geol., v. 59, p. 1032–1041, 1047–1059.

Trendall, A. F., and J. G. Blockley, 1970, The iron formations of the Pre-Cambrian Hammersley Group, Western Australia: Western Australia Geol. Surv. Bull., 119, 350 p.

34

Carbon isotopic evidence for the origin of a banded iron-formation in Western Australia

RICHARD H. BECKER
Department of Chemistry, University of Chicago

and

ROBERT N. CLAYTON
The Enrico Fermi Institute and the Departments of Chemistry and of the Geophysical Sciences, University of Chicago

(*Received* 5 *November* 1971; *accepted in revised form* 18 *December* 1971)

Abstract—Carbon isotope ratios were determined for carbonates from the banded iron-formation of the Dales Gorge Member of the Brockman Iron Formation and from the Wittenoom and Duck Creek Dolomite Formations of the Hamersley Range area of Western Australia. The iron-formation carbonates had δC^{13} values of -9 to -11 ‰, while the dolomitic limestones had δC^{13} values of $+2$ to -2 ‰. It is concluded that the iron formation was precipitated in a basin isolated from the ocean, but probably in close proximity to it and that organic activity may have played a significant role in the genesis of the iron-formation. The dolomitic limestones were deposited during periods when the basin was transgressed by the ocean.

A consideration of the available data on Precambrian marine carbonates leads to the conclusion that the oceanic reservoir of carbon has remained nearly constant for almost 3×10^9 years. The argument previously advanced for Phanerozoic samples, that this constancy implies a constant amount of atmospheric oxygen is reconsidered, and is found to rest on questionable assumptions.

INTRODUCTION

THE BANDED iron-formations, deposits of laminated chert, iron oxides and silicates and carbonates, have interested geologists and geochemists for many years. Because of their unusual properties, and their distribution in time and space, they are considered to be potential sources of information about conditions at the earth's surface during the Precambrian. A great deal of controversy exists, however, in the interpretation of the data available from investigations of iron-formations. Reviews are given by LEPP and GOLDICH (1964), SCHWEIGHERT (1965), GOVETT (1966), and JAMES (1966).

Among the points of dispute have been the site of deposition of iron-formation, whether in epicontinental seas (WOOLNOUGH, 1941), alkaline lakes (EUGSTER, 1969), or inland freshwater lakes (HOUGH, 1958), and the influence, if any, of organic matter in the derivation or deposition of iron and silica (GRUNER, 1922; LEPP and GOLDICH, 1964; JAMES, 1966; CLOUD, 1968). Stable isotope ratios, particularly for carbon, may be useful tools for settling these points.

Carbon isotope ratios can be used as tracers of environmental conditions. Carbon δ values, alone and in conjunction with oxygen δ values, have been used to distinguish between marine and non-marine carbonate deposits of Phanerozoic age (CRAIG, 1953; JEFFERY *et al.*, 1955; CLAYTON and DEGENS, 1959; OANA and DEEVEY, 1960; KEITH and WEBER, 1964), for example. Carbon isotope ratios in marine carbonates have also been related to the oxygen content of the Phanerozoic atmosphere (BROECKER, 1970). Data for Precambrian carbonates are relatively scarce, so that similar approaches have not been used to any great extent for the Precambrian.

Editor's Note: A row of asterisks indicates that material has been omitted from the original article.

The Hamersley Iron Province of Western Australia contains examples of extremely well-preserved iron-formation, as well as other rock-types, including thick carbonate deposits. A study of the carbon isotope ratios in these rocks could help to distinguish among the origins suggested for iron-formations, at least for this particular case. A few carbon isotope analyses from other iron-formations have been reported previously, ranging from values typical of present-day marine carbonates to values much lower than marine carbonates (OANA and DEEVEY, 1960; HOERING, 1962; HOERING, in BARGHOORN and TYLER, 1965; PERRY and TAN, 1972 a,b). An explanation for this range of about 15 ‰ might be found by studying one particular deposit in detail.

* * * * * * *

ANALYTICAL PROCEDURES

The carbonates in each sample were identified optically, and, if necessary, by X-ray powder patterns. They were then analyzed by the evolution of CO_2 in 100% phosphoric acid (MCCREA, 1950). When a single carbonate was present, the procedure was simply to collect the gas once, after what was assumed to be a sufficient time for complete reaction. Siderite, which reacts very slowly, was an exception There is evidence that the gas collected after reacting siderite for two months with 100% phosphoric acid is not significantly different from that collected after longer periods of time, up to six months (Clayton and Mayeda, unpublished). Therefore, it is assumed that no errors were introduced by using data from incompletely reacted siderite. The reaction times used were: one day for calcite, one week for dolomite, two weeks for ankerite, and two to three months for siderite.

When two carbonates were present, either calcite plus dolomite or ankerite plus siderite, a modification of the procedure of EPSTEIN *et al.* (1964) was used. Taking advantage of the differing reaction rates of the carbonates, collections of CO_2 were made at various times after the start of the phosphoric acid reaction. Early collections, if taken early enough, should contain CO_2 from the more reactive carbonate, while later collections should contain CO_2 representative of the less reactive carbonate. Time intervals were chosen by trial and error for each type of sample, to give the maximum separation of the carbonates. Similarities of δC^{13} values in consecutive portions of CO_2 taken very early or very late indicate that reasonably good values for the individual carbonates were probably obtained. Similarities between samples analyzed as single carbonates and those analyzed by the time-cut method seem to support this assumption.

The CO_2 was analyzed for its isotopic composition on a 60°, 15 cm, double-collecting mass spectrometer modified after NIER (1947) and MCKINNEY *et al.* (1950). The measured ratios were corrected for background, mixing at the inlet valves, and mass 44 tail, as described by CRAIG (1957). The analytical values are given in the δ notation (EPSTEIN, 1959), in per mil,where:

$$\delta C^{13} = \left[\frac{\text{R sample}}{\text{R standard}} - 1\right] \times 1000$$

with $R = C^{13}/C^{12}$ and the standard referred to being PDB-1 (CRAIG, 1957).

Samples were usually analyzed twice, except when there was insufficient material. In nearly all cases, duplicate values were within 0·15 ‰ and in many cases, they were within 0·10 ‰. The standard deviation for the analytical procedure, as measured for a single sample analyzed numerous times over a long period of time, is better than 0·10 ‰. The data are listed in Appendix 1. Information on the individual samples is given by BECKER (1971).

RESULTS

The distributions of carbon δ values obtained for the various formations are shown in Fig. 2. Values for coexisting carbonates are connected by lines. One additional δC^{13} value, of +0·42 ‰, was obtained from a metamorphosed basalt containing 1·7 per cent calcite. This greenstone is from the Mt. Jope Volcanics, which lies some 1·5 km below the Dales Gorge Member.

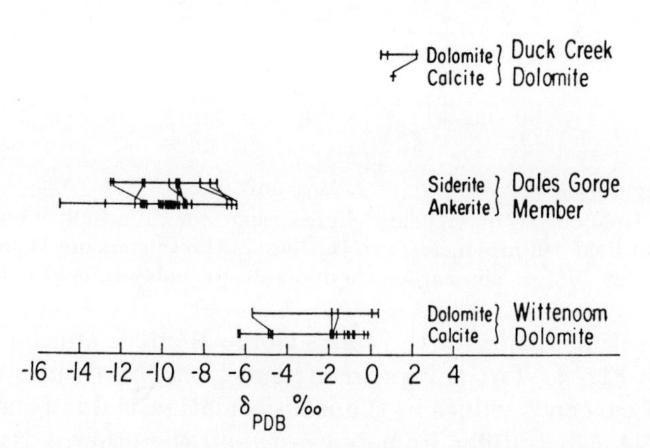

Fig. 2. Distributions of the carbonate δC^{13} values for the iron formation and dolomitic limestones. Lines connect different carbonates from the same samples.

The following observations can be made with respect to the data of Fig. 2. First, although the range of δC^{13} values in a given formation is several per mil, clustering is evident in all cases, with the dolomitic limestones having δC^{13} values near zero, and the iron-formation having δC^{13} values of about −10 ‰. Second, in each formation the range of values for different carbonates is similar. Third, there is no uniform relationship between δC^{13} values in coexisting carbonates. Sometimes one is lighter than the other, and sometimes it is heavier.

The large range of values in the Wittenoom Dolomite is misleading. A plot of carbon versus oxygen δ values, shown in Fig. 3, indicates that there are actually two distinct groups of samples from this formation. Those with low carbon δ values also have low oxygen δ values. Two samples do not fall into either group, but both are from veins, and will therefore not be considered further.

The samples with low isotope ratios are those with the low carbonate contents mentioned earlier, from the lowermost part of the formation. These samples do not represent the formation as a whole, and their significance will be discussed later. The remaining samples cover a much narrower range of δC^{13} values than do all the samples taken together.

The samples from the Duck Creek Dolomite and the Dales Gorge Member do not show any apparent relationships between their carbon and oxygen isotope ratios, and have therefore been omitted from Fig. 3.

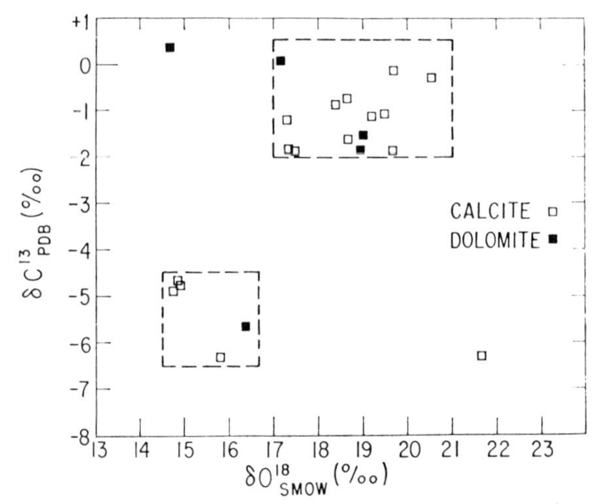

Fig. 3. Distribution of δC^{13} values versus δO^{18} values for carbonates from the Wittenoom Dolomite. Upper field delimits range for essentially pure carbonate rocks. Lower field delimits rocks from the base of the Wittenoom Dolomite, which contain about 50% of non-carbonate minerals, probably altered volcanic ash.

The carbon isotope ratios for the Dales Gorge Member are shown broken down by macroband in Fig. 4. Two things are evident from this figure. One is that most of the scatter of carbon δ values in the iron-formation is due to a few samples in BIF10 and BIF11 which differ from the rest, and the other is that a 1·5 ‰ shift in average carbon δ value occurs in going from BIF10 to BIF11.

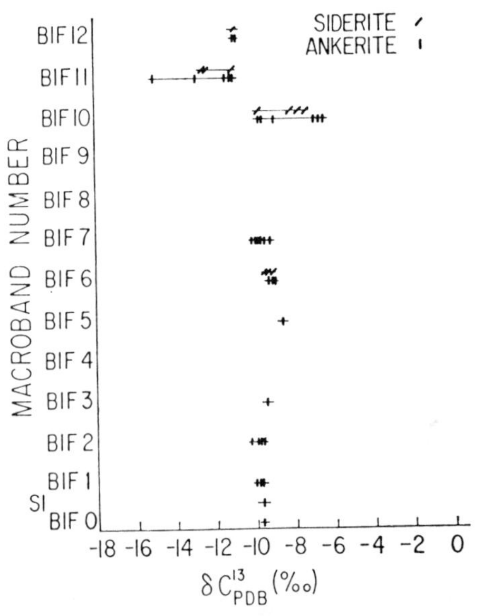

Fig. 4. Distribution of δC^{13} values for the Dales Gorge Member, broken down by macroband.

The first observation can be explained by considering the individual samples involved. Those in BIF11, with δC^{13} values lighter than -12 ‰, are from a few unusual mesobands designated here as "white cherts." Most chert mesobands are stained by traces of dispersed hematite, but the chert laminae in these mesobands are nearly pure white, indicating a lack of hematite. The most negative δC^{13} value occurs in a sample in which minnesotaite, the ferrous-iron analog of talc, is observed in abundance. The evidence seems to indicate reducing conditions relative to other mesobands. This, combined with the more negative carbon δ values, may mean that bleaching by trapped organic matter occurred in these particular mesobands. Such a mechanism was mentioned in connection with red beds by Craig (1953).

Those samples in BIF10 with δC^{13} values above -8 ‰ came from a single, non-microbanded, ankerite mesoband, which was sampled in two different drill cores. It was stained yellow, except for a small bleached portion in one core, which was sampled separately. This mesoband has a sharp lower contact with a magnetite mesoband, and it grades upward into a magnetite–silicate mixture. It appears to represent a sudden, short-term change in basin conditions, such as might perhaps be caused by a brief overflow from one basin into another containing a chemically different solution. The white portion of the mesoband has a δC^{13} value 0·25 ‰ heavier than the surrounding ankerite, opposite to what might be expected if organic matter caused the bleaching. Whether this difference in isotopic composition is significant is not known, as it is only slightly greater than experimental error.

The second observation noted above is not understood. Although some properties of the iron-formation, such as the amount of riebeckite, vary from one level to another of the Dales Gorge Member (Trendall and Blockley, 1970), none appear to be related to the 1·5 ‰ shift in carbon δ values. The size of the intervening S11 macroband is unusually large, but one just as large occurs between BIF5 and BIF6 with no corresponding shift in δC^{13} values. The possibility that the thickness of the S11 macroband is related to the carbon isotope ratio change cannot, however, be ruled out. The change may have been permanent, since BIF12 has δC^{13} values similar to BIF11.

It is assumed in the above that samples taken from cores centimeters in length are representative of macrobands meters in thickness. Since samples from different macrobands represent different portions of these macrobands, some near the top and some near the bottom, the fact that nearly all the δC^{13} values are the same indicates that the assumption may be valid. The change in δC^{13} values going from BIF10 to BIF11 may indicate a sampling bias, although this seems highly unlikely.

The drill cores cover a sampling distance of some 20 km laterally, and again, the assumption is made that they are representative of the basin as a whole. The remarkable lateral uniformity of the iron-formation (Trendall and Blockley, 1968, 1970) favors this assumption.

Very few samples from the Duck Creek Dolomite were available for analysis, which would account for the small spread of δC^{13} values observed. The samples are, however, from different outcrops, and it is felt that they may be representative of the total formation.

It thus appears that, when non-representative samples are omitted, a fairly clear-cut division of the carbonate-containing samples can be made, into dolomitic limestones with carbon δ values of $+2$ to -2 ‰, and iron formation with carbon δ values of -9 to -11 ‰.

Discussion

Since oxygen isotope ratios in carbonates are known to show an "age effect" (Degens and Epstein, 1962; Keith and Weber, 1964) attributed by some to post-depositional exchange with ground water (Degens and Epstein, 1962), it is necessary to consider whether the difference in carbon isotope ratios observed in the present study may be the result of some similar sort of exchange in relatively recent times. Such exchange of carbon in carbonates has been observed by Gross (1964).

It is possible to argue for the preservation of carbon isotope ratios in the iron-formation on the basis of observed internal variations. Vertical variations of 2·5 ‰ exist over distances of less than 1 cm, between adjacent mesobands, even though lateral variations in these same mesobands, over distances of kilometers, are fractions of one per mil. Such variations would be expected to have been wiped out if large scale exchange had occurred. Similarly, the lack of consistent differences between coexisting carbonates indicates that exchange between them has not occurred to any great extent, as might be expected if a major amount of exchange with a fluid phase has taken place. Other evidence, relating to the oxygen isotope ratios observed in the carbonates, can also be cited (Becker, 1971). These points make it seem unlikely that significant exchange of carbon has occurred in the iron-formation since its burial at depth.

In the dolomitic limestones, the present values would be difficult to explain as the result of exchange processes, if initial δC^{13} values had been similar to those of the iron-formation. At present, most of the sources of carbon in ground water are organic in nature, and they tend to lower carbonate carbon δ values (Gross, 1964; Gross and Tracey, 1966; Hodgson, 1966). Mechanisms for the enrichment of C^{13} are known (Murata *et al.*, 1969), but they are localized in thin beds and concretionary zones, and lead to widely scattered δC^{13} values. It seems unreasonable to propose that thick depositional units such as the Wittenoom and Duck Creek Dolomites have undergone large scale exchange of carbon, arriving at just the sort of δC^{13} values one finds in Phanerozoic marine carbonates, by such mechanisms. It is therefore felt that the observed isotope ratios are the original ones.

If the isotope ratios now seen in these formations do represent the original ones, then it is possible to make some statements about conditions existing at the time the formations were deposited. These are discussed below.

Marine carbon isotope ratios

As pointed out earlier, the Duck Creek Dolomite was almost certainly precipitated under marine conditions, and the same is likely to be true for much of the Wittenoom Dolomite, as it has chemical and isotopic compositions similar to those of the Duck Creek Dolomite. It is therefore significant that both formations have carbon δ values similar to those of present-day marine carbonates. Some Precambrian carbonate samples with δC^{13} values in the same range, or perhaps slightly lower, have been previously reported (CRAIG, 1953; HOERING, 1962; DEGENS and EPSTEIN, 1964; WEBER, 1967). South African marine carbonates of Archean age (SCHOPF *et al.*, 1971; PERRY and TAN 1972b) and Russian carbonates of Archean and Proterozoic age (GALIMOV *et al.*, 1968) have recently been analyzed, again with results similar to present-day marine carbonates. These data, in conjunction with those of the current study, seem to indicate that a world-wide oceanic reservoir of oxidized carbon isotopically similar to that in the present oceans has existed for at least $2{\cdot}2 \times 10^9$ years, and possibly as long as 3×10^9 years. The number of samples available is too small to place good limits on the amount of variation that might have occurred in the isotopic composition of the reservoir, but it is not likely to have been much larger than the range of about 4 ‰ seen in Phanerozoic carbonates (WEBER, 1967). This range of variation was attributed in part to the variations in the abundance of land plants through the Phanerozoic, a factor not expected to have been important in the Precambrian. In any case, the average δC^{13} value of crustal carbon appears to be around $-6{\cdot}5$ ‰ (SCHWARCZ, 1969), and, since the heavy isotope tends to be concentrated in the oxidized form, the marine reservoir would not be expected to have a value lighter than this.

Site of the basin

If the possibility of changes in the entire reservoir of oceanic carbon of 10 ‰ is discounted, at least over the period of time involved in the deposition of the Mt. Bruce Supergroup, then an explanation is required for the difference between the iron-formation and limestone carbon δ values. Differences in the equilibrium isotopic distribution of carbon between ankerite or siderite and bicarbonate ion as opposed to that between calcite or dolomite and bicarbonate ion can be ruled out. While it is known that different carbonates concentrate the carbon isotopes in different amounts from the same carbon reservoir, partition function calculations show that the theoretical fractionations are only 2 or 3 ‰, rather than 10 ‰ (Clayton and Rubinson, unpubl.).

Metamorphic decarbonation of carbonates can cause lowered carbon isotope ratios in the residual carbonate (SHIEH and TAYLOR, 1969; DEINES and GOLD, 1969). However, isotopic and other evidence indicates a maximum temperature for the Dales Gorge Member of under 300°C (BECKER, 1971). This is probably below the decomposition temperature for siderite (SEGUIN, 1971; FRENCH, 1971), so that decarbonation should not be important. It must be noted, however, that decarbonation of siderite has been discussed as a source of magnetite in iron-formations (LABERGE, 1964; AYRES, 1970), and the high carbonate content in S-type macrobands in the Dales Gorge Member has been explained as the result of the trapping of CO_2 evolved by the decarbonation of iron-formation beneath impermeable shale layers (TRENDALL and BLOCKLEY, 1970). The one analysis of a carbonate from the S-type macrobands falls within the range for the majority of the iron-formation carbonates, indicating that, even if decarbonation did lead to trapping of CO_2 beneath the shales, the isotopic effects were small.

The most reasonable explanation for the low carbon δ values of the Dales Gorge Member involves precipitation within a restricted basin. In such a basin, changes in the isotopic composition of carbon would not be diluted by a large oceanic reservoir, so that input of light carbon from some source in reasonable amounts could cause the required shift of 10 ‰. In fact, isopachs indicate that the Brockman Iron Formation was probably precipitated in such a restricted basin (TRENDALL and BLOCKLEY, 1970).

As evidence exists for incursions of ocean water on both a long time scale, during the precipitation of the dolomitic limestones, and on a short time scale indicated by the chemistry and isotopic composition of the ankerite mesoband, the basin is likely to have been near to, and perhaps at times in contact with, the ocean. Enrichments of riebeckite, a sodic amphibole, at some levels within the iron-formation indicates that sodium ion was abundant in the basin at times. For these reasons, it seems that a freshwater lake could not have been the site of deposition of the iron-formation, contradicting the proposal of HOUGH (1958). An epicontinental sea, or "barred basin," such as discussed by WOOLNOUGH (1941) or JAMES (1954) is preferred, although the alkaline lake model of EUGSTER (1969) cannot be ruled out. Oceanic deposition of iron-formation, by submarine concentration of iron derived from sediments (BORCHERT, 1960), appears to be ruled out by the carbon isotope ratios of the iron-formation.

Organic activity

A source of the light carbon of the iron-formation is necessary. One possibility is igneous activity, bringing either juvenile or recycled crustal carbon into the basin. There is some question as to whether such carbon would be sufficiently light, however. Carbonatites usually range from −3 to −8 ‰ (TAYLOR *et al.*, 1967; DEINES, 1970), although much heavier values have been reported for carbonate inclusions within a peridotite (DEINES, 1968). Volcanic gases have been estimated to contain carbon with a δC^{13} value of −8 to −12 ‰ (CRAIG, 1963). Only the reduced carbon of igneous rocks, in the range of −23 to −30 ‰ (CRAIG, 1953; GALIMOV and PETERSIL'YE, 1969), would appear to be light enough, but it occurs in only very small amounts, and its actual origin is debatable, as it may partially come from contamination by surface organic carbon (CRAIG, 1953).

A more reasonable source of light carbon is organic matter. It is well-known that evidence of microorganisms is found in cherts associated with iron-formations (BARGHOORN and TYLER, 1965; CLOUD and LICARI, 1968). Reduced carbon with isotopic ratios in the range of organic matter is found in the same formations (HOERING, 1962), and has been taken as evidence for the presence of photosynthesis in the Precambrian. Carbonates with carbon δ values of −9 to −14 ‰, similar to those of the Dales Gorge Member, are also found in these sediments (OANA and DEEVEY, 1960; HOERING, in BARGHOORN and TYLER, 1965). Fossils of algae in the Mt. Bruce Supergroup have already been mentioned. There is, therefore, good reason to believe that biological activity existed, and could therefore have played a part in the derivation, transport, or deposition of iron and silica, during the formation of the Dales Gorge Member. The white cherts of the Dales Gorge Member are additional evidence for the presence of organic matter, to the point of being buried in the sediment. Finally, small amounts of pyrite throughout the iron-formation (TRENDALL, 1966a) may further support the existence of organic material in the sediment, because in present-day deposits pyrite is almost always formed in the presence of organic material (BERNER, 1970).

The form in which the carbon entered the sediment is of interest, because it relates to the question of primary minerals in iron-formations. The evidence for reduced carbon in the original precipitate implies that ferrous carbonate and magnetite could have been formed by reduction of iron initially in the ferric form, as postulated for other iron-formations (PERRY and TAN, 1972a). While this mechanism may certainly have operated in the Dales Gorge Member, as evidenced by the white cherts, it is not likely to have been the major source of carbon. Textural evidence indicates that the initial deposit was a gel containing either siderite (AYRES, 1970) or ankerite (TRENDALL, 1965), so that some of the carbon was initially in oxidized form. The ankerite mesoband analyzed is almost certainly primary, and its intermediate carbon δ value indicates that light carbon must have existed as bicarbonate ion, rather than as reduced carbon, in the basin. Finally, the rarity of the white cherts in the Dales Gorge Member shows that carbon was not overabundant with respect to hematite in more than a few of the mesobands, and favors the conclusion that little organic matter was trapped in the sediment. It is possible that the isotopically light carbonate was formed near the bottom of the basin as a result of oxidation–reduction reactions involving ferric iron, but most of this reaction must have occurred above the sediment–water interface.

History of the Hamersley Basin

From the carbon isotope ratios observed, it is possible to construct a partial history of the development of the basin in which the Mt. Bruce Supergroup was deposited. It is for the most part similar to that given by MACLEOD (1966).

The initial deposits, including the Mt. Jope Volcanics, may have been laid down under marine conditions. The single carbonate sample from these rocks supports this, as it has a δC^{13} value typical of marine carbonates. TAYLOR and COLEMAN (1968) have interpreted their data on metabasalts from Ward Creek, California, as indicating that carbon δ values of marine carbonates were picked up by the small amounts of carbonate in their rocks, presumably during extrusion, and were then preserved during metamorphism. The same may be true in the present case.

By the time of deposition of the Marra Mamba Iron Formation, at the base of the Hamersley Group, the basin must have been closed. This can be concluded for two reasons. First, the Marra Mamba Iron Formation is similar, although not exactly the same, in general features to the Dales Gorge Member, and a similar basin would be required. Second, the intermediate carbon δ values of the lower part of the Wittenoom Dolomite pointed out earlier, can be interpreted as the result of mixing of carbonate of organic origin in a closed basin with oceanic carbonate, during a subsidence of the basin. The Wittenoom Dolomite would represent a marine transgression which ended the deposition of the Marra Mamba Iron Formation, and temporarily caused a return to open-sea deposition of carbonates. The first deposits would contain remnants of the organically derived carbonate ion, and would therefore be isotopically lighter than the marine value. The presence of what appears to be altered volcanic ash in these samples may be the result of a period of explosive volcanism accompanying subsidence of the basin. Analysis of carbonates from the Marra Mamba Iron Formation would help to clarify the matter.

Later adjustments of the basin, closing it off again, would lead to the deposition of the Brockman Iron Formation with its low carbon isotope ratios. Finally, after some later events for which isotopic evidence is lacking, the basin opened to the ocean, allowing deposition of the Wyloo Group, including the Duck Creek Dolomite.

One additional point can be made here. Based on the single analysis from an S-type macroband, it would appear that the alternation of macrobands occurred by a mechanism which did not alter the carbon isotope ratio of the basin appreciably. It would probably imply that the basin remained isolated from the ocean during macrobanding episodes, although data from several of the S-type macrobands would be needed before a positive statement could be made about this point.

Atmospheric oxygen

Recently, attempts have been made to relate the oxygen content of the atmosphere in the past to the amount of organic activity at the Earth's surface (TAPPAN, 1968; BROECKER, 1970). One measure of the amount of organic activity at a given time has been considered to be the isotopic composition of marine carbon at that time (WEBER, 1967; BROECKER, 1970). Because of a lack of data for the Precambrian, these attempts have been restricted to the Phanerozoic. The results have indicated that a steadily increasing atmospheric oxygen content, resulting from photosynthetic dissociation of CO_2 by organisms since the Cambrian (BERKNER and MARSHALL, 1965), is not compatible with the isotopic data (BROECKER, 1970). It appears, however, that the relationship between atmospheric oxygen and marine carbonate δC^{13} values is tenuous at best, and while the model of BERKNER and MARSHALL (1965) may be incorrect (BRINKMANN, 1969; SCHOPF and BARGHOORN, 1969), it cannot be so demonstrated using marine carbonate δC^{13} values.

The presence of carbonates of marine affinity at various times in the Precambrian, all with carbon δ values near 0 ‰ as noted earlier, would imply that oxygen levels in the atmosphere have remained near present-day levels for 3×10^9 years, if the arguments of Broecker were extended to these samples. Since arguments for much lower oxygen levels in the Precambrian have been made (HOLLAND, 1962; PERRY *et al.*, 1971), it is necessary to consider the assumptions on which Broecker's argument is based in some detail.

There are essentially three assumptions. The first of these, that a constant δC^{13} difference between the oxidized and reduced carbon reservoirs has existed through time, can be tested empirically. Analyses of reduced carbon in sediments of various ages seem to indicate that this reservoir has indeed been constant in δC^{13} value since the Archean (OEHLER *et al.*, 1972), although older samples may be slightly lighter than younger ones. This can perhaps be attributed to diagenetic effects (HOERING, 1962). The carbon in carbonates has already been shown to be relatively constant. The first assumption is probably valid, therefore, to the extent required for the argument.

The second assumption, which is that the total carbon at the earth's surface and in sediments has remained constant to within about 10% is certainly arguable. In the model of RUBEY (1951), for example, carbon is being outgassed from the mantle through time, so that the total amount at the surface has increased by a significant amount in 3×10^9 years. Assuming the rest of Broecker's arguments to be valid, the total amount of oxygen in the atmosphere would presumably have increased in a comparable way, as the juvenile CO_2 underwent partial photosynthesis and was divided between the oxidized and reduced reservoirs in the proper proportions. On the other hand, if outgassing occurred as a single step (Lafon and MacKenzie, 1971), and crustal materials have undergone partial or total recycling since (Garrels and MacKenzie, 1969; Barth, 1968), then crustal carbon and atmospheric oxygen may have been constant through the Precambrian. If the new global tectonics are considered (Isacks *et al.*, 1968), then a constancy of surface carbon would require a balance between material gained from and lost to the mantle over geologic time.

Finally, there is the question of the distribution of photosynthetically released oxygen between sediments and the atmosphere. According to Broecker (1970), only about 5 per cent of the oxygen equivalent to the reduced carbon in the crust is currently in the atmosphere, with the remainder tied up in sulfates and in ferric oxides. Since weathering is an ongoing process at the earth's surface, continuously using up atmospheric oxygen, a constant level of atmospheric oxygen would require a source that was somehow regulated by oxygen pressure in the atmosphere. Although Broecker (1970) suggests a mechanism for this regulation, based upon increased burial of organic matter to compensate for the loss of oxygen, it would seem that this involves a change in the ratio of oxidized to reduced carbon in sediments over time, which should show up in the isotopic ratios of the two carbon reservoirs. Metamorphic reactions in the buried sediments, involving reduction of sulfate and ferric iron by the buried carbon, might recycle the carbon, if the crust were a closed system, and maintain the ratio of reduced to oxidized carbon and the amount of atmospheric oxygen. However, loss of marine sediments to the mantle, as discussed by Gilluly (1971), for example, implies that the crust is not a closed system.

Possible controls on the level of atmospheric oxygen have also been considered by Van Valen (1971), who finds none particularly satisfying. Brinkmann (1969) suggests photodissociation as the controlling mechanism, and while it may be, it would not readily account for the apparently constant distribution of carbon between oxidized and reduced reservoirs.

It would therefore appear that, while δC^{13} values of marine carbonates have remained fairly constant over a period of 3×10^9 years, any conclusions about the constancy of atmospheric oxygen levels based on this observation are probably unwarranted.

Conclusions

Observations of the carbon isotope ratios in the Dales Gorge Member iron-formation, and in the associated carbonate formations, of the Hamersley Iron Province of Western Australia lead to the following conclusions:

(1) The iron-formation was deposited in a closed basin separated from but probably located near the open ocean.

(2) Organic activity was probably present and therefore may have played a part in the transport of, or deposition of, the iron and silica in the iron-formation, although volcanism cannot be ruled out as the source of light carbon in the iron-formation.

(3) The isotopic ratio of inorganic carbon in the oceans has remained near the present value for at least 2×10^9 years, and probably longer.

(4) Although carbon isotope ratios in the surface carbon reservoirs may have been constant over much of geologic time, this probably cannot be used as an argument for the constancy of the atmospheric content of oxygen. Some control over the isotopic compositions of oxidized and reduced carbon at the surface must, however, exist.

To the extent that other iron-formations show similar properties to those of the Hamersley basin, they may have formed under similar conditions. Thus, the banded iron-formation of the Transvaal System of South Africa may have had a similar origin to the Dales Gorge Member, while the iron-formations of the Lake Superior region may have differed in some ways (Trendall, 1968).

Acknowledgments—The authors would like to thank Dr. A. F. Trendall of the Geological Survey of Western Australia for providing most of the samples used in this study.

Acknowledgment is made to the donors of The Petroleum Research Fund, administered by the American Chemical Society, for support of this research. The research was also supported by National Science Foundation grants NSF-GA 1390 and NSF-GA 22711.

References

Achauer, C. W. and Johnson, J. H. (1969) Algal stromatolites in the James Reef complex (Lower Cretaceous), Fairway Field, Texas. *J. Sediment. Petrol.* **39,** 1466–1472.

Ayres, D. E. (1970) Iron oxide genesis in the Brockman Iron Formation and associated ore deposits, Western Australia. Ph.D. Thesis, University of Wisconsin.

Barghoorn, E. S. and Tyler, S. A. (1965) Microorganisms from the Gunflint Chert. *Science* **147,** 563–577.

Barth, T. F. W. (1968) The geochemical evolution of continental rocks. A model. In *Origin and Distribution of the Elements* (editor L. H. Ahrens), pp. 587–597. Pergamon.

Becker, R. H. (1971) Carbon and oxygen isotope ratios in iron-formation and associated rocks from the Hamersley Range of Western Australia and their implications. Ph.D. Thesis, University of Chicago.

Berkner, L. V. and Marshall, L. C. (1965) On the origin and rise of oxygen concentration in the earth's atmosphere. *J. Atmos. Sci.* **22,** 225–261.

Berner, R. A. (1970) Sedimentary pyrite formation. *Amer. J. Sci.* **268,** 1–23.

Borchert, H. (1960) Genesis of marine sedimentary iron ores. *Inst. Mining Metal. Trans.* **69,** 261–279.

Brinkmann, R. T. (1969) Dissociation of water vapor and evolution of oxygen in the terrestrial atmosphere. *J. Geophys. Res.* **74,** 5355–5368.

Broecker, W. S. (1970) A boundary condition on the evolution of atmospheric oxygen. *J. Geophys. Res.* **75,** 3553–3557.

Clayton, R. N. and Degens, E. T. (1959) Use of carbon-isotope analyses for differentiating fresh-water and marine sediments. *Bull. Amer. Assoc. Petrol. Geol.* **43,** 890–897.

Cloud, P. E., Jr. (1968) Atmospheric and hydrospheric evolution on the primitive earth. *Science* **160,** 729–736.

Cloud, P. E., Jr. and Licari, G. R. (1968) Microbiotas of the banded iron formations. *Proc. Nat. Acad. Sci. U.S.* **61,** 779–786.

Compston, W. and Arriens, P. A. (1968) The Precambrian geochronology of Australia. *Can. J. Earth Sci.* **5,** 561–583.

Craig, H. (1953) The geochemistry of the stable carbon isotopes. *Geochim. Cosmochim. Acta* **3,** 53–92.

Craig, H. (1957) Isotopic standards for carbon and oxygen and correction factors for mass-spectrometric analysis of carbon dioxide. *Geochim. Cosmochim. Acta* **12,** 133–149.

Craig, H. (1963) The isotopic geochemistry of water and carbon in geothermal areas. In *Nuclear Geology in Geothermal Areas* (editor E. Tongiorgi), pp. 17–53. Consiglio Nazionale delle Richerche, Pisa.

Degens, E. T .and Epstein, S. (1962) Relationship between O^{18}/O^{16} ratios in coexisting carbonates, cherts, and diatomites. *Bull. Amer. Assoc. Petrol. Geol.* **46,** 534–542.

Degens, E. T. and Epstein, S. (1964) Oxygen and carbon isotopic ratios in coexisting calcites and dolomites from recent and ancient sediments. *Geochim. Cosmochim. Acta* **28,** 23–44.

Deines, P. (1968) The carbon and oxygen isotopic composition of carbonates from a mica peridotite dike near Dixonville, Pennsylvania. *Geochim. Cosmochim. Acta* **32,** 613–625.

Deines, P. (1970) The carbon and oxygen isotopic composition of carbonates from the Oka Carbonatite complex, Quebec, Canada. *Geochim. Cosmochim. Acta* **34,** 1199–1225.

Deines, P. and Gold, D. P. (1969) The change in carbon and oxygen isotopic composition during contact metamorphism of Trenton limestone by the Mount Royal pluton. *Geochim. Cosmochim. Acta* **33,** 421–424.

Edgell, H. S. (1964) Precambrian fossils from the Hamersley Range, Western Australia, and their use in stratigraphic correlation. *Geol. Soc. Aust.* **11,** 235–262.

Epstein, S. (1959) The variations of the O^{18}/O^{16} ratio in nature and some geological applications. In *Researches in Geochemistry* (editor P. H. Abelson), pp. 217–240. John Wiley.

Epstein, S. Graf, D. L. and Degens, E. T. (1964) Oxygen isotope studies on the origin of dolomites. In *Isotopic and Cosmic Chemistry*, (editors H. Craig, S. L. Miller and G. J. Wasserburg), pp. 169–180. North-Holland.

Eugster, H. P. (1969) Inorganic bedded cherts from the Magadi area, Kenya. *Contrib. Mineral. Petrol.* **22,** 1–31.

French, B. M. (1971) Stability relations of siderite ($FeCO_3$) in the system Fe–C–O. *Amer. J. Sci.* **271,** 37–78.

Galimov, E. M., Kuznetsova, N. G. and Prokhorov, V. S. (1968) The composition of the former atmosphere of the earth as indicated by isotopic analysis of Precambrian carbonates. *Geokhimiya*, 1376–1381; *Geochem. Int.* **5,** 1126–1131 (1968).

Galimov, E. M. and Petersil'ye, I. A. (1968) Isotopic composition of carbon in bitumens of igneous and metamorphic rocks. *Dokl. Akad. Nauk SSSR* **182,** 186–189.

Garrels, R. M. and MacKenzie, F. T. (1969) Sedimentary rock types: relative proportions as a function of geological time. *Science* **163,** 570–571.

Gebelein, C. D. (1969) Distribution, morphology, and accretion rate of Recent subtidal algal stromatolites, Bermuda. *J. Sediment. Petrol.* **39,** 49–69.

Gilluly, J. (1971) Plate tectonics and magmatic evolution. *Geol. Soc. Amer. Bull.* **82,** 2383–2396

Govett, G. J. S. (1966) Origin of banded iron formations. *Geol. Soc. Amer. Bull.* **77,** 1191–1212.

Gross, M. G. (1964) Variations in the O^{18}/O^{16} and C^{13}/C^{12} ratios of diagenetically altered limestones in the Bermuda Islands. *J. Geol.* **72,** 170–194.

Gross, M. G. and Tracey, J. I. (1966) Oxygen and carbon isotopic composition of limestones and dolomites, Bikini and Eniwetok atolls. *Science* **151,** 1082–1084.

Gruner, J. W. (1922) The origin of sedimentary iron formations: the Biwabik Formation of the Mesabi Range. *Econ. Geol.* **17,** 407–460.

Hodgson, W. A. (1966) Carbon and oxygen isotope ratios in diagenetic carbonates from marine sediments. *Geochim. Cosmochim. Acta* **30,** 1223–1233.

Hoering, T. C. (1962) The stable isotopes of carbon in the carbonate and reduced carbon of Precambrian sediments. *Carnegie Inst. Wash., Yearb* **61,** 190–191.

Holland, H. D. (1962) Model for the evolution of the earth's atmosphere. In *Petrologic Studies: A Volume to Honor A. F. Buddington* (editors A. E. J. Engel, H. L. James and B. F. Leonard), pp. 447–477. Geol. Soc. Amer., New York.

Hough, J. L. (1958) Fresh-water environment of deposition of Precambrian banded iron-formations. *J. Sediment. Petrol.* **28,** 414–430.

Isacks, B., Oliver, J. and Sykes, L. R. (1968) Seismology and the new global tectonics. *J. Geophys. Res.* **73,** 5855–5900.

James, H. L. (1954) Sedimentary facies of iron-formation. *Econ. Geol.* **49,** 235–293.

James, H. L. (1966) Chemistry of the iron-rich sedimentary rocks. *U.S. Geol. Survey Prof. Paper 440-W*, 61 pp.

JEFFERY, P. M., COMPSTON, W., GREENHALGH, D. and DE LAETER, J. (1955) On the carbon 13 abundance of limestones and coals. *Geochim. Cosmochim. Acta* **7**, 255–286.

KEITH, M. L. and WEBER, J. N. (1964) Carbon and oxygen isotopic composition of selected limestones and fossils. *Geochim. Cosmochim. Acta* **28**, 1787–1816.

LABERGE, G. L. (1964) Development of magnetite in iron-formations of the Lake Superior region. *Econ. Geol.* **59**, 1313–1342.

LABERGE, G. L. (1966) Altered pyroclastic rocks in iron-formation in the Hamersley Range, Western Australia. *Econ. Geol.* **61**, 147–161.

LAFON, G. M. and MACKENZIE, F. T. (1971) Early evolution of oceans—a weathering model (abstract). *Bull. Amer. Assoc. Petrol. Geol.* **55**, 348.

LEPP, H. and GOLDRICH, S. S. (1964) Origin of Precambrian iron formations. *Econ. Geol.* **59**, 1025–1060.

LOGAN, B. W., REZAK, R. and GINSBURG, R. N. (1964) Classification and environmental significance of algal stromatolites. *J. Geol.* **72**, 68–83.

MACLEOD, W. N. (1966) The geology and iron deposits of the Hamersley Range area, Western Australia. *West. Australia Geological Survey Bull.* **117**, 170 pp.

MCCREA, J. M. (1950) On the isotopic chemistry of carbonates and a paleotemperature scale. *J. Chem. Phys.* **18**, 849–857.

MCKINNEY, C. R., MCCREA, J. M., EPSTEIN, S., ALLEN, H. A. and UREY, H. C. (1950) Improvements in mass spectrometers for the measurement of small differences in isotope abundance ratios. *Rev. Sci. Instr.* **21**, 724–730.

MURATA, K. J., FRIEDMAN, I. and MADSEN, B. M. (1969) Isotopic composition of diagenetic carbonates in marine Miocene formations of California and Oregon. *U.S. Geol. Survey Prof. Paper* 614-*B*, 24 pp.

NIER, A. O. (1947) A mass spectrometer for isotope and gas analysis. *Rev. Sci. Instr.* **18**, 398–411.

OANA, S. and DEEVEY, E. S., Jr. (1960) Carbon 13 in lake waters and its possible bearing on paleolimnology. *Amer. J. Sci.* **258-A**, 253–272.

OEHLER, D. Z., SCHOPF, J. W. and KVENVOLDEN, K. A. (1972) Carbon isotopic studies of organic matter in Precambrian rocks. In preparation.

PERRY, E. C., Jr., MONSTER, J. and REIMER, T. (1971) Sulfur isotopes in Swaziland System barites and the evolution of the earth's atmosphere. *Science* **171**, 1015–1016.

PERRY, E. C., Jr. and TAN, F. C. (1972a) Significance of carbon isotope variations in carbonates from the Biwabik Iron-Formation, Minnesota. In preparation.

PERRY, E. C., Jr. and TAN, F. C. (1972b) Significance of oxygen and carbon isotope determinations in Early Precambrian cherts and carbonate rocks of southern Africa. In preparation.

PLAYFORD, P. E. and COCKBAIN, A. E. (1969) Algal stromatolites: deepwater forms in the Devonian of Western Australia. *Science* **165**, 1008–1010.

RUBEY, W. W. (1951) Geologic history of sea water: an attempt to state the problem. *Geol. Soc. Amer. Bull.* **62**, 1111–1148.

SCHOPF, J. W. and BARGHOORN, E. S. (1969) Microorganisms from the Late Precambrian of South Australia. *J. Paleontology* **43**, 111–118.

SCHOPF, J. W., OEHLER, D. Z., HORODYSKI, R. J. and KVENVOLDEN, K. A. (1971) Biogenicity and significance of the oldest known stromatolites. *J. Paleontology* **45**, 477–485.

SCHWARCZ, H. P. (1969) The stable isotopes of carbon. In *Handbook of Geochemistry*, vol. II/1, (editor K. H. Wedepohl), pp. 6-B-1 to 6-B-15. Springer-Verlag.

SCHWEIGHERT, H. (1965) Genesis of the iron ores of the Pretoria Series, South Africa. *Econ. Geol.* **60**, 269–298.

SEGUIN, M. K. (1971) Phase relations in the Fe–C–O–S–H_2O system and its geological application. *Chem. Geol.* **7**, 5–18.

SHIEH, Y. N. and TAYLOR, H. P., Jr. (1969) Oxygen and carbon isotope studies of contact metamorphism of carbonate rocks. *J. Petrol.* **10**, 307–331.

TAPPAN, H. (1968) Primary production, isotopes, extinctions and the atmosphere. *Palaeogeogr. Palaeoclimatol. Palaeoecol.* **4**, 187–210.

TAYLOR, H. P., Jr. and COLEMAN, R. G. (1968) O^{18}/O^{16} ratios of coexisting minerals in glaucophane-bearing metamorphic rocks. *Geol. Soc. Amer. Bull.* **79**, 1727–1756.

TAYLOR, H. P., Jr., FRECHEN, J. and DEGENS, E. T. (1967) Oxygen and carbon isotope studies of carbonatites from the Laacher See district, West Germany and the Alnö district, Sweden. *Geochim. Cosmochim. Acta* **31,** 407–430.

TRENDALL, A. F. (1965) Progress report on the Brockman Iron Formation in the Wittenoom-Yampire area. *W. Aust. Geol. Survey, Ann. Rep.* 1964, 55–65.

TRENDALL, A. F. (1966a) Altered pyroclastic rocks in iron-formation in the Hamersley Range, Western Australia. *Econ. Geol.* **61,** 1451–1458.

TRENDALL, A. F. (1966b) Second progress report on the Brockman Iron Formation in the Wittenoom-Yampire area. *W. Aust. Geol. Survey, Ann. Rep.* 1965, 75–87.

TRENDALL, A. F. (1968) Three great basins of Precambrian iron-formation deposition: a systematic comparison. *Geol. Soc. Amer. Bull.* **79,** 1527–1544.

TRENDALL, A. F. (1969) The Joffre Member in gorges south of Wittenoom. *W. Aust. Geol. Survey, Ann. Rep.* 1968, 53–57.

TRENDALL, A. F. and BLOCKLEY, J. G. (1968) Stratigraphy of the Dales Gorge Member of the Brockman Iron Formation, in the Precambrian Hamersley Group of Western Australia. *W. Aust. Geol. Survey, Ann. Rep.* 1967, 48–53.

TRENDALL, A. F. and BLOCKLEY, J. G. (1970) The iron formations of the Precambrian Hamersley Group, Western Australia, with special reference to the associated crocidolite. *W. Aust. Geol. Survey Bull.* **119,** 366 pp.

VAN VALEN, L. (1971) The history and stability of atmospheric oxygen. *Science* **171,** 439–443.

WEBER, J. N. (1967) Possible changes in the isotopic composition of the oceanic and atmospheric carbon reservoir over geologic time. *Geochim. Cosmochim. Acta* **31,** 2343–2351.

WOOLNOUGH, W. G. (1941) Origin of banded iron deposits—a suggestion. *Econ. Geol.* **36,** 465–489.

35

Reprinted from *Proc. Kiev Symp. Genesis of Precambrian Iron and Manganese Deposits,* UNESCO, New York, 1973, pp. 299–305.

Significance of carbon isotope variations in carbonates from the Biwabik Iron Formation, Minnesota

E. C. Perry Jr and F. C. Tan

Department of Geology, University of Minnesota

Introduction

Most carbonates in a suite of 3–1 $\times 10^9$ year-old rocks from southern Africa and the Canadian shield have δC^{13} values[1] within ± 2 per mil of PDB, an isotopic standard described by Urey *et al.* (1951) which has a value typical of Phanerozoic marine carbonates (Perry and Tan, 1970 and in preparation). Carbon isotopic determinations on Precambrian carbonates by Hoering (1967) also give a range of values that is normal for Phanerozoic marine sediments.

Carbonates from iron-formation have δC^{13} values lower than PDB by as much as 18 per mil. The anomaly was first reported by Becker and Clayton (1970), who found that δC^{13} of limestones and dolomites stratigraphically above and below the Dales Gorge Member of the 1.9×10^9 year-old Brockman Iron Formation of Western Australia is similar to that of normal Phanerozoic carbonates, but that δC^{13} of iron carbonates within the iron-formation is about 10–15 per mil lower. They concluded that : '(1) the carbon isotope ratio in the world oceans has been nearly constant for at least 2×10^9 years; (2) the banded iron-formation of West Australia was deposited in a basin distinct from but with some connection to the ocean; (3) there probably was organic activity involved in either the transport of iron to the basin or in the precipitation of iron and silica. However, the possibility of juvenile or recycled carbon from volcanic sources supplying the lighter carbon, rather than organic activity, cannot be ruled out.'

Evidence about the contribution of carbon from volcanic sources is difficult to obtain and interpret. One clue may come from carbonates from iron-formations within the 3×10^9 year-old Onverwacht and Fig Tree Formations of South Africa which also have anomalously low δC^{13} values (Perry and Tan, 1970 and in preparation). Limestones and dolomites, sometimes associated with volcanics, and even carbonates from tuffaceous sediments in these formations have normal δC^{13} values, suggesting that there is no volcanic carbon contribution.

Experimental procedures

Composite samples and a few individual specimens from four continuous drill cores of Biwabik Iron Formation were analysed in this study. Composite samples were chosen because partial analyses were available (Pfleider *et al.*, 1968) and because there is no *a priori* way of determining equilibration volume within the iron-formation.

Carbon and oxygen isotopic data on carbonates were obtained from CO_2 liberated by 100 per cent phosphoric acid by the technique of McCrea (1950). The Biwabik Iron Formation contains coexisting ankerite and siderite (French, 1968), both of which react slowly with phosphoric acid, and successive gas fractions from iron-formation samples contain increasing proportions of gas from the carbonate with the slowest reaction rate. Analyses of such successive CO_2 fractions from mixed $CaCO_3$–$CaMg(CO_3)_2$ assemblages is discussed by Epstein, Degens and Graf (1964). Pending accurate determination of the carbonate phases involved and of the phosphoric acid-carbonate oxygen isotope fractionation factors for the appropriate carbonates, we have arbitrarily used the oxygen isotope fractionation factor for calcite.[2]

Oxygen from SiO_2 (chert) was liberated with BrF_5 and converted to CO_2 by the technique of Clayton and Mayeda (1963). δO^{18} for chert is reported with respect to Standard Mean Ocean Water (SMOW) (Craig, 1961).

Isotopic analyses of CO_2 gas were performed with a mass spectrometer having a 15 cm radius analyser and equipped with double inlet and double collector systems (McKinney *et al.*, 1950).

1. $\delta C^{13} = \left[\frac{(C^{13}/C^{12})\text{sample}}{(C^{13}/C^{12})\text{PDB}} - 1\right] \times 1\,000$. Similarly, $\delta O^{18} = \left[\frac{(O^{18}/O^{16})\text{sample}}{(O^{18}/O^{16})\text{standard}} - 1\right] \times 1\,000$. The standard used for carbonates is PDB.
2. Since this paper was prepared a phosphoric acid-siderite fractionation factor has been reported by Fritz *et al.* (1910). Using this factor would decrease our δO^{18} values of carbonates by about 1.6 per cent, but would have no significant effect on the relative values or on any of the conclusions presented here.

Discussion of data

Samples for this study were taken at intervals throughout the stratigraphic section of the Biwabik Iron Formation and the data are given in Tables 1 and 2. Stratigraphic logs of percentage iron from magnetite (Pfleider *et al.*, 1968), δO^{18} and δC^{13} are shown for 3 cores in Figure 1. It is apparent from this figure that isotope ratios show a strong stratigraphic trend. We shall explore whether this is a primary trend or the result of isotopic reactions between minerals and other components of the system during diagenesis and metamorphism.

The iron carbonate-rich top of the Upper Slaty Member, the Intermediate Slate Member, and the uppermost part of the Lower Cherty Member of the Biwabik Iron Formation are iron-formations in the sense of containing about 20 per cent or more Fe in the form of silicates and carbonates, but they contain little or no magnetite. A plot of δO^{18} versus δC^{13} (Fig. 2) shows that these units occupy a field different from that occupied by magnetite-bearing iron-formation units. In particular, most samples of magnetite-free iron-formations have a δC^{13} greater than — 4 per mil, whereas almost all magnetite-bearing iron-formations have a δC^{13} less than — 7 per mil.

The Intermediate Slate contains as much as 3 per cent reduced carbon (Gruner, 1946). In sample EP 2-66 this reduced carbon has a δC^{13} of — 33.2 per mil, a value which agrees well with Hoering's (1967) value of δC^{13} PDB = — 30.5 per mil for carbon from the Thomson Formation, stratigraphically equivalent to the overlying Virginia Formation, and δC^{13} PDB = 30.3 per mil for carbon from the correlative Gunflint Iron Formation. It also agrees well with the value of — 33.1 per cent reported by Smith *et al.* (1970) for the HF residue in chert from the Gunflint Iron Formation. As shown in Figure 2, this large quan-

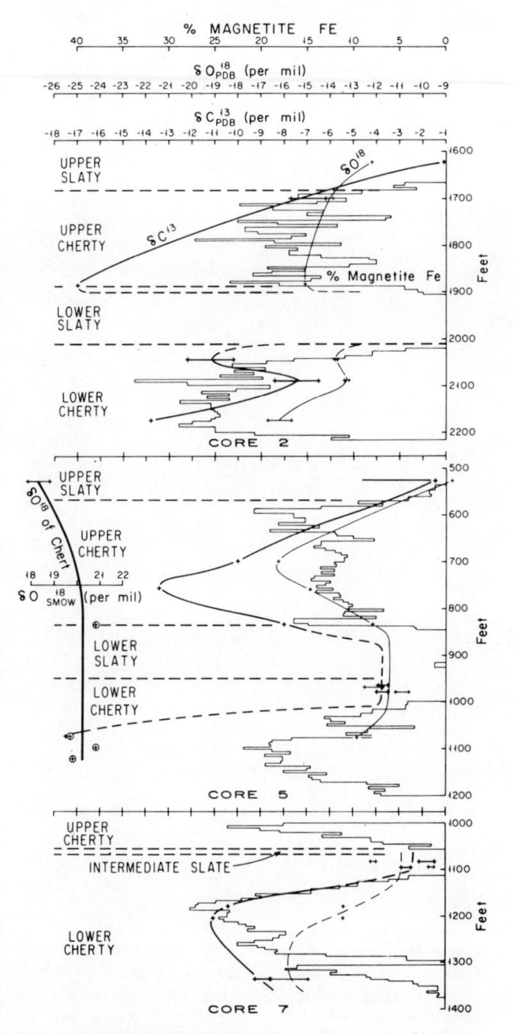

Fig. 1. Core log showing δO^{18} and δC^{13} of carbonates and percentage magnetite iron for three continuous core samples of Biwabik Iron Formation.

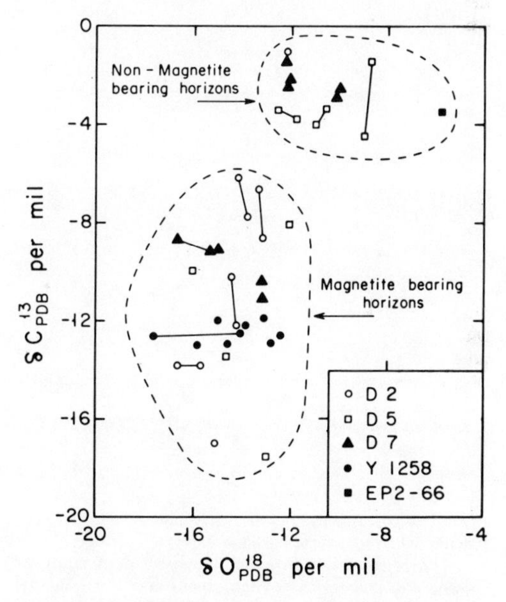

Fig. 2. δO^{18} versus δC^{13} of carbonates from Biwabik Iron Formation showing fields of magnetite-bearing and magnetite-free units.

TABLE 1. Isotopic and related data for core samples of Biwabik Iron Formation

Sample number[1]	δC^{13} (PDB) per mil	δO^{18} (PDB) per mil	Percentage Fe[2]	Percentage magnetite Fe[2]	Stratigraphic unit	Reaction time
D2 1620–1624.5	— 1.08	— 12.18	6.23	0	Upper Slaty	0–2 hours
D2 1697–1705	— 7.75	— 13.88	16.30	10.8	Upper Cherty	0–2 hours
	— 6.19	— 14.28				2 hours–1 day
D2 1882.4–1886.2	— 17.04	— 15.14	29.72	18.0	Upper Cherty	0–1 day
D2 2040–2045.8	— 12.20	— 14.19	27.57	16.6	Lower Cherty	0–2 hours
	— 10.16	— 14.33				2 hours–14 days
D2 2085–2090	— 8.44	— 13.19	37.87	33.8	Lower Cherty	0–2 hours
	— 6.47	— 13.40				2 hours–3 days
D2 2170–2175	— 13.82	— 15.73	29.40	25.5	Lower Cherty	0–1 hour
	— 13.81	— 16.69				1 hour–21 days
D5 524.1–530	— 4.58	— 8.99	17.42	0	Upper Slaty	0–1 hour
	— 1.45	— 8.70				1 hour–7 days
D5 692.5–700	— 10.00	— 16.16	25.60	10.9	Upper Cherty	0–3 days
D5 755–760	— 13.38	— 14.86	29.05	12.2	Upper Cherty	0–7 days
D5 829–835	— 7.99	— 12.18	26.05	14.8	Lower Slaty	0–4 days
D5 965–970	— 3.87	— 11.82	13.98	0	Lower Cherty	0–1 hour
	— 3.51	— 12.53				1 hour–3 days
D5 975–985	— 4.00	— 11.15	19.43	0	Lower Cherty	0–1 hour
	— 3.47	— 10.61				1 hour–3 days
D5 1070–1075	— 17.48	— 12.86	27.73	7.9	Lower Cherty	0–7 days
D7 1083	— 2.39	— 12.18	10.91[3]	0[3]	Lower Cherty	0–2 hours
	— 2.14	— 11.98				2 hours–4 days
	— 1.46	— 12.13				4–7 days
D7 1094	— 2.88	— 10.19	10.77[3]	0[3]	Lower Cherty	0–1 hour
	— 2.48	— 10.02				1 hour–10 days
	— 2.50	— 10.00				10–17 days
D7 1175–1180	— 10.39	— 13.37	32.31	27.1	Lower Cherty	0–1 day
D7 1200–1205	— 11.03	— 13.40	30.59	24.5	Lower Cherty	0–4 days
D7 1337	— 9.17	— 14.94	27.38[3]	6.1[3]	Lower Cherty	0–2 hours
	— 9.20	— 15.21				2 hours–4 days
	— 8.56	— 16.69				4–7 days
EP 2-66	— 3.71	— 5.84	20–30	0	Intermediate Slate	0–1 hour

1. Core 2 was taken near Biwabik, Minnesota (Sec. 22, T58N, R16W); core 5 was taken near Buhl, Minnesota (Sec. 36, T58N, R20W); core 7 was taken near Keewatin, Minnesota (Sec. 36, T57N, R22W).
2. Taken from Pfleider *et al.* (1968).
3. Single hand specimen, but analysis is for five foot composite.

tity of isotopically light carbon has not produced a significant δC^{13} shift in the carbonate.

The Intermediate Slate is composed dominantly of siderite and chamosite (French, 1968) and is considered to have a volcanic ash component (Morey, this volume, page 193). We conclude from the essentially normal δC^{13} values in this unit that it is unlikely that the δC^{13} anomaly in iron-formations is caused by a direct contribution of volcanic carbon to the sedimentary basin.

In a number of samples in which we have analysed successive fractions of CO_2 gas, these fractions shift according to a variety of trends (Tables 1 and 2, points connected by lines in Fig. 2). Because these shifts show no consistent trend, we reject the trivial interpretation

TABLE 2. Isotopic data and iron oxide percentage for composite samples of Biwabik Iron Formation (Hanna y 1258), Cooley, Minnesota

Sample number	δC^{13} (PDB) per mil	δO^{18} (PDB) per mil	Percentage magnetite	Percentage hematite	Stratigraphic unit	Reaction time
47–74	— 11.95	— 14.97	41.9	1.2	Lower Cherty	0–1 day
74–93	— 12.64	— 12.40	35.9	0	Lower Cherty	0–1 day
93–121	— 12.78	— 12.92	30.4	4.2	Lower Cherty	0–1 day
121–158	— 12.36	— 14.21	30.5	8.3	Lower Cherty	0–1 day
	— 12.43	— 17.66			Lower Cherty	1–3 days
158–172	— 11.92	— 13.25	28.7	2.3	Lower Cherty	0–1 day
172–194	— 12.82	— 15.85	27.7	1.3	Lower Cherty	0–1 day
194–208	— 12.33	— 14.01	34.1	1.8	Lower Cherty	0–1 day
208–241	— 13.15	— 14.78	27.3	1.2	Lower Cherty	0–1 day

that they are the result of surface exchanges with atmospheric CO_2. Instead, they probably represent carbonate components with differing reaction rates and different isotopic compositions and fractionation factors. Since the shifts are small in short core specimens (D 7 samples with single footage numbers, Table 1), we attribute the larger shifts to sampling intervals that exceed the volume of local equilibration. Although the shifts are a nuisance in the interpretation of data, they suggest that diagenesis and metamorphism in the Biwabik Iron Formation involved reactions in a number of small subsystems with little interaction between them.

All but one of the samples from core Y 1258 contain hematite and magnetite. We note, without explanation, that in this buffered system δC^{13} varies only from — 12.0 to — 13.2 per mil, whereas δO^{18} ranges from — 12.4 to — 17.7 per mil.

Interpretation

At least three interpretations of the data of Figures 1 and 2 are possible:

Both Fe for magnetite and carbon for carbonate are derived from a volcanic source characterized by low δC^{13}. We regard this as unlikely because the δC^{13} anomaly is not evident in the Intermediate Slate, the only unit of the Biwabik Iron Formation in which there is direct evidence (shards) of a volcanic contribution.

Iron is transported or precipitated by some organic process which produces carbonate with a low δC^{13} value. This is the model of Becker and Clayton (1970); its validity rests on whether the isotopic patterns in Figure 1 are primary stratigraphic features or are the diagenetic and metamorphic result of primary differences. Normal δC^{13} values for carbonates from zones containing about 20 per cent iron in the form of iron silicates and carbonates, but no magnetite, indicate that the δC^{13} anomaly is most probably not related to transportation of iron.

We propose here a model in which oxidation-reduction reactions during diagenesis and metamorphism produce shifts of carbon from an abundant reduced reservoir of organic carbon (less than — 30 per mil) to the carbonate reservoir (initially near 0 per mil); similar shifts may transfer oxygen from hematite to carbonate (a shift of over 20 per mil). Although this model is tentative, it can be extended to explain some of the perplexing features of deposition and diagenesis of iron-formation.

We postulate that much of the magnetite in iron-formation was precipitated as ferric-oxide-hydroxide simultaneously with a variable amount of organic matter. During diagenesis and low grade metamorphism the following reactions (or similar ones) occurred:

$$6Fe_2O_3 + C_{(organic)} \rightarrow 4Fe_3O_4 + CO_2 \quad (1)$$

$$C^{12}O_2 + FeC^{13}O_3 \rightleftarrows C^{13}O_2 + FeC^{12}O_3 \quad (2)$$

$$2Fe_3O_4 + 6CO_2 \rightleftarrows 6FeCO_3 + O_2 \quad (3)$$

A more complete set of possible reactions is given by Yui (1966). After exchange according to reaction (2), CO_2 is assumed to have escaped from the immediate system; because of the sandwich-like nature of the iron-formation, gaseous products may continue to react in other zones, but large local variations in isotope ratios discussed previously suggest that interaction between zones was limited.

We are not aware of CO_2–$FeCO_3$ isotope exchange experiments or calculations but, by analogy with dolomite (O'Neil and Epstein, 1966), the CO_2 produced by reaction (1) could be out of equilibrium with $FeCO_3$ by about 40 per mil for carbon. This is probably sufficient to produce the shifts of approximately 10 per mil that we observe in the carbonate values.

A similar shift occurs in δO^{18}, but this is complicated by possible exchange reactions in the system. Figure 1 shows the correlation in core 5 of δO^{18} between carbonates and coexisting chert. The large spread in carbonate values compared to the relative constancy of coexisting cherts suggests that oxygen exchange reactions associated with oxidation and reduction may not be completely masked. Clayton (1970) reports 5 per mil shifts in δO^{18} for magnetite compared to 1 per mil maximum shifts for chert in the Dales Gorge Member of the Brockman Iron Formation. He attributes this to late exchange and homogenization of the chert, but one might speculate that the large variations result from oxidation reduction reactions that do not affect the chert. Table 3 shows δO^{18} for selected chert samples from core 5.

TABLE 3. δO^{18} (relative to SMOW) of selected chert (SiO_2) samples from core 5

Feet	δO^{18} (per mil)
524–530	18.29 ±.50
755–760	20.02 ±.02
829–835	20.80
1070–1075	19.68
1115–1124	19.83

Implications

Our model can readily be extended to explain some of the intriguing features of iron-formation deposition. In this limited discussion we make no effort to deal extensively with the geochemical problems associated with iron-formations. A summary of the literature and an extensive bibliography are given by James (1966). Thermodynamics of diagenesis and metamorphism are discussed by Yui (1966).

One question which has concerned many people (Gruner, 1922; Lepp and Goldich, 1964) is how the large quantities of iron found in Precambrian iron-formations was transported. Our model is compatible with a generally reducing atmosphere in which ferrous iron could be transported to the site of deposition. Here it could be oxidized in the photo-synthetic zone by primitive organisms using the $Fe^{++} \rightarrow Fe^{+++}$ reaction as an electron donor, as suggested by Cloud (1968). Ferric oxide-hydroxide might then be precipitated and incorporated in the sediment together with dead organisms. The present day Fe_2O_3/Fe_3O_4 ratio in iron-formations would then depend on the depositional ratio of Fe_2O_3/C. Less than $\frac{1}{2}$ per cent would be sufficient for reaction (1) to go to completion in a rock containing 30 per cent magnetite and would produce CO_2 for exchange in a mole ratio of CO_2 (reduction)/$FeCO_3$ $= \sim.4$ in a sediment containing 10 per cent $FeCO_3$. Present concentration of reduced carbon in iron-formations is more than adequate for this mechanism.

This model is consistent with the facies concept of James (1954) since organic matter in shallow water deposits would be rapidly oxidized by water of high Eh, whereas in deeper water organisms and Fe_2O_3 would be deposited together. The model also provides an explanation for the puzzling coexistence of Fe_2O_3 and Fe_3O_4 in many iron-formations (Eugster, 1957). This coexistence merely implies that reaction (1) stopped when the local system became depleted in carbon.

Iron-formation of the Transvaal System in South Africa and the Brockman Iron Formation in Western Australia typically contain fine laminae that Trendall (1968) has suggested may represent annual accumulations. This is, of course, consistent with a mechanism for precipitation of iron oxides which depends on seasonal maxima in organic activity.

Magnetite and iron carbonates often display complex interrelated textures which have led several authors to postulate diagenetic or metamorphic conversion of $FeCO_3$ to Fe_3O_4 (LaBerge, 1964; French, 1968). Reaction (1) is probably an early reaction that stabilizes siderite by increasing CO_2 pressure (reaction (3)). Higher temperature can decompose siderite to produce magnetite (Yui, 1966). This complicated system, coupled with variability in the size of the equilibrating system, probably explains why we cannot demonstrate a direct relationship between δC^{13} and Fe_3O_4/$FeCO_3$.

Summary and conclusions

Figures 1 and 2 provide good circumstantial evidence that a negative δC^{13} shift in iron-formation carbonates is related to oxidation-reduction reactions involving magnetite which permit exchange between two carbon reservoirs differing by about 30 per mil in their carbon isotope composition. As an example of one possible reaction, we have postulated a model in which primary hematite could be converted to magnetite by oxidation of organic carbon; and we have suggested some implications of this model. Four approaches may be useful in testing this model: (a) more detailed correlations such as those shown in Figure 1; (b) a tracer study of hydrogen-deuterium ratios in chamosite and other hydrous iron-formation silicates; (c) a study of end member assemblages such as hematite-carbonate; and (d) a close correlation of textural relations to isotopic data. We are currently making a much more detailed study of carbon and oxygen isotope variations in carbonates and of oxygen isotope variations in silicates and oxides of the Biwabik Iron Formation (test 1). Our model may not be unique, but we emphasize that carbon isotopes provide an important tracer that can be used to help understand the petrology of iron-formations.

Acknowledgments

This research was sponsored by the Minnesota Geological Survey and the National Science Foundation (GP 10855). We wish to acknowledge the help of L. A. Mattson, J. S. Owens and R. D. Scamfer of the Hanna Mining Co. and R. Bleifuss, G. B. Morey and P. K. Sims of the University of Minnesota.

Résumé

Signification des variations des proportions des isotopes du carbone dans les carbonates des gisements de fer de Biwabik, dans le Minnesota (E. C. Perry Jr. et F. C. Tan)

Les rapports C^{13}/C^{12} dans les carbonates des formations de fer du Précambrien inférieur et moyen sont plus faibles que ceux des autres carbonates précambriens et des carbonates marins phanérozoïques. Dans la formation de fer de Biwabik, dans le Minnesota, qui appartient au Précambrien moyen, la perte de C^{13} varie de 7 à 8 ‰ par rapport à la calcite crétacée normale (PDB). De faibles rapports C^{13}/C^{12} ne caractérisent que les zones qui contiennent de la magnétite et dans lesquelles est absente l'ardoise intermédiaire, matière sidéritique finement laminée, sans magnétite, qui contient certains fragments volcaniques. Cependant, dans cette matière l'abondant carbone réduit voit le C^{13} diminué dans la proportion de 33 ‰.

L'auteur propose une réaction diagénétique d'oxydation-réduction avec production de magnétite à partir d'hématite, qui permettrait un échange entre le carbone organique et le carbone des carbonates :

$$6Fe_2O_3 + C_{(organique)} \rightarrow 4Fe_3O_4 + CO_2 \quad [1]$$

$$C^{12}O_2 + FeC^{13}O_3 \rightleftarrows C^{13}O_2 + FeC^{12}O_3 \quad [2]$$

Une conversion réversible de magnétite en carbonate est aussi possible :

$$2Fe_3O_4 + 6CO_2 \rightleftarrows 6FeCO_3 + O_2 \quad [3]$$

Ce modèle propose le transport de fer comme Fe^{++}, l'oxydation par des organismes photo-synthétiques en hydroxyde-oxyde (comme cela a été proposé par Cloud en 1968), la précipitation de l'oxyde ferrique hydraté avec des organismes morts, et une réaction diagénétique entre l'oxyde ferrique et les organismes morts, sauf quand ces organismes sont oxydés dans des eaux peu profondes à Eh élevé. Ce modèle peut expliquer les feuillets à caractère saisonnier, semblables à des varves, avec coexistence de magnétite-hématite et certaines structures de remplacement mettant en jeu de la magnétite et du carbonate. Cela s'accorde avec le transport de fer Fe^{+2} et n'introduit que de minimes modifications au concept de faciès de James (1954).

Bibliography / Bibliographie

Becker, R. H.; Clayton, R. N. 1970. C^{13}/C^{12} ratios in a Precambrian banded iron-formation and their implications, Abstract in *Trans. Amer. geophys. Un.*, no. 51, p. 452.

Clayton, R. N. 1970. Oxygen isotopes in ancient sediments. Abstract in the *14th annual report on research, The Petroleum Research Fund*, American Chemical Society, Washington, D.C.

——; Mayeda, T. K. 1963. The use of bromine pentafluoride in the extraction of oxygen from oxides and silicates for isotopic analysis. *Geochim. et cosmoch. Acta*, vol. 27, p. 43–52.

Cloud, P. E. Jr. 1968. Atmospheric and hydrospheric evolution on the primitive earth. *Science*, vol. 160, p. 729–36.

Craig, H. 1961. Standards for reporting concentrations of Deuterium and oxygen-18 in natural waters. *Science*, vol. 133, p. 3467.

Epstein, S.; Graf, D. L.; Degens, E. T. 1964. Oxygen isotope studies on the origin of dolomites. In: H. Craig, S. L. Miller, G. J. Wasserburg (eds.), *Cosmic and isotopic chemistry*, p. 169–180. Amsterdam, North Holland.

Eugster, H. 1957. Reduction and oxidation in metamorphism. In: P. H. Abelson (ed.), *Researches in geochemistry*. p. 397–426, New York, Wiley.

French, B. M. 1968. Progressive contact metamorphism of the Biwabik Iron-formation, Mesabi Range, Minnesota. *Bull. Minn. geol. Surv.*, vol. 45.

Fritz, P.; Binda, P. L.; Folinsbee, F. E.; Krouse, H. R. 1970. Isotope composition of diagenetic siderites from Cretaceous sediments of Western Canada. *J. sediment. Petrol.* (In press.)

Gruner, J. W. 1922. The origin of sedimentary iron-formations: the Biwabik formation of the Mesabi Range. *Econ. Geol.*, vol. 17, p. 407–60.

——. 1946. *Mineralogy and geology of the Mesabi Range*, St Paul, Minn., Minnesota Office of the Commissioner of the Iron Range Resources and Rehabilitation.

Hoering, T. C. 1967. The organic geochemistry of Precambrian rocks. In: P. H. Abelson (ed.), *Researches in geochemistry*, vol. 2. New York, Wiley.

James, H. L. 1954. Sedimentary facies of iron-formation. *Econ. Geol.*, vol. 49, p. 235–93.

——. 1966. Chemistry of iron rich sedimentary rocks. *Prof. Pap. U.S. geol. Surv.*, 440–W.

LaBerge, G. 1964. Development of Magnetite in iron-formations, The Lake Superior Region. *Econ. Geol.*, vol. 59, p. 1313–42.

Lepp, H.; Goldich, S. S. 1964. Origin of Precambrian iron-formations. *Econ. Geol.*, vol. 59, p. 1025–60.

McCrea, J. M. 1950. On the isotopic chemistry of carbonates and a paleotemperature scale. *J. chem. Phys.*, vol. 18, p. 849–57.

McKinney, C. R.; McCrea, J. M.; Epstein, S.; Allen, H. A.; Urey, H. C. 1950. Improvements in mass spectrometers for the measurement of small differences in isotope abundance ratios. *Rev. sci. Instrum.*, vol. 21, p. 724–30.

O'Neil, J. R.; Epstein, S. 1966. Oxygen isotope fractionation in the system dolomite-calcite-carbon dioxide. *Science*, vol. 152, p. 198–201.

Perry, E. C. Jr, Tan, F. C. 1970. Carbon and oxygen isotope ratios in 3,000 m.y. old rocks of southern Africa. Abstract in Geological Society of America Annual Meeting Program, Milwaukee.

Pfleider, E. P.; Morey, G. B.; Bleifuss, R. L. 1968. *Mesabi Deep Drilling Project, Progress Report no. 1*, Minnesota

Section, AIME Forty-first Annual Meeting, Minneapolis, University of Minnesota.

SMITH, J. W.; SCHOPF, J. W.; KAPLAN, I. R. 1970. Extractable organic matter in Precambrian cherts. *Geochim. et cosmoch. Acta*, vol. 34, p. 659–75.

TRENDALL, A. F. 1968. Three great basins of Precambrian banded iron-formation deposition: A systematic comparison. *Bull. geol. Soc. Amer.*, vol. 79, p. 1527–44.

UREY, H. C.; LOWENSTAM, H. A.; EPSTEIN, S.; MCKINNEY, C. R. 1951. Measurement of paleotemperatures and temperatures of the Upper Cretaceous of England, Denmark, and the southeastern United States. *Bull. geol. Soc. Amer.*, vol. 62, p. 399–416.

YUI, S. 1966. Decomposition of siderite to magnetite at lower oxygen fugacities: A thermochemical interpretation and geological implications. *Econ. Geol.*, vol. 61, p. 768–76.

VI
Hydrothermal Iron Deposits

Editor's Comments on Papers 36 and 37

36 Holser and Schneer: *Hydrothermal Magnetite*

37 Park: *The Iron Ore Deposits of the Pacific Basin*

As noted in the Introduction, the theme of this volume is on the processes that tend to enrich iron in the earth's crust. Most of the preceding papers have dealt with the geochemical behavior of iron in the surface cycle of matter. Iron also is locally concentrated by the internal processes in deposits classified by Bateman (1950) as magmatic, contact metasomatic, and replacement. Some of the iron deposits resulting from the action of endogenic processes are important commercially and the literature on them is voluminous. Because such deposits are small when compared to the sedimentary iron-formations which strike lengths of hundreds of miles, only a limited space was allotted to them here.

We have seen from the preceding papers on the surface cycle of iron that there are still many unresolved problems. The behavior of iron in the endogene cycle is even less well understood. There seems to be little doubt that iron and titanium oxides are locally concentrated by magmatic processes in some layered anorthositic igneous complexes. Whether this differentiation results from fractional crystallization and gravitative settling, or by residual liquid segregation, or whether the oxides were enriched by late hydrothermal activity or metamorphic processes is still a debated question. The magmatic affiliation of relatively pure intrusive magnetite bodies such as are found in the Kiruna district of Sweden is not so obvious. Whereas most geologists, such as Geijer (1960), Geijer and Magnusson (1952), and Schneiderhöhn (1958), consider the iron in these deposits to have been concentrated by magmatic processes, Landergren (in Paper 1) suggests that the initial concentration must have been affected in the surface cycle. He attributes the deposits to the remobilization of sedimentary iron deposits by the endogene processes.

Deposits of magnetite located near the contacts of igneous intrusives as replacements of lime rocks and those that occur as vein fillings are equally difficult to explain. Mackin (1968) concluded that the replacement magnetite ores in the Iron Springs district of Utah received their iron from nearby intrusives by a process he calls deuteric release. He suggests that the movement of iron from the intrusives was chiefly by diffusion. Some geologists hold that many iron-rich skarn deposits are sedimentary iron deposits that have been mobilized by proximity to intrusives. Magnusson (1960), for example, in a study of the skarn ores of central Sweden, which are considered by some to be contact metasomatic, notes the association between some of the skarns and quartz-banded iron formations. He concludes: "Remnants of the quartz-banded iron ores and limestone-dolomite-banded iron ores and of skarn-banded iron ores with or without quartz have, during later years, been found in so many iron ore occurrences that the author now can dare to put forward the statement that nearly all of our skarn iron ores in central Sweden from the beginning have been sediments."

In view of the popularity of the hydrothermal theory of ore deposition among American geologists during the first half of this century, it is not surprising that vein filling and replacement magnetite-hematite bodies were frequently assigned a genetic relationship to the nearest intrusive. The only disagreement seemed to be in whether the iron was carried in aqueous solution (hydrothermal) or in the gas phase (pneumatolytic). More recently an increasing number of geologists have begun to accept the idea that some vein and replacement iron deposits represent sedimentary concentrations mobilized during metamorphism.

Considering the many unresolved problems connected with iron deposits with plutonic affiliations, it seems presumptive to try to convey some appreciation of the subject in only two reprints. The papers selected do, however, give some appreciation of the problems related to iron deposits of plutonic affiliation. The reader is referred to other references listed here and in Papers 37 and 38 for additional information.

Paper 36, by W. T. Holser and C. J. Schneer, was selected to present some experimental data on the solubility of magnetite in hydrothermal media. Many articles on replacement or vein-filling magnetite deposits refer loosely to hydrothermal solutions or to ferrous chloride emanations as the carriers of iron for the deposits. Holser and Schneer evaluate some of the suggested means of iron transport.

William T. Holser is Professor and Head of the Department of Geology, University of Oregon, where he has been since 1970. He received his degrees from the California Institute of Technology and Columbia University and he has had past associations with Cornell University, Battelle Memorial Institute, University of California at Los Angeles, Chevron Oil Company, and the U.S. Geological Survey.

His interest in teaching and research cover a broad range of mineralogy and geochemistry. Other publications have dealt with theories of packing and twinning in crystal structures, radiofrequency wave propagation in rocks, and with the geochemistry of beryllium, iron, bromine, and sulfur.

Cecil J. Schneer teaches mineralogy and the history of science at the University of New Hampshire. He was educated at Harvard and Cornell Universities, and he has been academic guest at the Solid State Institute of the Zurich Polytechnic and the Mineralogical Institute of the University of Milan. He has published on the theory of polytypism, thermodynamics of phase change, and on the relationships between crystal form and structure. His books are on the origins of science and the history of geology.

Park received degrees from the New Mexico School of Mines, the University of Arizona, and the University of Minnesota. From 1930 to 1946 he was employed by the U.S. Geological Survey in the Section of Metalliferous Deposits. Since 1946 he has been at Stanford University, where he served as Dean of the School of Earth Sciences from 1950 to 1965. Park has been active as a consultant to various companies and governments and he has worked in more than fifteen countries. He is a past president of the Society of Economic Geologists and the recipient of a number of awards for outstanding achievement. He has published widely on mineral deposits in various professional journals and is the author of several books, including a textbook on ore deposits (Park and MacDiarmid, 1970).

References

Bateman, A. M., 1950, Economic mineral deposits: John Wiley & Sons, Inc., New York.

Geijer, P., 1960, The Kiruna iron ores: 21st Internat. Geol. Cong., Guide to excursions A25 and C20, p. 3–17.

Geijer, P., and N. H. Magnusson, 1952, The iron ores of Sweden: 19th Internat. Geol. Cong., Algiers, Symposium sur les gisements de fer du monde, v. 2, p. 483–485.
Mackin, J. H., 1968, Iron ore deposits of the Iron Springs district, Utah: *in* Ore deposits of the United States, Amer. Inst. Min. Met. Petr. Eng., v. II, p. 992–1019.
Magnusson, N. H., 1960, Iron and sulphide ores of central Sweden: guide to excursions A26 and C21, Internat. Geol. Congr., XXI Sess., Norden, Geol. Surv. Sweden.
Park, C. F., Jr., and R. A. MacDiarmid, 1970, Ore deposits: W. H. Freeman and Co., San Francisco, 522 p.
Schneiderhöhn, H., 1958, Die Erzlagerstätten der Frühkristallisation, v. I: Gustav Fischer, Stuttgart.

36

Reprinted from *Geol. Soc. America Bull.,* **72,** 369–386 (Mar. 1961)

WILLIAM T. HOLSER *California Research Corp., La Habra, Calif.*
CECIL J. SCHNEER *Dept. Geology, University of New Hampshire, Durham, N. H.*

Hydrothermal Magnetite

Abstract: The solubility of magnetite was measured in dilute aqueous solutions of HCl at high temperature and pressure. At 390° C., 440 bars, in 0.0002 M HCl, 300 ppm ferrous iron is dissolved. Solubility decreases with acid concentration; in pure water at the same conditions solubility is less than 0.02 ppm. Calculation of real-gas equilibria from thermodynamic data shows that the contribution of volatile Fe_2Cl_6 molecules is insignificant in such dilute solutions. Comparison with room-temperature data suggests that ferrous iron is brought into true solution mainly as Fe^{2+} ion, by reaction with H^+, although complexes such as $FeCl^{2+}$ and $FeOH^{2+}$ may participate.

Magnetite was synthesized by reaction of acidic iron chloride solutions with calcite at high temperature and pressure.

The amount of iron measured in solutions with HCl concentrations less than a hundredth of that of natural fluids is great enough to be geologically significant.

CONTENTS

HYDROTHERMAL IRON DEPOSITS

Geological Environment

A large class of iron deposits is neither sedimentary nor magmatic and has been variously designated as contact metamorphic, pneumatolytic, pyrometasomatic, or hypothermal. These deposits include both vein fillings and widespread replacements of sedimentary rocks (particularly the carbonates) and are characteristically associated with igneous activity. Evidence from structure, texture, and mineral associations has generally led to the conclusion that such deposits were formed from some kind of dilute fluid at moderate to high temperatures, and we will call them hydrothermal.

The general characteristics of the group are: (1) the associated silicates (some of which originated at an earlier time and a higher temperature than the magnetite) represent metamorphic equilibria in the amphibolite (in some cases pyroxene hornfels) facies; (2) magnetite is the principal iron mineral, with hematite and pyrite subordinate; (3) some of the magnetite is in the form of veins, in many cases indicating open-space filling as well as replacement of the host rock.

Theories of Formation

A complete theory must include: (1) the source of iron; (2) the state of iron during transportation; (3) the change of conditions responsible for deposition of the iron as magnetite crystals.

Iron must be concentrated from its general dispersion (5 per cent) in the earth's crust by a factor of six to make a minable deposit. The low concentration ratio allows practically any rock type to be an ultimate source of the iron. The mobilized iron might originate from a rock melt by some process of magmatic differentiation, or it may be mobilized directly from a crystalline rock: even solid granite may provide sufficient iron to form magnetite veins (Mackin, 1954).

The theories of mobilization generally fall into one of two categories. Many geologists (best summarized by Fenner, 1933) base their theories on the high "volatility" of a halide gas (Fe_2Cl_6, $FeCl_3$). Others have emphasized the importance of hydrothermal solutions in the transport of iron. They have generally been less specific in describing such a fluid, but a liquid aqueous solution involving hydration and some dissociation is implied. The conditions of temperature and pressure we are considering are above the critical point of any such fluid, and the strict distinction of gas and liquid is lost. However, even if both water and halide are present, there is still a valid question as to whether the system is acting mainly as a simple mixture of gases (including volatile compounds), or whether appreciable interactions between iron and water give it the aspect of a solution in the usual liquid sense.

The term pneumatolytic is often associated with theories that involve volatile halides. However, a pneumatolytic fluid is defined in terms of its origin as a gas in equilibrium with a denser liquid-phase solution. The term therefore concerns the origin of the mobilizing fluid and is not pertinent to considerations of any of its properties once it is on its way to deposit iron.

The principal object of this investigation is to test experimentally some of the possible modes of transport of iron and to apply theory toward an understanding of them.

Experimental and Theoretical Program

The program is essentially one of determining the manner in which the concentration of iron in a fluid phase varies with temperature, pressure, and composition of the system. We began with an attempt to measure the solubility of magnetite in pure water at high temperature and pressure. In a second phase of the measurements, we investigated the effect of HCl on the solubility. No doubt other components, such as CO_2 and HF are also important in nature.

In order to determine whether the concentration of iron in our system actually represented a solubility, rather than the formation of an iron halide gas, Holser calculated the equilibrium concentration of iron halide gas at various temperatures and pressures.

Finally, we made direct experiments of the deposition of magnetite by a change in composition of the system.

The experimental work and many of the theoretical calculations were done in the Department of Geology at Cornell University during 1951–1954. Some of the preliminary results were reported in an abstract (Holser and Schneer, 1953), and a complete report was distributed later (Holser and Schneer, 1957). The present paper summarizes some results that may be of general interest; readers wishing further details may obtain the earlier report.

ACKNOWLEDGMENTS

The experimental program was begun in 1949 with the assistance of E-an Zen. In early 1951 the Graduate School of Cornell University made a small grant for equipment. Later in 1951 The Geological Society of America generously provided funds for equipment and supplies under Research Grant 575-51. During 1952–1954 contract Nonr-40107 with the Office of Naval Research supported the purchase of additional equipment and supplies and the salary of a research assistant. The position was filled during summers by M. Blinder, H. H. Schlanger, and H. H. Vinnedge. In 1957 the Institute of Geophysics at the University of California, Los Angeles, provided facilities for writing this summary of our experimental program. We are also indebted to R. M. Garrels, G. C. Kennedy, E. F. Osborn, and H. S. Yoder for valuable suggestions concerning the experimental program and to A. F. Buddington, F. C. Dickson, H. P. Eugster, G. C. Kennedy, George Tunell, and H. S. Yoder for constructive criticism of the original report. The investigation has depended heavily on all this support and assistance.

PREVIOUS EXPERIMENTAL WORK

The program outlined above is concerned with parts of the system Fe–O_2–H_2–Cl_2, particularly in the regions Fe_3O_4–H_2O and Fe_3O_4–H_2O–HCl. These are not true binary and ternary systems. The data on various parts of the quarternary system are voluminous.

The system Fe–O_2 has been ably summarized by Darken and Gurry (1945; 1946), who included detailed studies of oxygen pressures over the various oxides. The thermodynamic relations for the system Fe–O_2–H_2 were summarized by Ralston (1929), with later additions in the hydrogen-rich portion by Emmett and Schultz (1933), Fricke and others (1941), and Muan (1958); and in the oxygen-rich portion by Schmahl (1941). (*See* Eugster, 1959.) In the system Fe–O_2–H_2, the stable phase in the presence of water was magnetite, when there is a low hydrogen pressure, and hematite when there is a very low oxygen pressure. These data were all gathered at temperatures higher than 1000° C. and low pressures, so that as far as high-pressure liquid-phase water is concerned, they tell us only what the equilibrium solid phase may be but not the extent of its reaction with water. The system Fe–O_2–H_2 has also been treated in studies of corrosion and electrochemistry. Most of such work was done with liquid water at room temperatures; the definitive experimental study is by Corey and Finnegan (1939). Gould and Evans (1947) investigated corrosion at 100° C., and Miller and others (In press) have done some related work at higher temperatures and pressures. Here again magnetite was found to be in equilibrium with "oxygen-free" water.

The system Fe_2O_3–$FeCl_3$–H_2O–HCl was first investigated in detail by Stirnemann (1925a) who applied his results to geological problems (Stirnemann, 1925b). Stirnemann's thesis has been superseded by the detailed work of Schäfer (1950). More recent results by Wilson and Gregory (1958) do not differ substantially from Schäfer's work. These experiments were at low pressures and high temperatures and therefore concerned with gaseous reactions among the components. As such they are important in the theoretical interpretation of our results. Some work on these systems at low temperatures and low pressures has been done by Schimmel (1952), and there is a considerable volume of data on the solution chemistry of iron chlorides (Brosset, 1941; Rabinowitz and Stockmayer, 1942). Some experiments pertinent to our problem have been done on the corrosion of iron by HCl solutions (at room temperature); in particular Pryor and Evans (1949) studied the solution mechanism of hematite in acid solutions.

In summary, considerable information is available on gas-solid reactions at high temperatures and low pressures, some information on systems involving aqueous solutions at room temperature, but no information on the reactions of iron oxides with pure water or acid solutions at high temperatures and high pressures.

EXPERIMENTAL PROCEDURES

Equilibration

Measurements were made by cooking coarsely crystalline natural magnetite in a solution at constant temperature and pressure, quickly cooling, and analyzing the fluid for ferrous and ferric iron. The magnetite was from Mineville, New York, Cornell No. 237–73. Although this particular material was not analyzed, magnetite from the same locality has been found to have nearly the ideal composition (Newhouse and Glass, 1936). In most cases crystals were ground to pass 60 mesh and the very fine material removed by washing. A few measurements were made of the solubility of hematite, using Baker and Adamson reagent-grade Fe_2O_3.

The pressure vessels were 20 cc closed bombs generally like those described by Morey and Ingerson (1937), made from 303 stainless steel. Liners were needed to eliminate contamination of the solution with iron from the stainless steel: for pure water a shrink-fit ⅛-inch-thick cup of Haines No. 25 alloy; for acid solutions, a close-fitting liner spun from 0.010-inch platinum sheet. Discs of sheet platinum sealed the top.

A bomb was charged with a weighed amount (about 1 g) of magnetite, and the required amount of distilled water or acid solution was measured in with a calibrated pipette. In most of the experiments with acid solutions, magnetite samples were placed on a pedestal above the solution, to avoid reaction at low temperature at the beginning and end of the run.

A major problem in all such experiments is to

keep the system free of oxygen, other than the equilibrium concentration that might be generated by reaction between magnetite and solution. This could be accomplished satisfactorily by using distilled water that had been boiled under a neutral atmosphere and had been continuously flushed with an inert gas during the loading process. The gases used were Seaford-grade nitrogen and welding-grade argon (National Cylinder Gas Co.). Tanks of these gases were specified to contain not more than 0.002 and 0.001 volume per cent oxygen, respectively, and were not further purified. These concentrations in the loading atmosphere correspond to a maximum partial pressure of oxygen of the order of 10^{-5} bars at the experimental conditions. Some oxygen adsorbed on the bomb walls was not detected until late in the experimental program. It was removed by baking the bomb in an argon atmosphere before use. Extrapolation to 400° C. of the thermodynamic data of Darken and Gurry (1946) indicates that an oxygen pressure as low as 10^{-25} should be necessary to prevent the oxidation of magnetite to hematite. As pointed out by Muan (1958, p. 177), this is considerably less than the equilibrium oxygen pressure because of the dissociation of pure water at this temperature. Our oxygen (or hydrogen) pressure was not measured. The thermodynamic data suggest that in our experiments either (1) the oxygen pressure was kept at a sufficiently low value by a minute amount of reaction with metallic iron in the bomb wall, or (2) a very small amount of hematite was formed by oxidation of the magnetite. A low Fe^{3+}/Fe^{2+} was attained in most of our experiments, and $Fe(OH)_2$ was colored only pale grayish green in similar runs. This indicates that the magnetite was not oxidized as in (2). Reaction with the bomb wall as in (1) should have been detectable in the very sensitive iron analysis of the blank runs.

The bombs were heated in two alundum core furnaces of standard design, with the usual control and measurement of temperature. The over-all uncertainty of temperatures was less than 2° C.

The closed liners made it necessary to generate a calculated pressure by degree of filling with water. The resulting uncertainty of the specific volume, about 0.5 per cent, is principally due to uncertainty in the diameter of the cavity. The pressure calculation assumed that: (1) none of the water leaked during the run, and (2) the p-v-T relations of the fluid were not appreciably affected by the presence of ions in the solution. These assumptions could be verified only approximately. The level of water in the bomb was checked qualitatively at the end of the run, and if it was low the run was rejected. However, only a very few runs showed any visual lowering of the water level unless they were dry. Thus leakage was probably negligible in most of the recorded runs, so that although one or two runs may have been considerably in error this would not seriously affect the mean of the large number of runs. The only measurements of partial molal volume at high temperature and pressure are those of Benson and others (1953) for NaCl in the range 385°–395° C. and 240–300 bars. In this range 0.001 N NaCl lowers the pressure (relative to pure water) 0.2–0.5 bars, or 1.0–0.2 per cent. The low dissociation of HCl in this range (Fogo and others, 1954, p. 216; Franck, 1956) suggests that the effect of 0.001 HCl on the specific volume will also be small and well within the precision of specific volume measurement.

The effects on the calculated pressure, of uncertainties in specific volume and temperature, are of the same order of magnitude. The total uncertainty in pressure ranges from 1 to 3 per cent. The p-v-T data of Kennedy (1950a) for pure water were used in all the calculations. Errors introduced by that data (Holser and Kennedy, 1958; 1959) are less than those introduced by other factors, and the results were not recalculated.

Sampling and Analysis

Reprecipitation of iron during cooling was minimized as far as possible by quenching the bomb under water in a few seconds. The cap was unscrewed, a hole punched in the top seal, and four samples of solution extracted by pipette for immediate analysis. The samples could be easily removed without contamination by the original coarse grains of magnetite. Any iron that may have reprecipitated during the quenching undoubtedly did so as a colloidal hydroxide, and such dispersed material would be sampled and analyzed with any iron still in true (supersaturated?) solution.

Iron was determined colorimetrically using 1,10-(ortho) phenanthroline (monohydrate from G. F. Smith Chemical Co.). The general procedures have been summarized by Sandell (1950, p. 375–378) and Smith and Richter (1944, p. 59–79). Modifications of their technique and extreme care in analysis gave a sensitivity of somewhat better than 0.1 ppm (parts per million by weight). Concentrated reagents were added by micropipette to the 1-ml samples in special long, narrow cuvettes. The analyses were carried out in a Lumetron type 402-E colorimeter, which is a null-type photoelectric instrument. For the determination of total iron, all iron was reduced to the ferrous state with hydroxylamine hydrochloride.

A comparison of 30 paired analyses (both for ferrous and for total iron) in the usable range (0 to 2 ppm) showed a standard deviation of 0.02 ppm, not particularly dependent on the concentration. Ferric iron was determined by difference, and consequently its precision is lower; how much lower depends on the relative levels of ferrous and total iron.

The concentration of dilute HCl solutions was determined at room temperature and pressure with an electronic pH indicator.

However, the concentration is recorded in the unequivocal terms of molar concentration of HCl as a component, rather than as ionic activity. Inasmuch as we are interested in the final equilibrium state, this measurement is of the concentration at the end of the run, after the solution had been removed from the bomb.

New data published since our experiments and calculations were completed allow interpretation of the molar concentrations (Tables 1, 2) in terms of hydrogen-ion activity (the pH, by definition), at the temperature and pressure of the experiment. Franck (1956, p. 200) calculates the dissociation constant of HCl at high temperature and pressure from his conductivity measurements. From his table we deduce, for example, that a 0.0002 M HCl solution at 390° C. and 440 bars has a pH of 3.8, compared with a pH of 3.9 at room temperature and pressure. The pH of "neutral" pure water is 5.3 at the high temperature and pressure (Franck, 1956, p. 203), compared with pH = 7.0 under standard conditions.

EXPERIMENTAL RESULTS

Pure Water

Experiments made in platinum liners showed that any iron dissolved from magnetite into pure water over a considerable range of temperatures and pressures was less than the limit of sensitivity of 0.02 ppm (Table 1). A blank (water and no magnetite) run at 400° C. and 485 bars gave a similarly low result.

Some earlier experiments of lower sensitivity indicated only that dissolved iron was less than 0.6 ppm for 200–300 bars at about 400° C. and less than 0.4 ppm ion in solution for 400–1300 bars at about 500° C. Times were 40–150 hours. A few experiments on the solubility of synthetic hematite were also of low sensitivity but still gave less than 0.2 ppm at 500–1100 bars and about 500° C. The length of runs was 40–100 hours.

TABLE 1.—EXPERIMENTS ON SOLUTION OF MAGNETITE IN PURE WATER AT HIGH TEMPERATURE AND PRESSURE

Experiment no.	Temperature (°C.)	Pressure (bars)	Time (hours)	Analysis of solution, ppm Fe^{2+}	Fe^{3+}
193	494	1185	94	0.02	0.01
194	509	1260	67	0.00	0.02
195	299	1025	46	0.01	0.01
196	183	690	93	0.00	0.03

HCl Solutions at High Temperature

Fifteen runs equilibrated to 0.0002 M HCl (starting concentrations 0.001 M HCl) at about 390° C. and 440 bars. An equal number of runs was made at other temperatures, pressures, and concentrations. (See Table 2.) Several blank (acid solution without magnetite) runs under various conditions gave total iron of less than 1 ppm.

The analyses in the range 380°–400° C., 499–480 bars, for about 0.0002 M HCl, fall into two groups (with a single exception): 0–25 ppm and 250–300 ppm ferrous (and total) iron. The latter are believed to approximate the true solubility, for the following reasons. Late in the series of experiments it was discovered that some of the runs giving low values also showed a thin deposit of hematite on the magnetite. Oxygen contamination was suspected as the cause of the low values, and this was confirmed by sweeping run 284 with oxygen instead of with an inert gas. The contamination was not observed in many of the runs, and therefore it probably did not come from the gas used for a loading atmosphere. It may have been adsorbed on the liner wall while the bomb was being cleaned in air between runs. This proposition was tested in the last two runs by baking the bomb and liner at 180° C. in an argon atmosphere just before loading in an argon atmosphere. High iron concentrations were obtained in both of these runs.

The experimental program had to be stopped at this point. Further experiments to check these conclusions would have been desirable. Removing the uncertainty of the solubility in this restricted range would have helped interpret the determinations made at other temperatures, pressures, and acid concentrations. The partial correlation between iron and acid concentration was significant (at the 5 per cent level). This is consistent with the iron concentration of 0.02 ppm previously obtained for zero acid concentration. The results of our experiments are too variable to indicate consistently any change of iron concentration with temperature or pressure in the range 200°–500° C. and up to 1100 bars. A similar lack of correlation between iron concentration and length of run indicates that the analyses represent equilibrium concentrations to at least the precision of these determinations.

TABLE 2.—EXPERIMENTS ON SOLUTION OF MAGNETITE IN HCl SOLUTIONS AT HIGH TEMPERATURE AND PRESSURE

Experiment no.	Loading atmosphere*	Molar concentration of HCl (final)	Temperature (°C.)	Pressure (bars)	Time (hours)	Analysis of solution, ppm Fe^{2+}	Fe^{3+}
202	N_2	0.000002	379	380	71	0.24	0.04
204	N_2	0.000005	383	400	42	0.00	0.03
205	N_2	0.000005	388	420	141	0.01	0.02
207	N_2	0.0003	388	420	119	4.7	1.1
221	N_2	0.00016	393	450	120	17.4	1.0
257	N_2	0.00009	382	360	49	14.8	2.7
259	A	0.00013	390	410	108	17.8	0.0
260	A	0.00009	389	410	163	297.	19.
262	A	0.00016	391	420	46	256.	8.
267	A	0.00015	375	320	47	265.	4.
273	A	0.00013	403	490	44	295.	2.
274	A	0.00013	391	430	44	264.	5.
275	A	0.00016	400	480	19	2.40	0.22
276	A	0.00016	391	420	17	254.	6.
277	A	0.00016	299	85†	24	165.	7.
278	A	0.00016	296	81†	24	193.	4.
279	A	0.00018	350	165	23	164.	4.
280	A	0.00017	345	155	23	87.	5.
281	A	0.00016	502	1130	19	14.9	0.6
282	A	0.00019	495	1090	19	7.4	0.6
283	A	0.00016	199	15†	18	4.6	0.5
284	O_2	0.00015	400	480	17	6.9	0.2
285	H_2	0.00014	401	480	17	26.	0.
286	H_2	0.00015	401	480	40	16.3	0.5
287	A**	0.0008	383	360	16	214.	3.
288	A**	0.00023	398	470	41	284.	0.

* All experiments were in bombs lined with platinum or tantalum sheet.
† Sample was in the denser of the two fluid phases.
** Bomb was baked out at 180° C. in A atmosphere before loading.

Eight earlier experiments were made in approximately 10^{-6} M HCl at 180°–300° C. and saturation pressure always in the vapor phase. Analyses did not exceed the sensitivity limit of 1 ppm.

Other Solutions at High Temperature

A few experiments with solutions other than HCl provide supporting data. The experiments gave only a maximum value of possible iron content.

A number of experiments were run at 500° C. and 1000 bars in solutions buffered at pH = 9.0 (sodium borate) and pH = 6.1 (sodium bicarbonate). Analyses were less than the background level of 1 ppm.

Four experiments were made with 0.0008 M NaOH solution in the range 330°–550° C. at about 1000 bars. The analyses on these early runs were made by a visual method with a sensitivity of 2 ppm iron, and neither the runs with magnetite nor the blank runs showed any detectable iron.

Another eight experiments were made with magnetite in (neutral) 0.20 M NaCl solution at about 500° C. and 500 bars. Solution of silver from the liner used in these experiments interfered with the iron analyses, but in no case was the amount above this background of 5 ppm.

HCl Solutions at Room Temperature

The variations of solubility of magnetite in HCl solutions at high temperature and pressure suggested a comparison with the similar variability at room temperature and pressure. It is well known that at room conditions magnetite dissolves in concentrated HCl at a rapid rate, and that no solubility is measured in pure water. If a reasonable assumption is made concerning the mechanism of solution, a theoretical curve of equilibrium iron concentration as it varies with, say, hydrogen-ion concentration, might be derived from available thermodynamic data. However, the lack of specific measurements and some uncertainty concerning the solution mechanism made it desirable to measure solubility.

An excess of −60-mesh magnetite, doubly washed to remove fines, was placed in about 100 ml of HCl of appropriate concentration, in a Pyrex Erlenmeyer flask. The HCl solution was swept with argon before adding the magnetite and during subsequent measurements. The flasks were sealed with wax between measurements. For convenience, they were kept at laboratory temperature, which ranged between 20° and 25° C. during the experiments. Diffusion, convection, and time, rather than mechanical mixing, were depended on for attainment of equilibrium.

Seven experiments were run at initial HCl concentrations ranging from 1 M to 10^{-6} M. The solutions were sampled with a micropipette at intervals of increasing length; the total lengths of the experiments were 330–490 days. The samples were analyzed for ferrous and total iron, and also for acid concentration by the pH meter.

Results of the numerous analyses are outlined in Figure 1. Final analyses for ferrous and ferric iron are plotted against final acid concentration. Approximate equilibrium concentrations are indicated by lines, as determined by the following considerations. For HCl concentrations below 10^{-4}, analyses reached a steady value in 20 or 30 days, and this was assumed to be an equilibrium concentration. With higher concentrations of HCl, the iron concentration continued to increase with time until the end of the runs. Therefore, the solution rate was plotted against concentration to find an approximate value toward which the data were trending. This approximation became increasingly uncertain with increasing HCl concentration because the data showed no decrease of solution rate with time. The relative precision of the analytical method decreases to zero between 0.1 and 0.01 ppm, and ferric iron is determined by difference. Many of the very low values are probably overestimates.

Hydrothermal Synthesis of Magnetite

After we established that measurable amounts of iron could be mobilized in HCl solutions at high temperature and pressure, but not in neutral or alkaline solutions, it was evident that such a solution should deposit magnetite with an increase in the pH. At room temperature, the acidity of a solution of iron chlorides could be reduced by reaction with calcium carbonate. However, this change in pH is accomplished at the expense of adding another component to the system. Calcite is a likely candidate for such a reaction in view of the natural occurrence of iron oxides in limestones, and qualitative experiments were made with it. Magnetite had previously been synthesized from iron chlorides and calcite (for example, *see* Vinogradov and Dontsova, 1952), but always at low pressures.

Iron chloride solutions were made up to about 1000 ppm Fe^{3+} and 500 ppm Fe^{2+}, with a pH of about 2. A measured quantity of the solution was placed in the bottom of the bomb, and a weighed calcium carbonate sample placed on a platinum pedestal above the solution. The experiments were made using temperatures and pressures along the steam saturation line in order to minimize reaction while the bomb was being raised to temperature. In two of the experiments, finely ground calcite was packed inside a short length of capillary Inconel tubing in order to slow down the rate of reaction. In four other experiments, a cleavage rhomb of optical grade calcite was placed in the open on the pedestal. The runs lasted 24 to 77 hours.

At a temperature of 320° C. with either arrangement, the principal product was crystalline magnetite. Under high magnification the cleavage surface of the calcite was found to be covered with minute etch pits, many of them occupied by sharp octahedra of magnetite (truncated slightly by dodecahedral faces). (*See* Plate 1.) The X-ray-powder diffraction pattern was identical with that of our standard Mineville magnetite.

At temperatures of 240° and 150° C. the X-ray diffraction patterns of the products indicated approximately 70 and 90 per cent hematite, respectively, with the remainder magnetite. There are not sufficient observations to attach very much significance to this variation of reaction product with temperature.

Analyses of the solutions after the runs showed less than 200 ppm Fe^{2+} and less than 20 ppm Fe^{3+}, with pH between 5 and 6. Some of the iron probably precipitated at preparation pressure and temperature. Although these experiments did not necessarily establish equilibrium, the magnitude of the iron concentrations is consistent with the solubility measurements.

These qualitative experiments confirm the anticipated deposition of magnetite by neutralization of iron chloride solutions at geologically significant temperatures and pressures and emphasize the disproportionately greater effect on solubility of composition as compared with temperature and pressure.

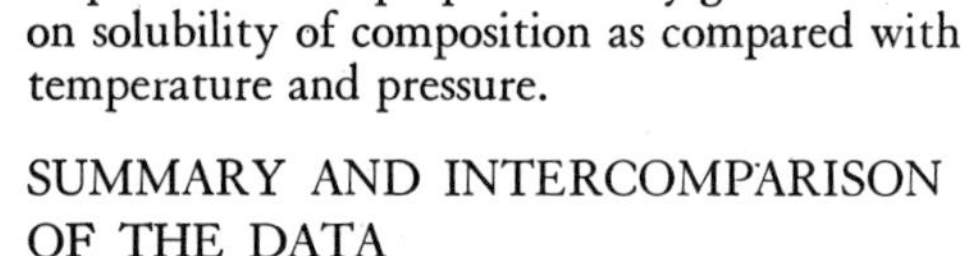

SUMMARY AND INTERCOMPARISON OF THE DATA

Variations with Temperature and Pressure

The best value of iron concentration in acid solution was 300 ppm in 0.0002 M HCl at about 390° C., 440 bars, and a specific volume of 1.77. The data for 22° C., 1 bar, specific volume 1.00 (Fig. 1) may be interpolated to give a value of 1.3 ppm at the same HCl concentration. The measurements were too rough to show any consistent trend among the high-temperature measurements themselves.

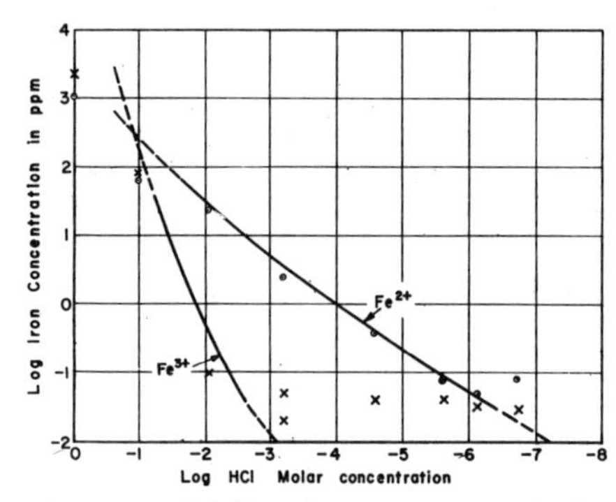

Figure 1. Solubility of magnetite in HCl solutions at room temperature and pressure. Concentrations measured at the end of 300–500 days experiments are indicated by circles for Fe^{2+} and crosses for Fe^{3+}. The equilibrium concentrations shown by the lines are inferred from this data as discussed in the text.

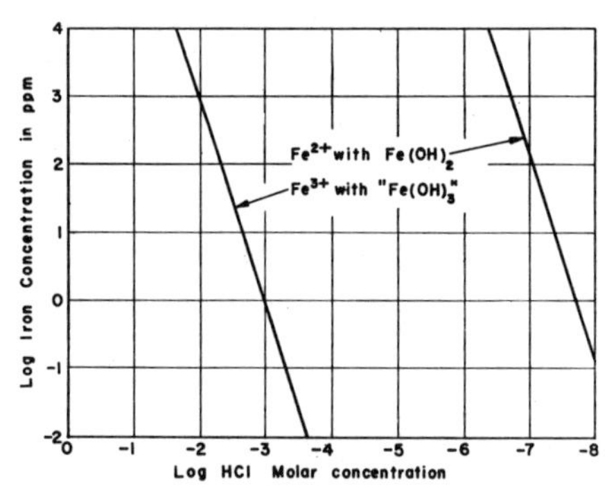

Figure 2. Theoretical solubility of iron hydroxides at room temperature and pressure as calculated from thermodynamic data (equations 7–11). This diagram may be compared with the solubility determination for magnetite, which is shown in Figure 1 at the same scale.

Variations with Acid Concentration

The decrease of iron with decreasing acid concentration, as indicated roughly by analysis of Table 2, is consistent with the value of less than 0.02 ppm iron in pure water (Table 1). Note the very low iron in HCl concentrations of about 10^{-6} M (Table 2, experiments 202–205). The maximum established for iron concentration in "buffered" solutions is also consistent with this correlation of solubility with acid concentration. They furthermore suggest that the observed decrease may be continued into the range of basic solutions, and that it may be in some measure independent of the acidic anion.

Figure 1 confirms the analogous decrease of iron with decreasing acid concentration that would be expected at room temperature and pressure.

Relations of Ferrous to Ferric Iron in Solution

The best analyses of supercritical HCl solutions showed very low concentrations of ferric iron, of the order of 1 ppm. Inasmuch as ferric iron was determined by difference, and the precisions of the ferrous and total iron determinations are about 2 per cent each, the measured values of ferric iron may only be interpreted as rough upper limits to the possible concentration. Figure 1 indicates that for a similar acid concentration at room temperature, ferric iron in solution also is at an unmeasurably low value. At room temperature the concentration of ferric iron in equilibrium with magnetite rises steeply as the HCl concentration is increased above that of 10^{-2} M. Thus the rather surprising result, that all the iron in solution at high temperatures and pressures is ferrous iron, may possibly be understood in terms of the results at room temperatures, as discussed below.

Comparison with Other Published Data

The only pertinent solubilities at high temperature were published by Morey (1957, p. 242; Morey and Hesselgesser, 1951), who measured the solubility in pure water of a number of oxides, including hematite but not magnetite. Morey found 90 ppm of Fe_2O_3 dissolved from hematite at 500° C. and 1000 bars. However, Morey found some iron oxide dissolved in all his experiments with other minerals. Presumably this came from solution of the walls of his Inconel X bomb, although no blank runs were made. Morey's method was a dynamic one, in which the solution was moved through the bomb under pressure. The conditions of the experiments indicate that each portion of water remained in the bomb in contact with mineral for only about 30–60 minutes. The short duration of these runs therefore would tend to make his values low, if anything. Therefore contamination of Morey's samples by solution from the metallic iron of the bomb may not be sufficient to explain the discrepancy between his results and ours. Although most other oxides (Morey, 1957, p. 242) had lower solubilities than hematite, the lowest solubility (0.2 ppm for uraninite) was higher than those we obtained for magnetite in pure water.

INTERPRETATION

Solubility and Volatility

We believe that the mechanism mainly responsible for the mobility of iron in our HCl–H_2O mixtures at high temperature and pressure is of the same general type that operates in similar mixtures in the liquid phase at room temperature and pressure. We wish to demonstrate the complete inadequacy of another sort of process that can operate in gaseous systems, in which iron might be mobilized as a gas in molecular combination with chlorine. This distinction is particularly important, in view of the extensive speculation on gas processes in the geological literature.

A common type of solution is that of a salt in liquid water. One may also think of a solution of a salt in steam. In both cases the solubility of the salt is a result of an interaction, "solvation," of the salt component and the water to form the solution. On the other hand, a salt may have an appreciable vapor pressure by itself—this might be called its volatility—an entirely different sort of effect. If a fluid contains a given amount of a salt component in equilibrium with the solid salt, what part of that amount is a result of a simple volatility of the salt, and what part is due to interaction of the pure fluid and the salt component? The part due to fluid-salt interaction might be thought of as a "true," or "liquid-type," solubility and will hereafter be called solubility, with due recognition of the fact that even a simple mixture of gases is a solution in strict thermodynamic nomenclature.

Solubility, as defined above, is found by subtracting from the total of mobilized component the fraction due to volatility. At low total pressure the amount due to volatility can be calculated directly from the applicable thermodynamic equilibrium constant, taking into account any compounds formed by the mobile component as it vaporizes. Then as total pressure is increased, some of the changes in concentration of the mobile component are characteristic of the molecular species already present at low pressure, not of new phenomena of interaction with the "solvent." These are: (1) the increase in vapor pressure of the solid due to change in total pressure, and (2) the departure of individual gases from their low-pressure ideality.

The following calculations show that the iron concentrations measured in the present study were not significantly affected by volatility of iron chloride but represented solvent action. An HCl concentration of 2.7 M would be needed to volatilize as little as 1 ppm of iron as $FeCl_2$ gas under the conditions of temperature and water pressure of the experiments. This is several orders of magnitude different from the 300 ppm iron measured at 0.0002 M HCl.

Calculation of Theoretical Iron Halide-Gas Equilibria at High Temperature and Pressure

The volatility of iron chlorides is demonstrated by their vapor pressures in approximately single component systems. For example, at 500° C. ferric chloride is a liquid with a vapor pressure of 9.5 bars Fe_2Cl_6 gas (Stirnemann, 1925a, p. 353; Schäfer, 1950, p. 143) and 0.2 bars $FeCl_3$ gas (Schäfer, 1949, p. 68; 1950, p. 143). This is not strictly a single component system, inasmuch as the ferric chloride dissociates slightly to crystalline $FeCl_2$ and gaseous Cl_2. For the stated conditions the chlorine pressure is 0.1 bar (Schäfer and Oehler, 1953, p. 212). In contrast the vapor pressure of crystalline $FeCl_2$ at 500° C. must be less than 10^{-5} bar, found by extrapolating the higher-temperature liquid–vapor pressure data of Schäfer and Krehl (1952, p. 36).

At earth pressures any system involving only one of these components would be "condensed." But if an inert gas was present, the iron could be concentrated in the vapor in proportion to its vapor pressure. If we neglect the small increase of vapor pressure with increase of total pressure and assume a geological temperature of 500° C. and total pressure of 500 bars, a vapor pressure of 10^{-4} bars might be significant (see below). Evidently Fe_2Cl_6 is the only volatile species of importance. In the following calculations we shall make the generous assumptions that the volatile iron is present as Fe_2Cl_6 molecular gas, that the HCl concentration (relative to water) is as high as 0.001 M, and that the temperature and pressure are as high as 500° C. and 500 bars.

It has long been known that the simple single-component volatility of the iron halides is not even a first approximation to a natural situation. The concentration of iron halides in the vapor state is very sharply restricted by the presence of component water, because it reacts to form iron oxide. The equation

$$Fe_2O_3(c) + 6HCl(g) \rightleftharpoons Fe_2Cl_6(l) + 3H_2O(g) \quad (1)$$

(where the nature of a phase is indicated by *c*-crystal, *l*-liquid, and *g*-gas) is displaced strongly to the left. In measuring the thermodynamic equilibrium constant

$$K_1 = \frac{[Fe_2Cl_6]\,[H_2O]^3}{[HCl]^6} \quad (2)$$

at very low pressures (ideal gas), each bracketed fugacity may be replaced by a formal partial pressure, p_x, or a product of the mole fraction, n, times the total pressure, p:

$$K_1 = \frac{p_{Fe_2Cl_6} \cdot p^3_{H_2O}}{p^6_{HCl}} = \frac{n_{Fe_2Cl_6} \cdot n^3_{H_2O}}{p^2 n^6_{HCl}} \quad (3)$$

The value measured by Schäfer (1949, p. 71) for 500° C. (and pressure in bars) is $9.38 \cdot 10^{-7}$. Solving for a concentration of iron chloride would give

$$n_{Fe_2Cl_6} = K_1 p^2 \frac{n^6_{HCl}}{n^3_{H_2O}} = 9.38 \cdot 10^{-7} \cdot 500^2 \cdot \frac{(1.81 \cdot 10^{-5})^6}{1.00} = 8.9 \cdot 10^{-30}\ mole/mole, \text{ or } 5.5 \cdot 10^{-23}\ ppm\ Fe \quad (4)$$

if the gases were still ideal at that pressure. Stated in another way, a concentration of 8.9 M HCl is required to keep as little as 1 ppm iron in the gas phase. The value for the equilibrium constant, determined by Stirnemann (1925a) and used in his similar calculations, was larger than Schäfer's by a factor of 200; this led to a correspondingly larger iron concentration.

For nonideal gases, we assume that the fugacity of a gas depends only on its formal partial pressure, and not on interactions with other components. This is a precise assumption in that it defines the conditions of volatility that we are trying to calculate; otherwise "true" fugacities that take account of interactions would give results that are really a form of solubility. It is convenient to use the fugacity coefficient ν_x, which is the ratio of fugacity to the actual partial pressure. In these terms equation (2) becomes:

$$K_1 = \frac{n_{Fe_2Cl_6} \cdot n^3_{H_2O}}{p^2 \cdot n^6_{HCl}} \cdot \frac{\nu_{Fe_2Cl_6} \cdot \nu^3_{H_2O}}{\nu^6_{HCl}} \quad (5)$$

The fugacity coefficient of water was calculated for this purpose (Holser, 1953) from Kennedy's (1950a) p-v-T data. Fugacity coefficients for HCl and Fe_2Cl_6 were estimated by the principle of corresponding states (Hirschfelder, Curtiss, and Bird, 1954, p. 235–239). Using critical points measured for HCl and guessed from empirical rules for Fe_2Cl_6

(Hirschfelder, Curtiss, and Bird, 1954, p. 238, 252), we entered reduced temperatures and pressures for 500 bars and 500° C. on Newton's (1935) average graphs. Substituting these fugacity coefficients in equation (5) gives:

$$n_{Fe_2Cl_6} = K_1 p^2 \frac{n^6_{HCl}}{n^3_{H_2O}} \cdot \frac{\nu^6_{HCl}}{\nu_{Fe_2Cl_6} \cdot \nu^3_{H_2O}} \tag{6}$$

$$= 8.9 \cdot 10^{-30} \frac{1.01^6}{0.042 \cdot 0.655^3}$$

$$= 8.0 \cdot 10^{-29} \; mole/mole \text{ or } 5.0 \cdot 10^{-22} \; ppm \; Fe.$$

This is 90 times as much iron as calculated for an ideal gas but is still an insignificant amount, and no reasonable variation of our approximations could make it significant. The corresponding concentration of HCl necessary to mobilize 1 ppm Fe as Fe_2Cl_6 gas is 2.7 M.

We conclude that volatility of iron halides does not account for any significant proportion of the equilibrium concentration of iron in HCl solutions equilibrated with magnetite. The measured iron concentration may be confidently assigned to some sort of interaction between fluid and solid and designated as true solubility. This conclusion seems to contradict calculations recently published by Krauskopf (1957), who finds 0.5 ppm Fe in a magmatic vapor 0.06 M in HCl at 600° C. and 1000 bars. Although Krauskopf took into account the effect of reactions with sulfides, he did not allow for the reaction of water with the iron chloride (equation 1), which is the principal deterrent to halide gas transport of iron in a natural system.

Mechanism of Solution

General statement. The nature of iron solutions has been studied previously at room temperature by a wide variety of measurements of E.M.F., conductivity, vapor pressure, and spectrophotometry. The solubility of magnetite in acid solutions at room temperature can be interpreted first in relation to these data. Then the interpretation may be tentatively extrapolated to the high-temperature measurements.

Relation of room-temperature measurements to hydroxide solubilities. The solution of ferrous hydroxide may be represented by

$$Fe(OH)_2(c) \rightleftharpoons Fe^{2+}(aq) + 2(OH)^-(aq), \tag{7}$$

where *aq* indicates an aqueous solution phase. The solubility product has been evaluated by Miller and others (In press) from new measurements made by four methods:

$$K_7 = [Fe^{2+}][OH^-]^2 = 10^{-15.60} \tag{7a}$$

including a critical evaluation of 18 earlier determinations. The hydroxyl-ion activity in equation (7a) is in turn related to the hydrogen-ion activity through the ionization constant of water

$$K_8 = [H^+][OH^-] = 10^{-14.17}. \tag{8}$$

From these two constants one can calculate how the Fe^{2+} activity increases with hydrogen-ion activity (pH), according to the equation

$$Fe(OH)_2(c) + 2H^+(aq) \rightleftharpoons Fe^{2+}(aq) + 2H_2O(l)$$

$$K^9 = \frac{[Fe^{2+}]}{[H^+]^2} = \frac{K_7}{K_8^2}. \tag{9}$$

At these great dilutions the activities may be equated to the respective ionic concentrations. The results of this calculation are graphed in Figure 2.

The analogous calculation for ferric hydroxide is not so clearly defined. The reaction is usually written

$$Fe(OH)_3(c) \rightleftharpoons Fe^{3+}(aq) + 3\,OH^-(aq) \tag{10}$$

with a solubility product as evaluated from available data by Cooper (1937):

$$K_{Fe(OH)_3} = [Fe^{3+}][OH^-]^3 = 10^{-38.6}.$$

But while $Fe(OH)_2$ is a crystalline species whose unit activity is closely approached by the material measured by Miller, $Fe(OH)_3$ is an indefinite term either for a red ferric oxide sol, which insofar as it is crystalline has the hematite structure, or for a yellow ferric oxide monohydrate sol, with the geothite structure (Weiser, 1935, p. 39, 44). Most of the measurements have probably been made on the former material, but even this material is highly variable in particle size and content of adsorbed ions, both of which affect its activity and the calculated solubility product (Lamb and Jacques, 1938, p. 1224; Evans and Pryor, 1949). Hematite is unstable relative to goethite at room temperature (Smith and Kidd, 1949; Schmalz, 1959). With these reservations in mind, we calculated and plotted the total ferric iron in equilibrium with "$Fe(OH)_3$" from the above constant (Fig. 2).

The increasing solubility of magnetite with increasing acid concentrations follows a similar trend, which suggests that a reaction with

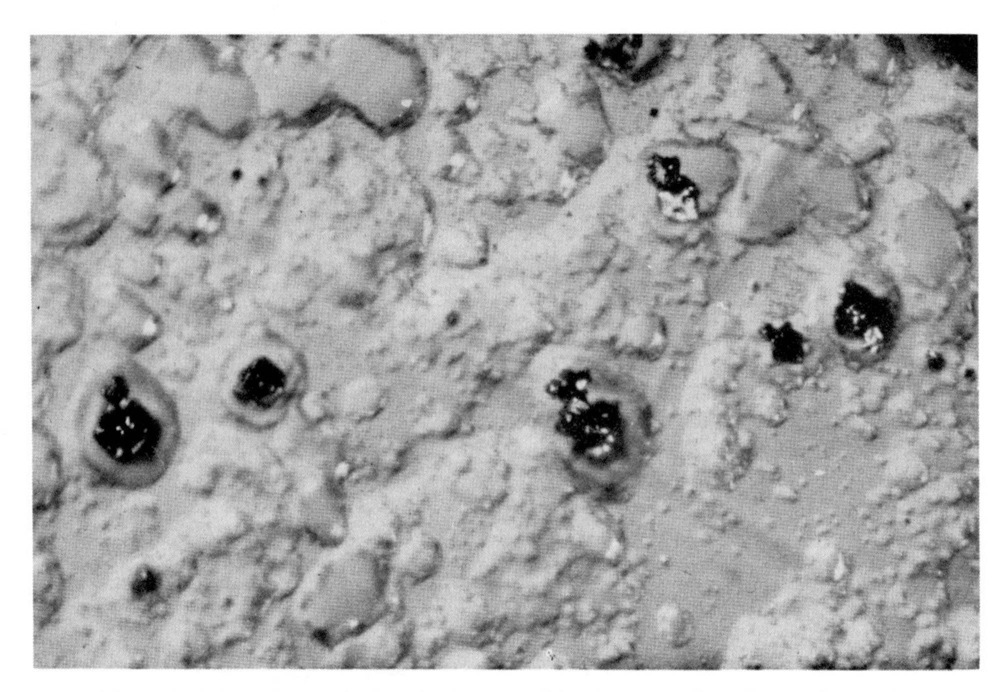

Figure 1. Magnetite crystals in etch pits on a calcite cleavage surface. Formed by reaction of iron chloride solutions with calcite in the gas phase at 320° C. ×100

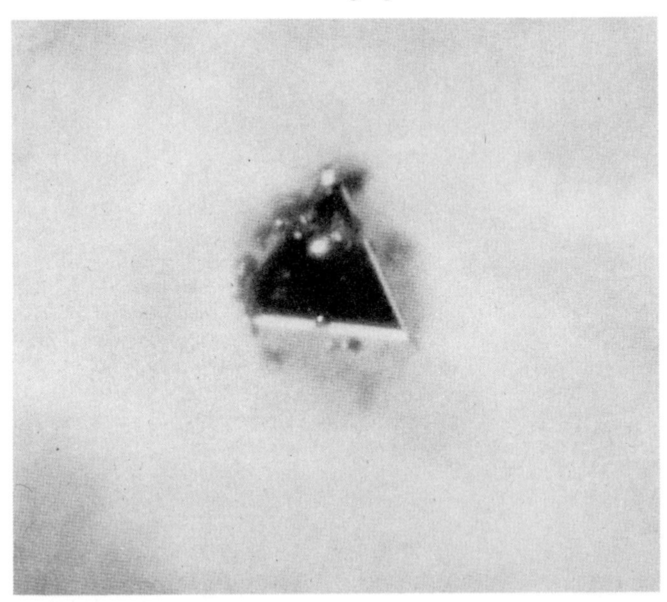

Figure 2. A single magnetite crystal in an etch pit. Same conditions as Figure 1. ×500

PHOTOMICROGRAPHS OF SYNTHETIC HYDROTHERMAL MAGNETITE

HOLSER AND SCHNEER, PLATE 1

hydrogen ion is responsible for the solution of magnetite at room temperature. However, the amount of ferrous iron in equilibrium with magnetite should be substantially lower than that in equilibrium with ferrous hydroxide at the same acid concentration, because ferrous hydroxide decomposes to magnetite in oxygen-free water, according to the following equation:

$$3Fe(OH)_2(c) \rightleftharpoons FeFe_2O_4(c) + 2H_2O(l) + H_2(g). \quad (11)$$

This reaction has been studied by Hüttig and Moldner (1931), Corey and Finnegan (1939), and Fricke and Rihl (1943).

The above considerations show why the solubility of ferrous iron from magnetite should lie below the solubility curve for ferrous hydroxide, as observed. However, if the solution of magnetite were to proceed strictly by analogy with equation (9):

$$FeFe_2O_4(c) + 8H^+(aq) \rightleftharpoons Fe^{2+}(aq) + Fe^{3+}(aq) + 4H_2O(l); \quad (12)$$

then the concentration of ferric iron should always be twice that of ferrous iron. In fact (Fig. 1) ferric iron is less than ferrous iron for concentrations of HCl below 10^{-2} and is imperceptible for concentrations below 10^{-3}. This suggests that the solution of magnetite in low HCl concentrations goes according to an equation like

$$2FeFe_2O_4(c) + 12H^+(aq) \rightleftharpoons 6Fe^{2+}(aq) + 6H_2O(l) + O_2(g) \quad (13)$$

which may also be written

$$FeFe_2O_4(c) + 6H^+(aq) + H_2(g) \rightleftharpoons 3Fe^{2+}(aq) + 4H_2O(l). \quad (13a)$$

Equation (13) also accounts for the strong inhibition of solubility by presence of small amounts of oxygen. It does not account for the shallow slope of the curve (Fig. 1) for ferrous iron vs acid concentration.

Another possibility is that the ferric ions in the magnetite structure are not reduced into solution. An equation may be written as follows:

$$FeFe_2O_4(c) + 2H^+(aq) \rightleftharpoons Fe^{2+}(aq) + \text{``}Fe_2O_3\text{''} + H_2O(l). \quad (14)$$

This equation is nonspecific in that "Fe_2O_3" is a component of an unspecified solid phase. In this respect there seem to be three possibilities: (1) the ferric oxide is present as "colloidal Fe_2O_3," (2) it is present as crystalline hematite, or (3) it is present as ferric ions in the magnetite structure. Ferric iron may remain behind either as a new precipitate, as crystalline hematite, or as a solid solution in the magnetite-maghemite series. We observed a thin irregular film of red hematite coating the magnetite charge in some of the runs.

Pryor and Evans (1949) studied the dissolution of hematite in acid solutions. Their procedure was similar to ours, although most of their experiments were for only 1 hour. Their resulting curve of ferric iron from hematite lies near our curve for ferrous iron from magnetite, down to their minimum concentration of 10^{-3} M HCl, but has even smaller slope. They also found a small amount of ferrous iron in longer runs at low acid concentrations. They interpreted this as preferential solution of non-stoichiometric ferrous ions from the hematite structure, but it may also be due to reduction of ferrous iron in dilute acid. (*See* equations 13–14.)

Role of Complex Ions in Iron Halide Solutions. The formation of complex ions can increase the total iron in solution, if other conditions are equal.

The iron complex $FeOH^{2+}$ is particularly important at high pH. The investigations of Cooper (1937), Lamb and Jacques (1938), and Brosset (1941) give association constants that indicate more iron as the complex than as free Fe^{3+} ions, at pH above 2.5. Lamb and Jacques (1938), Arden (1951), and Ito and Yui (1953) also postulate a further association to $Fe(OH)_2^+$. Therefore this complex may be important in stabilizing the small amount of ferric iron detected by us in the range of concentrations from 10^{-2} to 10^{-3} M HCl.

As the concentration of the HCl solutions increases, ferric iron associates with chlorine to form the complex ions $FeCl^{2+}$, $FeCl_2^+$ (Brosset, 1941; Rabinowitz and Stockmayer, 1942; Siddall and Vosburgh, 1951), and finally in very concentrated solutions $FeCl_4^-$ (Friedman, 1952), or Fe_2Cl_6 (Brady, 1958). The first of these is the major complex in the acidity range of our measurements on magnetite, and the measured equilibrium constants indicate that it may be important in fixing the total ferric iron in solution at concentrations of HCl greater than 10^{-2}.

The solution chemistry of ferrous iron contrasts strikingly with the above data on ferric iron. Stokes and Robinson (1948) show by detailed measurements that ferrous chloride is a strong electrolyte, dissociating completely in aqueous solution, although a small concentration of $Fe(OH)^+$ may be present at high pH (Leussing and Kolthoff, 1953). The Fe^{2+} ion is hydrated with about 12 water molecules, as are many other simple cations (Robinson and Stokes, 1949). Even in very concentrated solutions it does not form complexes with HCl (Schimmel, 1952).

Summarizing the information for room-temperature solutions, we conclude that although not all features of the experiments have been satisfactorily explained, the principal cause of solution over most of the range of concentration is probably the reaction with hydrogen ions represented by equation (13). At HCl concentrations greater than 0.1 M, equation (12) becomes important, and ferric iron increases sharply. The solution of ferric iron in these highly acid solutions is aided by the formation of the complex ion $FeCl^{2+}$, and in the less acid solutions the small amount of ferric iron is enhanced by $FeOH^{2+}$. Ferrous iron does not form complex ions.

Solubility Mechanism at High Temperature and Pressure. At high temperature and pressure the experiments (Table 2) show an increase of iron concentration with increasing acid concentration, and a lack of ferric iron in the solution, both of which parallel the more detailed observations at room temperature. The decomposition of $Fe(OH)_2$ to magnetite (equation 13) is even faster at high temperature; it has been observed up to 290°C. (Berl and van Taack, 1928; Miller and others, in press). All this suggests that the dissolution of magnetite at high temperature and pressure also proceeds by a hydrogen-ion reaction similar to that of equation (13) above.

The importance of complex ions in the solutions at high temperature and pressure is difficult to evaluate, particularly in view of the fact (Franck, 1956; Fogo and others, 1954, p. 216) that HCl is no longer a strong electrolyte under these conditions. Rabinowitz and Stockmayer (1942, p. 340–341) observed that the stabilities of $FeOH^{2+}$ and $FeCl^{2+}$ ions increase markedly with temperature in the range 25°–45° C., and this is interpreted in terms of an endothermal process in formation of complex ions. Friedman (1952) studied the spectra of one of the complex ions, $FeCl_4^-$, in media of low dielectric constant, and found the complex still stable. The weak dissociation of NaCl and HCl, at 390° C. and critical density, suggests that the usually strong electrolyte $FeCl_2$ may also tend to be more highly associated under these conditions. Thus the formation of complex ions might be important in the solubility process at high temperature, even for ferrous iron.

Table 3.—Equivalent Molar Concentration of HCl in Some Natural Fluids

Source	Maximum	Minimum	Mean	Number	Reference
Kilauea volcanic gases	0.22*	0.00	0.04	24	Shepherd (1938, p. 321)
Vesuvius volcanic gases	0.09	0.00	0.03	3	Gautier (1909)
Katmai fumarolic gases	0.31	0.003	0.07	15	Allen (1922, p. 80)
White Island fumarolic gases			0.25	4	Wilson (1953)
Amygdules in Japanese lavas	0.0006	0.000	0.0001	5	Kokubu and others (1957, p. 157)
Gases from various rocks in vacuo	0.29*	0.004	0.17	20	Shepherd (1938, p. 326)
Fluid inclusions in various pegmatitic minerals	0.05	0.00	0.02	6	Wahler (1956, p. 129, 135)

* Less a single erratically high analysis.

Geological Implications

Anything less than 1 ppm iron in solution is not significant in the formation of hydrothermal iron-ore deposits. Huber and Garrels (1953, p. 354) use 3 ppm for sedimentary iron ores. Evidently pure water cannot provide even this small amount in solution.

But what HCl concentrations are available to increase solubility in natural fluids? Table 3 was calculated on the assumption that H_2 and Cl_2 are combined at equilibrium into HCl, and this is mixed with the H_2O to form an HCl solution. At 500° C. the thermodynamic equilibrium constant for the formation of HCl is $4.5 \cdot 10^{16}$ (Lewis and Randall, 1923, p. 503), and this is reduced only as far as $2.5 \cdot 10^{16}$ when the effect of real gases at 500 bars is taken into account. Effectively all the

H_2 or all the Cl_2 (in some cases Cl^- was used) will react to form HCl, depending upon which is in the least concentration.

When the diversity of the analytical methods and the sources of material are considered, it is surprising that this series of analyses is concordant in order of magnitude. Only two single analyses from Kilauea (Shepherd, 1938) and from Mihara (Iwasake, 1951) show exceptionally high values of .66 and 1.4 M HCl respectively. Possibly much of the chlorine in igneous rocks corresponds to a similar concentration of HCl in the original magma or its derivative solutions. Kuroda and Sandell (1953) found 0.022 per cent Cl in granitic rocks; if this were HCl dissolved in the usual 1 per cent water, the concentration would be 0.6 M.

These considerations place some restrictions on the chloride and possible HCl concentrations that may be expected in natural fluids. Concentrations in the range 0.01–0.1M are probably common, but concentrations higher than 0.5 M are unlikely. Similar considerations led Krauskopf (1957, p. 793) to find a concentration of 0.06 M HCl. The simple assumptions neglect many reactions that may have changed the compositions of the solutions (Fyfe, Turner, and Verhoogen, 1958, p. 144–146; Ellis, 1957, p. 423).

Our measurements show that geologically significant concentrations of iron can be mobilized at temperatures and pressures similar to those at which hydrothermal deposits were formed and in solutions two orders of magnitude more dilute in HCl than these natural fluids. Transport by HCl solutions can therefore be important in the formation of some magnetite deposits. Further high-temperature experiment is necessary to compare solubilities in HCl solutions with those in other important acids such as HF and H_2CO_3. The importance of the latter is well attested by the geological work of Behrend (1934), the low-temperature experiments of Huber and Garrels (1953, p. 355), and a few observations by Morey (Abelson, 1954, p. 123) at high temperature and pressure.

The solubility of iron compounds in all these solvents will undoubtedly decrease with decreasing acid concentration, and we can suggest no mechanism by which it will increase in basic solutions. Shand (1947) was forced to depend upon a ferrous hydroxide hydrosol for transport in an alkaline medium. However, the instability of this sol at high temperatures has already been pointed out above (Solubility Mechanism at High Temperatures), and the ineffectiveness of colloidal suspensions in the replacement process has been discussed in detail elsewhere (Holser, 1947, p. 387–388). On the other hand, it is difficult to reconcile acid transport of iron with the cogent arguments of many petrologists (Shand, 1947; Kennedy, 1955, p. 498; Ridge, 1956; Fyfe, Turner, and Verhoogen, 1958, p. 143–144) that the final derivative of many magmas is probably alkaline rather than acid. If HCl is important in the transport of iron, the common deposition of magnetite in carbonate rocks is easily explained by the reaction between the acid solution and calcium carbonate. The experiments suggest that the mechanism of solution depends principally on acidity; then the mechanism of deposition depends on neutralization.

Our limited data are insufficient to give quantitative conclusions concerning the effect of temperature and pressure changes on the deposition of dissolved material in acid solutions. But the calculated volatility at very low pressure, compared with the measured values of real solubility at high pressure, indicates that the dissolved load must be dropped during a pressure drop. This is of course a general feature of supercritical solutions (Kennedy, 1950b, p. 648–649; *see* Fyfe, Turner, and Verhoogen, 1958, p. 135–137). But much more experimental work remains to be done before we can interpret in detail the deposition with lowered pressure and analogous deposition expected with lowered temperature.

In his detailed discussion of the ore-forming fluid Graton (1940, p. 344) concluded that ". . . The venerable thesis that metals and other components for mineral formation are transferred as volatile compounds of the halogen elements is found to require a great pyramiding of favoring assumptions." But techniques as new as isotopic analysis have been called to its defense (Vinogradov and Dontsova, 1952), although the reasoning is far from clear. A comparison of our experimental data with the theoretical calculations for real-gas equilibria should make it abundantly clear that HCl solutions are capable of transporting far more iron, under conceivable earth conditions, than can possibly be accounted for by the volatility of a halide gas. If the natural occurrence of these dilute aqueous solutions of HCl is doubtful, then concentrations of HCl sufficiently anhydrous to volatilize $FeCl_2$ are certainly out of the question. These conclusions might be juxtaposed in the following way: calculation indicates that water prohibits iron chloride volatility, but experiment shows that the dilute acid solutions formed by this water are capable of transporting iron in true solution.

REFERENCES CITED

Abelson, P. H., 1954, Annual report of the Director of the Geophysical Laboratory: Carnegie Inst. Washington Year Book 1954, p. 95–145

Allen, E. T., 1922, Chemical aspects of volcanism with a collection of the analysis of volcanic gases: Franklin Inst. Jour., v. 193, p. 29–80

Arden, T. V., 1951, The hydrolysis of ferric iron in sulphate solution: Chem. Soc. London Jour., p. 350–363

Behrend, Fritz, 1934, Rezenter Vulkanismus und die Bildung von Eisenerzen: Zeitschr. Deutsch. Geol. Gessel., v. 66, p. 360–367

Benson, S. W., Copeland, C. S., and Pearson, David, 1953, Molal volumes and compressibilities of the system NaCl–H_2O above the critical temperature of water: Jour. Chem. Physics, v. 21, p. 2208–2212

Berl, E., and Von Taack, F., 1928, Über die Schutzwirkung von Natriumsulfat bei der Einwirkung von Laugen und Salzen auf Flusseisen unter Hochdruck: Arch. für Warmewirtschaft, v. 9, p. 165–169

Brady, G. W., 1958, Structure in ionic solutions. III.: Jour. Chem. Physics, v. 29, 1371–1375

Brosset, Cyril, 1941, The ionic equilibrium in acid ferric chloride solutions of fixed ionic strength: Svensk Kemisk Tidskrift, v. 53, p. 434–440

Cooper, L. H. N., 1937, Some conditions governing the solubility of iron: Royal Soc. London. Proc., v. 124B, p. 299–307

Corey, R. C., and Finnegan, T. J., 1939, The pH, dissolved iron concentration and solid product resulting from the reaction between iron and pure water at room temperature: Am. Soc. Testing Materials Proc., v. 39, p. 1242–1260

Darken, L. S., and Gurry, R. W., 1945, The system iron-oxygen. I. The wustite field and related equilibria: Am. Chem. Soc. Jour., v. 67, p. 1398–1412

—— 1946, The system iron-oxygen. II. Equilibrium and thermodynamics of liquid oxide and other phases: Am. Chem. Soc. Jour., v. 68, p. 798–816

Ellis, A. J., 1957, Chemical equilibrium in magmatic gases: Am. Jour. Sci., v. 255, p. 416–431

Emmett, P. H., and Schultz, J. F., 1933, Equilibria in the system Fe–Fe_3O_4–H_2O–H_2 at 400, 500, and 600 C: Am. Chem. Soc. Jour., v. 55, p. 1376–1389

Eugster, H. P., 1959, Reduction and oxidation in metamorphism, p. 397–426 *in* Abelson, P. H., Researches in geochemistry: New York, John Wiley & Sons, 511 p.

Evans, U. R., and Pryor, M. J., 1949, The passivity of metals. Part IX. The solubility product of freshly precipitated $Fe(OH)_2$: Chem. Soc. London Jour., Supp., p. 157–160

Fenner, C. N., 1933, Pneumatolytic processes in the formation of minerals and ores, p. 58–106 *in* Ore deposits of the Western states (Lindgren Volume): Am. Inst. Min. and Metal. Engineers, 797 p.

Fogo, J. K., Benson, S. W., and Copeland, C. S., 1954, Electrical conductivity of supercritical solutions of sodium chloride and water: Jour. Chem. Physics, v. 22, p. 212–216

Franck, E. V., 1956, Hochverdichteter Wasserdampf III, Ionendissoziation von HCl, HOH, und H_2O in uberkritischem Wasser: Zeitschr. Physikal. Chemie, v. 8, p. 192–206

Fricke, R., and Rihl, S., 1943, Zur Beständigkeit des $Fe(OH)_2$: Naturwiss., v. 31, p. 326–327

Fricke, R., Walter, K., and Lohrer, W., 1941, Über die Beeinflussung des Gleichgewichtes Fe/Fe_3O_4 mit H_2O/H_2 durch den physikalischen Zustand der festen Reaktionsteilnehmer: Zeitschr. Elektrochem., v. 47, p. 487–500

Friedman, H. L., 1952, The visible and ultraviolet absorption spectrum of the tetrachlorferrate (III) ion in various media: Am. Chem. Soc. Jour., v. 74, p. 5–10

Fyfe, W. S., Turner, F. J., and Verhoogen, J., 1958, Metamorphic reactions and metamorphic facies: Geol. Soc. America Mem. 73, 260 p.

Gautier, Armand, 1909, Sur les gaz des fumarolles volcaniques: Acad. Sci. Paris Compte Rendu, v. 148, p. 1708–1715

Gould, A. J., and Evans, U. R., 1947, Corrosion of steel by boiling water: Iron and Steel Inst. Jour., v. 155, p. 195–200

Graton, L. C., 1940, Nature of the ore-forming fluid: Econ. Geology, v. 35, supp. 2.

Hirschfelder, J. O., Curtiss, C. F., and Bird, R. B., 1954, Molecular theory of gases and liquids: New York, John Wiley & Sons, 1219 p.

Holser, W. T., 1947, Metasomatic processes: Econ. Geology, v. 42, p. 384–395

—— 1953, The fugacity coefficient of water at high temperature and pressure: Jour. Phys. Chemistry, v. 58, p. 316–317

Holser, W. T., and Kennedy, G. C., 1958, Properties of water, Part IV. Pressure-volume-temperature relations of water in the range 100–400 C, 100–1400 bars: Am. Jour. Sci., v. 256, p. 744–754

—— 1959, Properties of water, Part V. Pressure-volume-temperature relations of water in the range 400–1000 C, 100–1400 bars: Am. Jour. Sci., v. 257, p. 71–77

Holser, W. T., and Schneer, C. J., 1953, Deposition of high-temperature nonmagmatic magnetite (Abstract): Geol. Soc. America Bull., v. 64, p. 1435

—— 1957, Hydrothermal geochemistry of iron: U.S. Office of Naval Res., Final Rept. on Project NR 081–120: U.S. Dept. Commerce, Office Tech. Services Doc. PB 147802, 61 p.

Huber, N. K., and Garrels, R. M., 1953, Relation of pH and oxidation potential to sedimentary iron mineral formation: Econ. Geology, v. 48, p. 337–357

Hüttig, G. F., and Moldner, H., 1931, Das System Eisen (II)–oxyd/Wasser und sein Ubergange zu dem System Eisen (III)–oxyd/Wasser: Zeitschr. anorg. allg. Chemie, v. 196, p. 177–187

Ito, T., and Yui, N., 1953, The hydrolysis constants of ferric iron in nitrate solution: Sendai, Japan, Tohoku Univ. Sci. Repts., v. 37, p. 19–27

Iwasaki, I., 1951, Geophysics of volcano Ooshima, Izu: Jour. Geography, Tokyo, v. 60, p. 140–143

Kennedy, G. C., 1950a, Pressure-volume-temperature relations in water at elevated temperatures and pressures: Am. Jour. Sci., v. 248, p. 540–564

—— 1950b, A portion of the system silica-water: Econ. Geology, v. 45, p. 629–653

—— 1955, Some aspects of the role of water in rock melts: Geol. Soc. America Special Paper, v. 62, p. 489–504

Kokubu, Nobuhide, Watanabe, Syosuke, and Ide, Yasusi, 1957, Liquid inclusions in the amygdaloidal cavities of olivine-basalt from Imazu, Hukuoka City, Japan: Fukuoku, Japan, Kyushu Univ. Fac. Sci. Mem., ser. C, v. 2, p. 151–160

Krauskopf, K. B., 1957, The heavy metal content of magmatic vapor at 600°C: Econ. Geology, v. 52, p. 786–807

Kuroda, P. K., and Sandell, E. B., 1953, Chlorine in igneous rocks: Geol. Soc. America Bull., v. 64, p. 879–896

Lamb, A. B., and Jacques, A. G., 1938, The slow hydrolysis of ferric chloride in dilute solution. II. The change in hydrogen ion concentration: Am. Chem. Soc. Jour., v. 60, p. 1215–1225

Leussing, D. L., and Kolthoff, I. M., 1953, The solubility product of ferrous hydroxide and the ionization of the aquoferrous ion: Am. Chem. Soc. Jour., v. 75, p. 2476–2479

Lewis, G. N., and Randall, Merle, 1923, Thermodynamics and the free energy of chemical substances: New York, McGraw-Hill Book Co., 653 p.

Mackin, J. H., 1954, Geology and iron-ore deposits of the Granite Mountain area, Iron County, Utah: U. S. Geol. Survey Mineral Invest. Field Studies maps, MF 14

Miller, P. D., and others, in press, The solubility product of ferrous hydroxide: Am. Chem. Soc. Jour.

Morey, G. W., 1957, The solubility of solids in gases: Econ. Geology, v. 52, p. 225–251

Morey, G. W., and Hesselgesser, J. M., 1951, The solubility of some minerals in superheated steam at high pressures: Econ. Geology, v. 46, p. 821–835

Morey, G. W., and Ingerson, Earl, 1937, A bomb for use in hydrothermal experimentation: Am. Mineralogist, v. 22, p. 1121–1122

Muan, Arnulf, 1958, Phase equilibria at high temperatures in oxide systems involving changes in oxidation states: Am. Jour. Sci., v. 256, p. 171–207

Newhouse, W. H., and Glass, J. P., 1936, Some physical properties of certain iron oxides: Econ. Geology, v. 31, p. 699–711

Newton, R. H., 1935, Activity coefficients of gases: Industrial and Engineering Chemistry, v. 27, p. 302–306

Pryor, M. J., and Evans, U. R., 1949, The passivity of metals. X. The mechanism of direct dissolution of ferric oxide: Chem. Soc. London Jour., p. 3330–3336

Rabinowitz, Eugene, and Stockmayer, W. H., 1942, Association of ferric ions with chloride, bromide and hydroxyl ions (a spectroscopic study): Am. Chem. Soc. Jour., v. 64, p. 335–347

Ralston, O. C., 1929, Iron oxide reduction equilibria: U. S. Bur. Mines Bull. 296, 326 p.

Ridge, J. D., 1956, Transportation and deposition of hydrothermal minerals: Intern. Geol. Cong. 20th Sess. Resumes, p. 100

Robinson, R. A., and Stokes, R. H., 1949, The role of hydration in the Debye-Hückel theory: New York Acad. Sci. Annals, v. 51, p. 593–604

Sandell, E. B., 1950, Colorimetric determination of traces of metals: 2d ed., New York, Interscience Publishers, Inc., 673 p.

Schäfer, Harald, 1949, Die Einwirkung von Chlorwasserstoff auf Eisenoxyd und die Auswertung der Reaktionsgleichgewichte: Zeitschr. anorg. allg. Chemie, v. 259, p. 53–74

—— 1950, Das System Fe_2O_3–$FeOCl$–$FeCl_3$–H_2O–HCl zwischen etwa 100 und 1000°C: Zeitschr. anorg. allg. Chemie, v. 261, p. 142–152

Schäfer, Harald, and Krehl, Kurt, 1952, Das Reaktionsgleichgewicht $FeCl_2$ gas$+H_2=Fe+2HCl$: Zeitschr. anorg. allg. Chemie, v. 268, p. 35–46

Schäfer, Harald, and Oehler, Eberhard, 1953, Der Chlordurck über den festen Bodenkorpern $FeCl_3$ und $FeCl_2$: Zeitschr. anorg. allg. Chemie, v. 271, p. 206–216

Schimmel, F. A., 1952, The ternary systems ferrous chloride-hydrogen chloride-water, and ferric chloride-ferrous chloride-water: Am. Chem. Soc. Jour., v. 74, p. 4689–4691

Schmahl, N. G., 1941, Die Beziehungen zwischen Sauerstoffdruck, temperatur und zusammensetzung im System Fe_2O_3–Fe_3O_4: Zeitschr. Elektrochem., v. 47, p. 821–835

Schmalz, E. F., 1959, A note on the system Fe_2O_3–H_2O: Jour. Geophys. Research, v. 64, 575–579

Shand, S. J., 1947, The genesis of intrusive magnetite and ores: Econ. Geology, v. 42, p. 634–636

Shepherd, E. S., 1938, The analysis of gases obtained from volcanoes and from rocks: Jour. Geology, v. 33, p. 289–369

Siddall, T. H., and Vosburgh, W. C., 1951, A spectrophotometric study of the hydrolysis of iron (III) ion: Am. Chem. Soc. Jour., v. 73, p. 4270–4272

Smith, F. G., and Kidd, D. J., 1949, Hematite-goethite relations in neutral and alkaline solutions under pressure: Am. Mineralogist, v. 34, p. 403–412

Smith, G. F., and Richter, F. P., 1944, Phenanthroline and substituted phenanthroline indicators: Cincinnati, Ohio, G. Frederick Smith Chem. Co., 103 p.

Stirnemann, Ernst, 1925a, Das System Eisenchlorid-Wasser bei höherer Temperatur: Neues Jahrb. Min. Pet., Beil. B., v. 52A, p. 334–377

—— 1925b, Ueber die Bildungsverhaltnisse der Eisenerzlagerstatten im System Eisenchlorid-Wasser: Neues Jahrb. Min. Pet., Beil. B., v. 53A, p. 59–94

Stokes, R. H., and Robinson, R. A., 1948, Thermodynamic study of bivalent metal halides in aqueous solution. XVII. Revision of data for all 2:1 and 1:2 electrolytes at 25°: Faraday Soc. Trans., v. 44, p. 295–307

Vinogradov, A. P., and Dontsova, E. I., 1952 (Isotopic composition of oxygen in minerals of a skarn origin): Akad. Nauk SSSR Doklady, n. s., v. 85, p. 1341–1343

Wahler, William, 1956, Über die in Kristallen eingeschlossenen Flussingkeiten und Gase: Geochim. et Cosmochim. Acta, v. 9, p. 105–135

Weiser, H. B., 1935, Inorganic colloid chemistry, v. II. The hydrous oxides and hydroxides: New York, John Wiley & Sons, Inc., 429 p.

Wilson, L. E., and Gregory, N. W., 1958, Vapor-solid equilibria in the iron-chlorine system: Jour. Phys. Chemistry, v. 62, p. 433–437

Wilson, S. H., 1953, Chemical investigations of the hot springs of the New Zealand thermal region: Pacific Sci. Cong., 7 Sess., v. 2, p. 449–469

Manuscript Received by the Secretary of the Society, June 19, 1959

37

Reprinted from *Econ. Geol.*, **67**(3), 339–349 (1972)

The Iron Ore Deposits of the Pacific Basin

Charles F. Park, Jr.

Abstract

Magnetite-hematite bodies are widely distributed throughout the highly deformed rocks bordering the Pacific ocean basin. The origin of these interesting deposits has been the subject of extensive debate and is highly controversial. Study of the deposits as a unit has furnished ideas that help to clarify the discussion.

Evidence is advanced to show that these deposits result from partial mobilization of iron in various types of rocks below, and that the process is directly related to the mobile belt along the continental margins. The resulting deposits may be classed as magmatic injection deposits, contact metamorphic deposits, metasomatic or replacement deposits, and the magnetite flows of Laco, Chile.

The Iron Ore Deposits of the Pacific Basin

During many years of mine examination throughout the Pacific Basin, the differences between the iron ores of this basin and those of the Atlantic and Indian ocean basins, have been recorded with growing interest. In these latter basins, the borders of the large stable continental shields are underlain by sedimentary itabirites or taconites of Precambrian age, and by sedimentary iron-bearing beds of more recent geologic time, such as the well known Clinton and Minette formations. That the sedimentary beds around the "Pacific ring of fire" are few in number and small in size involves more than chance. Other types of deposits, usually described as of replacement or contact metasomatic origin, predominate (Fig. 1). These deposits are described below; they have many features in common with iron ores associated with zones of strong deformation and volcanism elsewhere in the world. The purpose of this paper is to discuss the origin of these interesting deposits.

For purposes of study, the iron-bearing deposits of the Pacific basin are divided into three categories, based upon their origins: 1) magmatic segregation deposits in ultramafic rocks, 2) sedimentary deposits, and 3) magnetite-hematite deposits that include those described by some geologists as contact metamorphic or pyrometasomatic, by others as replacement deposits, and by still others as magmatic segregation and injection deposits accompanied by abundant volatile and probably watery fluids. The examination of these mineralized bodies in a regional setting has furnished ideas and evidence concerning origin that supplement and may differ from those obtained by study of smaller areas and individual deposits. As a result of the broad general examination, a pattern of origin has emerged that enables reasonable explanation of the type three deposit.

Magmatic Segregation Deposits in Ultramafic Rocks

These deposits are exemplified by Lodestone Mountain, British Columbia, Canada (Rice, 1947), Klukwan, Alaska (Taylor and Noble, 1960), and the Savage river, Tasmania (Hughes, 1965). The deposits at Lodestone Mountain are similar to that at Klukwan and to many others throughout southeastern Alaska. The partly serpentinized ultramafic complex at Lodestone Mountain is of Mesozoic age and intrudes silicic granitic rocks of the Coastal batholith and sedimentary and volcanic rocks of Upper Triassic age. It occupies an area about 10 miles long by a maximum width of 3 miles. It ranges in composition from peridotite-pyroxenite at Lodestone Mountain in the south, to the dunite of Olivine Mountain in the north. Much of the intrusive rock contains magnetite as an accessory mineral; locally the quantity increases and at Lodestone Mountain as much as 25 percent iron in magnetite is present. Pods and lenses of nearly pure magnetite also are present and in places are conspicuous.

Lodestone Mountain is no exception to the generalization that iron deposits of magmatic segregation types in ultramafic complexes contain enough titanium (1.5–2.5 percent titanium in ilmenite) to discourage economic development.

The Savage river deposits in Tasmania are of late Precambrian or early Paleozoic age. They are somewhat different from the disseminated segregation deposits of Lodestone Mountain and Klukwan, though they too have been attributed directly to magmatic processes (Hughes, 1965). A zone of magnetite-hematite lenses is irregularly distributed along a thick sill of amphibolite or gabbro. This sill intrudes a sequence of quartzite, phyllite, and schist,

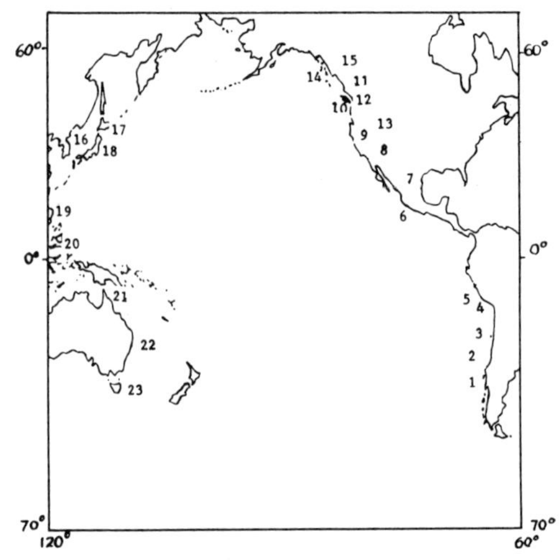

FIG. 1. Partial list of the Iron Ore Deposits of the Pacific Basin.

1. Nahuelbuta,* Nueva Imperial,* Relun;* Chile
2. Cemento Melon,* Chiliquaquen, La Higuera,* Romeral,* El Tofo;* Chile
3. Algarrobo,* Mercedita,* Paipote;* Chile
4. El Laco,* San Sebastian; Chile
5. Acari,* Cerro Casco, Marcona;* Peru
6. Peña Colorado, Las Truchas;* Mexico
7. Cerro Mercado;* Mexico
8. Eagle Mountains;* California U. S. A.
9. Lake Hawley and Spencer Lakes,* Shasta Iron;* U. S. A.
10. Power River, Vancouver Island, Texada Island, Zeballos; Canada
11. Kamloops Lake,* Canada
12. Lodestone Mountain,* Canada
13. Atlantic City; U. S. A.
14. Kasaan Peninsula, Klukwan,* Prince of Wales Island; U. S. A.
15. Snake Range, Canada
16. South Korea
17. Kamikimobetsu,* Kuchan;* Japan
18. Kamaishi,* Japan
19. Larap,* Yandayao; Philippine Islands
20. Shih-lu, Hainan Island, China
21. Cape York Peninsula, Australia
22. Cadia,* Australia
23. Savage River, Australia

* Indicates deposits examined by the writer.

and is about 24 kilometers long by about 900 meters wide.

Closely related to the magmatic segregation deposits are those in volcanic rocks where the iron minerals are primary constituents. Such a deposit was described by Salas et al. (1965) at San Sebastian, in the high country east of Arica in northern Chile. Here, at an altitude of approximately 4,000 meters, a member of the Pliocene Oxaya formation contains large amounts of hematite. The Oxaya formation is about 1,000 meters thick and ranges from andesite flows and tuffs at the base to dacite and rhyolite ignimbrites in the upper members. One of the ignimbrite members is bright red at the top and bulk analyses gave 52 percent of iron in hematite. Salas thinks that the hematite is a primary constituent and that the deposit should be classed as magmatic segregation, though he stated that the evidence was inconclusive. This flow possibly marks a late stage and surface expression of the end products of the same process that gave rise to the Lodestone Mountain body.

Another closely related type of deposit is that at Laco, also in the high Andes mountains of northern Chile, around the base of a modern volcano. Here, at four places, flows of nearly pure magnetite, locally oxidized to hematite, have broken through a sequence of tuffs and flows and have spread for short distances over the surface (Park, 1961; Ruiz, 1965; Rogers, 1968). The origin of the Laco deposits is of special interest in the study of ore genesis, as the deposits show extensive features unknown in magmatic deposits elsewhere. Did the mobile magnetite-hematite result from segregation in a magma chamber, or did it become concentrated through partial mobilization of deeply buried, iron-rich rocks? This question will be discussed later.

Sedimentary Deposits

The second type of iron ore in the Pacific basin is of sedimentary origin, and all deposits of this class either crop out in small areas or are of uneconomic grade. Such sedimentary deposits as the taconites of the Snake range, Yukon Territory, Canada, and the Atlantic City district, Wyoming, are east of the deformed coastal belt being discussed. Sedimentary deposits within the belt of deformation include the Nahuelbuta or Relun and Nueva Imperial localities in southern Chile, thought to be of Precambrian age. These deposits have been likened to the itabirite of eastern South America, though chert layers are usually absent and, in general, the iron content is lower than in the larger, better known deposits (Flores and Hornkohl, 1947), Figure 2A. Farther north in Chile, a banded iron formation is reported at Chiliquaquen, about 35 kilometers northeast of Valparaiso (Ruiz, 1965) and at the Mercedita property about 44 kilometers by road northwest of Inca del Oro, figure 2B. Ferruginous quartzites, possibly related to itabirites, are recognized in small amounts near both the Romeral and El Tofo orebodies in central Chile (A. A. Bookstrom, personal communication, 1970).

At least two deposits of possible sedimentary origin are known in Peru. One is at Cerro Casco or Tarpuy near Arequipa (Concha, 1956), and the other is just south of Arica in the Province of Ica, Figure 3. The layered material near Arica contains minor lenses of

FIG. 2A. Photograph of a polished slab of banded iron formation from Nahuelbuta, southern Chile. B. Photograph of a hand specimen of banded iron formation from the Mercedita property, northern Chile.

massive magnetite into which the itabirite appears to grade.

Gallagher (1963) discussed the sedimentary iron formations in South Korea, and Leningston (1954) and others described iron formation near the east coast of Cape York peninsula, northeastern Australia. Canavan (1965b) said that the Cape York peninsula deposits were "Banded iron formations which comprise regularly and irregularly banded magnetite quartzite, and/or hematite quartzite." These beds are also thought to be Precambrian or Lower Paleozoic in age.

Other small and low grade sedimentary deposits probably will be found in the Pacific basin, especially within the rather limited Precambrian rock outcrops. It is not the purpose of this paper to discuss the origin of itabirites and sedimentary iron; the subject will not be brought up again. It is, however, pertinent to the problem to point out that Precambrian exposures around the Pacific basin are few, but these few commonly contain showings of iron formation. Buried Precambrian iron formation may be more common than is generally supposed.

Spring and bog deposits of limonite have been recognized in several places in the Pacific basin and should probably be mentioned under sedimentary ores, though they are of minor interest to our discussion. The Kuchan and Kamikimobetsu deposits of Hokkaido, Japan, and the Yandayao deposit at Tupi, Cotobato Province, Philippine Islands (Santos Yñigo, 1961) are examples of spring deposits. The Japanese deposits are apparently being laid down by present day cold springs, while the Yandayao spring is warm. Several bog iron deposits are known elsewhere around the Pacific basin, but their origin is unimportant to the present discussion.

Contact Metamorphic, Pyrometasomatic, and/or Replacement Deposits

The third type of deposit in the Pacific basin is by far the most interesting from an economic as well as from a genetic point of view. These deposits are principally cross-cutting, irregular bodies of magnetite that are superficially oxidized to hematite. They number, literally, in the hundreds, and are widely distributed from eastern Australia and Malaysia northward along the islands from Hainan through the Philippine Islands and Japan, to Korea and Kamchatka (Bartlett, 1956; Harrington and Page, 1952; Ichimura, 1931; Kato, 1939; Mitsuchi, 1952; Santos Yñigo, 1952, 1953).

Along the eastern border of the Pacific ocean the deposits are recognized from Alaska southward through Canada, the United States, Mexico, Central America, and along the coastal and mountainous belts of western South America (Bacon, 1951; Bacon and Black, 1952; Bennett, 1962; Broughton, 1943; Dueñas, 1918; Gonzales Reyna, 1952; Hodge, 1935, 1938; Jenkins and Cooper 1922; Kindle, 1964; MacKevett and Blake, 1963; Mapes et al., 1959; McConnell, 1914; Meave and Echegoyen, 1961; Rice and Jones, 1959; Richter and Herreid, 1965; Stevenson; 1950; Zoldak, 1947; Zoppis de Sena, 1957). Such well known deposits as El Tofo, Romeral, and Algorrobo, in Chile, Marcona and Acari in Peru, Las Truchas and Peña Colorada in Mexico, Eagle Moun-

FIG. 3A. Photograph of an outcrop of banded iron formation south of Acari, Province of Ica, Peru. B. Photograph of a boulder detached from the outcrop shown in Figure 3A.

tains and Shasta Iron in California, Zeballos and Texada Island in Canada, Prince of Wales Island, Alaska, Kamaishi in Japan, Larap, Philippine Islands, Shih-lu on Hainan Island, Dungun in Malaysia, and Cadia, New South Wales, Australia, are examples, though many others might be listed. It is perhaps significant that of the 17 deposits of magnetite-hematite described by Canavan (1965) in Australia, all are along the eastern seaboard; each state from Tasmania northward through Queensland, has such deposits. While all of the Australian magnetite deposits of this class appear to be small, physically they closely resemble larger deposits distributed around the periphery of the Pacific ocean (Bell, 1959; Brooks, 1957; Brüggen, 1913; Flores, 1949, 1959; Griffin and Wynn, 1961; Pittman, 1910; Raggatt, 1953; Ruiz, 1943, 1961, 1965; Twelvetrees, 1910; Olmeda, 1913).

The host rocks of the deposits are of many varieties and the magnetite-hematite appears to have formed without dependence upon the type of country rock. Limestones, sandstones, and shales are generally present near the Mesozoic and older deposits, and the tendency has been to attribute the presence of ore to the reaction between iron-bearing fluids and carbonate rocks. However, in Chile, and to a lesser extent elsewhere, but especially in the Tertiary and younger deposits, the common associates are volcanic rocks, mainly andesites and andesite breccias. Locally the host rocks are intrusive bodies, and at Acari, Peru, the ore was in a long plunging rod surrounded by undeformed granodiorite. The contacts between ore and country rock are sharp and show little evidence of replacement, gradation, assimilation, or dilution by the granodiorite. The ore is massive and contains only minor quantities of elements other than the iron oxides. Indications of extensive faulting around the ore are lacking, though the main intrusive body is thought to lie along a major longitudinal fault. Mine workings in the granodiorite beneath the orebody failed to disclose any indication of data relevant to the origin. Why and how the long thin rod of magnetite formed in the massive granodiorite is debatable; a possible, but seemingly unlikely, explanation is total replacement of a roof pendant.

Most deposits of magnetite-hematite are recognizably close to intrusive bodies, and zoning around the intrusives is at places well developed. Zoning is most conspicuous in those deposits where skarn is present.

Most deposits are associated with faults, many of which parallel the borders of the Pacific basin, and the geologists who have studied the region frequently emphasize the relations of ore to structure (Andal, 1953; Eastwood, 1965; Frost, 1965; Ruiz, 1965; Simons and Bellido, 1956). The faults are thought to have tapped the sources of both magma and ore-bearing fluids at depth, and to have acted as channelways for their passage. The fractures that parallel the coastline are considered to be directly related to zones of deformation—the geosynclinal and mobile belt around the borders of the continental masses. Insofar as peripheral fractures and mobile deformed zones around the continents are related to plate tectonics, the associated iron ores also may be considered as products of sea floor spreading.

The origin of this interesting group of deposits has been much debated. Most are considered to be related to contact metamorphic or metasomatic types, but they range considerably from ore in and near massive skarn and garnet zones through deposits where the principal alteration mineral is amphibole, to bodies where only an occasional garnet or skarn mineral is present. In a few deposits no indication of skarn mineralization is recognized; elsewhere no intrusive rocks are known. Massive skarn zones are more numerous and best developed in the northern and western parts of the Pacific basin. Although much skarn is present locally, skarn free deposits are most numerous in Chile and Peru and a few are present in other parts of the basin. Differences in character among the deposits are caused perhaps by differences in depths of erosion and deposition. Many geologists prefer to describe the ore as of "replacement origin," and to avoid the term contact or igneous metamorphism or metasomatism, used in the sense that the ores originated in the local intrusive masses (Lamey, 1961; Muñoz Cristi, 1950b; Ruiz, 1965; Simons and Bellido, 1956; Sutherland Brown, 1962). Use of the term replacement to describe the origin leaves open any commitment as to the source and nature of the ore-bearing fluids. It also ignores and leaves unexplained the facts that many, but not all, ores are in veins or dikes, lenses, and irregular bodies that have knife-edged contacts with the host rock. In many deposits replacement is obvious, in others, evidence of replacement is difficult to obtain.

The magnetite-hematite deposits are so closely associated with igneous processes and igneous rocks that the tendency naturally has been to relate the ores to magmas, either known or inferred. The intrusive masses are dominantly of intermediate composition, diorite, granodiorite, quartz diorite, monzonite, tonalite, or similar materials. Irregular bodies and dikes of aplite and bleached country rock are conspicuous near several of the ore deposits and Brüggen (1913) suggested that removal of iron from magmas of intermediate composition gave rise to magnetite and aplite. Many of the intrusive bodies have both skarn and ore in them; clearly they were in part emplaced before the ore.

Dikes of andesite, diorite, or of other silicic or intermediate composition, commonly cut the magnetite-hematite orebodies, and Flores (1959) recorded fragments of diorite enclosed in magnetite. The open pit at the Romeral mine, central Chile, shows the relationships between ore and dikes very clearly; the ore is post-major intrusive rock and at least in part is pre-dike.

Ages of the magnetite-hematite deposits range from Precambrian to Recent. Deposits in eastern Australia are thought to be Lower Paleozoic or Precambrian; on Hainan island the deposits are in metamorphosed Paleozoic rocks intruded by granite, but the age of the mineralization is unknown. Kamaishi, Japan, and many of the deposits along the western coast of North America are thought to be of Mesozoic age. Possibly the deposit at Larap, Philippine Islands, is Tertiary, as may also be some of the deposits in South America. Other deposits, such as those of El Laco and San Sebastian in northern Chile are Recent or Late Tertiary. Ages of many of the deposits are unknown.

All geologists who have described these deposits think that the ore components originated at depth, were transported either as highly mobile hydrothermal fluids or magmas along permeable fault zones or other controlling structures, and either have replaced favorable rocks or have intruded them. Flores (1959) very well summarized the conclusions of the many workers in Chile when he said that localization of the deposits could best be explained as resulting from pneumatolytic and hydrothermal activities. He continued, however, that the possibility of a magmatic segregation and injection origin could not be excluded in some areas, especially in those districts where later hydrothermal activities obscure the original characteristics.

Tanton (1952) described the deposits of British Columbia, Canada, as contact metamorphic replacement deposits, and he visualized the magnetite being introduced not as a magnetite magma by ore injection, but by a "slow, gradual progressive replacement of limestone, tuff, andesite, or diorite, by tenuous solutions of considerable penetrability."

Young and Uglow (1926) had earlier described the British Columbia deposits and they also considered that most ores replaced the rocks in which they are emplaced. But they conceded that in several places "the deposits possess all of the essential characteristics of fissure fillings." Near Kamloops lake, the "veins" are characterized by the presence of variable, and in places, large amounts of apatite.

Eastwood (1965) called the deposits of Vancouver Island, Canada, replacement deposits, and he distinguished them from contact metamorphic deposits which he defined as requiring "proximity of an intrusion, high temperature and pressure, and replacement of limestone predominantly." He pointed out that on Vancouver Island magnetite is a common constituent of the skarns. However, at Power river, the magnetite contains a little pyroxene, but otherwise is essentially skarn-free. He emphasized structural controls of deposition and stated that an origin by refusion of old, deeply buried iron formation seems unlikely from the geologic history of the island. Eastwood also stated (p. 146) that: "The iron for the magnetite was probably derived from the somewhat iron-rich Karmutsen volcanics via granodiorite magma." He brought out the fact that most of the intrusive rocks on Vancouver Island are older than the magnetite deposits.

Swanson (1925) gave an excellent description of the iron ore deposits of Texada island, Canada, just south of Vancouver Island. The country rock is a sequence of metamorphosed limestones, schists, quartzites, and volcanics intruded by quartz diorite. Both the country rock and the main intrusive mass were replaced by extensive skarn zones that contain masses of magnetite. Swanson traced the geologic history in detail and showed that the diorite porphyry dikes cut the magnetite; the dikes are manifestations of the latest igneous activity.

The ores on Texada island contain considerable pyrite, calcite, and quartz, and in places as much as 1 percent copper. Swanson clearly demonstrates the efficacy of replacement. He considered the possibility that the massive magnetite bodies had been injected as molten magnetite, but rejected the idea in favor of replacement. He thought that the skarns and magnetite were the end products of the igneous processes that gave rise to the main intrusive body of quartz diorite.

At the Kamaishi mine in Japan, a body of granodiorite and associated igneous rocks intrudes a sequence of Mesozoic limestones, shales and sandstones. An extensive skarn and hornfels zone was developed along the contact, particularly in the limestone, and lenticular bodies of massive magnetite were deposited in and adjacent to the skarn. Minor amounts of hematite, chalcopyrite, bornite, pyrite, pyrrhotite, sphalerite, galena, gold, and silver are disseminated in the magnetite. The largest single orebody is the Shinyama lens, 400 m long, 80 m wide, and 550 m deep. This orebody is entirely similar to many others widely distributed in Japan, but is larger than most. A description of the Kamaishi deposits reads almost the same as a description of the Texada island ores.

Muñoz Cristi (1950a, b) stated that the iron ore deposits of Chile are in the covers of batholiths and near their contacts. He pointed out that amphiboles are abundant with the iron minerals and he related the mineralization to that of the copper ores (chalcopyrite), as at Higuera in Coquimbo Province, where amphibole and magnetite are plentiful around the borders of a dioritic body. Warner et al. (1961) also brought out the relationships between magnetite and copper mineralization of the Kasaan peninsula, Alaska. Many other deposits contain small amounts of copper.

In addition to magnetite and hematite, many of the deposits contain irregularly distributed grains and nodules of pyrite, chalcopyrite, and other sulfides. Apatite can generally be recognized, and minor amounts of titanium in sphene are not uncommon. Minerals of the skarn types are abundant in many iron ores and are present in small amounts in many more. They include appreciable amounts of amphiboles, pyroxenes such as hedenbergite and diopside, quartz, biotite, grossularite and andradite garnets, epidote, scapolite, and chlorite, as well as minor amounts of many others. Ruiz (1965) described the apatite in the Chilean deposits as being chlorapatite, though elsewhere fluorapatite has been identified.

Apatite-Magnetite-Amphibole Rock

One of the more interesting features of many of these deposits is the association of magnetite with apatite and green amphibole, particularly in the de-

Fig. 4. Photographs to show relationships among apatite (white) and magnetite-amphibole (dark). A. From Pleito y Zapallo deposit, Chile. Veinlets of magnetite in apatite. B. From Tambillos property, Chile. Apatite crystals and veinlets in magnetite and amphibole. C. From Protrero Seco deposit, Chile. Skeleton crystals of apatite in magnetite and amphibole. Note the basal section at the upper right.

posits of South America. In Chile, where the apatite-bearing dikes are probably the best developed and most extensive, they have been studied thoroughly by many geologists. Locally the dikes are so abundant that they have been mined and used as a source of phosphate rock. At Cemento Melon, a small mine in Coquimbo Province, the dikes are up to 25 feet or more wide, contain about 30 percent of phosphorus in the upper levels, and are used in the manufacture of fertilizers. The apatite-rich dikes are common around the edges of larger massive magnetite deposits that contain much smaller amounts of phosphorus and that are being mined locally for iron ore. In places in Chile so many of these dikes are present that they have been mapped and used as possible guides to the location of the larger bodies. Where followed at depth, the dikes tend to become poorer in apatite; magnetite and green amphibole correspondingly increase, Figure 4A. At an area near Paipote, northern Chile, a mass estimated to contain a minimum of 6 million tons, consists about half and half of magnetite and apatite, with minor amphibole. Green amphibole is the only mineral recognized in many of the dikes in addition to apatite and magnetite.

Apatite-magnetite-amphibole dikes are common throughout the southeastern part of the Pacific basin, and are present, though inconspicuous, at many places elsewhere. Atchley (1956) described them from the area around the well known ore deposits at Marcona, Peru, and similar dikes have been mapped near Acari, Peru. Many of the iron ore deposits of Mexico are locally bordered by inconspicuous dikes and other bodies of magnetite-apatite, and at Cerro Mercado, near Durango, the clear yellowish apatite is sought as gem material (Foshag, 1929). Apatite-magnetite dikes are recognized at many places in California, and Durrell and Proctor (1948) described them from Lake Hawley and Spencer Lakes in the northern Sierra Nevada Mountains. Young and Uglow (1926) described apatite-magnetite rock from near the south shores of Kamloops lake, British Columbia, Canada, where they that in places it is present in large amounts. Many other authors who describe the iron ores of western Canada, Alaska, Korea, Japan, and Australia, make no mention of apatite. Certainly in these areas apatite is not as common as it is in Chile; all magnetite bodies carry some apatite, but the very small mineral grains in the larger bodies are easily overlooked. Warner et al. (1961) refer to apatite as a minor constituent in the iron ores of the Kasaan peninsula, Alaska. Frost (1965) described small exposures of magnetite-apatite rock around the orebodies at Larap, Philippine Islands, and very minor amounts of apatite-magnetite rock has been recognized in eastern Australia.

Considerable time has been devoted to the study of the apatite-magnetite-amphibole dikes in the field and to hand specimens and sections in an effort to establish the paragenesis and to obtain clues as to genesis. The walls of the dikes and bodies generally are sharp; the dikes appear to be fissure fillings and they yield little or no information that indicates extensive replacement of the host rocks. The bordering walls of some dikes are surprisingly unaltered and no indication of assimilation or unusual hydrothermal alteration is present. On the other hand, A. A. Bookstrom (personal communication, 1970) states that he has observed extensive development of amphibole in the wall rocks of some of the apatite-magnetite bodies in Chile. He also noted that the long axes of the amphibole crystals are oriented normal to the walls of the dikes. One is almost forced to the conclusion that some of the dikes were intruded as molten apatite-magnetite-amphibole magma, very rich in highly mobile fluids; the dikes are regarded as a variety of pegmatite. Their study lends credence and support to Geijer's (1931) explanation of similar dikes at Kiruna, Sweden, which he thought resulted from the injection of magnetite magma. Recently Geijer (1961) published an excellent review of the relations between apatite and magnetite in the type of deposit here being considered.

A sequence of deposition has not been established that will permit generalization, and it is concluded that the minerals were essentially contemporaneous. A sample from one deposit may contain a vein of apatite cutting magnetite, another sample may show magnetite veins cutting apatite. In several dikes, crystals of apatite contain crystals of magnetite; within the magnetite are smaller crystals of apatite, which in turn contain more magnetite, Figure 4. Similarly, relationships with amphiboles are indeterminate. Especially in the narrower dikes, the apatite grains tend to be oriented with their long axes normal to the walls of the dikes, but are separated from the walls by at least a few millimeters of magnetite (Geijer, 1967, p. 12).

It is recognized, of course, that the melting temperature of magnetite at atmospheric pressures, is just below 1,600° C, and that this temperature is above that considered reasonable for normal volcanic processes. It seems likely, though, that the presence of phosphorus, chlorine, fluorine, water, and possibly other highly mobile elements allows persistence of iron-rich liquids at lower temperatures. According to Jahns (personal communication, R. H. Jahns, 1970), results of preliminary experiments support this thesis.

Discussion

Since the apatite-magnetite-amphibole bodies are frequent offshoots of, and grade imperceptibly into, more massive, large bodies of magnetite ores, it follows logically that some of the ores have an origin similar to that of the dikes; they were formed by direct injection of the molten ore magma. This is the view expressed by many geologists a generation or more past, but is less popular at present (Brüggen, 1913; Linnemann, 1920; Geijer, 1931; Revorede, undated). The mobility of the iron ore was explained by these geologists as resulting from late stage hydrothermal and pneumatolytic activities. Here it must be added in haste, that replacement has indeed been the dominant process in many deposits; not all deposits were injected as molten material. No single type of emplacement will explain the diversities of the magnetite bodies. The deposits range from those injected as molten ore magma to those transported in highly mobile, watery fluids which reacted with and replaced the country rock (Saksela, 1970).

The process of genesis envisioned here is one of partial mobilization of iron in the rocks below, possibly in large part the deeply buried Precambrian iron formations. This thesis is perhaps supported by the presence of ferruginous quartzites and small bodies of banded iron formation near some of the ore deposits. Other iron-rich rocks, especially the volcanics such as those described at San Sebastian, Chile (Salas et al., 1965), may well be involved. Such mobilization would be particularly effective along the deforming continental margins where intrusive rocks and their companion mobile fluids are working their way through iron-rich materials. Iron may also be contributed directly from the magmas, especially from the ultramafic complexes such as those of Lodestone Mountain, Canada, and Klukwan, Alaska. Direct contributions from the magma are both possible and in places are reasonable, though they are unnecessary to explain many of the presently known orebodies.

The molten magnetite or "ore magma," in places charged with large amounts of volatile and other highly mobile constituents—phosphorus, chlorine, fluorine, water, and probably others contributed by the magma or activated by the magma, rose along faults and along the borders of the intrusions until an environment favorable for deposition was reached. Here the ore was deposited. The present day character of the resulting deposit depends, not only upon the nature of the transporting fluids, but more especially upon the environment of deposition. At Laco, Chile, the magma broke through to the surface and cooled quickly. At Cemento Melon, Chile, where the magnetite-apatite-amphibole dikes are abundant and skarn minerals are few or absent, the ore magma and its volatile constituents reached within a few thousand feet of the surface. Here both injection and replacement would be active. Injection of magnetite magma appears to have been especially common where movement toward the surface has been rapid, as in areas of explosive volcanic activities. And where skarns abound, as on Vancouver Island, Canada, and at Kamaishi, Japan, temperatures and pressures were probably high and communication with the surface was impeded. Here the iron ores had time to replace the favorable country rock, aided by adequate ground preparation in advance and by abundant transient fluids. Deposition of the iron was not limited to any geologic period, but seems to have taken place at intervals at least since late Precambrian.

The distribution of magnetite-hematite ores of the Pacific basin has proven to be a stimulating and interesting study. Such examination might well be applied to the distribution of disseminated copper deposits and to the Kuroko-type sulfide ores of Japan, which have recently been described as well from Fiji and the Philippine Islands (Matsukuma and Horikoshi, 1970).

Acknowledgments

Laboratory work on the study of the iron ores of Chile and Peru has been in part supported by a grant from the National Science Foundation. The manuscript has been read by A. A. Bookstrom, F. W. Dickson, F. C. Kruger, and K. L. Williams, whose friendly comments and helpful discussion are gratefully acknowledged.

Department of Mineral Engineering,
Stanford University, California,
April 14, 1971; January 3, 1972

REFERENCES

Andal, Gregorio, 1953, Iron in the Philippines: Phil. Bur. Mines, Info. Circ., No. 17.

Atchley, F. W., 1956, Geology of the Marcona Iron Deposits, Peru: Ph.D. Thesis, Stanford University.

Bacon, W. R., 1957, Magnetite deposits of the coastal area of British Columbia: *In* Structural geology of Canadian ore deposits, v. 2, Commonwealth Min. and Met. Cong., p. 1–7.

——, and Black, J. M., 1952, Iron ore deposits of Vancouver Island and Texada Island: Minister of Mines, B. C., Ann. Rept., p. 217–234.

Bartlett, A. H., 1956, Iron ore at Nowa Nowa, East Gippsland: Min. and Geol. Jour. (Dept. Mines, Victoria), v. 6, No. 1, p. 32–34.

Bell, G., 1959, The iron ore deposits of Nowa Nowa, Eastern Gippsland: Geol. Survey Victoria (Australia), Bull. 57.

Bennett, W. A. G., 1962, Mineralogy and geochemistry of the Read magnetite deposit, Southwestern Stevens County, Wash.: Econ. Geol., v. 57, p. 941–949.

Brooks, J. H., 1957, Summary report, iron ore resources of Queensland: Queensland Geol. Survey, Pub. No. 283.

Broughton, W. A., 1943, The Buckhorn iron deposits of Okanogan County, Wash.; Results of a magnetic survey: Wash. Div. Mines and Geol., R. I. Circ. 8, 21 p.
Brüggen, J., 1913, Contribucíon a la Geología del Valle del Huasco y del Departamento de la Serena con una breve Descripcion de los Yacimientos de Fierro: Bol. Soc. Nac. Mineria, 3rd. Ser., v. 25, p. 447–458.
Canavan, F., 1965a, Iron ore deposits of Australia: *In* Geology of Australian ore deposits, 8th Commonwealth Min. and Met. Cong., v. 1, p. 13–23.
——, 1965b, Iron and manganese deposits of Iron range: *In* Geology of Australian ore deposits, 8th Commonwealth Min. and Met. Cong., v. 1, p. 391–393.
Concha, J. F., 1956, El Yacimiento de Fierro del Cerro Casco o Tarpuy, Arequipa (Peru): Soc. Geol. del Peru, Bol. 30, p. 167–175.
Duenas, E. I., 1918, El Yacimiento de Fierro de Huacravilca: Bol. Cuerpo de Ing. de Minas del Peru, No. 87.
Durrell, C., and Proctor, P. D., 1948, Iron ore deposits near Lake Hawley and Spencer Lakes, Sierra County, California: Calif. Div. Mines, Bull. 129, p. 165–192.
Eastwood, G. E. P., 1965, Replacement magnetite on Vancouver Island, British Columbia (Canada): Econ. Geol., v. 60, p. 124–148.
Flores Williams, H., 1949, Geología de los Yacimientos de Fierro de Chile: Revista del Inst. de Ing. de Minas de Chile.
——, 1959, Apuntes de Geología Economica de Yacimientos Minerales: pt. 2, Santiago, Chile.
——, and Hornkohl, H., 1947, Informe Preliminar sobre los Yacimientos de Fierro de Relun: Santiago (Chile), Dept. Minas Petrol., Informe Inedito.
Foshag, W. F., 1929, Mineralogy and geology of Cerro Mercado, Durango, Mexico: U. S. Natl. Museum, Proc. 75, Art. 23.
Frost, J. E., 1965, Controls of ore deposition for the Larap mineral deposits, Camarines Norte, Philippine Islands: Ph.D. Thesis, Stanford Univ.
Gallagher, D., 1963, Mineral resources of Korea, v.IV, Iron ore deposits: Mining Branch, Ind. and Min. Div., USOM/Korea.
Geijer, P., 1931, The iron ores of the Kiruna type: Sveriges Geologiska Undersökning, ser. C, Avhandlinger och uppsater, No. 367, Arsbok 24, No. 4.
——, 1967, Internal features of the apatite-bearing magnetite ores: Sveriges Geol. Undersökning, ser. C, NR 624, Arsbok 61, NR9, 32 p.
Gonzales Reyna, J., 1952, Los Yacimientos de Fierro de Mexico y su Geologia: Symposium sur les gisements de fer du Monde, 19th Intern. Geol. Cong. (Algiers), p. 435–454.
Griffin, R. S., and Wynn, D. W., 1961, Iron. The mineral industry of N.S.W.: Geol. Survey New South Wales, Bull. 21.
Harrington, J. F., and Page, B. M., 1952, Sources of iron ore in Asia: Gen. Hdqrs., Nat. Res. Div., Supreme Commander for the Allied Powers, Rept. No. 154.
Hodge, E. T., 1935; 1938, Report on available raw materials for a Pacific Coast iron industry: v. 4, 1935; v. 5, 1938; U. S. Army. Off. Div. Engrs., Portland, Oregon.
Holser, W. T., and Schneer, C. J., 1961, Hydrothermal magnetite: Geol. Soc. Amer., Bull. 76, p. 369–386.
Hughes, T. D., 1965, Iron ore deposits of Savage River: *In* Geology of Australian ore deposits, 8th Commonwealth Min. and Met. Cong., v. 1, p. 525–526.
Ichimura, T., 1931, Notes on the titaniferous magnetite deposits of Shoenpe-to, Korea: Taihoku Imperial Univ., Mem. Fac. Sci. and Agri., v. 3, No. 4, ser. 1, p. 249–265.
Jenkins, O. P., and Cooper, H. H., 1922, A study of the iron ores of Washington: Wash. Div. Mines and Geol., Bull. 27, p. 11–115.
Kato, T., 1939, Origin of the Mozan iron ore (Korea): Japan Jour. Geol. Geog., v. 16, p. 233–238.
Kindle, E. D., 1964, Copper and iron resources, Whitehorse copper belt, Yukon Territory: Canada Geol. Survey, Paper 63-41, 46 p.
Lamey, C. A., 1961, Contact metamorphic iron deposits of California: Geol. Soc. Amer. Bull., v. 72, p. 669–677.
Leningston, K. R., 1954, Iron range: Queensland Govt. Min. Jour., v. 55, No. 633, p. 583–586.
Linnemann, Cl., 1920, Los Yacimientos de Fierro en el Sur de Atacama: Bol. Soc. Nac. Minería (Chile), p. 691–705.
MacKevett, E. M., Jr., and Blake, M. C., Jr., 1963, Geology of the North Bradfield River iron prospect, Southeastern Alaska: U. S. Geol. Survey, Bull. 1108-D, p. D1–D21.
Mapes V., E., Porraz Z., R., Alexandri R., R., Gutiérrez, C. G., Pesquera V., R., Guillén y, J. J., and Camacho C., M., 1959, Los Yacimientos Ferriferous de Las Truchas, Michoacan: Mexico Consejo Rec. Naturales no Renovables, Bol. 46, 128 p.
Matsukuma, T., and Horikoshi, E., 1970, Kuroko deposits in Japan, a review: *In* Volcanism and Ore Genesis (Watanabe Commerative Volume), ed. Tatsumi, Tatsuo, Univ. of Tokyo Press, p. 153–179.
McConnell, R. G., 1914, Texada Island, B. C.: Canada Geol. Survey, Mem. 58, p. 74–90.
Meave T., E., and Echegoyen S, J., 1961, Estudio Geologico-Economico sobre algunos Yacimientos de Mineral de Hierro en los Municipios de Pihuamo y Tecalitlan, Jalisco: Mexico Consejo Recursos Naturales no Renovables, Bol. 53, 88 p.
Mitsuchi, T., 1952, Iron ore deposits in Japan: Symposium sur les gisements de fer du Monde, 19th Intern. Geol. Cong. (Algiers), p. 537–560.
Muñoz Cristi, J., 1950a, Geología del Distrito Minero de la Higuera ubicado en la Provincia de Coquimbo: Fac. de Ciencias Fis. y Mat., Univ. Chile, Inst. Geol., Pub. 1, p. 49–50.
——, 1950b, Geología: In Geografía Economica de Chile, Corp. de Fomento de la Produccion, t. 1, Santiago, Chile, p. 55–187.
Olmeda, D. P., 1913, Yacimientos de Fierro de la Serena: Inspeccion de Geog. y Minas, Dir. Gen. Obras Publicas, Bol., Ano 9, p. 258–279, Santiago (Chile).
Park, C. F., Jr., 1961, A magnetite "flow" in Northern Chile: Econ. Geol., v. 56, p. 431–436.
Pittman, E. F., 1910, The iron ore deposits of the state of New South Wales: Intern. Geol. Cong. (Stockholm), v. 2, Iron Ore Resources of the World, p. 846–871.
Raggatt, H. G., 1953, The mineral resources of Australia: Geol. Australian Ore Deposits, p. 15–17.
Revorede, A., Undated mimeograph notes, Geología Economica de Yacimientos Minerales, 250 p.
Rice, H. M. A., 1947, Geology and mineral deposits of the Princeton map-area, British Columbia: Canada Geol. Survey, Mem. 243.
——, and Jones, A. G., 1959, Geology, Vernon-Kamloops, Osoyoos, and Kootenay districts, British Columbia: Canada Geol. Survey, Map 1059A.
Richter, D. H., and Herreid, G., 1965, Geology of the Paint River area, Iliamna Quadrangle, Alaska: Alaska Div. Mines Minerals, Geol. Rept. 8, 18 p.
Rogers, D. P., 1968, The extrusive iron oxide deposits "El Laco," Chile: abs., Econ. Geol., v. 63, p. 700.
Ruiz F., C., 1943, Los Yacimientos de Hierro de la Region Noroccidental de Copiapo, un Tipo no Descrito de Yacimiento de Contact Metamorfico: Bol. Minero, Santiago (Chile), Año 59, v. 55, No. 522, 523, p. 820–827; 906–915.
——, 1961, Exploracion por metodos geofisicos aereos y terrestres de las anomalías ubicada en la region de Cerro Chanar-Boqueron, con una discusion sobre genesis de los Yacimientos de Hierro de Atacama: Santiago (Chile), Aptdo Rev. Minerales, No. 75, p. 23–30.
——, 1965, Geología y Yacimientos Metaliferous de Chile: Inst. de Inves. Geol., Chile, p. 221–247.
Saksela, M., 1970, Über Magmatische Ausscheidungen von Eisenerzen in Sauren und Mässig Sauren Eruptivgestei-

nen: Ann. Acad. Sci. Fennicae, ser. A, III, Geol.-Geog., 106, 119 p.

Salas, R., Kast, R. Montecinos, F., and Salas, I., 1965, Geología del Departamento de Arica, Provincia de Tarapaca: Santiago (Chile), Inst. Inves. Geol., Bol. 21.

Santos Yñigo, L., 1952, The geology of iron ore deposits of the Philippines: Symposium sur les gisements de fer du Monde, 19th Intern. Geol. Cong. (Algiers), p. 583–608.

——, 1953, The geology of iron ore deposits of the Philippines: The Phil. Geologist, v. 7, p. 122–164.

——, 1961, Geology of the Landayao iron deposits at Tupi, Cotabato Province: The Phil. Geologist, v. 15, No. 4, p. 147–169.

Simons, F. S., and Bellido, E., 1956, The iron deposits of Cerro Huacravilca, Junin: Soc. Geol. Peru, Bull. 30, p. 359–374.

Stevenson, J. S., 1950, Geology and mineral resources of the Zeballos Mining Camp, B. C.: British Columbia (Canada), Dept. Mines, Bull. 27, p. 125–128; 131–134.

Sutherland Brown, A., 1962, Pyrometasomatic iron-copper deposits on the West Coast: Western Miner and Oil Rev., v. 35, No. 2, p. 44–45.

Swanson, C. O., 1925, The genesis of the Texada Island magnetite deposits: Canada Geol. Survey, Summ. Rept., 1924, pt. 4, p. 106–144.

Tanton, T. L., 1952, Iron ores in Canada: *In* Symposium sur les gisements de fer du Monde, 19th Intern. Geol. Cong. (Algiers), v. 1, p. 311–352.

Taylor, H. P., and Noble, J. A., 1960, Origin of the ultramafic complexes in Southeastern Alaska: 21st Intern. Geol. Cong. (Copenhagen), pt. 13, p. 175–187.

Twelvetrees, W. H., 1910, Iron ore deposits of Tasmania: *In* Iron ore resources of the world, Intern. Geol. Cong. (Stockholm), v. 2, p. 881–884.

Warner, L. A., Goddard, E. N., Walton, M. S., Jr., Bressler, C. T., Stefansson, K., Ray, R. G., and Flint, G. M., Jr., 1961, Iron and copper deposits of Kasaan Peninsula, Prince of Wales Island, Southeastern Alaska: U. S. Geol. Survey, Bull. 1090, 136 p.

Young, G. A., and Uglow, W. L., 1926, Iron ore in British Columbia and Yukon: Canada Geol. Survey, Econ. Geol. Ser., No. 3.

Zoldok, S. W., Cole, J. W., and Dougherty, E. Y., 1947, Iron deposits of Buckhorn Mt., Meyers Creek mining district, Okanogan County, Washington: U. S. Bur. Mines, R. I. Circ. 4051, 22 p.

Zoppis de Sena, R., 1957, Informe sobre el Yacimiento de Hierro de Monte Carmelo, Departamento de Zelaya, Nicaragua: Nicaragua Serv. Geol. Nac., Bol. 1, p. 13–27.

Additional Bibliography

Aldrich, H. R., 1929, The geology of the Gogebic iron range of Wisconsin: Wisconsin Geol. Nat. Hist. Survey, Econ. Ser., Bull. 71, 279 p.

Alexandrov, E. A., 1973, The Precambrian banded iron ores of the Soviet Union: Econ. Geol., v. 68, p. 1035–1062.

Alling, H. L., 1941, Diagenesis of the Clinton hematite ores of New York: Geol. Soc. America Bull., v. 58, p. 991–1018.

Amstutz, G. C., and L. Bubenicek, 1967, Diagenesis in sedimentary mineral deposits: *in* Diagenesis in sediments, G. Larsen and G. V. Chilingar, eds., Elsevier Publishing Co., Amsterdam, p. 455–466.

Ayres, D. E., 1972, Genesis of iron-bearing minerals in banded iron formation mesobands in the Dales Gorge Member, Hammersley Group, Western Australia: Econ. Geol.. v. 67, p. 1214–1233.

Baas-Becking, L. G. M., and D. Moore, 1959, The relation between iron and organic matter in sediments: Jour. Sed. Petrology, v. 29, p. 454–458.

Baldwin, A. B., and W. H. Gross, 1967, Possible explanations for the localization of residual hematite ore on a Precambrian iron formation: Econ. Geol., v. 62, no. 1, p. 95.

Barnes, H. L., and W. Back, 1964, Geochemistry or iron-rich ground water of southern Maryland: Jour. Geol., v. 72, p. 435.

Bayley, R. W., and H. L. James, 1973, Precambrian iron-formations of the United States: Econ. Geol., v. 68, p. 934–959.

Berg, G., 1925, Die Entstehung der sedimentären Eisenerze: Geol. Rundschau, v. 15, p. 97–110.

Berge, J. W., 1974, Geology, geochemistry, and origin of the Nimba itabirite and associated rocks, Nimba County, Liberia: Econ. Geol., v. 69, p. 80–92.

Beukes, N. J., 1973, Precambrian iron-formations of South Africa: Econ. Geol., v. 68, p. 960–1004.

Bleifuss, R. L., 1964, Mineralogy of oxidized taconites of the western Mesabi and its influences on metallurgical processes: Amer. Inst. Min. Eng. Trans., v. 236, p. 235–244.

Borchert, H., 1952, Die Bildungsbedingungen mariner Eisenerzlagerstätten: Chem. Erde, v. 16, p. 49–74.

Boyle, R. W., and J. L. Davies, 1973, Banded iron formations: Geochim. Cosmochim. Acta, v. 37, p. 1389.

Brandt, R. T., 1964, The genesis of the Mount Goldsworthy iron ore deposits of northwest Australia: Econ. Geol., v. 61, p. 999–1009.

______, 1973, The origins of the jaspilitic iron ores of Australia: *in* Genesis of Precambrian iron and manganese deposits, Kiev symposium, 1970, UNESCO, New York.

Bromfield, S. M., 1954, Reduction of ferric compounds by soil bacteria: Jour. Genet. Microbiol., II, I.

Bruce, E. L., 1945, Pre-Cambrian iron formation: Geol. Soc. America Bull., v. 56, p. 589–602.

Butozova, G. Y., and L. E. Shterenberg, 1962, Distribution of dispersed manganese, iron and phosphorous in the manganiferous sediments of Georgia: Doklady Acad. Sci. USSR, v. 142, p. 1395–1398 (Russian); English Trans. Amer. Geol. Inst., 1964, p. 164–166.

Campbell, J. M., 1917, Laterite, its origin, structure, and minerals: Min. Mag., v. 17, p. 67–77, 120–128, 171–179, 220–229.

Cissarz, A., 1924, Mineralogisch-microskopische Untersuchungen der Erze und Nebengesteine des Roteisensteinlagers der Grube Maria bei Braunfels a.d. Lahn: Mitt. Kaiser-Wilhelm Inst., Eisenforsch, Düsseldorf.

Cochranc, G. W., and A. B. Edwards, 1960, The Roper River oolitic ironstone formations, Australia: Comm. Sci. Ind. Res. Org. Min. Inv. Tech. Paper 1, 28 p.

Collins, W. H., and J. T. Quirke, 1926, Michipicoten iron ranges: Geol. Surv. Canada Mem. 147, 120 p.

Cooper, L. H. N., 1953, Iron in the sea and in marine plankton: Roy. Soc. London Proc., ser. B, v. 118, p. 419–439.

———, 1938, Some conditions governing the solubility of iron: Roy. Soc. London Proc., ser. B, v. 124, p. 299–307.

Correns, C. W., 1952, Zur Geochemie des Eisens: 19th Internat. Geol. Congr., Algiers, Symposium sur les gisements de fer, v. 2, p. 23–27.

Cullen, D. J., 1963, Tectonic implications of banded ironstone formations: Jour. Sed. Petrology, v. 33, p. 387–392.

Dorr, J. V. N., and A. L. M. Barbosa, 1963, Geology and ore deposits of the Itabira district, Brazil: U.S. Geol. Surv. Prof. Paper 341C, 110 p.

Doyle, R. W., 1964, The origin of the ferrous ion-ferric oxide Nernst potential in environments containing dissolved ferrous iron: Amer. Jour. Sci., 266, 840.

Drever, J. I., 1974, Geochemical model for the origin of Precambrian banded iron-formations: Geol. Soc. Am., Bull., v. 85, p. 1099–1106.

Dunham, K. C., 1960, Syngenetic and diagenetic mineralization in Yorkshire: Yorkshire Geol. Soc. Proc., v. 32, p. 229–284.

Dunn, J. A., 1935, Origin of iron ore in Singhbhum, India: Econ. Geol., v. 30, p. 643–654.

Eckel, E. B., 1938, The brown iron ores of eastern Texas: U.S. Geol. Surv. Bull. 902, 157 p.

Eichler, J., 1967, Das physicalisch-chemische Milieu bie der Verwitterung von Itabiriten in Minas Gerais, Brasilien: Chem. Erde, v. 26, p. 119–132.

Erhart, H., 1973, Itinéraires géochimiques et cycle géologique de l'aluminium: Doin, Éditeurs, S. A., Paris, 253 p.

Eugster, H. P. and I-M. Chou, 1973, The depositional environments of Precambrian banded iron-formations: Econ. Geol., v. 68, p. 1144–1168.

Evrard, P., 1947, Statistical relation between TiO_2, Fe_2O_3 and FeO in rocks and ores during differentiation of a titaniferous magma: Geol. Soc. America Bull., v. 58, p. 127–210.

Flaschen, S. S., and E. F. Osborn, 1957, Studies in the system iron oxide–silica–water at low oxygen partial pressures: Econ. Geol., v. 52, p. 923–943.

Frietsch, R., 1967, The relationship between magnetite and hematite in the iron ores of the Kiruna type and some other iron ore types: Sver. Geol. Unders., ser. C, 645.

———, 1970, Trace elements in magnetite and hematite mainly from northern Sweden: Sver. Geol. Unders., ser. C, 646.

Geijer, P., 1957, Die Herkunft der quarzgebänderten Eisenerze, Eine Übersicht der Problemage: N. Jb. Mineral., Abh. 91, p. 223–238.

Gokhale, K. V. G. K., and T. C. Bagchi, 1961, Preliminary investigation of banded iron ore formations of Perumalai Hills, Salem district, Madras: Quart. Jour. Geol. Min. Met. Soc. India, v. 33, p. 49–53.

Goldschmidt, V. M., 1954, Geochemistry, A. Muir, ed., Clarendon Press, Oxford, 730 p.

Goodwin, A. M., 1964, Geochemical studies at the Helen iron range: Econ. Geol., v. 59, p. 684–718.

Grass, G. A., 1968, Geology of iron deposits in Canada; vol. III, Iron ranges of the Labrador geosyncline: Geol. Surv. Canada, Econ. Geol. Rept. 22, 179 p.

Gross, W. H., and D. W. Strangway, 1961, Remanent magnetism and the origin of hard hematites in Precambrian banded iron formation: Econ. Geol., v. 56, p. 1345–1362.

Grubb, P. L. C., 1971, Silicates and their paragenesis in the Brockman iron formation: Econ. Geol., v. 66, p. 281–292.

Gruner, J. W., 1924, Contributions to the geology of the Mesabi range: Minnesota Geol. Surv. Bull. 19, 71 p.

Hallimond, A. F., K. C. Dunham, J. E. Hemingway, J. H. Taylor, W. Davies, R. J. M. Dixie, and F. A. Bannister, 1951, The constitution and origin of sedimentary iron ores, a symposium: Yorkshire Geol. Soc. Proc., v. 28, p. 61–101.

Harder, H., 1954, Beitrag zur Petrographe and Genese der Hämatiterze des Lahn-Dill-Gebietes: Heidelberger Beitr. Miner. Petrogr., v. 4, p. 54–66.

———, 1963, Zur diskussion über die enstehung der quartz banderze (Itabirite): N. Jb. Mineral., v. 12, p. 303–314.

Hawley, J. E., 1942, Origin of some siderite, pyrite, chert deposits, Michipicoten district, Ontario: Roy. Soc. Canada Trans., v. 36, sec. 4, p. 79–87.

Hayes, A. D., 1915, Wabana iron ore of Newfoundland: Canada Geol. Surv. Mem. 78, 163 p.

Hegemann, F., and F. Albrecht, 1954, Zur Geochemie oxydischer Eisenerze: Chem. Erde, v. 17, p. 81–103.

Hem, J. D., and W. H. Cropper, 1959, Survey of ferrous-ferric chemical equilibria and redox potentials: U.S. Geol. Surv. Water-Supply Paper 1459-A, p. 1–31.

Huber, N. K., and R. M. Garrels, 1953, Relation of pH and oxidation potential to sedimentary iron mineral formation: Econ. Geol., v. 48, p. 337–357.

James, H. L., 1969, Comparison between Red Sea deposits and older ironstone and iron-formations: *in* Hot brines and recent heavy mineral deposits in the Red Sea, E. T. Degens and D. A. Ross, eds., Springer-Verlag, New York, p. 525–531.

Kehrer, P., 1972, Zur geologie der Itabirite in der sudlichen Serra do Espinhaco (Minas Gerais, Brasilien): Geol. Rundschau, v. 61, no. 1, p. 216–248.

Knyazev, G. I., V. A. Reshit'ko, and L. I. Fedorovskaya, 1969, Genesis of ferruginous quartzite: Akad. Nauk SSSR Izv. Ser. Geol., v. 12, p. 33–46 (English translation in Internat. Geol. Rev., v. 12, p. 1096–1106.)

Kornilov, N. A., 1970, Age of high-grade hematite ores of Precambrian iron-formations and the physiochemical conditions of Precambrian weathering: Akad. Nauk SSSR Dokl., v. 115, no. 4, p. 919–922 (English translation in Acad. Sci. USSR Dokl., v. 195, p. 68–70).

Krishna Rao, J. S. N., and D. S. N. Murthy, 1971, The lateritic iron ores, itabiritic quartzites and epidiorites of the Kemmangundi area, Mysore State: Miner. Deposita, v. 7.

Kulish, Y. A., 1970, Amount of oxygen in the Archean atmosphere of Alden: Akad. Nauk SSSR Dokl., v. 191, no. 4, p. 921–923 (English translation in Acad. Sci. USSR Dokl., v. 191, p. 196–197).

La Berge, G. L., 1966, Altered pyroclastic rocks in the iron-formation of the Hammersley range, Western Australia: Econ. Geol., v. 61, p. 147–161.

———, 1967, Microfossils and Precambrian iron formations: Geol. Soc. America Bull., v. 78, p. 331–342.

Lacroix, A., 1913, Les latérites de la Guinée et les produits d'altération qui leur sont associés: Nouv. Archs. Mus. Hist. Nat., Paris, p. 255–356.

Leith, C. K., 1925, Secondary concentration of Lake Superior iron ores: Econ. Geol., v. 26, p. 274–288.

Lepp, H., 1966, Chemical composition of the Biwabik iron formation, Minnesota: Econ. Geol., v. 61, p. 243–250.

Lovering, T. S., 1923, The leaching of iron protores: Econ. Geol., v. 18, p. 523–540.

Maksimov, A. A., 1960, Types of manganese and iron-manganese deposits in central Kazakhstan: Internat. Geol. Rev., v. 2, p. 508–521.

Mann, V. I., 1953, Relation of oxidation to the origin of soft iron ores of Michigan: Econ. Geol., v. 48, p. 251–281.

Marmo, V., 1956, Banded ironstones of the Kangari Hills, Sierra Leone: Econ. Geol., v. 51, p. 798–810.

Martin, R. F., and A. J. Piwinskii, 1969, Experimental data bearing on the movement of iron in an aqueous vapor: Econ. Geol., v. 64, p. 798–803.

Moore, E. S., 1918, The iron formation on Belcher Islands, Hudson Bay; with reference to its origin and associated algal limestones: Jour. Geol., v. 26, p. 412.

Morey, G. B., 1973, Mesabi, Gunflint, and Cuyuna ranges, Minnesota; in Genesis of Precambrian iron and manganese deposits; Kiev Symp., 1970, UNESCO, New York, p. 193–208.
Norton, S. A., 1973, Laterite and bauxite formation: Econ. Geol., v. 68, p. 353–361.
Oftedahl, C., 1958, A theory of exhalative-sedimentary ores: Geol. fören. Stockholm Förh., v. 8, no. 1, p. 1–19.
Palmquist, S., 1935, Geochemical studies on the iron-bearing Liassic series in southern Sweden: Lunds Geol.-Miner. Inst., Medd. no. 60, 204 p.
Park, C. F., Jr., 1959, Origin of hard hematite intabirite: Econ. Geol., v. 54, p. 573–587.
Percival, F. G., 1931, The iron-ores of Noamundi: Trans. Min. Geol. Inst. India, v. 26, p. 119–271.
———, 1967, Possible explanations for the localization of residual hematite ore on a Precambrian iron formation—discussion: Econ. Geol., v. 62, p. 739–742.
Perry, E. C., Jr., and B. Bommichson, 1966, Quartz and magnetite: oxygen-18–oxygen-16 fractionation in metamorphosed Biwabik iron-formation: Science, v. 153, p. 528–529.
———, F. C. Tan, and G. B. Morey, 1973, Geology and stable isotope geochemistry of the Biwabik iron formation, northern Minnesota: Econ. Geol., v. 68, p. 1110–1125.
Pettijohn, F. J., 1949, Sedimentary rocks: Harper & Row, New York, 526 p.
Pichamuthu, C. S., 1974, On the banded iron formations of Precambrian age in India: Jour. Geol. Soc. India, v. 15, p. 1–30.
Prescott, J. A., and R. L. Pendleton, 1952, Laterite and lateritic soils: Commonwealth Bur. Soil Sci. Tech. Commun., 47.
Pride, D. E., and A. F. Hagner, 1972, Geochemistry and origin of Precambrian iron-formation near Atlantic City, Wyoming: Econ. Geol., v. 67, p. 329–338.
Quiring, H., 1955, Eisenerzlager vom Lahn-Dill-Typus in Nordspanien: Neues Jb. Paläontologie, Monatsh. 2, p. 49–52.
Ramberg, H., 1948, Titanic iron-ore formed by dissociation of silicates in granulite facies: Econ. Geol., v. 43, p. 553–570.
Ramdohr, P., 1926, Beobachtungen an Magnetit, Ilmenit, Eisenglanz und Ueberlegungen ueber das System $FeO–Fe_2O_3–TiO_2$: Neues Jb. Min. Geol. Paleo., v. 54, A, p. 320–379.
Renaud, L., and L. Delaire, 1955, Notice explicative sur la feuille Conakry-Est: Direction Mines A.O.F., p. 1–16.
Ruckmick, J. C., 1963, The iron ores of Cerro Bolivar, Venezuela: Econ. Geol., v. 58, p. 218–236.
Sastry, A. V. R., and R. Vaidhyanadhan, 1968, Structure and petrography of the quartz-magnetite and associated rocks of Vamparla area, Nellore district: Jour. Geol. Soc. India, v. 9, p. 49–57.
Schmidt, R. G., 1963, Geology and ore deposits of the Cuyuna North range, Minnesota: U.S. Geol. Surv. Prof. Paper 407, 96 p.
Scholl, W. U., 1972, Der sudwestliche Randbereich der Espinhaco-Zone, Minas Gerais, Brasilien: Geol. Rundschau, v. 61, no. 1, p. 201–215.
Schweighert, H., 1965, Genesis of the iron ores of the Pretoria Series, South Africa: Econ. Geol., v. 60, p. 269–298.
Serdyachenko, D. P., 1959, The origin of Archean iron ores of south Yakutia: Akad. Nauk SSSR Izv., Ser. Geol. (English translation Amer. Geol. Inst. in Izv. Acad. Sci. USSR, Geol. Ser., no. 8, p. 28–41).
Silverman, M. P., and H. L. Ehrlich, 1964, Microbial formation and degradation of minerals: Adv. Appl. Microbiol., v. 6, p. 153–206.
Sims, P. K., 1973, Banded iron-formations in the Vermilion district: *in* Geology of Minnesota, P. K. Sims and G. B. Morey, eds., Minnesota Geol. Surv., p. 79–81.
Spears, D. A., 1964, The major element geochemistry of the Mansfield Marine Band in the Westphalien of Yorkshire: Geochim. Cosmochim. Acta, v. 28, p. 1679–1696.
Starkey, R. L., and H. O. Halvorson, 1927, Studies on the transformation of iron in nature, II, Concerning the importance of microorganisms in the solution and precipitation of iron: Soil Sci., v. 26, p. 381–402.
Stephens, C. G., 1961, The soil landscapes of Australia: C.S.I.R.O. Austr., Soil Publ., 18.

Strong, M.W., 1956, Marine iron bacteria as rock forming organisms: Advancement of Science, v. 12, no. 49, p. 583–585.

Svitalski, N., 1937, Krivoi Rog and the iron ores of this district: Handbook No. 7, Southern Excursion, Ukranian Soviet Socialistic Republic, Inter. Geol. Congress, Moscow.

Taylor, S. R., 1964, Abundance of the chemical elements in the continental crust: a new table: Geochim. Cosmochim. Acta, v. 28, p. 1273–1285.

Trendall, A. F., 1973, Varve cycles in the Weeli Wolli Formation of the Precambrian Hammersley Group, Western Australia: Econ. Geol., v. 68, p. 1089–1097.

———, and J. G. Blockley, 1969, The iron formations of the Pre-Cambrian Hammersley Group, Western Australia: Western Australia Geol. Survey Bull., 119, 350 p.

Troshanov, E. P., 1965, Bacteria which reduce manganese and iron in bottom deposits: *in* Applied capillary microscopy, Consultants Bureau, Inc., New York, 106 p.

Tyler, S. A., 1948, Itabirite of Minas Gerais, Brazil: Jour. Sed. Petrology, v. 18, p. 86–87.

———, 1949, Development of Lake Superior soft iron ores from metamorphosed iron formation: Geol. Soc. America Bull., v. 60, p. 1101–1124.

Vogt, J. H. L., 1927, On the genesis of the iron deposits of the Kiruna type: Geol. Fören. Stockholm, Förh., v. 49, p. 153–195.

Wagner, P. A., 1928, The iron ore deposits of the Union of South Africa: Geol. Surv. South Africa Mem. 26.

Walter, R. M., 1972, A hot spring analog for the depositional environment of Precambrian iron formations of the Lake Superior region: Econ. Geol., v. 67, p. 965–972.

Walther, J., 1915, Laterite in West-Australien: Z. Deut. Geol. Ges., v. 57, p. 113–132.

Wright, C. M., 1965, Syngenetic pyrite associated with a Precambrian iron ore deposit: Econ. Geol., v. 60, p. 998–1019.

Yui, S., 1966, Decomposition of siderite to magnetite at lower oxygen fugacities: a thermochemical interpretation and geological implications: Econ. Geol., v. 61, p. 768–776.

Author Citation Index

Subject Index